Making Math Meaningful®

A Source Book for Teaching High School Math

By Jamie York

Jamie York Press

August 2015

Making Math Meaningful®

A Source Book for Teaching High School Math

ISBN: 978-1-938210-19-8

Catherine Douglas was a student at Shining Mountain Waldorf School when she designed the cover to this book. It is an impressive example of how equiangular spirals emerge from nested octagons.

JAMIE YORK PRESS

Meaningful Math Books for Waldorf Public, Private, and Home Schools

www.JamieYorkPress.com

Table of Contents

—— About this Book ——

What is this book?

Largely, this book is the result of more than twenty years of gathering and developing material for the high school math classroom. It is intended both to help a new high school math teacher get started, and to serve as a resource for all high school math teachers. It is packed with material that standard high school math textbooks never seem to have time for – great stuff that will help to inspire students.

This book is also an essential teacher's companion for our high school math workbooks, which are designed to develop students' math skills, preparing them for anything they might encounter in college. I like to emphasize a healthy balance between developing skills and having mathematical experiences, and this source book is all about giving students those amazing mathematical experiences.

Who can use this book?

While most of my teaching experience is within the Waldorf school system, the material presented here can be effectively used by any teacher wishing to bring meaningful, age-appropriate material to their students.

A Word of Caution

This book should not be viewed as a recipe for teaching mathematics in any school. Indeed there is no such recipe. This book is merely a resource that reflects the experiences and opinions of the author.

The reader (presumably a teacher) should not simply follow instructions or carry out a plan just because it is stated in this book. As always, it is the teacher's job to develop the inner sense of what is right at a particular moment for the class and to create an effective lesson. It is ultimately the teacher's love and creativity that will bring the material alive for the students. No book can give this to the teacher.

Order of topics

The topics in this book are mostly arranged by grade, according to subject area. It is not intended that a teacher should cover the topics in the order that they appear in this book. Teachers using my workbooks will likely find it best to cover topics in the order that they appear in the workbook. *Many of the topics found in this book don't appear in the workbooks at all.*

Permission

As stated in the front page of the book: "There are several sheets in this book intended for use and distribution in the classroom. *The publisher grants teachers permission to copy individual pages of this book for distribution to students.* For all other purposes, no part of this book may be reproduced in any form or by any means, without permission in writing from the publisher."

What are we preparing them for?

Certainly, any student graduating high school should be prepared for whatever step comes next in life. While most of my students go to college, some of them will never take another math course after high school. But for those who struggle the most with math in high school, I believe that math may be the most important part of their education – not because of the content they are learning, but because of the life lessons (e.g., how to persevere through difficulties, etc.).

Other students have a talent for math and may plan on majoring in mathematics, engineering, or science in college. These students need a thorough math education in high school so that they are well prepared.

All of our books (including this book and our workbooks) are written to meet the needs of all students. It is certainly one of the great challenges of the teacher to make it work for everyone.

Mainstream and non-traditional math

Generally speaking, our math curriculum consists of two types of topics: "mainstream" and "non-traditional". Both are important. Mainstream math is what we are all familiar with – the topics that always appear in any algebra, algebra II, or precalculus textbook. Mainstream math is very skills oriented. What I am referring to as non-traditional math, is the math included in my curriculum that is unfamiliar to most math teachers. It is a combination of Waldorf math topics and other topics which develop mathematical thinking, problem-solving abilities, and a general sense of wonder for mathematics.

This book has a heavy emphasis on non-traditional topics. This may give the reader the impression that most all of my classroom time is spent on non-traditional math and that I am neglecting mainstream math skills. This is not true. My students are exposed to a balance of mainstream and non-traditional math.

I have written this book with the assumption that teachers are familiar with typical mainstream math topics, therefore leaving out detailed explanations of these topics. I also assume that the non-traditional topics require many examples, explanations, and resources for the teacher.

The best way to get a sense of how I teach the mainstream topics is to read through our workbooks.

Main Lessons and Track Classes

Some of the material presented here assumes familiarity with the Waldorf idea of "main lesson". A main lesson is a three or four-week intensive course which meets daily for about 100 minutes. In Waldorf schools, the students in a particular year have nine or ten main lessons over the course of the year. The subject material for main lessons varies between math, science, and the humanities. Of course, main lessons could be integrated into any school. A few other school systems and colleges have a "block system", which is similar to the idea of a main lesson.

Waldorf schools don't have all of their courses in main lesson blocks. There is only one main lesson class per day, and the rest of the day consists of four or five "track classes", which typically run all year long, and meet between three and five times per week, each time for about 45 minutes. The math curriculum is covered in a combination of math main lesson blocks and math track classes.

In general, main lessons tend to be more about the "big picture" and less about developing skills. Main lessons are not split according to ability. Main lessons often require a fair bit of writing from the students. My math main lessons are often an integration of history, philosophy, writing, and math. The students don't have a textbook for a main lesson class; they create their own "main lesson book", which often consists of a collection of essays summarizing the experience of the course.

Math track classes tend to be more skills oriented. It is in the math track classes that students use our workbooks.

Why so much tenth grade?

Of course, the reality is that tenth grade math occupies only about one-quarter of the whole math curriculum, yet it occupies a higher proportion of this book. This is simply because our tenth grade math curriculum includes many non-traditional topics unfamiliar to most teachers, which therefore requires more space in this book.

Our workbooks, puzzle and game book, and more!

The following *Making Math Meaningful* books are available from Jamie York Press:

- *Workbooks for grades 6-12.* Our middle school and high school workbooks are an integral part of our math curriculum. While our workbooks largely focus on standard skill development, they also provide mathematical experiences and give the students a feeling of discovery. The teacher's editions for the high school workbooks include a unit-by-unit commentary, the student workbook, and the answer key.
- *Fun with Puzzles, Games and More!* Our math puzzle and game book is intended as a resource in order to supplement the normal classroom material and provide for that "something different".
- *Source Books* for math teachers: grades 1-5, middle school, and high school.

Our website

Making Math Meaningful books has a website: **www.JamieYorkPress.com**. On this site, you can purchase our books, view main lesson book pages and drawings, and download (for free!) a variety of documents, lesson plans, and other resources related to *Making Math Meaningful* books. You can also contact us there with questions and comments.

Acknowledgements

We would like to heartily thank Jeff O'Brien for his inspirational work with surveying and his willingness to write the surveying unit in this book.

—— *Today's Challenge* ——

The *LIST*

Today, mathematics education is predominantly focused on skill development. Over time this has degenerated into the *LIST* – a horrifically long list of skills that are supposedly necessary for our students to move to the next level (e.g., middle school, high school, or college). The *LIST* manages to put pressure on teachers at all levels of education. They fear that if they don't get through the entire *LIST*, then their students won't be prepared. We are led to believe that this *LIST* is getting longer and longer, and more and more daunting. Such an over-emphasis on skill development is boring or overwhelming (or both) for many students, and for the teacher as well.

I believe that basic skills are important, but the list of topics needed to move forward is not horrifically long; it is actually quite manageable (see "What are the essential math skills?" under *Will our Students be Prepared?*). I also believe there is much more to math than just learning skills. With so much emphasis going toward the mastery of a long list of skills, some of the most interesting aspects of mathematics become neglected.

The need for higher-level thinking

All too often in today's world, students graduate from high school and college unable to think for themselves. Even when doing math, their thinking is largely imitative; they can do math problems as long as they have seen something similar before. We often hear from university professors and people in industry that today's education isn't able to adequately produce graduates who are good problem-solvers and can think creatively. As educators, our goal is to have our students graduate from high school able to think flexibly, creatively, and independently.

What is math?

All of this leads to an important question: *What is math, really?*

Why does our modern educational system have such difficulty teaching math effectively? A significant part of the problem is that we don't really understand what math is. And then comes the shocking realization: *We aren't actually teaching real math.*

Blind procedures

Much of the focus of mainstream mathematics curricula today seems to be to cram as much material into the students' heads as possible. This emphasis on learning "math skills" is often at the expense of understanding the math behind the math. Students just want to be fed a formula or be told how to follow some procedure blindly in order to "solve" the problem. In summary:

> *Most people think that math is a collection of blind procedures to be used to solve meaningless problems.*

In contrast, I believe that it is critically important for students to understand the math behind the math, to realize that math isn't something that's "out there somewhere", but rather that math is one of those things that makes us human.

> *We want our students to experience math as an adventure, and to feel that math is a profoundly human endeavor.*

Meaningless math

What is society's view of math? Math is often not seen as meaningful in and of itself. A widespread belief is that "good math" must be practical and useful. It then follows that the main reason to study math is that it can be useful for some other purpose or subject. All of these attitudes toward math can make it challenging to teach math in a meaningful way.

I believe that practical applications of math can be helpful, but I also feel that there is a higher purpose to learning math.

What is the higher purpose of teaching math?

- *Math teaches us how to think.* We want our students to be able to think for themselves, think analytically, and we hope that their thinking is heart-felt and imbued with imagination.
- *Character development.* Math teaches students discipline, perseverance, patience, and how to deal

with mistakes. For many students, math teaches them how to (work through) struggle.

- *Combating cynicism.* In today's world, our youth can easily come to believe that things are meaningless and without purpose. Cynicism is a pervasive social disease today. By teaching math in the right way, we can show our students that the world is true and is filled with awe and wonder.
- *Spiritual and moral development.* Rudolf Steiner, the founder of Waldorf education, talks about the importance of math as part of the students' future spiritual development[1]:

  > "The student of mathematics must get rid of all arbitrary thinking and follow purely the demands of thought. In thinking in this way, the laws of the spiritual world flow into him. This regulated thinking leads to the most spiritual truths."
- *Math is human.* Not everything we teach has to be practical. Math, like music, drama, painting, and literature, is an art. Through these subjects, a true and complete education teaches us what it means to be human.

—— *Thoughts on Teaching Math* ——

Phenomenological Math and the Path of Discovery

Often, when a new topic is introduced, math textbooks start off with the finished product – a statement of a theorem, a formula, or a procedure for solving a new type of problem. Following this, examples of the new concept are shown, the students are expected to practice several of these new types of problems, and finally the students are given a test on the topic. This approach essentially feeds the concepts to the students, and leaves them with the impression that math is something that is magically pulled out of a hat. This is the essence of the "blind procedures" approach to math that is so prevalent today (see *Blind Procedures*, above).

I have intentionally reversed the process in this book, and in our workbooks. With a *phenomenological* approach, we begin with a collection of examples, and through the students' own observations, they discern a hidden pattern or shared quality. With the *path of discovery* approach, we serve as the students' guide – being careful not to give too much away. With both of these approaches, students formulate the statement of a rule, property, or theorem for themselves. They create the math (to some degree) rather than having it fed to them.

This book and our workbooks can only be so useful in this regard; ultimately it is part of the art of teaching math to ensure that the students experience math in this real and engaging way.

Balancing skills and mathematical experiences

It is a common misconception that everything we teach should be learned, tested, and retained. Perhaps people think this way because today's math classrooms are dominated by skill development. While I acknowledge that math skills are important, I feel strongly that it is equally important for the students to experience "real math", and to develop mathematical thinking.

It can be helpful to consider that math topics can be divided into two categories: *skills* (i.e., material that needs to be mastered) and *mathematical experiences.*

<u>Skills</u> (a topic that needs to be mastered). Here the teacher needs to create a dance between introducing, deepening, practicing, sleeping, and reviewing. The bigger the topic, the greater the number of times it needs to be put to sleep, and then later reviewed. It is quite typical to introduce a skills topic one year, but not to have the students reach mastery until the next year, or the year after.

<u>Mathematical experiences</u>. While our workbooks allow the students adequate time to practice essential skills, they also create opportunities for discovery. This discovery process is part of a broader category of *mathematical experiences* – something that is critical for developing true mathematical thinking capacities, yet so neglected in today's math classrooms. Mathematical experiences include discovery, puzzles, games, and problem solving. We teach these topics because they stretch our students' minds, they teach mathematical thinking, and they engender enthusiasm and wonder for math. This book and our workbooks can only do so much. *It is ultimately the responsibility of the teacher to create opportunities for mathematical experiences.* As a guideline, I recommend that between 25% and 50% of classroom time be spent on mathematical experiences.

---

[1] Rudolf Steiner, *Spiritual Ground of Education,* lecture given at Oxford, August 21 1922, GA 305

And one more thing that we should always keep in mind: students develop mathematical thinking when we model mathematical thinking for them. This happens most deeply when the students follow a complex explanation, and, better yet, follow the flow of a mathematical thought developing over the course of several days or weeks.

Repetition and review

I think of the word "review" in two ways: (1) daily review, which helps the student recall what was done during the previous day's lesson, and (2) review of material that was covered some time ago. Both are an important part of the learning process.

The teacher needs to systematically integrate repetition and review into the lessons in order to strengthen the students' skills. And here's the added bonus…if the teacher wants the students to remember something, then briefly reviewing the concept every day, maybe even for just one minute, will make it possible for the students to learn and remember it without having to practice as much.

The three myths of math

- *Myth #1: Only people born with math ability can become good at math.*
  In reality, hard work can help develop math ability. A student in high school who is seen as being strong in math, might very well have once struggled with math.
- *Myth #2: Confusion is bad.*
  In reality, confusion is part of learning math. Every time we learn a new topic in math, we must go through a period of confusion as we gain clarity.
- *Myth #3: Forgetting is bad.*
  In reality, forgetting is an important part of learning. In fact, for important topics, you need to forget it three times in order to learn it permanently!

Four steps towards math trauma

1. *Confusion.* Everyone experiences confusion when learning math.
2. *Struggling.* Most students struggle with math at least occasionally.
3. *Frustration.* Many students get frustrated with math.
4. *Shutting down/trauma.* Some students shut down and become "math traumatized".

One of the jobs of the teacher is to guide the students through the challenges they encounter in school and in life. In today's world, our children are often shielded from discomfort; they come to expect that things should be easy. They have little patience. It is therefore not surprising that so many students have little tolerance for confusion and struggle. If we compound this with a variety of emotional issues, then we can see how important it is for us, as teachers, to *coach* these students through these challenges.

What makes a student good at math?

As teachers, we all hope our students will become good at math. But to realize this we need to fully understand what math is, and what it isn't (see *Blind Procedures*, above). So now we ask: What are the key attributes that enable a student to become good at math? Here is my short list:

- *Striving to understand deeply.* We want our students to understand the concepts they encounter. Good math students are never satisfied with going through a procedure without understanding what they are doing.
- *Asking good questions.* Good math students are curious, and wonder "what if…?" They question why something is true, and they become skillful at articulating questions.
- *Making mistakes.* Contrary to what many people think, mistakes are an important part of learning math. Good math students don't let mistakes discourage them. In fact, mistakes can motivate students to find the truth and make mathematical discoveries. We want our students to become comfortable with making mistakes, and to learn from their mistakes.
- *Attitude and work ethic.* This includes many things, such as: enthusiasm, determination, and discipline. Good math students persevere through their challenges; they are determined to succeed.

All of the above shows how our students learn many life lessons through studying mathematics. (And, yes, the same may be said about the proper teaching of other subjects as well.)

Teaching the "Big Topics"

The "big topics" in middle school math are fractions, decimals, percents, and ratios. In high school we add basic algebra, trigonometry, logarithms, and Cartesian geometry. There are two common mistakes made with these big topics:

The first is to do *too much too soon.* The topic may have been introduced in a wonderful and effective way, but if we build too much on the new foundation then many of the students may drown. The second mistake is *not enough follow-up and review.* Take percents as an example. It is introduced and practiced (perhaps too much!) in sixth grade, and then the students might never see it again.

So how should percents be done? It should be introduced in a wonderful sixth grade main lesson – not too much – and kept very simple. Then, one year later, the topic is reviewed and deepened – again being careful that it isn't too much. And then, once again, it is put to sleep. Now the stage has been set for going into depth in eighth grade. A similar three-step plan can be followed with any "big topic". If we want the students to learn something well and permanently, then we need to create a "dance" between introducing, deepening, practicing, sleeping, and reviewing.

What makes math meaningful?

For starters, no workbook or textbook (not even ours) can make math meaningful. Only the teacher can make math meaningful and inspire the students. Here are some ideas to help make math meaningful:

- *Make it developmentally appropriate.* The question should not be: "Are the children able to learn this material now?", but rather: "Are the children developmentally ready for this material?"
- *Work with questions.* Does the topic at hand answer a real question that lives within the student? It is meaningful for the students when they are able to answer a question that they have been living with.
- *Allow for depth.* The tendency in the mainstream is to teach too many topics. This leads to superficiality. By covering a topic in depth, we allow thinking to develop more effectively.
- *Challenge the students.* Every student should be challenged appropriately. The teacher needs to ensure that the level of challenge is manageable and allows for the students to feel successful.
- *Transform struggle into success.* The greatest feeling of success doesn't come from doing something easy. It comes from working through struggle, and accomplishing something significant.
- *Offer interesting material.* Engaging the students in the material is an important part of the art of teaching. Practical applications can make the material interesting to the students. But often a good puzzle, or a new type of problem can catch the students' interest, as well.
- *Provide the historical context.* It makes it quite meaningful for the students to realize that they are living and breathing the same thoughts that the greatest minds in history have also struggled with.

Regular and advanced track classes

In general, I feel that it is best to keep a class together until the end of eighth grade. This can be quite the juggling act for the teacher – to ensure that the top students are adequately challenged and to make adjustments so that the weakest students are still doing fine. To some degree, it is possible to keep a middle school class together using my seventh and eighth grade curriculum and workbooks because the topics completely change every unit (i.e., a student who struggled with *Number Bases* gets a completely fresh start with the *Pythagorean Theorem*).

This all changes in ninth grade when algebra is the main theme for the year. Given the sequential nature of algebra (and the curriculum after that), it becomes necessary to split the math track classes (starting in ninth grade) into a faster and slower group – or what I call: an *advanced* and a *regular* group. The question then arises: how do we determine which students are placed in the two sections? Splitting a class into two sections is particularly difficult because we are splitting down the middle. (Ideally, it would be best to split a class into three sections if the school's enrollment allowed for it.) The mistake can be made to allow too many students into the advanced class, and to have a smaller regular class. Inevitably this leads to having an advanced class that isn't advanced, and a regular class that ends up being rather remedial. Although each class comes with its own considerations, I generally recommend that the advanced class be somewhat smaller than the regular class. What then are the criteria for a student to be placed into the advanced class? These are my criteria (in order of importance):

- a willingness and/or need to be challenged,
- not needing much review and repetition when learning a new topic,
- solid math skills (as shown on tests, etc.),
- a strong work ethic.

Regarding homework

In a variety of ways, teachers often feel pressured to give homework. If we didn't give homework, our parents and colleagues would think that we didn't take academics seriously.

My views on homework have shifted dramatically over the past few years. The only courses I teach that require a significant amount of homework are main lessons with essay writing. I give almost no homework in my math track classes.

Students often enter high school hating math homework, and this can make them hate math. The purpose of homework – to facilitate learning – is lost on most students. Homework is seen as something to simply get done; the goal is to avoid getting a bad homework grade or to avoid getting in "trouble". Years ago, I got tired of policing homework – trying to make sure that students weren't cheating on homework. They were clearly missing the point of what the homework was intended to do: strengthen their math skills. So I stopped grading homework. Now I don't even check to see if they did it. There is no homework grade. There is only one purpose for doing the assigned problems: to learn. In the short term, this usually means learning the material so that they can do well on a test. But I want my students to take responsibility for their own learning, and to realize that their work will help them, in the long term, to become stronger math students.

In my math track classes, I set aside a good deal of time in class (on average about 50% of the whole class period) for students to work on their assignments. This also allows me to answer most of their questions. The stronger students rarely need to take their work home.

Whatever homework we give should serve a real purpose. Perhaps the guiding question should be: "Will this homework assignment further their love and enthusiasm for learning?" When homework goes too far – and I believe that for high school it should be no more than an average of 90 minutes per night (in total, for all subjects) – then it inevitably dampens the students' natural enthusiasm for learning.

And, after all, shouldn't our students have the time to pursue their own passions outside school?

Regarding grades

Ideally, I would like to eliminate grades. In a world of inflated GPAs and grade-obsessed students, I see grades as having an overall detrimental effect on students' learning. Many teachers use grades as a way of motivating students; grades serve as a constant, and often unspoken, threat: "Do what I say or your grade will suffer!" And what are the consequences? Students cheating on homework and tests, students trying to motivate themselves to do work that they aren't interested in, and students becoming cynical about school and losing their interest in learning. By removing grades, teachers would have a hard time getting their students to do meaningless work; teachers would need to truly inspire their students. And students would need to find genuine inner motivation to do their work. Would this make a teacher's job more challenging? Perhaps in some ways, for some teachers.

The primary argument against eliminating grades is that our students wouldn't be able to get into colleges. This does not appear to be true. When going through a stack of applications, college admissions officers put applications without grades into a separate pile that require closer inspection. There are many high schools, with students going to excellent colleges, that don't give grades.

All of the above being said, I realize that eliminating grades would be rather unthinkable at most schools. At the very least, faculty should make space to have in-depth discussions about the various aspects of grades and grading.

Regarding tests

Any test should have a genuine purpose. It is easy to fall into the trap of thinking that every topic brought into the classroom must be practiced, thoroughly learned, and then tested. This is true for a skills-based topic, except if it's the introduction to a "big topic" (see above), in which case I usually don't give a test (e.g., intro to trigonometry in tenth grade). Otherwise, a test at the end of a skills topic serves a purpose: it gives focus and a clear goal by which the material must be learned. I make these tests quite challenging because I want my students to be prepared for the SAT and for tests they will encounter in college. However, there are many topics that are not skills-based (see *Balancing Skills and Mathematical Experiences*, above), such as a problem solving exercise, *Math and Music* (from our *10th Grade Workbook*), and most main lessons. In many of these cases I don't give a test at the end because I don't see that it serves a genuine purpose. But if I do give a test at the end of a main lesson block, then I design the test so that the students have an opportunity to show what they have learned. I want them to walk away with a positive feeling about the block.

Regarding functions

The major purpose for studying functions is preparation for calculus. I have found that ninth graders find work with functions to be perplexing; they are left wondering: why are we doing this? I feel that functions should be delayed until eleventh grade. As with Cartesian geometry, eleventh graders can learn and understand function much more quickly than ninth graders. And we can also honestly say: you will need this to be prepared for the twelfth grade calculus main lesson and for the SAT test.

Regarding vectors

In general, it is best to avoid teaching a topic that never leads to anything interesting or significant. This is why we delay the introduction of probability until ninth grade, when we can actually build up to problems that are challenging and thought provoking. Similarly, I advise coordinating the introduction to vectors with the mechanics main lesson. It could either be introduced briefly in the math track class, just before the start of the mechanics main lesson, or it could be introduced during the first few days of the main lesson itself. Done in this way, the students can experience a real application of vectors, which therefore gives it more meaning.

Regarding calculators

Our workbooks are in direct contrast to the common "wisdom" that a modern high school math textbook should be technology integrated. Homework assignments from standard textbooks often require scientific calculators, graphing calculators, and various forms of software in an attempt to make math entertaining. Math is not entertainment; math should be thought provoking and mind-expanding.

I am not anti-technology, but I am opposed to the inappropriate use of technology. The obvious question to ask should be: is the use of a calculator (or other form of technology) actually benefitting the students' learning? The answer is neither always "yes", nor always "no". High school students should not be required to do tedious calculations (e.g., long division) by hand. For these types of calculations, a calculator has its obvious benefits.

In our note *To the Student*, at the start of the student's workbook, we state: "A calculator should be a tool, not a crutch. The less you use one, the sharper your mind will become." This statement points to a problem in today's world: we are losing our ability to do simple calculations in our heads; we are losing our sense of number.

As educators placed in such an important role in the development of these young people, we must also wonder what harm is done, in terms of the development of one's thinking capacities, when a calculator makes simple mental calculations a thing of the past. I encourage teachers to think carefully about when to allow students to use calculators, and when not to. Unless there is a good reason to use a calculator, the default should be: *no calculator allowed!*

The problem with algebra

We live in a society where education has become a mad race. This has led to our schools pushing more and more material down the throats of children at an increasingly young age.

One of our most important goals for middle school math should be to have the students enter high school saying, "I love algebra, and I'm good at it!" If we teach a wonderful but simple algebra main lesson in seventh grade, and then spend just a few weeks in eighth grade reviewing and deepening what was introduced a year earlier, then our goal is achievable.

I advocate for saving most of "Algebra I" for ninth grade. In contrast, many schools today are succumbing to the pressure to teach a full year of algebra in eighth grade, or earlier. My concern with this is not just with the regular or struggling students; it also has negative consequences for the advanced students. These consequences (for pushing a full year of algebra in eighth grade) are:

1. The eighth grade teacher has no alternative but to offer a watered-down version of an *Algebra I* course.
2. Students get put into higher-level high school math courses (e.g., *Algebra II, Geometry*) but their algebra skills are not strong enough.
3. The majority of eighth grade is spent on algebra, and therefore other wonderful and necessary math topics are neglected (e.g., number bases, ratios, percents, proportions, etc). *Students then end up with weak basic math skills.*
4. Students end up entering high school with an antipathy toward algebra. They say: "I hate algebra, and I'm bad at it."

The problem with calculus

Calculus is not the Holy Grail.

For several decades now, the math curriculum in this country has revolved around preparation for calculus, and now, increasingly, we push our brightest students into calculus as soon as possible. For most students, this turns out to be something of a cruel joke – their whole math education is geared toward preparing for something that they will never experience; their last math course they will ever take may very likely be precalculus.

But it also has negative consequences for our brightest students. As with pushing students in middle school to take algebra before they are truly ready, students who take a full-year of calculus in twelfth grade (or earlier) suffer from three problems:

1. Their basic "precalculus" and algebra skills are not strong enough to be truly ready for calculus. In particular, their knowledge of trigonometry, logarithms, functions, and Cartesian geometry is lacking.
2. Largely because they are not ready for a proper calculus course, the teacher has a grim choice: either leave the majority of students in the dust, or water down the course. Usually the latter choice is made. The students then often go off to college thinking that they have had a true calculus course, then get placed into *Calculus II* during their first semester in college – and they don't have the proper foundation to succeed in this important course.
3. What was tossed aside in the quest for the grail? I know that if I don't cover a particular calculus topic in twelfth grade, then those going in math/science/engineering will get it in their *Calculus I* course during their first semester of college. I also know that if I don't cover my final unit of trigonometry, final unit of Cartesian geometry, polar graphing, or the philosophy of mathematics, then my students will never encounter these valuable topics.

I am not anti-calculus. I believe that calculus is very important. But I want to ensure that my top math students are prepared for whatever courses they will take in college, and I want to make sure that all of my students end their high school math experience with the most amazing math that they have yet encountered.

And I do, of course, teach some calculus in twelfth grade: one main lesson for everyone in the class, and two units of calculus (culminating with related rate/max min problems) to those in the advanced class, so that these students will be fully prepared – perhaps even a bit ahead – for a *Calculus I* course during their first semester in college.

Introducing Cartesian geometry: ninth grade or eleventh?

We recommend that the introduction to Cartesian geometry takes place in eleventh grade, and therefore our *11th/12th Grade Workbook* begins with *Cartesian Geometry – Part I*. In spite of our reservations, we have also included the same unit, *Cartesian Geometry – Part I*, in our *9th Grade Workbook*; we recognize that schools and teachers feel pressured to introduce Cartesian geometry in ninth grade, or earlier, and we wish to make our books accessible to these schools.

We know that it sounds radical to delay the introduction of the x and y-axis until eleventh grade, but there are good reasons. Here are some reasons why we feel it is best to wait until eleventh grade:

- If Cartesian geometry (also known as "coordinate geometry" or "analytical geometry") is introduced too early, it can be quite meaningless for the students. By introducing it later, the students can be brought to a deeper level of understanding. Additionally, eleventh graders can learn the material more quickly and more deeply than eighth or ninth graders.
- Historically, the creation of Cartesian geometry was a huge step in the history of mathematics, but this union of algebra and geometry came relatively late. The students can gain more of an appreciation of this human achievement if we first fully develop the subjects of algebra and geometry in ninth and tenth grade.
- If Cartesian geometry is introduced as part of an eleventh grade main lesson block (titled, *The Philosophy and Geometry of René Descartes*), there are many wonderful philosophical discussions in which the eleventh grader can engage. What were the implications for the development of mathematics? How did Descartes' work alter the course of science and influence our philosophical worldview? These conversations are much more fruitful in eleventh grade than in ninth grade.
- We feel that students should live as long as possible with a pure and imaginative picture of geometry (i.e., all of the Waldorf geometry main lessons) before introducing the more reductionist, algebra-based geometry.

- We are not saying that all types of graphing should be delayed until eleventh grade. Indeed, statistical graphs and many types of scientific graphs should be introduced as early as sixth grade. We are only advocating for delaying proper Cartesian geometry, which represents equations as geometric curves and attaches equations to geometric figures.

Twelfth grade regular track class

It's worth repeating: all students should end their high school math career with the most amazing math that they have yet encountered. This includes those who do not have ambitions to study math in college. Yet, often, the students in the "regular" class end their high school math careers in a fairly mundane fashion. Perhaps the topic covered was something from precalculus or "business math" (which sounds like something for sixth graders). All too often, the math teacher for the regular class sees the final math class for the regular twelfth graders as a last chance to save them from their weak math skills. Instead it should be seen as a last chance for them to have an incredible mathematical experience. In fact, I believe that we should be mostly finished with math skills work by the middle of eleventh grade (for this group of students), which would free them up to spend more than a year doing the best math they have ever encountered. What topics would that be? Well that depends upon the teacher. For me, it is the philosophy of mathematics. For another teacher it might be chaos theory and fractals, or maybe problem solving, or statistics. There are numerous possibilities.

What if the students have weak math skills?

Despite our best efforts, and the best efforts of our middle school colleagues, there are often some students who enter high school with weak math skills. After concluding that a class has weak math skills, or is behind grade level, it is not uncommon for a high school math teacher to decide to spend several months reviewing lower grades math topics – fractions, decimals, percents, measurement, etc.

Even though the assessment may be accurate, it is critical that a class not get bogged down reviewing math from earlier grades. The students – no matter how weak – need to experience grade-level, challenging, and interesting material. As difficult as it may be, the teacher needs to find ways to weave review material together with new, grade-level material. All too often, the message teachers give to their students – even if unconscious and unintentional – is that they are behind and have weak skills. Therefore they aren't ready for grade-level math; they need "dumbed-down" material so they can manage it. This message is detrimental. Instead, we need to convince them (and perhaps ourselves, as well) that we have confidence in their abilities, that they learned more in the lower school than they may realize, and that if we work hard together, we can do even the most challenging math. They need to know we believe in them!

I question the notion that the weakest students should spend the most time on developing math skills. It is often best to pair down the skills work for these students to the bare essentials (and make sure they learn these skills well), and free up a significant amount of classroom time to do real math (e.g., puzzles, problem solving, etc.).

Will our Students be Prepared?

Preparation for life

Of course, there is much more to a high school education than preparation for college. Patrick Bassett, the former head of NAIS (National Association of Independent Schools), asks the question: "What are the skills and values that will be necessary for students to succeed and prosper in the 21st century?"[1]

In order to answer this question, Bassett refers to several sources, including: a Harvard-based study; the government's commission on education; a think tank for higher education; the academic testing industry; public opinion surveys; Tony Wagner's *Seven Survival Skills*; and Howard Gardner's book, *Five Minds for the Future*. What Bassett finds is a surprisingly high degree of congruence between these very different sources.

In the end, Bassett's list of six skills and values needed for the 21st century is:

1. *Character.* This includes a variety of qualities, such as empathy, integrity, resilience, courage, etc.
2. *Creativity.* Later in life, this quality manifests itself as adaptability and developing an entrepreneurial spirit.
3. *Critical thinking.* This includes problem solving, the ability to analyze information (filtering, analysis, and synthesis), questioning what you are "told" in the media, and thinking for yourself.
4. *Communication.* The emphasis here is public speaking. In today's information world of media and computer screens, children (and adults!) are losing their ability to speak articulately.
5. *Teamwork.* Working together productively and collaboratively has become more important than ever.
6. *Leadership.* Today, perhaps more than ever, the world is in need of inspirational leaders, who have strong values, and the courage and will to "stand up for the good".

I believe that the above six skills and values speak for the strength (and need!) of Waldorf education.

Preparation for college math

Broadly speaking, I believe that there are three critical ingredients that our students need in order to be prepared for the math they will encounter in college:

1. *Enthusiasm for learning.* If our students are truly enthusiastic about learning math, this naturally leads to interest in the material, and a motivation to do excellent work.
2. *Mathematical thinking.* If we can effectively develop true mathematical thinking in our students, they will be able to think analytically and problem solve as adults in the world.
3. *Basic math skills.* Yes, skills are important! However, the list of necessary skills isn't as daunting as we are often led to believe. The list is relatively short and is quite manageable.

[1] Patrick Bassett, *Demonstrations of Learning for 21st Century Schools*, Independent Perspective (Journal), Fall 2009.

What are the essential math skills?

Math educators often agree that there is too much of an emphasis on procedural skills in math education today. They say that we need to find more time to develop problem-solving skills and creative thinking capabilities. Yet, many teachers complain that there is never enough time for these "extras". We can begin to feel that there is an overwhelming amount of material that the students must learn, and, if they don't learn it all, they won't be ready for their future math studies. As stated above (see "The *LIST*" under *Today's Challenge*, above) the actual list of necessary skills is relatively short.

- Notes:
    - The below lists are simply intended as benchmarks in two-year intervals.
    - Each skill should be mastered by the time given; "mastered" means testable after a brief review.
    - Any skill listed under a certain year may very well be mastered a year earlier.
- *Skills needed by the end of fourth grade:* Arithmetic facts learned "by heart", and a *sense of number*. (Most teachers spend far too much time practicing procedural skills in grades 2-4.)
- *Skills needed by the end of sixth grade:* The four processes, fractions, decimals, measurement, estimation.
- *Skills needed by the end of eighth grade:*
    - Percents.
    - Area and volume.
    - Basic algebra (signed numbers, formulas, and basic equations) – no need for more!
    - Dimensional analysis (i.e., unit conversions).
    - Ratios, proportions, and rates
- *Skills needed by the end of twelfth grade for the regular math class*:
    - Basic algebra (mostly from our 9th *Grade Workbook*), including: work with formulas, exponents, polynomials and factoring, solving linear and quadratic equations, basic word problems, graphing linear equations, two-variable equations, systems of equations.
    - Basics of geometry: Pythagorean Theorem, angles of triangle add to 180°, etc.
    - Functions
    - Basic trigonometry: sin, cos, tan; right triangle trigonometry.
    - The ability to think mathematically and problem solve.
- *Skills needed by the end of twelfth grade for the advanced math class*: Everything listed under the twelfth grade regular math class, plus…
    - Logarithms
    - Advanced trigonometry (e.g., law of sines and cosines, $\cos^2 x + \sin^2 x = 1$, etc.)
    - Advanced Cartesian geometry (e.g., graphing polynomial functions)
    - Rational expressions and equations (e.g., $\frac{2}{x} + \frac{3}{x-1} = 4$)
    - Imaginary/complex numbers

The SAT test

I think the SAT is a fantastic experience for my students. I say this as a high school teacher in a private Waldorf school where the SATs are the first standardized test that our students encounter. The SAT test gives my eleventh graders the chance to "measure up" against their mainstream peers at a time when they are beginning to look out into the world and wonder what their destiny might be. The SAT occurs at a developmentally appropriate time. My math curriculum is designed, in part, to bring everything together (Cartesian geometry, functions, word problems, etc.) by the middle of eleventh grade so that the students will be ready to take the SAT for the first time at the end of eleventh grade. I tell my students that they should plan to take the SAT test three times, and expect to do their best in the fall of their twelfth grade year.

I feel strongly that my students should not be at a disadvantage on the SAT because they went to a Waldorf school; I want them to do well – and they do. How is it possible to have students do well on the math section of the SAT test? First of all, I refuse to make significant sacrifices in the curriculum just so that my students will be prepared for the SAT; I don't "teach to the test", but I do ensure that my students are "ready for the test". If we are successful in developing both math skills and mathematical thinking with our students, then we can get them ready for the test with fairly minimal classroom time.

I do an SAT prep math unit in the middle of eleventh grade that takes about 2½ weeks of track class time (7½ hours). I begin by giving them a three-page handout titled "Math SAT Summary Notes" (which can be downloaded from our website). This handout includes a few topics I left out of my curriculum but will likely appear on the SAT test (number lines, intersections and union of sets, inequalities, etc.). Most of the students are motivated enough to learn the new material quite quickly. Each night, their homework is to do a single 20 or 25 minute SAT practice test. I spend most of the classroom time teaching strategies for the test and going over problems.

The SAT is my students' first experience with a standardized test. While I am grateful that my students' education wasn't dominated by standardized testing, I feel that preparing for the SAT, just before they complete their Waldorf journey, is a hugely valuable experience. Many of my students wish to prepare more seriously for the SAT, so they take an SAT prep course that meets after school in the spring of their eleventh grade year.

Other standardized tests

ACT test. What's the difference between the ACT and the SAT? According to the ACT website: "The ACT is an achievement test, measuring what a student has learned in school. The SAT is more of an aptitude test, testing reasoning and verbal abilities." Put in other terms: the ACT tests more content and the SAT tests more critical thinking – although they both do both. I find that my approach to teaching math (mathematical thinking instead of blind procedures) fits best with the SAT.

PSAT test. Students typically take the PSAT in the fall of tenth grade or the fall of eleventh grade. The two most common reasons given for students to take the PSAT is: (1) it is practice for the SAT, and (2) that, if you do well, then you can win a National Merit Scholarship. This test comes too early for my students to be adequately prepared, so I am opposed to them taking it. I advise that if the students feel the need for extra practice for the SAT, the best thing to do is to take extra practice tests at home or take the SAT one extra time rather than take the PSAT at all. As far as the National Merit Scholarship, only about 1 out of 200 students who take the PSAT are awarded the scholarship, which is for $2500. There are many other college scholarships for students to consider.

Standardized state tests. Almost every state requires its public schools to administer standardized tests to its students. My intention here is not to take a stance for or against such testing. Public school teachers, who feel pressure to prepare their students for standardized tests, often ask me how it could be possible for them to use my curriculum. My response is similar to my situation with the SAT – avoid the temptation to "teach to the test". In any school, we need to make adjustments in order to meet the needs and requirements of the system and society in which we live. As a general guideline, I believe that 85% of our classroom time should be dedicated to teaching our "ideal" curriculum, and 15% of our time can be spent making necessary "adjustments" due to external pressures, such as standardized testing. If we instead make too many sacrifices to our curriculum in order to completely prepare our students for some standardized test, then likely our students will fare slightly better on the upcoming test, but over time they will not learn to think critically or creatively. It's short-term gain against loss-term loss. We have to ask ourselves: what's really important?

Tips for Success in Math

(a handout for students in grades 7-12)

Below are some thoughts to help you strive to become the best math student you can be.

- **Three Goals**: Math skills, mathematical thinking, and enthusiasm. The time you spend working on math problems will develop your math skills. Focusing in class, following the teacher's thought process, and working through challenging problems will all help to develop your mathematical thinking capacities. Perhaps it is most important to find ways to keep yourself enthusiastic about learning. After all, if you are excited about learning, then everything is more enjoyable and you will make better progress.
- **Things to Avoid**. Avoid or minimize the memorization of formulas and blindly following procedures.
- **Understand Deeply**. Good math students are never satisfied with going through a procedure without understanding what they are doing. Always question why something is true, and never be satisfied until you understand it deeply.
- **Make Lots of Mistakes**. Contrary to what many people think, mistakes are an important part of learning math. There is great value in becoming comfortable with being wrong and making mistakes. Learning from your mistakes is a critical part of becoming a good math student.
- **Organize Your Work**. You need to be able to follow your own work, but it doesn't have to be perfectly neat. Do hand calculations (fractions, multiplication, etc.) off to the side, or on a separate scratch sheet, but be sure to label it in case you need to find a mistake later.
- **Short Term vs. Long Term**. Don't fall into the trap of quickly getting through assignments just to get them done, or learning things superficially for an upcoming test. Take the time to learn things deeply. This will save you time in the long run, and lead to greater success.
- **Be Present**. Be fully present in class at all times. Every minute you spend in math class is an opportunity to learn. Before the start of each math class, tell yourself that your goal is to get as much out of class as possible.
- **Ask Questions**. Asking good questions is an important skill to develop in order to become a successful student. Find the courage to ask questions in class even if you are afraid of what others might think.
- **Keep Up**. Ask yourself every day if you understand the material. Try to clear up any confusion now, even if there is no test on the horizon. By keeping up on a day-to-day basis, you will not need to panic just before the test.
- **Follow Up**. When you get a problem on an assignment wrong, be sure to follow up – find out why you got it wrong, and figure out how to do it correctly. When you encounter something that you don't know how to do, make a note of it, and get your questions answered.
- **Be Determined**. You learn math best when you get confused and then work through that confusion. Struggle and frustration are part of doing math. Never get discouraged; get determined!
- **Responsibility**. Take responsibility for your own learning. Find the inner motivation to do your work for yourself – not for your teachers or your parents. By the time you graduate from high school, you should be fully independent.
- **Math and Life**. You will notice that most of the above tips can be applied to other subjects and other areas in life. We learn much about life by learning math. If math (and life) were always easy, we would miss out on important opportunities for personal growth.

A High School Math Curriculum Summary

9th Grade

Main Lessons

1. Possibility and Probability
2. Descriptive Geometry

Track Classes

Review middle school algebra
Laws of exponents
Arithmetic with polynomials
Solving systems of equations
Factoring
Solving quadratic equations
Word problems
Simplifying square roots
The quadratic formula and al-Khwarizmi's work
Rational expressions and equations
Negative and fractional exponents
Introduction to logarithms
Review of percents, unit conversions, proportions
Possibility and Probability

10th Grade

Main Lessons

1. Greek Geometry (Intro to Proofs)
2. Sequences and Series <u>or</u> Trigonometry and Surveying

Track Classes

Euclidean constructions (from 6th & 7th gr.)
Area transformation problems
Circle geometry
The Geometry of the Triangle
Writing proofs
The works of Archimedes (sphere and π)
Laws of proportionality (Euclid, Book V)
Mensuration (incl. volume and scale factors)
Proof of Heron's formula for triangle's area
Thorough review of 9th grade algebra
Intro to Trigonometry (up to Law of Sines)
Vectors (might be done in the physics lesson)
Sequences and Series (if not done in main lesson)
Logarithms (building from 9th grade)
Exponential growth, including the number *e*
Math and Music
Symmetry, patterns and tessellations (optional)

11th Grade

Main Lessons

1. The Philosophy and Geometry of René Descartes.
2. Projective Geometry.

Track Classes

Introduction to functions
Possibility and Probability (review & deepen)
Problem solving (in depth)
Cartesian Geometry
- Graphing linear equations
- Graphing conic sections
- Graphing polynomial equations
- Graphing systems of equations

Logarithms (building from 10th grade)
Trigonometry
- The Six Trig Functions
- Law of Cosines; Law of Tangents
- The unit trig circle and radian measure

Imaginary and Complex Numbers
- The complex number plane
- De Moivre's Theorem

12th Grade

Main Lesson: Introduction to Calculus

Track Classes

Precalculus Topics
- Analytical trig (identities and equations)
- Graphing trig functions
- Graphing exp. and logarithmic functions
- Graphing rational functions (asymptotes)

Calculus Topics
- Review and furthering of ML material
- Chain rule and implicit differentiation
- Related rate and max/min problems

Other Possible Topics
- Business math topics (e.g., mortgage formula)
- Topics from economics
- Statistics in the media
- Statistics (up to Central Limit Theorem)
- Spherical trigonometry
- 3-D coordinate geometry
- Chaos theory and fractals
- Philosophy of math (including Gödel's proof)

—— *Ninth Grade* ——

Developmental overview of ninth grade[1]

As the freshmen plunge into the high school, they are also plunging with new intensity into the materiality of their bodies (with the unfolding of puberty) and into the immateriality of abstract thinking. There is tension in this opposition – often struggle, occasionally even revolt. The ninth grade curriculum is sensitive to these tremendous developmental changes and struggles. It allows the students to see their inner experience reflected back to them in outer phenomena.

Ninth graders do not want to live in the past; they want to gain an understanding of how the modern world works through their own experiences. They can be largely focused on themselves, yearning to prove themselves, to test their emerging cognitive powers, and to see where they stand in the world.

The ninth grade math project – building algebra skills

In seventh and eighth grade math, the students study a great variety of topics (percents and growth, measurement, volumes, number bases, ratio and proportions, etc.), and hopefully also receive a wonderful but brief introduction to algebra. The ninth grader is ready to delve deeply into the intricacies of algebra in ways that the eighth grader is not. The goal of ninth grade math – quite an ambitious goal – is to build a solid foundation of algebra skills, a foundation which will serve the students well throughout the rest of their mathematical education. Ninth grade is the perfect year for building these algebra skills. The eighth grader is not mature enough to take it in deeply; the tenth or eleventh grader has moved on developmentally and no longer has the interest or patience for this kind of skills work.

Many of the algebra problems found in our *9th Grade Workbook* are quite complicated and require many steps. This poses the perfect challenge for ninth graders who are trying their best to hold themselves together, despite the drastic, sweeping changes that are happening to their physical bodies. The challenge is to come as close to perfection as one can in one's algebra technique. This requires extraordinary care, focus, and precision.

In many ways, we become more of a coach than a teacher – encouraging students when they feel defeated, and inspiring them to become the best they can become. In this way, ninth grade math is like learning a sport or a musical instrument; the only way to get better is to practice, practice, practice.

Yet, as the teacher, we still need to be mindful that the ninth grade math year doesn't become a grind for the students. We need to be sure that the students aren't just following *blind procedures* (see *blind procedures*, above). We must create situations for the students so that they have true mathematical experiences involving discovery, problem solving, and perplexing puzzles.

The units in our *9th Grade Workbook* are:

- Pre-Algebra
- Algebra Basics
- Exponents & Polynomials
- Factoring
- Word Problems
- Midyear Review
- Fractions & Square Roots
- The Quadratic Formula
- Logarithms, Part I
- Possibility & Probability, Part I
- Cartesian Geometry, Part I

A general unit-by-unit commentary with detailed explanations of the topics found in each unit is given in the introduction of the *Teacher's Edition of our 9th Grade Workbook.*

What is "Algebra I"?

While the bulk of our *9th Grade Workbook* covers topics found in any standard *Algebra I* course, there are some notable differences. We recommend delaying the first unit of Cartesian geometry until eleventh grade (although we do have the same unit at the end of the *9th Grade Workbook* – see more about this under *Thoughts on Teaching Math: Introducing Cartesian Geometry*, above). We also delay the introduction to functions until eleventh grade. Eleventh graders are developmentally ready to deeply and quickly learn these critically important topics (Cartesian geometry and functions) in order to be fully

---

[1] Part of each of these overviews is taken from Douglas Gerwin's *Genesis of a Waldorf High School*, "Waldorf High School Curriculum Guide", p12-15. www.waldorfresearchinstitute.org

prepared for the SAT test at the end of eleventh grade, and for an introduction to calculus in twelfth grade.

The delay of some topics until eleventh grade gives space for other topics in our *Algebra I* course. Our *9th Grade Workbook* therefore includes some topics that are not typically part of an *Algebra I* course – specifically: a review of eighth grade topics (percents, ratios, proportions, dimensional analysis), *Possibility & Probability*, al-Khwarizmi's derivation of the quadratic formula, and logarithms.

Main lessons for ninth grade math

- *Possibility & Probability.* This main lesson block, which includes permutations and combinations, offers a real mathematical experience in a branch of mathematics that, while completely numerical in nature, is nothing like what the students have seen before. This change of perspective is healthy for them; it allows them to realize that the world of mathematics is rich and varied. They tackle problems that at first glance seem impossible, such as: how many possible seating charts are there for a class of 25 students? Or, what is the probability of flipping five coins and getting all heads? As with the study of algebra, this block helps the ninth grader find order in a world that often seems chaotic. They learn that there is lawfulness in this world and that probability is a powerful tool that can be used to predict the outcome of events in the real world.

  This main lesson is described in detail later in this book. Following the completion of this main lesson, further practice of this topic appears as a unit towards the end of our *9th Grade Workbook*, and then again as a unit in our *11th/12th Grade Workbook*.
- *Descriptive Geometry.* This block is essentially a course in technical drawing. Whereas perspective drawing (seventh grade) offers a subjective view of a scene or object, descriptive geometry aims for a more objective truth. Through the use of multiple orthographic projections, objects are accurately and completely described in space. Careful drawing, relying upon both theoretical understanding and refined mechanical skill, improves our ability to see and strengthen our powers of imagination. In many ways, this block is in complete contrast to the rest of ninth grade math. However, as with algebra, descriptive geometry meets the ninth grader developmentally, requiring extraordinary care, focus, and precision. This main lesson is described in detail later in this book.

—— *Tenth Grade* ——

Developmental overview of tenth grade

From the turmoil of ninth grade, the tenth grader begins to discover a certain balance or midpoint between the violent collision of opposites. Physiologically, one may observe in boys a steadier gait, and, in girls, greater measure of poise and self-assurance. Mentally, the sophomores may begin to seek a certain order in the confusion, a midpoint to opposition. The curriculum responds to this search with subjects that incorporate balance: in chemistry, the study of acids and bases; in physics, the principles of mechanics; in embryology, the play of masculine and feminine influences.

Through these studies of balance in natural and human phenomena, students can begin to find their own fulcrum. In doing so, they are called to exercise powers of comparison, weighing in the balance contrary phenomena to determine their value and significance. This, in turn, prompts the desire to explore the origin of things and to find the source of their forms in the beginnings of history. The study of ancient times can now begin at a deeper level.

Tenth grade math – the development of logical thinking

While the ninth grade mathematics curriculum largely focuses on the development of algebraic skills, the tenth grade math curriculum allows for the study of a great variety of topics.

Tenth grade is thus the year of transition, and in math, the transition is from ninth grade algebra (pure number) to tenth grade geometry (pure form), and then, by the end of the year to mensuration and trigonometry (number and form intertwined). The Greek Geometry block is ideally placed for the tenth grade, as this is the year when many students start to wonder if anything they have been taught is really true. The question of the Greeks is: "How do we know what we know?"; the tenth graders are asking the same question. Thus, geometry and proof become a way for a tenth grader, who is struggling through the morass of adolescence, to begin the process of reconstructing everything that has recently fallen apart from childhood.

For this reason, it should not surprise the math teacher if a tenth grader, in the throes of his or her slump, cannot seem to remember even simple algebra from the year before. This is natural and to be expected. Forgetting is an important part of mathematics, and we should feel confident that, once the slump subsides, these skills will return in a more mature way.

Geometry is taught in both the block and the track in the first semester, as is deductive proof. This kind of logical scaffolding is very good for the tenth grader. It gives him the sense that there is a way to start from (almost) nothing and construct something quite beautiful and rigorous.

Main lessons and other material for tenth grade math

- *Main Lesson #1: Greek Geometry and Deductive Proofs.* This is a huge step in thinking for the tenth grader, so naturally it belongs in a main lesson block near the start of the year. There is a number of ways that the idea of a proof could be introduced, but we recommend the central focus to be Euclid's book, *The Elements*. The intention of this main lesson should be for the students to come to a deep understanding of what a proof really is, the idea of an axiomatic system, and the historical role of proofs in the world of mathematics. This main lesson is described in detail later in this book.
- *Main Lesson #2.* The second main lesson varies greatly depending upon the school – assuming that the school even has space for a second math main lesson in its curriculum. We recommend either *Sequences and Series* or *Trigonometry and Surveying* as the best option. Both of these subjects are described in detail later in this book.
- *Vectors and Mechanics.* Vectors tie in wonderfully to the tenth grade physics (mechanics) main lesson. There are two choices here, as we see it. Vectors can be introduced in the math track class just before the start of the mechanics main lesson, or it can be introduced during the first week of mechanics. Working together cooperatively between these two subject areas serves both well; it gives the background necessary for a successful mechanics main lesson, and it gives meaningfulness to the introduction to vectors. Obviously, the unit on trigonometry needs to precede an introduction to vectors. If the trigonometry foundation is adequate, then the intro to vectors need not take much time.
- *Proofs of Beauty.* The objective here is for students to see significant proofs – works of art – done by great mathematicians and experience it with a sense of awe. They can be brought either in main lesson or in track class. These proofs, all fully described later in this book, are:
    - Euclid's proof of the Pythagorean Theorem (Th. I-47 from *The Elements*)
    - Ptolemy's Quadrilateral Theorem.
    - Archimedes' derivation of the formula for the volume of a sphere.
    - Archimedes' calculation of π.
    - Archimedes' derivation for the area of a parabolic segment.
    - The proof of Heron's formula for the area of a triangle.

The units in our *10th Grade Workbook* are:

- Geometry Basics
- Circle Geometry
- Triangle Geometry
- Proofs
- Mensuration
- Algebra Review (levels A and B)
- Logarithms, Part II
- Trigonometry, Part I
- Exponential Growth
- Sequences & Series
- Math & Music

A general unit-by-unit commentary with detailed explanations of the topics found in each unit is given in the introduction of the *Teacher's Edition of our 10th Grade Workbook.*

—— *Eleventh Grade* ——

Developmental overview of eleventh grade

The eleventh grade year is a time of newfound depths to the inner life of thoughts, feelings, and deeds. Deeper and more individualized questions often begin to burn. In these inner promptings, a new and urgent voice speaks. "Leave behind what you have been given," it says, "and get on with your own journey!"

The junior year curriculum can be characterized by a theme of invisibility; we study subjects that are inaccessible to the experience of our senses. The curriculum becomes more philosophical and less practical. Such a journey requires a new type of thinking – thinking not anchored in what our senses give us – and a confidence that this type of thinking will not lead us astray.

Eleventh grade math – real mathematical thinking

The eleventh grader is now equipped to tackle real, modern mathematics. To some degree, their whole mathematics education has led them to this point: in the early grades, they learned arithmetic skills and developed a sense of number; in middle school, they learned to think both more abstractly (with the introduction to algebra, ratios, and number bases), and more practically (with business math, percents, the Pythagorean Theorem, and unit conversions); in ninth grade, they learned the language of algebra; and in tenth grade, they learned to think logically as they studied the mathematics of the ancient Greeks. Now, in eleventh grade, they are ready to go further and take their mathematical thinking to a new level. They should encounter topics and problems which demand serious problem solving and have a more philosophical nature. They can begin to get a genuine taste of the thinking required of real mathematicians, scientists, and engineers. Both of the eleventh grade main lessons (*Projective Geometry* and *The Philosophy and Geometry of René Descartes*) lend themselves to this endeavor, as do themes found in our *11th/12th Grade Workbook*: infinity, the number *e*, alternative coordinate systems, complex numbers, and a general theme of problem solving. Yet we still have a need to continue building math skills that will be needed for college (especially for the advanced class), including trigonometry, Cartesian geometry, and functions.

Unfortunately, all too often, the eleventh grade math year is nothing but skills work. The eleventh graders need something more. We must find a way to dedicate significant classroom time to mathematical experiences and real problem solving. Our *11th/12th Grade Workbook* has an entire section on problem solving exercises, some of which take the students on mathematical journeys that can last several class periods. Give it a try!

Eleventh grade main lessons

- *The Philosophy and Geometry of René Descartes*

  Once again, we go back to the source, as we investigate how Descartes discovered his new geometry – what we now call Cartesian geometry. His geometrical work is embedded within a greater philosophical work, *A Discourse on the Method of Rightly Conducting One's Reason and Searching for the Truth in the Sciences*, which was both a pioneering work in modern philosophy and served as a catalyst for the emerging scientific method. His geometry is dense and difficult reading. Most surprising, perhaps, is that nowhere do we see what we assumed must be his starting point – the X-Y coordinate plane. As we penetrate his work further, we feel ourselves begin to think as he did, and we go back in time, to an earlier stage of the evolution of consciousness.

  This main lesson is described in detail later in this book.

- *Projective Geometry*

  Projective geometry may be the most radical aspect of the Waldorf math curriculum. Rudolf Steiner saw great benefit in this topic as a means for developing imaginative and creative thinking. Projective geometry transcends the limits imposed by Euclidean geometry – which still dominates most people's conception of geometry – by asking the unthinkable: "What would happen if parallel lines actually met at infinity?" The journey is philosophical, mind-bending, and somehow very satisfying.

  This main lesson is described in detail later in this book.

The units in our *11th/12th Grade Workbook* are:

- Cartesian Geometry, Part I
- Trigonometry, Part II
- Complex Numbers, Part I
- Cartesian Geometry, Part II
- Possibility & Probability, Part II
- Trigonometry, Part III
- Cartesian Geometry, Part III
- Logarithms, Part III
- Complex Numbers, Part II
- Trigonometry, Part IV
- Cartesian Geometry, Part IV
- Calculus, Part I
- Calculus, Part II
- Statistics, Part I
- Statistics, Part II
- Problem-Solving Exercises

A general unit-by-unit commentary with detailed explanations of the topics found in each unit is given in the introduction of the *Teacher's Edition of our 11th/12th Grade Workbook.*

— *Twelfth Grade* —

Developmental overview of twelfth grade

The central theme of twelfth grade is synthesis. The senior year is intended, on the one hand, to be the gradual synthesis of our students' education – the great stock-taking and preparation for the next stage in learning – and, on the other, the fully conscious placement of oneself in the center of this panorama. By twelfth grade, the student is asking, "Who am I? What does it all mean?" The twelfth grade curriculum serves these purposes by offering subjects that synthesize many themes and relate these themes to the centrality of the human being.

Twelfth grade math– The Grand Finale

If we have been successful, students enter twelfth grade in a very different place than one year earlier. Their knowledge of mathematics – both in terms of skills and the ability to think mathematically – has greatly expanded. They are ready for something big. The *Introduction to Calculus* main lesson nicely serves this purpose. It gives students a sense of how far they have come, as they learn to appreciate the historical significance that calculus played in the development of thinking.

Other than the calculus main lesson, the twelfth grade math curriculum can be quite different for the advanced and the regular sections. For the advanced group, these students are likely looking toward further mathematics studies in college. They want to know that they are prepared. For these students, the first quarter of the twelfth grade is both a time to consolidate all of their algebra skills (including Cartesian geometry, trigonometry, functions, and logarithms) and an opportunity to bring everything to a new level. The material must be engaging and challenging. Following the completion of these "precalculus" topics, we have set the stage for the advanced section to go further with calculus, beyond the general introduction to the subject given in the main lesson.

The regular group should be freed from a skills dominant approach. (Read more about this in the above *Introduction* under "Twelfth Grade Regular Track Class".)

It is important for both the advanced and regular sections to end their high school mathematics studies with something of a bang; it's the Grand Finale! For me, it is the *Philosophy of Mathematics* which runs for a quarter of the year of track class, and includes the whole twelfth grade class together. For another teacher, it would likely be something else. There are endless possibilities.

Twelfth grade main lesson: *The Introduction to Calculus.*

This course gives the students an experience of the essence of one of the most important fields in mathematics. The goals of the course are very ambitious: (1) to give the twelfth graders an experience of discovering the two fundamental concepts of calculus: the derivative and the integral; (2) for the students to appreciate the historical and philosophical significance of the development of calculus; (3) to give the advanced students a strong foundation for further calculus studies; (4) to give the regular students a genuine calculus experience while allowing them to walk away saying: "I can do calculus!"

This main lesson is described in detail later in this book.

The units in our *11th/12th Grade Workbook* are given above (under *Eleventh Grade*) and explained in the unit-by-unit commentary of the *Teacher's Edition of our 11th/12th Grade Workbook.*

—— *Al-Khwarizmi's Algebra* (9th Grade) ——

Note: Muhammad ibn Musa al-Khwarizmi is known as the "father of algebra". His work, *Hisab al-jabr wal-muqabala*, written in 825AD, is considered to be the first book on algebra. These sections of al-Khwarizmi's book are found in our *9th Grade Workbook*; it focuses on his derivation of a version of the quadratic formula. I have reworded much of the text from Frederic Rosen's translation of *The Algebra of Mohammed Ben Musa* (pp 5-21).

On Calculating by Completion and Reduction

INTRODUCTION

When I considered what people generally want in calculating, I found that it is always a number. I also observed that every number is composed of units, and that any number may be divided into units.

Furthermore, I observed that the numbers which are required when calculating by completion and reduction are of three kinds, namely: roots, squares, and simple numbers[1]. Of these, a root is any quantity which is to be multiplied by a number greater than unity, or by a fraction less than unity. A square is that which results from the multiplication of the root by itself. A simple number [henceforth called only "number"] is any number which may be produced without any reference to a root or a square.

Of these three forms, then, two may be equal to each other, for example: squares equal to roots, squares equal to numbers, and roots equal to numbers[2].

Section I. CONCERNING SQUARES EQUAL TO ROOTS

The following is an example of squares equal to roots: "A square is equal to five roots". The root of the square then is five, and twenty-five forms its square, which is indeed equal to five times its root.

Another example: "One-third of a square equals four roots." Then the whole square is equal to 12 roots. So the square is 144, and its root is 12. Another such example: "Five squares equal ten roots." Therefore one square equals two roots. So the root of the square is two, and four represents the square.

In this manner, that which involves more than one square, or is less than one square, is reduced to one square. Likewise, the same is done with the roots; that is to say, they are reduced in the same proportion as the squares.

Section II. CONCERNING SQUARES EQUAL TO NUMBERS

The following is an example of squares equal to numbers: "A square is equal to nine." Then nine is the square and three is the root. Another example: "Five squares equal 80." Therefore one square is equal to one-fifth of 80, which is 16. Or, to take another example: "Half of a square equals 18." Then the whole square equals 36, and its root is six.

Thus any multiple of a square can be reduced to one square. If there is only a fractional part of a square, you multiply it in order to create a whole square. Whatever you do, you must do the same with the number.

Section III. CONCERNING ROOTS EQUAL TO NUMBERS

The following is an example of roots equal to numbers: "A root is equal to three." Then the root is three and the square is nine. Another example: "Four roots equal 20." Therefore one root is five, and the square is 25. Still another example: "Half a root is equal to ten." Then the whole root is 20 and the square is 400.

[In addition to the three above cases] I have found that these same three elements can produce three compound cases, which are:

Squares and roots equal to numbers,
Squares and numbers equal to roots, and
Roots and numbers equal to squares.

[These three above cases are variations of a quadratic equation. Sections IV, V, and VI give methods for solving each of these cases. Only section IV, which deals with the first case, is included in this source book and in our *9th Grade Workbook*.]

---

[1] The term "roots" stands for multiples of the unknown, our x; the term "squares" stands for multiples of our x^2; "numbers" are constants.

[2] In our modern notation, this is $x^2 = bx$, $x^2 = c$, $x = c$.

Section IV. CONCERNING SQUARES AND ROOTS EQUAL TO NUMBERS

The following is an example of squares and roots equal to numbers: "A square and ten roots are equal to 39." The question here is: "What must the square be such that when it is combined with ten of its own roots, it will amount to a total of 39?" To solve this, you take half the number of roots, which in this case gives us five. Then you multiply this by itself to get 25, and then add that result to 39, which gives us 64. Now take the root of this, which is eight, and subtract from it half the number of roots, resulting in three. This is the root of the square which you sought; the square itself is then nine.

This method is the same when you are given a number of squares. You simply reduce them to a single square, and in the same proportion you reduce the roots and simple numbers that are connected with them.

For example: "Two squares and ten roots equal 48." The question therefore is: "What must the amount of the two squares be such that when they are summed up and then combined with ten times their root, the result will be a total of 48?" First of all it is necessary that the two squares be reduced to one. So we take half of everything mentioned in the statement. It is the same now as if the original question had been: "A square and five roots equal 24", which means: "What must the amount of a square be such that when it is combined with five times its root, the result will be a total of 24?" To solve this, we halve the number of roots, which gives us 2½, and multiply that by itself, giving 6¼. To this we add 24, which yields a sum of 30¼, and then take the root of this, which is 5½. Subtracting half the number of roots, which is 2½, from this makes a remainder of three. This is the root of the square, and the square itself is nine.

[In section V Al-Khwarizmi gives a solution for solving *Squares and Numbers Equal to Roots* ($10x = x^2 + 21$). Section VI gives a solution for solving *Roots and Numbers Equal to Squares* ($3x + 4 = x^2$). We are skipping over these two sections. We will now pick up with the last paragraph of section VI, which reads as follows:]

I have now explained the six types of equations, which I first mentioned at the beginning of this book. I have taught how the first three must be solved; with these, it was not required that the roots be halved. And I showed how, with the other three, halving the roots is necessary. I now think it is necessary to explain the reason for halving.

Section VII. A DEMONSTRATION OF THE CASE "*A Square and Ten Roots Equal 39.*"

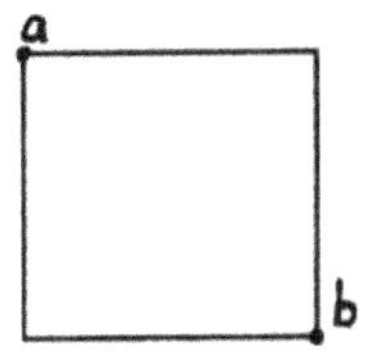

First, we construct a square ab of unknown sides. This square represents the square which, together with its root, you wish to find. Any side of this square represents one of the roots that we wish to know. We will now take one-fourth of the number of roots, namely one-fourth of ten, to get 2½. Combining this with the side of the square gives us four new rectangles (c, d, e, f), which we will place onto the sides of the square [as shown in the middle drawing].

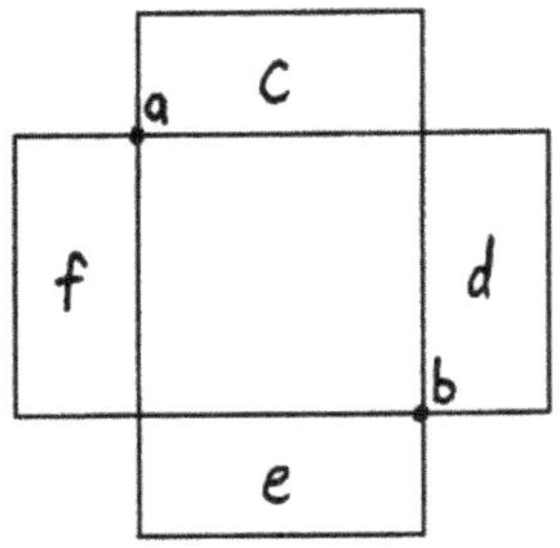

We now have a new, larger square except that small square pieces are missing from its four corners. These four corners each have an area of 2½ times 2½. When we add these four corners to our figure [as shown in the lower drawing], we have increased the area by four times the square of 2½, which is 25.

From the original statement we know that the square ab combined with the four rectangles, which together represent ten roots, must be equal to a total of 39. To this we add 25 (the area of the four small corners) to get a total of 64, which is the area of the great square GH. One side of this great square must then be eight. If we subtract twice a fourth of ten, which is five, from this eight then we get three – the root of the square which we sought.

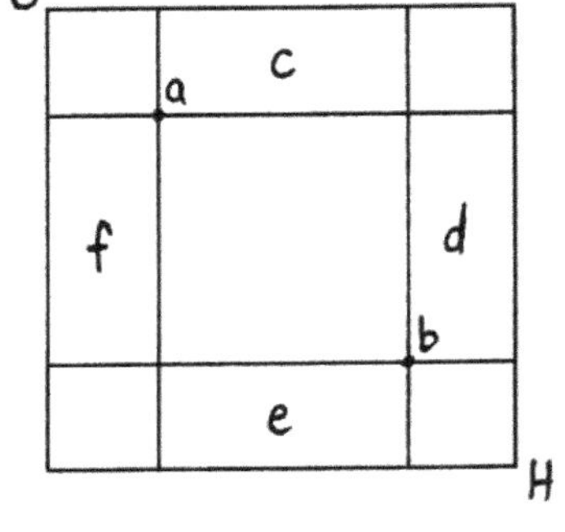

It must be observed that here we have taken one-fourth the number of roots, multiplied that result by itself, and then multiplied that by four, which is the equivalent of taking half the number of roots and then multiplying that by itself [which is what was done in section IV].

Section VIII. A DEMONSTRATION OF THE CASE "*Ten Roots Equals a Square and 21.*"

[This is our rewording of Section VIII.[1] This section *is not* found in our *9th Grade Workbook.*]

This is the type of quadratic equation that yields two (positive) solutions. The two solutions emerge from whether we draw the rectangle having a height more or less than half of the base (assuming the base is greater than the height).

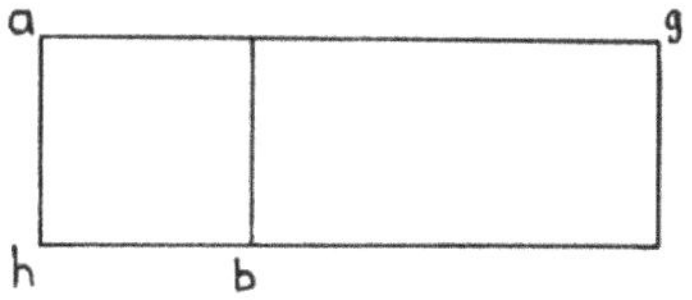

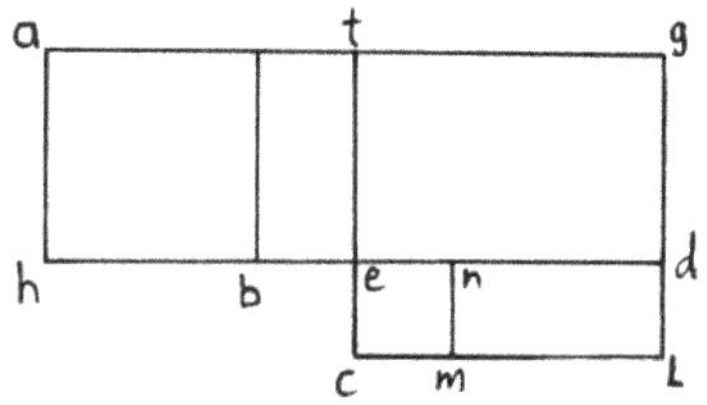

Solution #1 (The height of the rectangle is less than half its base.)

First, we draw square *ab* (which represents x^2) and then attach to it rectangle *bg* (which represents the 21 units) so that it is larger than the square *ab*. This now forms a larger rectangle *hg* (which represents 10x). At this moment, the diagram clearly represents the equation $10x = x^2 + 21$. Our goal is to determine x, the length of the side of the square, *ah*.

Al-Khwarizmi bisects *ag* at *t*, constructs square *cg*, and then constructs square *nc* (so that *en* = *ec*). The rectangle *tb* is congruent to rectangle *md*. This means that rectangle *bg* and gnomon *tenmlg* both have equal areas of 21. Since *ag* is 10, *tg* is 5, and the square *tg* has an area of 25. Now, the square *nc* has an area of 4 (the area of the square *cg* minus the area of the gnomom). So, *ec* must be 2, and *tc* minus *ec* then gives a length of **3** for both *te* and *ah*, which is the desired length of the side of the square *ab*.

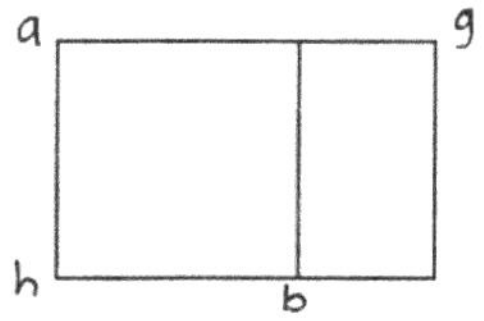

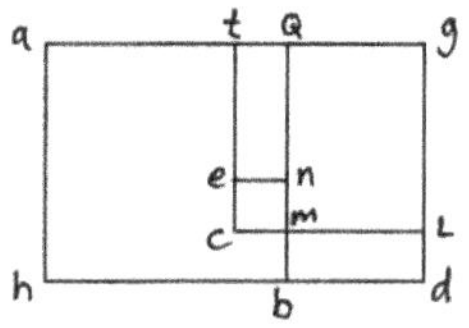

Solution #2 (The height of the rectangle is greater than half its base.)

This time we begin our drawing by making rectangle *bg* smaller than the square *ab*. Our goal, once again, is to find the length of the side of the square, *ah*. Again, we bisect *ag* at *t*, construct square *cg*, and then construct square *nc* (so that *en* = *ec*). The rectangle *tn* is congruent to rectangle *md*. This means that rectangle *bg* and gnomon *tenmlg* both have equal areas of 21. Since *ag* is 10, *tg* is 5, and the square *tg* has an area of 25. Now, square *nc* has an area of 4 (the area of the square *cg* minus the area of the gnomom). So, *nm* must be 2, which is also the length of *mb*. Therefore, Q*m* (which is 5) plus *mb* gives a length of **7** for Q*b*, which is also the desired length of *ah*, the side of the square *ab*.

Section IX. A DEMONSTRATION OF THE CASE "*A Square Equals Three Roots and 4.*"

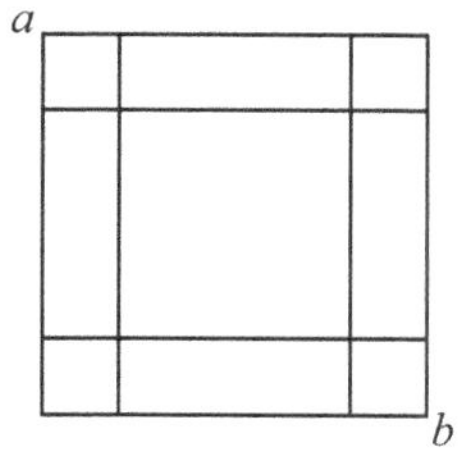

[Al-Khwarizmi uses a diagram similar to the last one in order to prove this last case. I, however, have come up with the following proof, which is more similar to his first proof given in section VII, which is the best known. This section *is not* found in our *9th Grade Workbook*]

We start with square *ab*. Our goal is to find the length of the side of this square. Since the rectangle ("three roots") is smaller than the square, we cut it parallel to its base into four thin strips and then put these four strips *inside* the square such that where they overlap forms four small squares at the corners of the larger square (as shown on the right). Given that the original rectangle had a width of 3, we know that the small squares each have an area of $(3/4)^2$, which is $9/16$. If we move all of these small squares toward the center (shown in the lower drawing) then the rectangle has now been cut into eight pieces that fit inside the original, large square in a way that the pieces no longer overlap. Since the original problem states that the area of the square is 4 greater than the area of the rectangle, the shaded region represents how much larger the original square is than the rectangle. The shaded region thus has an area of 4, and when combined with the four small corner squares (each with an area of $9/16$) we get a medium-sized square (the shaded area sits inside this square) with an area of 6¼. The side of this square is then the square root of 6¼, which is 2½. By looking at the diagram, we can see that the desired length of the side of the original square *ab* must be 2½ + ¾ + ¾, which is **4**.

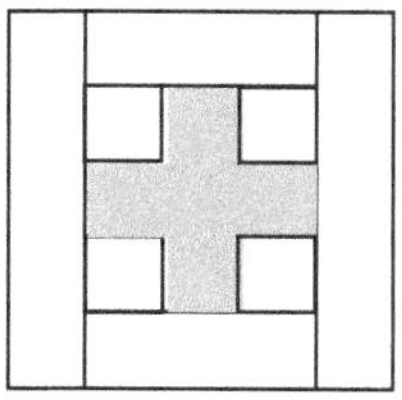

[1] See a *History of Mathematics*, by Carl Boyer, pp231-232, John Wiley & Sons, 1991.

—— *Possibility and Probability* (9th Grade Main Lesson) ——

Overview

The subject of *possibility and probability* (which includes permutations and combinations) concentrates on answering questions such as: How many possible (shortest) routes are there for going between two points marked on a grid? How many ways are there for twenty students to get in line? How many different committees of three can be formed from a group of ten people? What is the probability of flipping five coins and getting all heads?

These questions often yield surprising results. It is through careful thinking that we can overcome the task of making sense of these difficult problems. We recognize patterns and similarities with previously encountered problems and learn to solve the problems in a systematic way.

The students work both independently and in groups to solve problems. Carefully worded explanations of a few solutions are written in their lesson books. Each student is challenged at some point during the course, and hopefully develops confidence in their thinking.

Lesson plans

Detailed day-by-day lesson plans can be downloaded from our website: **www.JamieYorkPress.com**.

The big picture

This block is only intended to be an introduction to this subject area. These problems can get very difficult. In this block we are working with the big picture. We only do a few central problems very thoroughly. The purpose here is not to work on skills; we don't expect the students to become proficient at these problems during this main lesson block. Later in the year, they will revisit this topic in the track class as they work with the *Possibility & Probability* unit in our *9th Grade Workbook.* This is when the students get to practice solving many of these problems. Then in eleventh grade they revisit the topic once again and work with more challenging problems in the *Possibility & Probability* unit of our *11th/12th Grade Workbook.*

Learning to think independently

At the start of this block, I give a motivational speech about the importance of learning to think for yourself. I make the point that most people today simply believe what they are told (e.g., in the TV news, or on the Internet). I say to the students: "In the lower grades, you were expected to believe what your teacher told you. Your teacher probably told you that π was approximately 3.14. You believed your teacher. It is now time for you to start thinking for yourself." Here is the key thought for our block:

> *"Don't just believe what you're told. Believe it only when you know – in your own thinking – that it's true."*

Central questions

- With each of the below questions, I try to get the students to discover the answer as much as possible on their own; I resist the temptation to give them answers. Students present their ideas to the class, and slowly everyone comes to clarity about the correct solution.
- After they have reached clarity about a solution, they write up the problem in their main lesson books. For each essay, I expect a statement of the question, a description of what they did (even if they made an error), and a full explanation of the correct solution.
- *The Street Problem.* How many shortest routes are there from A to B?

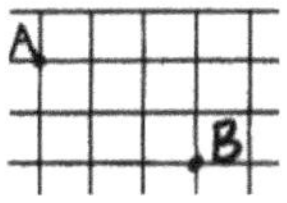

  - I begin the block with this question. The students inevitably draw out all of the possible routes, and usually come up with the correct answer (10).
  - Then I ask how many possibilities would there be for a 5x6 grid? Finding a method to answer this question becomes a goal for the block.
- *The Wardrobe Problem.* How many possible outfits can you choose to wear if you have 3 pants and 5 shirts to choose from?
  - This leads to the *Fundamental Counting Principle* (see the Summary Sheet below).
- *The Seating Chart Problem.* How many possibilities are there for making a seating chart for the class?
  - This leads to the idea of factorial.

- I also ask the following question (which leads to surprising results):
  Question: If you rearranged the class into a different seating chart every second, how long would it take before you exhausted every possibility?
  Solution: For a group of size n, we get: t = n! seconds÷3600sec/hour÷24hr/day÷365days/year
  If n=13, n!=6,227,020,800 $t \approx 197$ years.
  If n=18, $n! \approx 6.40 \cdot 10^{15}$ $t \approx 203{,}000{,}000$ years
  If n=25, $n! \approx 1.55 \cdot 10^{25}$ $t \approx 492{,}000{,}000{,}000{,}000{,}000$ years
- *The License Plate Problem.* How many possibilities are there for a license plate that has 3 digits followed by 3 letters? (Answer: $10^3 \cdot 26^3$) This is an extension of the *Fundamental Counting Principle.*
- *The Prize Problem.* How many possibilities are there for giving out 1st, 2nd, 3rd place prizes in a race that has 53 participants?
  - This leads to the idea of a *Permutation* (see the Summary Sheet, below).
  - The notation is ${}_nP_r$, which means the first r numbers of n factorial multiplied together.
- *The Committee Problem.* How many possibilities there are for selecting 3 people out of 5 to be on a committee.
  - First ask: how many possibilities are there for selecting a Pres, VP, and Sec from a group of 5 people? Then ask the above question and make sure they understand the difference.
  - This is probably the most difficult step in the block. We should build up slowly to an understanding of the below table:

Total # of people	# of people selected	# of possibilities for prize problem	# of possibilities for committee problem
5	3	${}_5P_3 = 60$	${}_5C_3 = \frac{{}_5P_3}{3!} = \frac{60}{6} = 10$
7	2	${}_7P_2 = 42$	${}_7C_2 = \frac{{}_7P_2}{2!} = \frac{42}{2} = 21$
10	3	${}_{10}P_3 = 720$	${}_{10}C_3 = \frac{{}_{10}P_3}{3!} = \frac{720}{6} = 120$
20	4	${}_{20}P_4 = 116{,}280$	${}_{20}C_4 = \frac{{}_{20}P_4}{4!} = \frac{116280}{6} = 4845$
75	5	${}_{75}P_5 = 2{,}071{,}126{,}800$	${}_{75}C_5 = \frac{{}_5P_3}{3!} = \frac{60}{6} = 17{,}259{,}390$

  - This leads to the idea of a *Combination* (see the Summary Sheet, below).
  - The notation is ${}_nC_r$, which means ${}_nP_r$ divided by r!
- *Word Scrambling.*
  - Build up to this slowly by asking students to figure how many ways there are to arrange the letters in these words: MARK, TARA, MOMO, JESSE, BOBBY, etc.
  - This leads to the idea of *Distinguishable Arrangements* (see the Summary Sheet, below).
- *Introduction to Probability.*
  - We only give a brief intro to probability in this block. We go into much more detail, and do much more challenging problems, in eleventh grade with the *Possibility & Probability* unit of our *11th/12th Grade Workbook.*
  - Introduce the formula $P = \frac{\text{number of successful outcomes}}{\text{number of total possible outcomes}}$
  - But we must make clear – this formula assumes that each possibility is equally likely.
    Example: When flipping a coin, we have a 50% chance of getting "heads" because each of the two possible outcomes is equally likely. When shooting a basketball, there are two possible outcomes when taking a shot: either you make a basket, or not. However, it is not correct to then say that you have a 50% chance to make a basket. The probability of making it depends upon many factors. Likewise, we can think that there are 11 possible outcomes (2-12) for (the sum of) rolling two dice. However, there isn't a $^1/_{11}$ probability of rolling a 10 because each of the 11 possible outcomes is *not* equally likely.

- *Rolling Two Dice.* What is the probability of rolling a (sum of) 10 with two dice?
    - We begin this problem by doing an experiment. Each student rolls a pair of dice 50 times and records the number of occurrences of each value. They then create a spreadsheet (e.g., Excel) to record the results in a table. (This is a good opportunity to do a brief lesson on how to use formulas in a spreadsheet.) If there are 20 students in the class, we will have 1000 results. The compiled results should then be studied, and interesting observations noted.
    - Then we can begin to address the main question: what is the (theoretical) probability of rolling a 10 with two dice? We list all 36 *equally likely* possibilities in order to see that three of them result in a 10. Therefore the probability is $^3/_{36} \approx 8\frac{1}{3}\%$.
    - Now we can fill out the following table:

    <u>Theoretical Probabilities for Rolling Two Dice</u>

total roll	# successes	Probability (%)
2	1	2.78
3	2	5.56
4	3	8.33
5	4	11.11
6	5	13.89
7	6	16.67
8	5	13.89
9	4	11.11
10	3	8.33
11	2	5.56
12	1	2.78

    - Now we can discuss how our experimental data compares with our theoretical answer. What can we say about this? How would it be different if we had rolled only 20 times? Or if we had rolled one million times?
    - This should lead to the *Statistical Probability Law*: *The more an event is repeated, the closer the average outcome gets to the expected (theoretical) outcome.*
- *Pascal's Triangle.* (See the next Summary Sheet for details.)
    - Have students point out various patterns that they notice.
    - Pascal's Triangle can help us solve probability problems.
- *The Street Problem – Revisited*: The 5x6 Street Grid problem.
    - Point out that the Street Grid problem is found within Pascal's Triangle – e.g., the number of possible routes with a 3x2 grid is ${}_5C_3$ (= 10), and with a 6x5 grid it is ${}_{11}C_6$ (=462).
        - To get to any point (x) in the middle of the grid, you have to come either from the point above x, or the point to the left of x. Therefore the number of possible (shortest) routes to x must be the sum of the number of routes to get to those two neighboring points.
    - With a 6x5 street grid, one route is to travel first 6 blocks east, and then 5 blocks south. This can be represented as EEEEEESSSSS. Therefore each possible route is simply a rearrangement of the string of letters EEEEEESSSSS $\rightarrow \frac{11!}{6!\,5!}$ (=462).
    - Amazingly, we now see how rearranging letters, the committee problem, the street grid problem, and Pascal's triangle are all related.
- *Birthday Problem.* In a (random) group of 50 people, what is the probability that at least two people have the same birthday?
    - This is the most advanced probability problem that we solve.
    - We ask instead: What is the probability that no two people have a common birthday?
        - If a twentieth person enters a room, the probability that he will not have a common birthday with anyone else in the room (all having different birthdays) is 346/365. This allows us to say that the probability of 50 people having no common birthday is: $P = \frac{365}{365} \cdot \frac{364}{365} \cdot \frac{363}{365} \cdot \frac{362}{365} \cdot \ldots \cdot \frac{316}{365} \approx 0.030$, which means there is only a 3% chance that the 50 people all have different birthdays. Therefore, there is a 97% probability that there is at least one common birthday.

Summary Sheet for
Possibility and Probability

The Fundamental Counting Principle (wardrobe problem)

The combined number of ways for two (independent) things to happen is the product of the number of ways for each of those things to happen separately.

Example: How many different outfits can Fred wear if he has 10 shirts and 8 pairs of pants?
Solution: For each of the 10 shirts he has 8 options for pants. Therefore, $10 \cdot 8 =$ **80**.

Permutations (prize problem)

The number of ways to select r *out of* n *items, and put them into order is:*

$${}_nP_r = \frac{n!}{(n-r)!} \quad \text{which is the first r items in n!}$$

Example: How many ways can the top 5 prizes be given out if there are 12 participants?
Solution: ${}_{12}P_5 = \frac{12!}{7!} \rightarrow 12 \cdot 11 \cdot 10 \cdot 9 \cdot 8 \rightarrow$ **95,040**

Combinations (committee problem)

The number of ways to choose a group of r *out of* n *items is:*

$${}_nC_r = \frac{{}_nP_r}{r!} = \frac{n!}{(n-r)!\,r!}$$

Example: How many committees of 5 people can be chosen from a group of 12?
Solution: ${}_{12}C_5 = \frac{12!}{7!\,5!} \rightarrow \frac{12 \cdot 11 \cdot 10 \cdot 9 \cdot 8}{5 \cdot 4 \cdot 3 \cdot 2 \cdot 1} \rightarrow$ **792**

Distinguishable Arrangements (rearranging letters)

With a total of n *items, of which* a *items are indistinguishable from each other, as are a further* b *items, etc., the number of distinguishable arrangements (or permutations) is:*

$$\frac{n!}{a!\,b!\,c!\,\ldots}$$

Example: How many ways are there to reorder the letters AAABBCCCCDEEE
Solution: $\frac{13!}{3!\,2!\,4!\,3!} \rightarrow$ **3,603,600**

The Probability of an Event

The probability of an event successfully occurring, P(E), *is equal to the number of possible (equally likely) success outcomes divided by the total number of possible (equally likely) outcomes.*

$$P(E) = \frac{\text{number of successful outcomes}}{\text{number of total possible outcomes}}$$

Example: One card is drawn from a standard deck. Find the probability of getting a spade.
Solution: The probability is $\frac{13}{52}$ or **25%**.

Sets that are not Mutually Exclusive

If A and B share members, then the number of members that are either in A or B is A plus B minus the number of members in both A and B.

$$A \cup B = A + B - (A \cap B)$$

Example: Everyone in a class is either a sophomore or a girl. 15 are sophomores and 12 are girls. If there are 8 students who are sophomore girls, how many are in the class?
Solution: $15 + 12 - 8 =$ **19**.

Summary Sheet for Possibility and Probability (continued)

Two Independent Events

If A and B are independent events, the probability that both A and B will occur is the product of probabilities of each occurring separately.

$$P(A \text{ and } B) = P(A) \cdot P(B)$$

Example: If you roll a die and flip a coin, what is the probability of getting a 2 and a head?

Solution: $\frac{1}{6} \cdot \frac{1}{2} = \frac{1}{12}$

Statistical Probability

The more an event is repeated, the closer the average outcome gets to the expected (theoretical) outcome.

Example: If we flip a coin n times, we expect that the number of heads will get closer to 50% for larger values of n.

Example: Since the probability of rolling a sum of a 9 with two dice is 11.1%, we expect that if we roll two dice one thousand times, then we will get a 9 about 11% of the time.

The Probability of a Complement

If A is the complement of B, then the sum of their probabilities is equal to one, or 100%.

Example: What is the probability of flipping three coins and getting at least one head?
Solution: The complement (or opposite) of this is getting no heads, which has a probability of $\frac{1}{8}$. Therefore, the probability of getting at least one head is $1 - \frac{1}{8} = \frac{7}{8}$.

Pascal's Triangle

1
1 1
1 2 1
1 3 3 1
1 4 6 4 1
1 5 10 10 5 1
1 6 15 20 15 6 1
1 7 21 35 35 21 7 1
1 8 28 56 70 56 28 8 1
1 9 36 84 126 126 84 36 9 1
1 10 45 120 210 252 210 120 45 10 1

Some properties of Pascal's Triangle:

- If we start counting with zero, then the number in the nth row and r^{th} column is ${}_nC_r$.
- From the property that was used to generate the triangle, we have ${}_{n-1}C_r + {}_{n-1}C_{r-1} = {}_nC_r$
- The sum of the numbers in the nth row is 2^n. In other words: $\sum_{r=1}^{n} {}_nC_r = 2^n$
- *The Binomial Theorem.* The nth row is the set of coefficients in the expansion of the binomial $(x+y)^n$, or $(x+1)^n$.
- The sum of the numbers in each "shallow" diagonal is a Fibonacci number.

—— ***Descriptive Geometry*** (9th Grade Main Lesson) ——

Overview

This main lesson block is essentially a course on technical drawing. It continues a theme begun in the eighth grade stereometry main lesson: the visualization of three-dimensional form. This drawing course focuses on producing exact drawings of three-dimensional solids from various perspectives.

The primary technique used is called orthographic projection, where the vanishing point, or the point of view of the observer, has moved to infinity. For each object placed inside the "viewing" box, the student initially draws the top view and front view. The main concept is that once the top and front views are known, the side view (or any other desired view) mechanically falls into place.

Lesson plans

Detailed day-by-day lesson plans can be downloaded from our website: **www.JamieYorkPress.com**.

Progression of drawings

Here is a possible progression of major concepts:

- *Freehand drawing of a dodecahedron.* The students simply look at a dodecahedron, and try to draw it as accurately as possible. This exercise helps them to appreciate what we will do later.
- *Six photos of a cube* (see next page). The students should compare the first two photos, and then photos #3 to #6. In comparing photo #3 with photo #6, we can conclude with photo #3 that the photographer was much further away from the cube, but zoomed in so that the cube appears to be about the same size. The point here is to discuss the ideas of perspective and point of view.
- *Two boxes.* The drawing shows two different perspectives of a box. (See drawing on next pages.) This is their first official drawing of the block – and therefore should be done with care. This is a brief review of one-point parallel perspective from seventh grade.
- Intro to the *viewing box* and the *three principle views*
  - An object (e.g., a point) sits inside the viewing box, and we imagine taking a photo (from far away) from above the box (top view), from in front of the box, and from the side.
  - It is important that we build up to a clear understanding of how this works. As an introduction, I use *Zome Tools* to build a viewing box, and then have the students start by drawing the three views of a point, and then a stick. (See below.)
  - Now we ask this question: What does each view tell us?
    - The front view tells us how far from the top and side it is. (We can't tell depth.)
    - The top view tells us how far from the front and side it is. (We can't tell height.)
    - The side view (also known as the "profile view") tells us how far from the front and top it is. (We can't tell left/right.)
- *The three principle views of a point floating inside the viewing box*
  - We start out by showing the top view of a point. It can be anywhere.
  - Now we ask: where can the point be located as drawn in the front view? Answer: the point in the front view must be located (in the drawing) directly below where it is in the top view. Since the top view tells us nothing about the height, we can choose any height we wish for the front view. We can now draw the front view of the point.
  - This is the central idea of the block: **Once you have the top and front views, then the side view is determined**. The front view tells the height, and the top view tells us the depth (i.e., the distance from the front face of the box). We can now locate the point in the side view as shown in the drawing here.

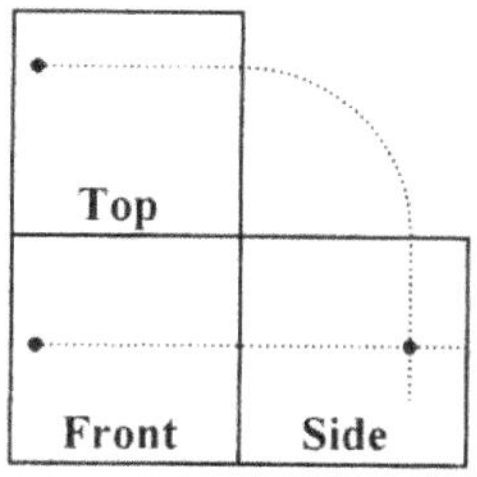

Three Views of a Point

- *The three principle views of a stick floating inside the viewing box*
  - Once the students understand the three views of a point, then we can have them practice drawing the three views of a stick. It just means that we are dealing with two points instead of one. (See drawing at right.)
  - *Descriptive Geometry – Problem Sets A and B* (downloaded from our website) give the students great practice with this.

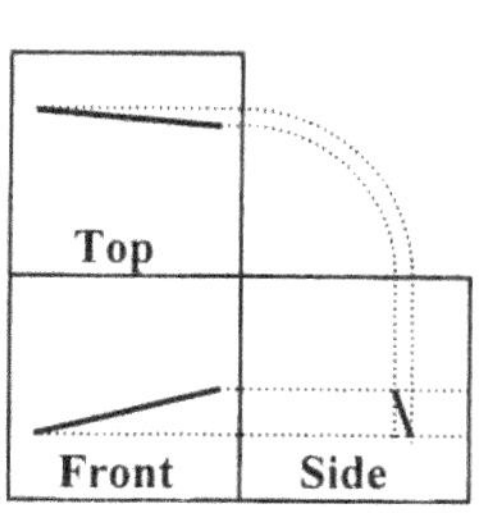

Three Views of a Stick

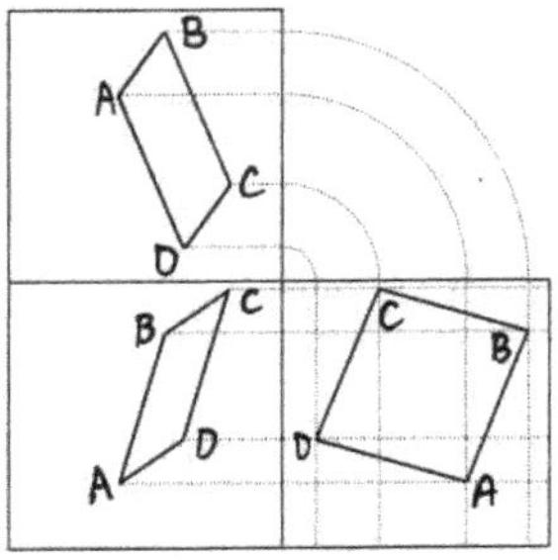

Three Views of a Square

- *The three principle views of floating polygons* (see drawing at right).
  - *Descriptive Geometry – Problem Set C* (downloaded from our website) gives the students practice completing the third view of various polygons.
  - This is the last step needed before drawing a 3-D solids.
- *Floating triangle.* This drawing is similar to the final drawings found in the problem sets, but now the students do the drawing from scratch. (See drawing on next pages.)
- *Three principle views of a pentagonal pyramid.* This is their first three-dimensional drawing. I often give the pyramid a pentagonal base because it gives some practice for the dodecahedron drawing, which comes next. (See drawing on the next page.)
- *The three principle views of a solid.*
  - This drawing is perhaps the centerpiece of the entire main lesson.
  - Once successful with the dodecahedron, students can then do three views of other solids, such as the icosahedron, or rhombic triacontahedron.
  - See the instructions and drawings on the following pages.
- *Rotated view of a solid.*
  - This is also known as a "primary auxiliary" view, or sometimes an "edge" view.
  - This takes the previous drawing one step further.
  - Once successful with the dodecahedron, students can then do rotated views of other solids, such as the icosahedron, or rhombic triacontahedron.
  - See the instructions and drawings on the following pages.
- *Rotated and lifted view of a solid.*
  - This is also known as a "secondary auxiliary" view, or an "arbitrary" view.
  - This takes the previous drawing one step further.
  - Once successful with the dodecahedron, students can then do rotated and lifted views of other solids, such as the icosahedron, or rhombic triacontahedron.
  - See the instructions and drawings on the following pages.

Six Photos of a Cube

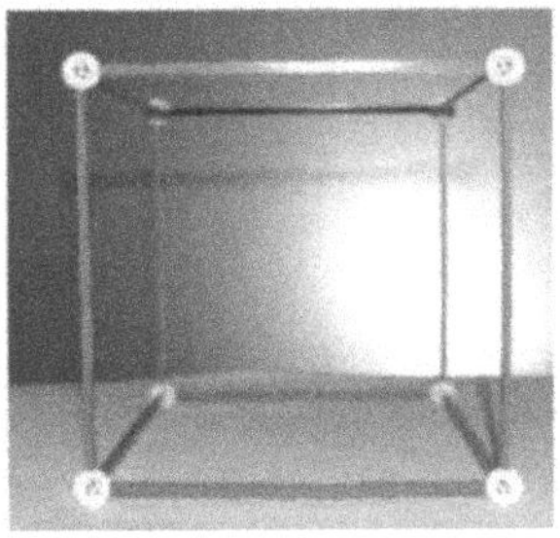

Photo #1

Photo #2

Photo #3

Photo #4

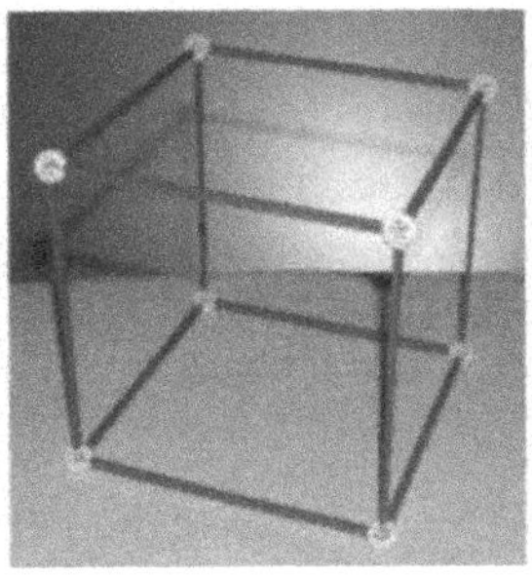

Photo #5

Photo #6

Two Boxes

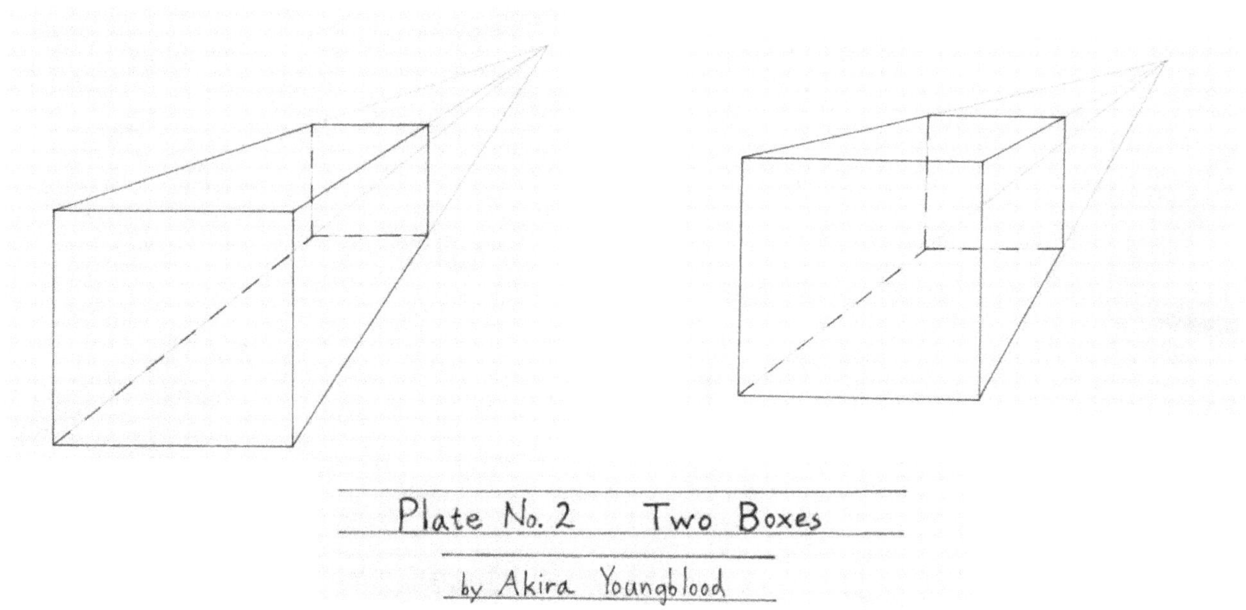

Our First 3-D Drawings

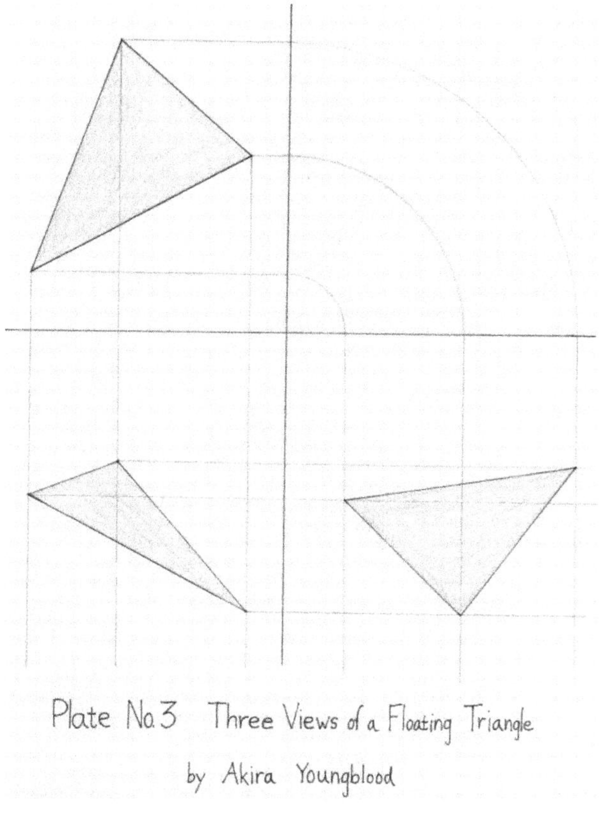

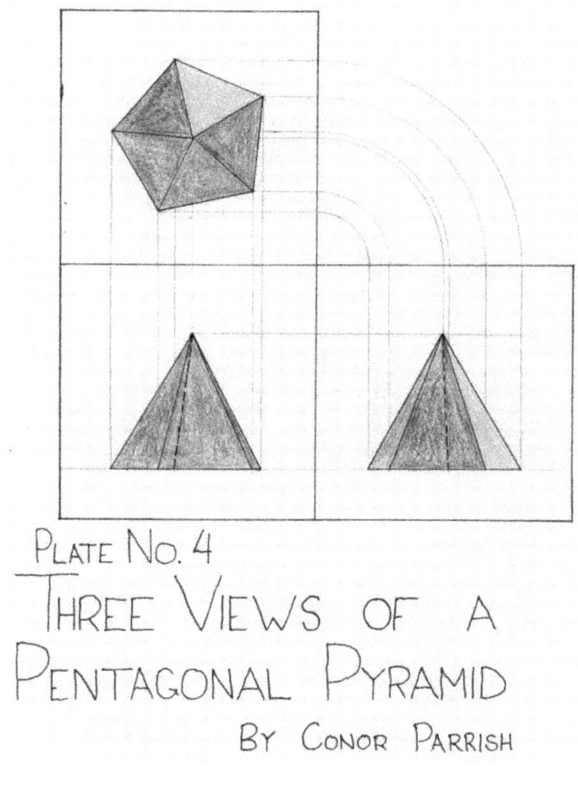

Instructions for Drawing a Dodecahedron

Note for the teacher: Before doing this, the students need to understand that any edge is drawn to actual size in a particular view only if the edge is parallel to the image plane (front, top or side).

The Top View:

- Start with ten evenly spaced points on a circle, such that two of the points are placed on the circle's horizontal diameter. In black ink, draw the decagon that connects these ten points.
- Draw an inner circle (lightly) that has a radius equal to the length of the side of the decagon (why is this?). Use the five diameters of the decagon in order to mark ten points on the smaller circle. Connect every other point of the inner circle thereby drawing two pentagons inscribed in this smaller circle. Make sure that the pentagon with solid (ink) lines has its left-most edge drawn vertically on the page (because this edge is perpendicular to the front face of the viewing box). The other pentagon is drawn with dotted lines.

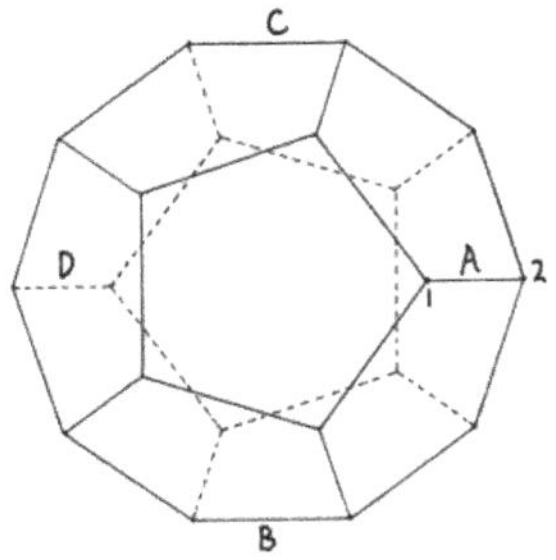

Top View

- Draw the remaining ten pentagonal faces of the dodecahedron, some of which are visible (with solid lines) and others are hidden (with dotted lines).

The Front View: (Carefully read through these instructions before trying them!)

- In the front view, all 20 points of the dodecahedron will be located on one of four horizontal lines drawn across the front view (with 5 points on each line). The five points of the dodecahedron's top face will be placed on the top-most of the four horizontal lines. The five points of the dodecahedron's bottom face will be placed on the bottom-most of the four horizontal lines. The rest of the dodecahedron's ten points will be placed alternately on the two remaining horizontal lines. *Our goal is to determine exactly how far apart the spacing must be between these horizontal lines.* This spacing is not arbitrary!
- Of the dodecahedron's 30 edges, four of them will be drawn to actual size in the front view. These edges (labeled as A, B, C, D) are the ones that are parallel to the front view and drawn in the top view horizontally across the page. The end points of edge A are labeled #1 and #2.
- In the top view, draw vertical lines (lightly in pencil) through each point that run down through the front view. In most cases, two points share the same vertical line. Label the vertical line through point #2 as line ***ℓ***, and the vertical line through point #1 as ***m***. (Lines ***ℓ*** and ***m*** are not shown here.)
- Point #1 in the front view of the drawing must be located on line ***m***. Choose point #1 to be about one inch from the top of the front view. (The rest of the points of the dodecahedron have now been determined.) Lightly draw a horizontal line through point #1, and locate the positions of the top face's other four points along this horizontal line.
- Now, we will determine the location of point #2 in the front view, which will thereby determine the spacing between the top two horizontal lines. The location of point #2 in the front view is determined by two things: the length of edge A must be actual size, and point #2 must be located on line ***ℓ***. To do this, we set our compass to the length of any edge that is of actual size in the top view drawing (i.e., any edge of the top face), place the compass needle on point #1 in the front-view drawing, and then mark the place where point #2 must be located on line ***ℓ***.

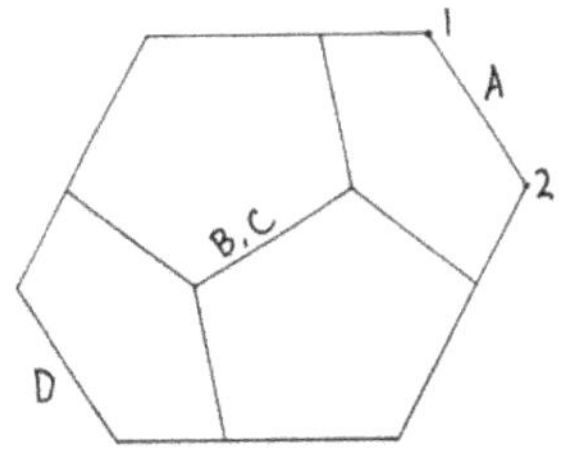

Front View

- Lightly draw a horizontal line through point #2, and locate the positions of the other four points of the dodecahedron that must also appear on this same horizontal line. (These four points, along with point #2, are all at the same elevation above the table on which the dodecahedron sits.)
- In the same way that we used edge A to determine the spacing between the top two horizontal lines, we can now determine the spacing between the middle two horizontal lines by using edge B (or C). Then we can determine the spacing between the bottom two horizontal lines by using edge D. Again, the key to this stems from the fact that these edges must appear in actual size in the front view.
- We can check the spacing between the horizontal lines of the front using these two facts: the distance between the top two (and the bottom two) horizontal lines should be equal to the radius of the smaller circle in the top view, and the distance between the two middle horizontal lines should be equal to the difference of the radii of the two circles in the top view.
- Now the rest of the front view, as well as the side view, can easily be completed according to the normal procedures. See the completed drawing on page 39.

Instructions for Drawing an Icosahedron

Notes for the teacher:

- It is helpful to make a model of an icosahedron from Zometools in order to best visualize what the various views look like.
- The process for drawing an icosahedron is very similar to the process for drawing a dodecahedron.
- Once the students have learned how to draw the dodecahedron, it may be best to have them figure out a process for drawing the icosahedron. They might figure out a different process than what is shown here.

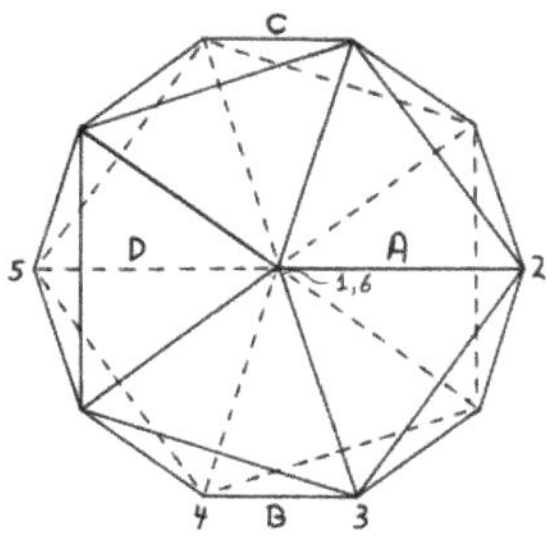

The Top View:

- Start with ten evenly spaced points on a circle, such that two of the points are placed on the circle's horizontal diameter. In black ink, draw the decagon that connects these ten points. Now the top view can be completed as shown in the drawing on the right.

The Front View: (Read through these instructions before trying them!)

- In the front view, one point is at the top, five points are located on a horizontal line a bit lower than the top, five more points are then located on another horizontal line somewhat further down, and the last point is the bottom point. *In order to draw the front view, we must first determine exactly how far apart the spacing between these four horizontal lines must be.* This spacing is not arbitrary!

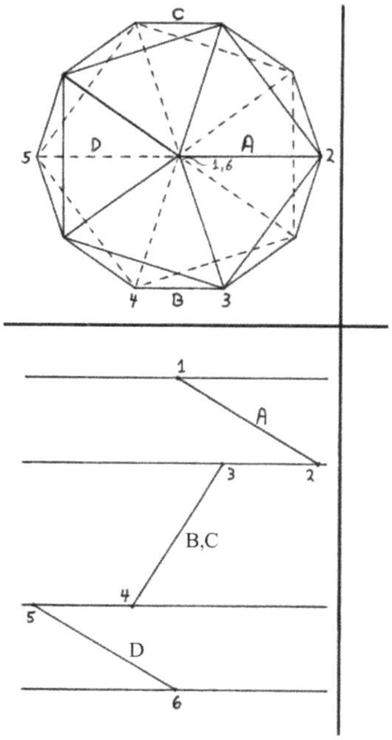

- Of the icosahedron's 30 edges, four of them will be drawn to actual size in the front view. These edges are the ones that are parallel to the front view, and are drawn horizontally across the page; they are labeled as A, B, C, D in the top-view drawing, shown here. The end points of edge A are labeled #1 and #2.
- Through each point in the top view, draw vertical lines (lightly in pencil) that run down through the front view. In most cases, two points share the same vertical line. Label the vertical line through point #2 as line ℓ, and the vertical line through point #1 as ***m***. (These lines are not shown in the drawing here.)
- Point #1 in the front view of the drawing must be located somewhere on line ***m***. Choose point #1 to be conveniently about one inch from the top of the front view. (The rest of the points of the icosahedron are now fixed.)
- Now, we need to determine the location of point #2 in the front view. The location of point #2 in the front view is determined by two things: the length of edge A must be actual size, and point #2 must be located on line ℓ. To do this, we set our compass to the length of any edge that is of actual size in the top view drawing (i.e., the edge connecting points #2 and #3), place the compass needle on point #1 in the front view drawing, and then mark the place where point #2 must be located on line ℓ.
- Lightly draw a horizontal line through point #2, and locate the positions of the other four points of the icosahedron that must also appear on this same horizontal line. (These four points, along with point #2, are all at the same elevation above the table on which the icosahedron sits.)
- In the same way that we used edge A to determine the spacing between the top two horizontal lines, we can now determine the spacing between the middle two horizontal lines by using edge B (or C), and we can determine the spacing between the bottom two horizontal lines by using edge D. Again, the key to this stems from the fact that these edges appear in actual size in the front view. (See above drawing.)
- Once the placement of the four horizontal lines has been determined, the rest of the front view, as well as the side view, can easily be completed according to the normal procedures. Notice that there should be no dotted lines in the front view. See the completed drawing on page 39.

Instructions for Drawing a

Truncated Icosahedron (a.k.a. Soccer Ball)

Notes for the teacher:

- The truncated icosahedron is quite challenging, and should only be attempted by advanced students.
- It is helpful to make a model of a truncated icosahedron from Zometools (all blue sticks) in order to best visualize what the various views look like.
- The truncated icosahedron has 32 faces, 60 points, and 90 edges. However, once the drawing of the icosahedron has been mastered, the truncated icosahedron is quite workable.
- Conceptually, the truncated icosahedron is the product of "chopping off" the 12 points of the icosahedron, whereby each point is replaced with a regular pentagon and each triangular face of the icosahedron transforms into a regular hexagon.
- Once the students have learned how to draw the dodecahedron and icosahedron, it may be best to have the students figure out a process for drawing the truncated icosahedron. They might figure out a different process than what is shown here.

Outline of the process for the drawing:

- Lightly in lead pencil, draw the top view of an icosahedron according to the instructions given for the icosahedron. (Some of the lines will be erased later.)
- With the front view of the icosahedron, the points were located on four different levels shown by horizontal lines. (The top and bottom lines only had one point, so drawing these lines weren't actually necessary. But we will leave them here for reasons that will soon be evident.) Lightly in lead pencil, draw these four lines (with the proper spacing) across the front view of the truncated icosahedron.
- With the front view and the four lines just drawn, draw two more horizontal *evenly-spaced* lines (do you understand why?) between the top two lines (lightly in lead pencil), two more horizontal *evenly-spaced* lines between the middle two lines, and two more horizontal *evenly-spaced* lines between the bottom two lines. Erase the original top and bottom lines. You should now have eight horizontal lines across the front view.
- *Drawing the Top View.* Each of the 30 edges of the icosahedron in the top view (including dotted edges that are in the background) needs to have two evenly spaced points (at distances of $\frac{1}{3}$ and $\frac{2}{3}$ the length of the edge) marked on it. Carefully and accurately locate these 60 new points with very small dots in black ink. Erase the lead pencil lines in the top view, and then connect the 60 inked points to complete the top view. Start by drawing the small pentagon in the center, and then the five hexagons connected to that pentagon. This top view should have dotted background lines (which aren't shown in the drawing here).
- *Drawing the Front View.* We have already drawn 8 horizontal lines in the front view. Of the 60 points in the front view, the middle four horizontal lines should have ten points each, and the top two and bottom two lines should have five points each. Locate these 60 points and then complete the front view. Notice that there should be no dotted lines in the front view.
- The *Side View* can now be completed.

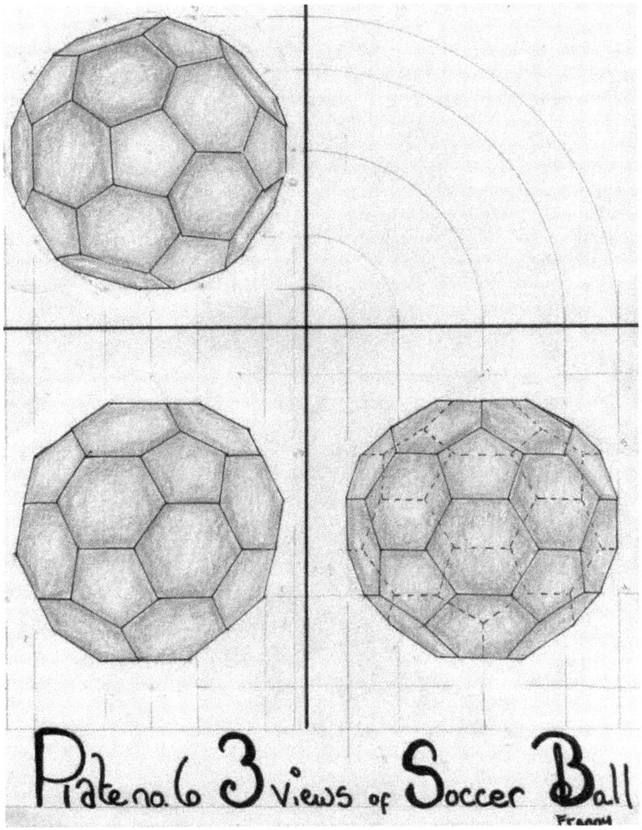

Instructions for Drawing a
Rhombic Triacontahedron

Notes for the teacher:

- The rhombic triacontahedron is quite challenging, and should only be attempted by advanced students.
- It is helpful to make a model of a rhombic triacontahedron from Zometools (all red sticks) in order to best visualize what the various views look like.
- The rhombic triacontahedron has 30 rhombic faces, 32 points and 60 edges.
- It emerges as the result of either growing (shallow) pentagonal pyramids off the faces of a dodecahedron, or by growing (shallow) triangular pyramids off the faces of an icosahedron.
- If the short diagonals are drawn onto every rhombic face of the rhombic triacontahedron, and then the rhombic triacontahedron disappears (but the diagonals remain), we are left with a dodecahedron. If the long diagonals are drawn onto every rhombic face of the rhombic triacontahedron, and then the rhombic triacontahedron disappears (but the diagonals remain), we are left with an icosahedron.
- Once the students have learned how to draw the dodecahedron and icosahedron, it may be best to have the students figure out a process for drawing the rhombic triacontahedron. They might figure out a different process than what is shown here.

The Top View:

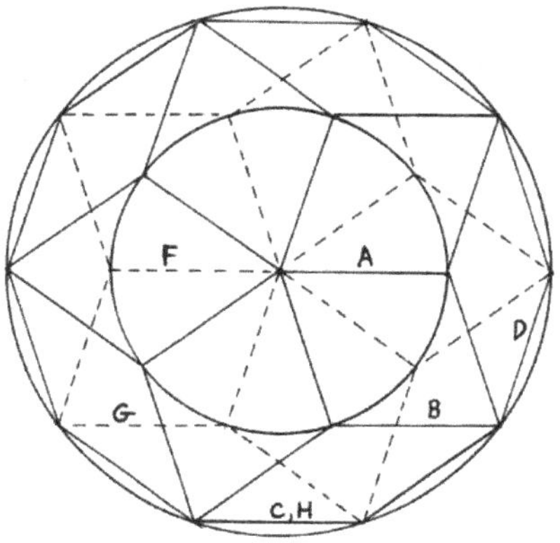

- As with the drawing for the dodecahedron, start with ten evenly spaced points on a circle, such that two of the points are placed on the circle's horizontal diameter. In black ink, draw the decagon that connects these ten points. Draw an inner circle (lightly in pencil) that has a radius equal to the length of the side of the decagon. Locate and mark the ten points on the inner circle that fall on the diagonals of the outer decagon. (The two circles should be erased in the end.)
- Now, in black ink, draw the five rhombuses that come to a point at the top center, and then the five rhombuses that fit into the between spaces around the perimeter of the circle.
- With dotted lines in black ink, draw in all of the edges that are in the background.

Some key observations:

- We have now drawn a total of 40 edges (15 of which are dotted), and 20 faces (ten of which are in the background). Where are the other 20 edges and ten faces? To fully understand this, it is best to look at a model of a rhombic triacontahedron. It is then clear that ten of the rhombic faces are "hiding" (i.e., lying on planes that are perpendicular to the top view) under the edges of the outer decagon in the top view. For example, under the edge labeled C, there is a hidden rhombic face. Edge H sits under and is parallel to edge C; they are both part of this same rhombus. This rhombus is the center face in the front view (as shown in the last drawing on the next page). The ten faces that are hidden in the top view (under the outer decagon) account for the 20 hidden edges – ten of the hidden edges sit under another edge (in the same way that edge H sits under edge C), and *ten of the hidden edges have a vertical orientation, meaning that they are both perpendicular to the top view and parallel to the front and side views*. (This last fact is important.)
- There are no edges parallel to the top view or the side view. Therefore, none of the edges in the top view are actual size. We will find a way to work around this.
- This particular view is unique because every edge that is drawn in the top view appears as the same length. (Do you understand why?) Because of this fact, we can say that the drawn length of edges D and A must be the same. *This allows us to understand why, when we drew the top view of the dodecahedron, the inner circle has a radius equal to the length of the edge of the outer decagon.*

(Continued on next page →)

(Instructions for Drawing a Rhombic Triacontahedron, continued)

The Front and Side Views:

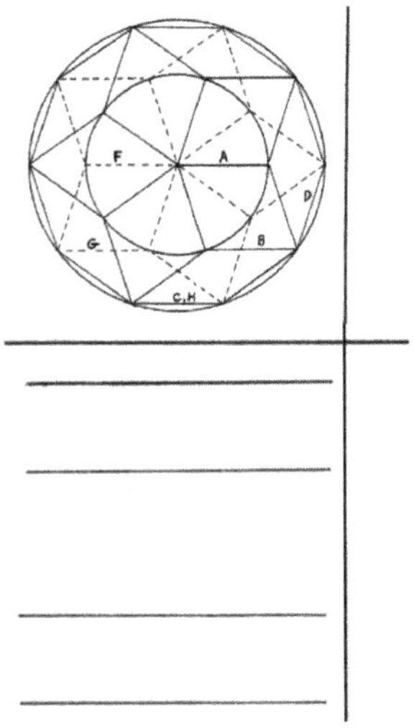

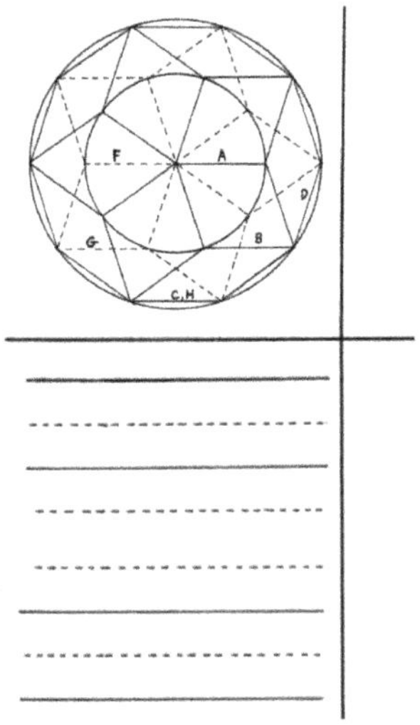

- The rhombic triacontahedron's 32 points lie on eight horizontal lines in the front (and side) view. The top four of these lines are evenly spaced, and the bottom four of these lines are evenly spaced.
- We will start by drawing the first four lines, which come from the icosahedron. (Recall that we get an icosahedron by drawing the long diagonals on the rhombic faces.) Follow the instructions for the icosahedron's front view in order to draw the first four horizontal lines. (See the first drawing shown here.)
- The rhombic triacontahedron sits balanced on its point. Therefore, one point falls on the top horizontal line of the front view, and five points fall on the second horizontal line (shown in the above-left drawing). These five points fall on the top view's outer circle. There are five more points in the front view which fall on a horizontal line that is exactly halfway between the two above-mentioned lines. These five points fall on the top view's inner circle. Once we draw this "in-between line", we add three more lines with this same spacing. All four of these new lines in the front view are shown as dotted lines in the above-right drawing. Note that the two dotted lines in the middle are spaced slightly further apart than the other lines.
- In the below-left drawing, we have begun to draw in some of the edges in the front view. These edges (labeled A, B, C, H, G, F) are six of the ten edges which are parallel to the front view *and* actually appear in the top view. Therefore, they must appear actual size in the front view. There are also ten edges with a vertical orientation. These edges are also parallel to the front view (and therefore actual size) and they are perpendicular to the top view, which caused them to not appear in the top view.
- The rest of the front view, as well as the side view, can be completed according to the normal procedures. Notice that there should be no dotted lines in the front view.
- In the completed drawing (shown below, right), the third view is a rotated view (rotated by about 13°), which is explained on the next page.

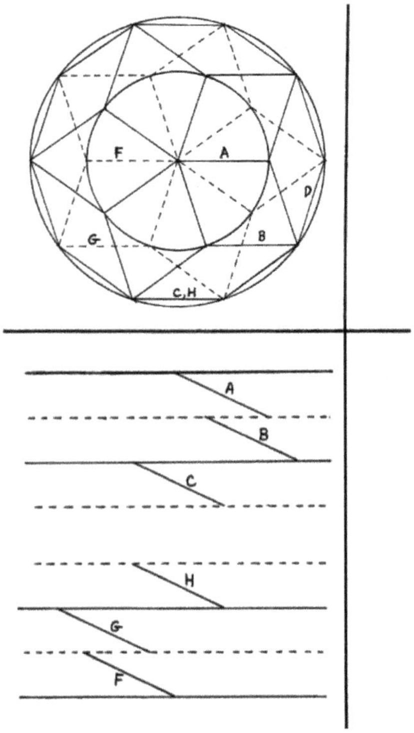

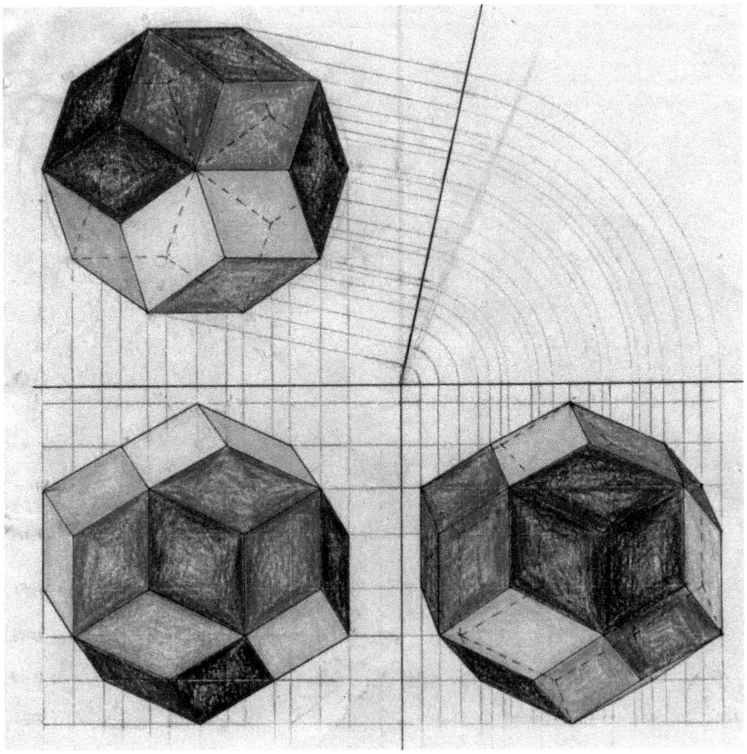

Instructions for Drawing a Rotated View

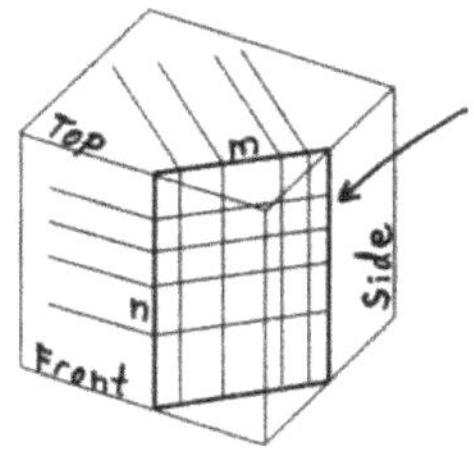

The **rotated** new image plane is perpendicular to the top view, and rotated 42° from the side view toward the front view.

Creating the image plane for a rotated view:

- The desired rotated view is achieved by creating an image plane which is a vertical section of the viewing box. The rotation we are dealing with here is between the front view and the side view. We can imagine that this rotated image plane serves as our painter's canvas, upon which we draw our view of the solid. (See drawing on the right.)
- A rotated view (also called a primary auxiliary view) must be perpendicular to one of the three principle views – top view, front view, or side view. Here, we will create a rotated view that is perpendicular to the top view.

Drawing a rotated view:

- As we mentioned before, once we know the top view and the front view, we have enough information to construct any desired view. In the same manner that we employed to construct the side (or profile) view, we simply follow the below steps (in this case, to draw a 42° rotated view of a pentagonal pyramid with an arbitrary height):
  - **Step #1.** Draw the top view and the front view.
  - **Step #2.** From each point in the front view, draw (horizontal) construction lines perpendicularly to the fold line (lines n in the drawing). Extend these lines past and perpendicular to the fold line in the rotated view. The fold line, m, is drawn at a 48° angle in the top view. Therefore the construction lines from the points in the top view do not go horizontally across the page (as they did in for the normal side view construction); the construction lines run at a 42° angle. In the below drawing, note the following:
    - The points on line m (which is the folding line between the top and rotated views) are copied with a compass from the top view onto the rotated view.
    - In the rotated view, line m looks as if it is the same line as line p (the folding line between the top and front views).
    - In the top view, line m can be drawn starting anywhere on line P, as long as the 48° angle is maintained, and all of the points of the solid can be successfully projected (by the perpendicular construction lines) onto line m.
  - **Step #3.** We can now locate and label all of the points in the rotated view, and finally draw all of the edges of the solid, carefully considering which edges are in the background, and should therefore be dotted. With the final drawing, we have erased all construction lines (which the students shouldn't do) and have labeled the faces that are in the foreground (which the students should instead show with color).
- Additional drawings of rotated views are shown on the following pages.

Step #1

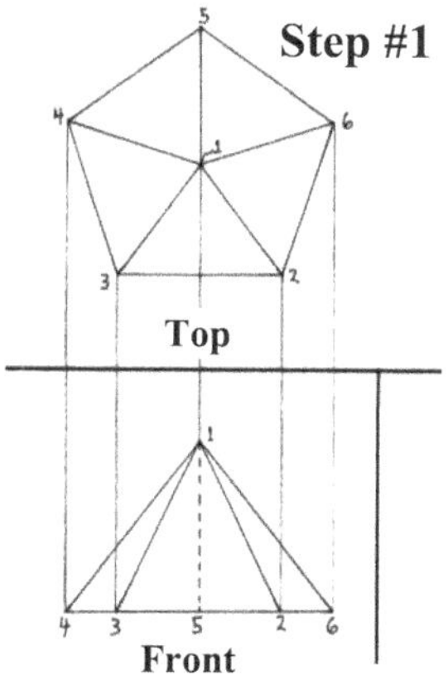

Step #2

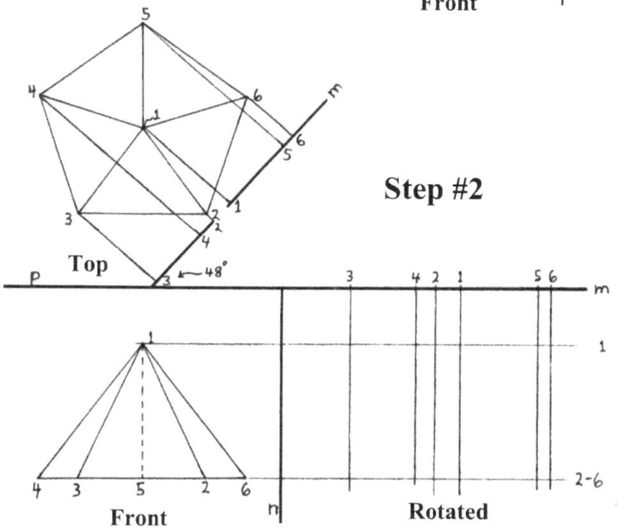

Step #3

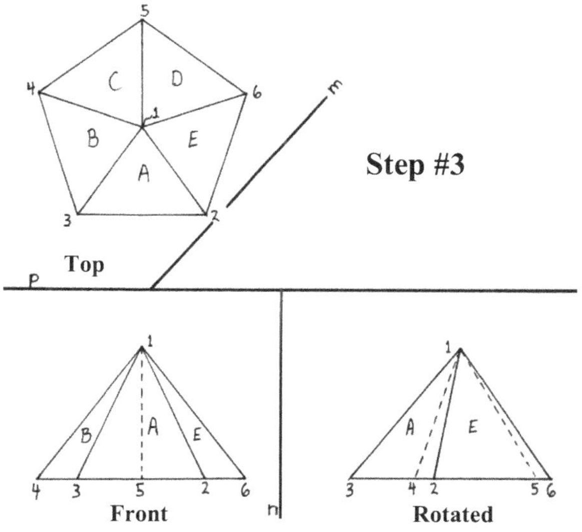

Instructions for a Rotated and Lifted View

(Four Views of a Solid)

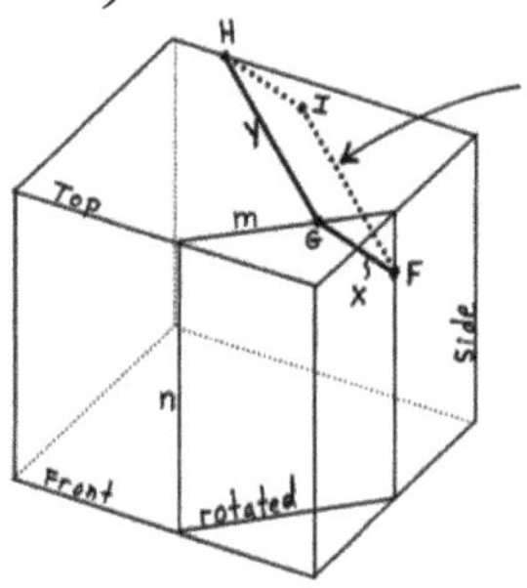

The **rotated and lifted** image plane is perpendicular to the rotated view, and then lifted 53° from vertical.

<u>Creating the image plane for a rotated and lifted view</u>:

- An arbitrary rotated and lifted view (also called a secondary auxiliary view) must have an image plane that is perpendicular to a rotated view. We will therefore build upon the rotated view from the previous page.
- Recall that the previous page's rotated view came from rotating 42° from the side view toward the front view. The new image plane takes that rotated view and turns it counter-clockwise by 90°. This results in the new view being a rotation of 42° from the back view toward the side view. Lastly, we rotate (lift) upwards by 53°. The resulting image plane is shown as rectangle FGHI in the above drawing. Note that point I is not on the viewing box.

<u>Drawing a rotated and lifted view</u>:

- The below explanation shows how to construct a view of a pentagonal pyramid (as shown on the previous page) which has been rotated clockwise 42° from the back view toward the side view, and then lifted 53° from vertical. All of the steps are reflected in the below drawing.
  - **Step #1.** Draw the top view, the side view, and the rotated view as shown on the previous page. Note that the final image plane for the rotated and lifted view will be additionally rotated counter-clockwise by 90°, and then lifted by 53°. (See above drawing.)
  - **Step #2.** Starting with the drawing of the three views from the previous page, we need to first add the two folding lines (lines x and y in the above drawing) that result from adding the new image plane. Because the new image plane must be perpendicular to the rotated view, folding line y, in the top view, must be perpendicular to folding line m (which was used in the previous drawing). Folding line x is the intersection of the new image plane with the plane of the rotated view. Since the new image plane is 53° from vertical, it is drawn above the rotated view at an angle of 37° from horizontal. (See below drawing.)

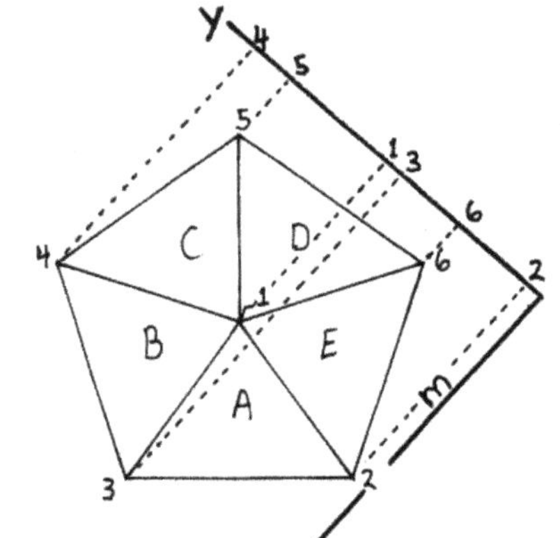

  - **Step #3.** In the top view, draw construction lines from points 1-6 at right angles to line y. In the rotated view, draw construction lines from points 1-6 at right angles to line x.
  - **Step #4.** Copy line x (and the points on it) to a vertical orientation (shown below, right) and copy line y (and the points on it) at a right angle to line x.
  - **Step #5.** As usual, construction lines (which aren't shown in the drawing) can be drawn from lines x and y in order to locate all of the points in the desired rotated and lifted view.
  - **Step #6.** The edges of the pyramid are drawn and the faces are shaded in with colors that are consistent with the other views.

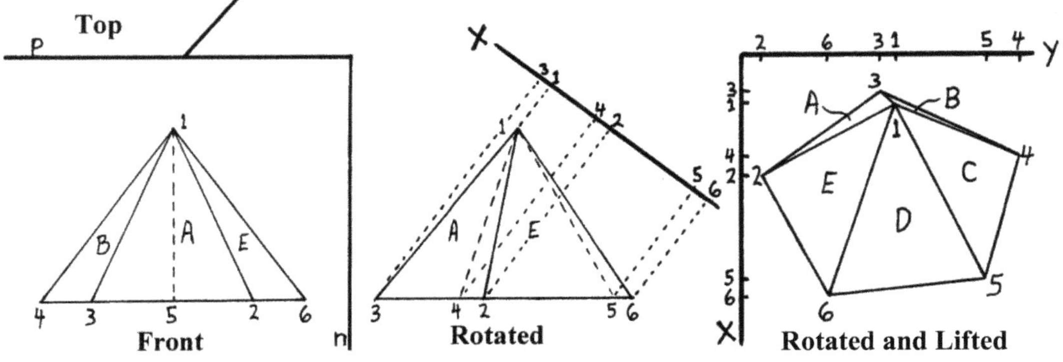

- Additional drawings of rotated and lifted views are shown on the following pages.

Three Views of Various Solids

(Note that the drawings on the right are "rotated" views.)

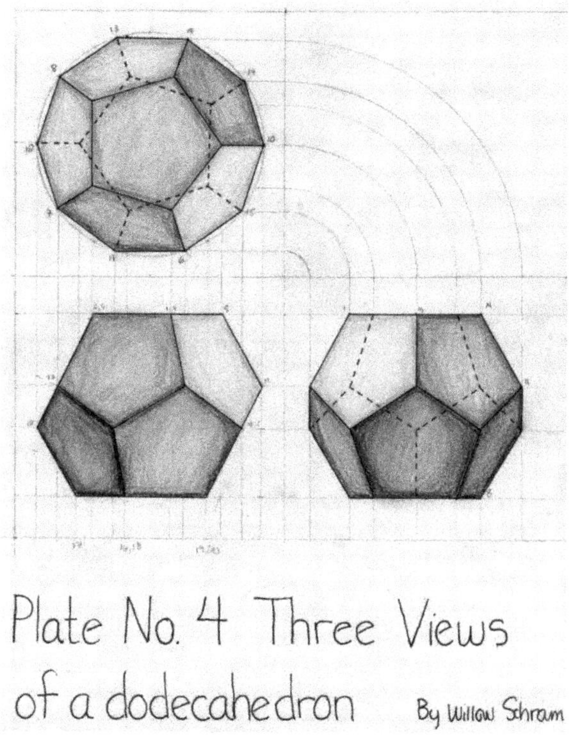

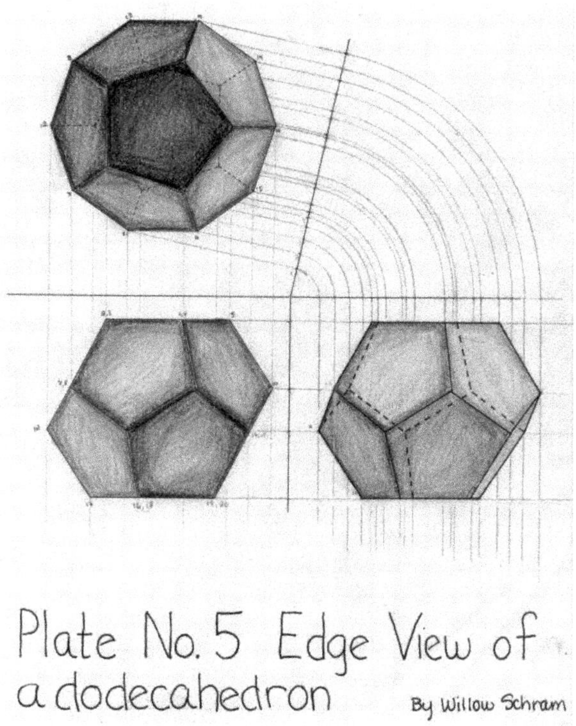

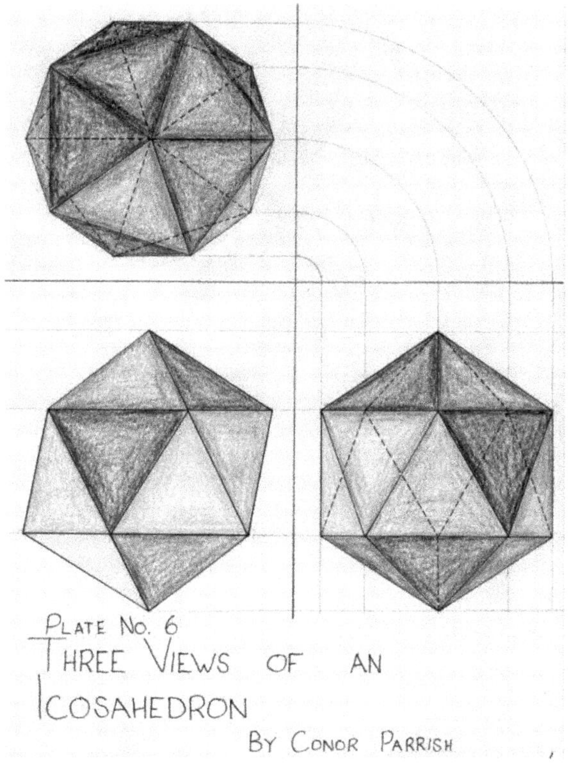

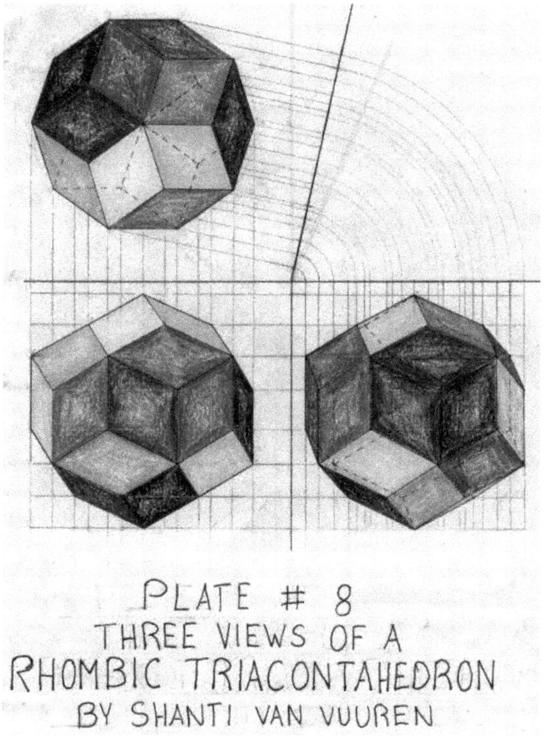

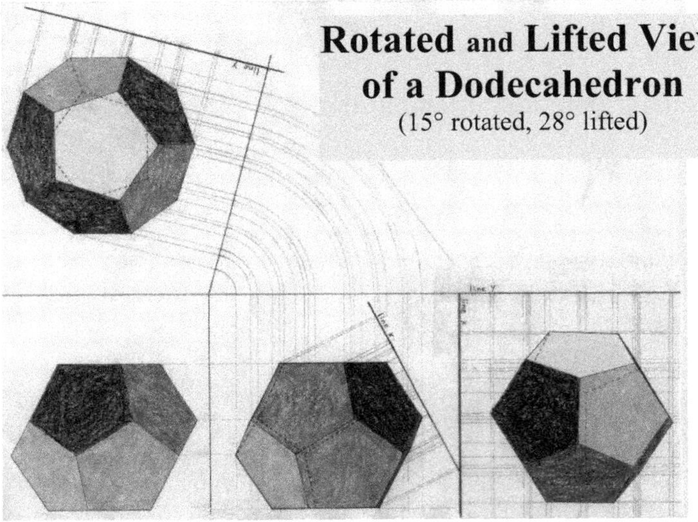

Rotated and Lifted View of a Dodecahedron
(15° rotated, 28° lifted)

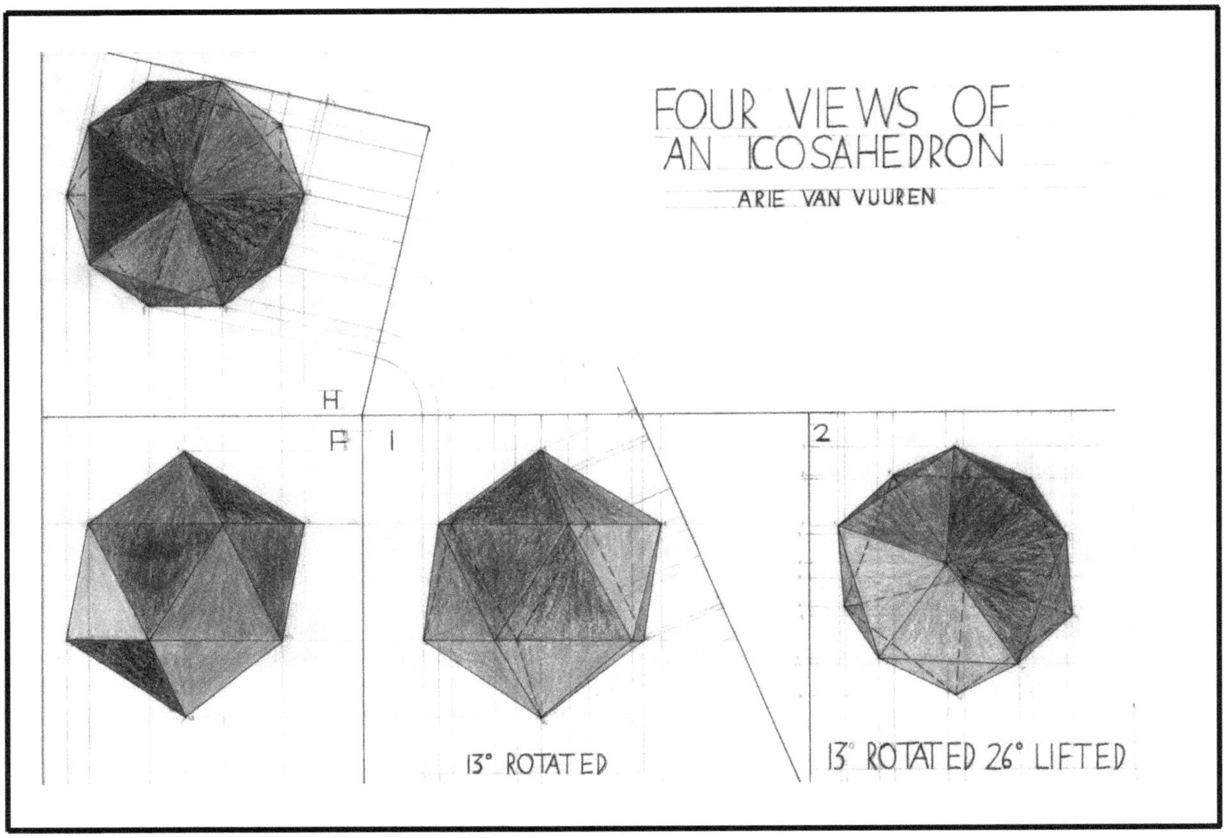

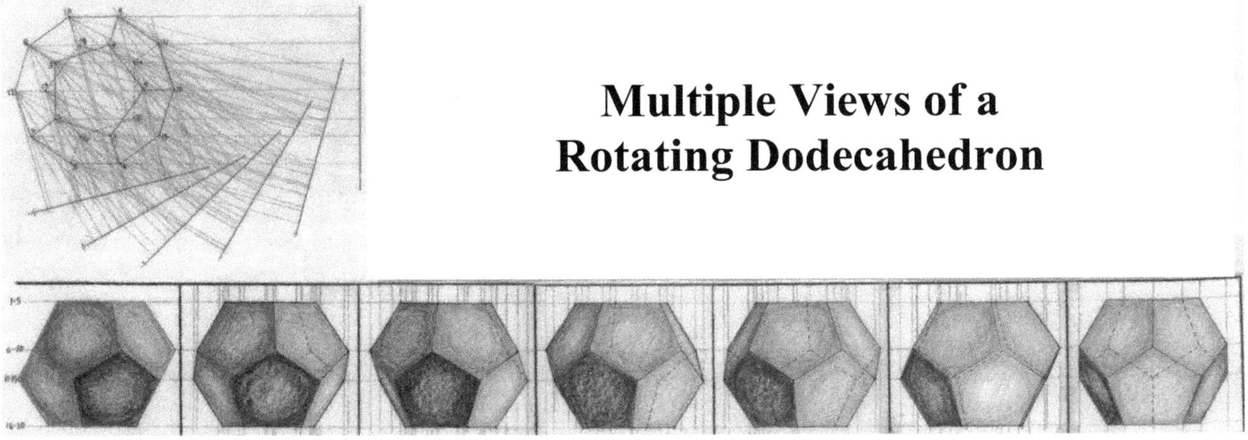

Multiple Views of a Rotating Dodecahedron

—— *Greek Geometry* (10th Grade Main Lesson) ——

Full course title: *Greek Geometry and Deductive Proofs*

Course overview

This course traces the evolution of Greek thought in mathematics from the school of Pythagoras up until the works of Euclid and the brilliant mind of Archimedes. To a large degree, this entails a history of mathematical proofs, which aids the students as they learn the art of deductive reasoning. The students are exposed to a variety of different styles of proofs, including visual proofs, indirect proofs, and Euclidean proofs.

At the start of the course, the students begin to answer the question, "What is a proof?", by studying six different proofs of the Pythagorean Theorem and the Pythagorean proof that the $\sqrt{2}$ is irrational. This leads naturally to the question, "What is a *good* proof?", and then, finally, to the idea of an axiomatic system of proofs. Much attention is then given to Euclid's 13-volume work, *The Elements*, and its impact on the world of mathematics. We thoroughly study *The Elements'* Book I, which consists of 48 theorems and culminates in Euclid's proof of the Pythagorean Theorem.

This main lesson block falls at the start of the tenth grade year and is intended to be an introduction to deductive, Euclidean-style proofs. Further work with proofs is continued in the tenth grade geometry track class with the *Proofs* unit in our *10th Grade Workbook.*

Lesson plans

Detailed day-by-day lesson plans can be downloaded from our website: **www.JamieYorkPress.com**.

Preparation for the Greek Geometry main lesson (To be done in track class)

- *The Geometry Basics unit in our 10th Grade Workbook.* This unit in our workbook is designed to give the students a solid foundation for the Greek Geometry main lesson and for other further studies in the math track class.
- *Review Euclidean Constructions*, especially:
    - To bisect a given line
    - To bisect a given angle
    - To copy a given angle
    - To draw a line perpendicular to a given line from a given point ON that line
    - To draw a line perpendicular to a given line from a given point NOT on that line
    - To draw a line parallel to a given line through a given point not on that line
    - To divide a given line into n equal segments
    - To construct regular polygons (square, triangle, hexagon, etc.) inside a given circle
- *Angle Theorems*
    - Angles forming a complete circle add to 360°.
    - *The X Theorem.* Vertical angles are equal.
    - *The Y Theorem.* Supplementary angles add to 180°.
    - *The Z Theorem.* Alternate interior angles are equal.
    - *The F Theorem.* Corresponding angles are equal.
    - Same-side interior angles add to 180°.
    - The sum of the angles in a triangle is 180°.
- *Triangle Congruency Theorems*
    - SAS. If two sides and the included angle of one triangle are congruent to two sides and the included angle of another triangle, then the two triangles are congruent.
    - SSS. If the three sides of one triangle are congruent to the three sides of another triangle, then the two triangles are congruent.
    - AAS, ASA. If two angles and a side of one triangle are equal, respectively, to two angles and a side of a second triangle, then the triangles are congruent.
    - HL. In general, SSA doesn't work. The students should understand why SSA can be ambiguous (see "Triangle Constructions" under *Euclidean Constructions*). However, if the known angle is a right (or obtuse) angle, then it works. Therefore, the Hypotenuse-Leg Theorem (HL) states: *"If the leg and hypotenuse of a right triangle are congruent to the leg and hypotenuse of another right triangle, then the two triangles are congruent."*

Historical background

- Earlier civilizations had advanced math and geometry, but had no proofs. It was the Greeks who first developed proofs.
- Earlier civilizations were more interested in using math for practical purposes.
- The Greeks were not interested in practical mathematics. Proofs were the most important part of mathematics, and this was truly a philosophical endeavor.
- Pythagoras was the first to call himself a philosopher, which means "lover of wisdom", but for him, it really meant a "seeker of the truth".
- For the Greeks, the important questions were not *"What is true?"*, but rather *"Why is it true?"*, or *"How can we say that this is definitely true?"*

Comments on Greek schooling

- The seven liberal arts took hold in the Middle Ages (Neo-Platonism). They are the Trivium (Grammar, Rhetoric, and Logic), and the Quadrivium (Arithmetic, Geometry, Music, Astronomy). Their origins go back to the ancient Greeks.
- The Pythagoreans and Plato's Academy studied the subjects of the Quadrivium. Pythagoras had more of an emphasis on music, and Plato had more an emphasis on stereometry.

Thales (ca. 600B.C.)

- "The primary question is not what we know, but how we know it." --Thales
- While Thales was in Egypt, he calculated the height of one of the pyramids by using similar triangles. Although today it is doubted, Thales was believed to have predicted a solar eclipse that occurred in 585 B.C.
- Theorems attributed to Thales:
  1. A circle is bisected by a diameter.
  2. The base angles of an isosceles triangle are equal.
  3. Vertical angles are equal.
  4. ASA, AAS. If two triangles are such that two angles and a side of one are equal respectively to two angles and a side of the other, then the triangles are congruent.
  5. (Theorem of Thales) An angle inscribed in a semicircle is a right angle. Thales' proof of this is believed to be the first mathematical proof. We prove it during the Circle Geometry unit of our *10th Grade Workbook.*

The Six Proofs of the Pythagorean Theorem

- This handout appears in the pages that follow.
- This serves as a transition from the School of Pythagoras to Euclid's *Elements*.
- The central purpose of this handout is for the students to fully understand that a theorem can have many different proofs, and that each proof can have its own strengths and weaknesses.
- The last of the six proofs is the one that appears in most geometry textbooks and it is the only one where area is not mentioned. The "geometry-ness" of the Pythagorean Theorem has been removed!
- We will see one more proof (Euclid's) of the Pythagorean Theorem later in the main lesson. Euclid wanted to prove it as perfectly as possible. But he first proved 46 other theorems to lead up to it!
- In 1940, Elisha Loomis published his book, *The Pythagorean Proposition*, in which he gives 370 proofs of the Pythagorean Theorem, including one by Leonardo da Vinci, and one by James Garfield (U.S. President in 1881).

Euclidean Constructions

- *Track class or main lesson.* This vast topic can be done either in the track class or in this main lesson. Usually I introduce Euclidean constructions (largely a review of what should be covered in the geometric drawing main lesson) in track class, just before the start of the Greek Geometry main lesson, go into significant depth during the main lesson, and then continue the theme later in track class. Euclidean constructions can be a nice hands-on activity to complement the otherwise cerebral topic of proofs.
- *Details of Euclidean constructions.* See the *Euclidean Constructions* section later in this book.

- *Handouts and worksheets*. A handout which summarizes *Basic Euclidean Constructions*, often introduced in sixth grade, is found is the *Euclidean Constructions* section later in this book. Additionally, Euclidean construction worksheets can be downloaded from our website.
- *Playing the Greek Geometric Game*. It is best to have the students try to figure out some constructions on their own. The following are taken from our Euclidean construction worksheets:
    1. The division of an angle into four equal parts.
    2. The division of a line into 7 equal parts.
    3. The division of an angle into three equal parts. (The trisection of an angle.)
    4. The construction of a 12-gon.
    5. The construction of a 10-gon.
    6. The construction of a 15-gon.
    7. The construction of a 9-gon.
    8. The construction of a 7-gon.
    9. The construction of a 17-gon.
    10. Finding the center of a given circle.

    Notes:
    - #10 and #6 are good challenges, but many students can solve them.
    - #2 is very difficult – a great challenge for an exceptional student.
    - #3, #7, and #8 are all impossible. Students might try these for several days before I break the news to them. It's great for them to engage in some of the great classical problems even if they are impossible. I console them later that at least they found this out after just a few days of effort. Some mathematicians tried for many years and died without knowing they were impossible! (See *Which regular polygons are possible?* in the *Euclidean Constructions* section, below.)
    - No student would be able to figure out #9, but it is possible. I hand out the instructions and have the students attempt it – it's quite fun!
      (See *Construction of a 17-gon* in the *Euclidean Constructions* section, below.)

The idea of commensurability

- *In terms of geometry*. To make two lengths (or numbers) "commensurable" means to find a "common measure", which has a longer length (or number) that both of the original lengths can go into an even number of times.
  Example: If one line is 20m long and the other is 12m long, we can make these commensurable with a 60m long line, since they both go into 60 evenly.
- *In terms of numbers*. Making two numbers commensurable is the same as finding the LCM (least common multiple) for the two numbers.
  Example: The LCM of 20 and 12 is 60.
- *Regarding rational numbers*. It should be emphasized that any two rational numbers (whether thought of as the lengths of two lines, or simply as two numbers) are commensurable, although finding the desired LCM (or line length) can be tedious.

  Example: Find the LCM of $2\frac{1}{3}$ and $5\frac{1}{2}$.

  Solution: We change them to improper fractions with a common denominator to get $\frac{14}{6}$ and $\frac{33}{6}$. Since these are in a ratio of 14:33, we can see that the LCM will have 14 times 33 in the numerator. Our final answer is $\frac{14 \cdot 33}{6}$, which works out to <u>77</u>. Of course, we can check our answer by dividing $2\frac{1}{3}$ into 77 (which is 33) and then $5\frac{1}{2}$ into 77 (which is 14).

  Example: Find the LCM of $2\frac{4}{15}$ and $3\frac{7}{10}$. (It's complicated, but it works!)

  Solution: We change them to improper fractions with a common denominator to get $\frac{68}{30}$ and $\frac{111}{30}$. Since these are in a ratio of 68:111 we can see that the LCM will have 111 times 68 in the numerator. Our final answer is $\frac{111 \cdot 68}{30}$, which works out to $\underline{251\frac{3}{5}}$, which is, of course, a multiple of both of our original numbers.

<u>The ratio in a square</u> (of its side to its diagonal)

- *Guessing the ratio.* Start by drawing a square on the board and ask the students to guess what the ratio of the diagonal to the side of the square might be. Certainly, they should be able to see that it must be less than 2:1 (the diagonal is less than twice the length of the side). They might guess that it is 3:2 or 5:3. The best (lucky) guess would be 7:5.
- *The Great Pythagorean Crisis.*
  One of the central tenets of the School of Pythagoras was that God had made the world so that it was imbued with harmony and perfection. Perfect ratios were a key theme. For example, they knew that in music the ratio of two notes an octave apart was 2:1, and that if the notes were a fifth apart, then the ratio was 3:2. (See the *Math and Music* unit.)
  Similarly, they believed that any two lengths were *commensurable*, meaning that they could be expressed as an exact ratio in whole number form. For example, with a rectangle that measures 2.5m by 4.25m, the ratio of the length to the width can be expressed as 17:10, which means that 17 times the width is *exactly* equal to 10 times the length.
  Yet the square, one of the most fundamental geometrical forms, did not yield such a simple ratio. No one could determine *exactly* what the ratio of the diagonal to the side of a square was. Then, after much effort to find this elusive ratio, someone within the Pythagorean School *proved* that no such ratio could possibly exist; there is no way to express the ratio exactly in whole number form. (See the proof that $\sqrt{2}$ is irrational, below.)
  This news was so horrifying to them that it was forbidden to leak the secret outside of their school. As one version of the story goes, one person did leak it, and when this was found out, that person was drowned! This marked the discovery of a new type of number, which was so disturbing that it is known as an *irrational number.* (See *Irrational Numbers*, below.)
- *Changing the question.* The following argument is quite complicated, but can be quite valuable if done successfully.
  The big question is: "*What is the ratio of a square's diagonal to its side?*"

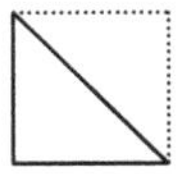

  As the Pythagoreans tried to answer this question, they knew that it was the same as asking, "*What is the length of the diagonal of a square that has sides of length equal to one?*" In order to answer this, we first take a unit square (e.g., a square with sides of length equal to 1) and cut it in half. The Pythagorean Theorem says that the sum of the areas of the squares off the smaller sides of the triangle must be equal to the area of the square off the hypotenuse. Since the areas of the squares off the smaller sides are each equal to 1, then the sum of these two smaller squares must be 1+1 = 2. Since the area of the square off the hypotenuse (which is the diagonal of the original square) is 2, the big question now becomes, "*What must the length of the side of a square be so that its area is exactly equal to 2?*"

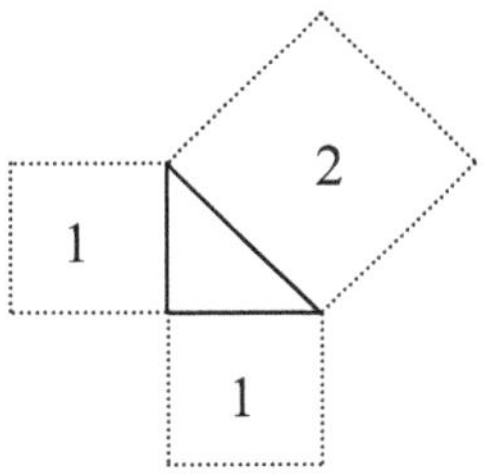

  Some students can have difficulty in answering this question. In order to reach an answer, it is helpful to first answer a simpler, but different, question, such as, "If the area of the square is 25, what is the length of the side of that square?" Most students can quickly see that this square would have sides of length 5. And then we ask, "What if the square had an area of 49?" The answer is that the side of the square would have to have a length of 7. And how did we find the answers to these last two questions? We took the square roots. Therefore, in order to find the length of the side of a square that has an area of 2, we need to find the $\sqrt{2}$.
  Most importantly, our original question, "*What is the ratio of a square's diagonal to its side?*", has now been transformed into the question, "*What is the exact value of the $\sqrt{2}$?*"
- *$\sqrt{2}$ As a Fraction.*
  The goal for the Pythagoreans became to find out *exactly* what the $\sqrt{2}$ was as a fraction (or ratio). We will now attempt to do this using decimals (which were invented well after the Greeks). Clearly, the $\sqrt{2}$ must be greater than 1, but less than 2. Our first guess might as well be 1.5. We check this guess by squaring it. Since $1.5 \cdot 1.5$ is 2.25, which is greater than 2, we can say that 1.5 is too big; the $\sqrt{2}$ must be less than 1.5. So we try 1.4, and since 1.4 squared is 1.96, which is less than 2, we know that $\sqrt{2}$ must be greater than 1.4. Since we already know that it must be less than 1.5, we can say that it must be one-point-four-something. So we try 1.45, and find out that it is too big. Likewise, both 1.43 and 1.42 are too big, and 1.41 is too small. Now we know that $\sqrt{2}$ must be one-point-four-one-something. We continue guessing and checking in this way. Some students may be quite determined,

as the Pythagoreans were, to find out the value that works exactly (e.g., to find the exact value for $\sqrt{2}$) but sooner or later they will be able to appreciate the fact that it can never be *exactly* found.

The $\sqrt{2}$ is an irrational number that is approximately equal to 1.4142135623730950488016887242097

As a fraction, $\sqrt{2}$ can be approximated, in order of increasing accuracy, as follows (the Pythagoreans only knew about the first few; the rest are the results of a computer program).

$\frac{7}{5}, \frac{17}{12}, \frac{140}{99}, \frac{1393}{985}, \frac{8119}{5741}, \frac{114243}{80782}$

- *In summary*:
  - The original question, "*What is the ratio of a square's diagonal to its side?*", is the equivalent of asking, "*What is* the *exact value of the* $\sqrt{2}$*?*"
  - The $\sqrt{2}$ cannot be expressed *exactly* as any fraction or decimal; it is an irrational number. (see below proof.)
  - Therefore, the ratio of a square's diagonal to its side cannot be expressed exactly.
  - It is possible to come up with two numbers (one simply has to be irrational) such that they share no common multiple. For example, using $\sqrt{3}$ and 7, there is no number that they both go into evenly.

The proof that $\sqrt{2}$ is irrational

- This proof is an indirect proof (or proof by contradiction).

1. Assume that $\sqrt{2}$ can be expressed *exactly* as a *reduced* fraction. Let this fraction be $\frac{X}{Y}$, where X and Y are both whole numbers and have no common factor.
2. Squaring both sides of $\frac{X}{Y} = \sqrt{2}$ we get: $\frac{X^2}{Y^2} = 2$, which becomes <u>$X^2 = 2Y^2$</u>
3. Whether Y is even or odd, $2Y^2$ must be even. Therefore X^2 is even, and <u>X must be even</u>.
4. Since $\frac{X}{Y}$ is a reduced fraction, <u>Y must be odd</u>.
5. Since X is even, half of X (call it P) must be a whole number. <u>$X = 2P$</u>.
6. Since $X = 2P$, we can substitute 2P in for X with the equation given in step 2. So we get $(2P)^2 = 2Y^2 \rightarrow 4P^2 = 2Y^2 \rightarrow$ <u>$2P^2 = Y^2$</u>.
7. $2P^2$ is even, therefore Y^2 is even, and <u>Y must be even</u>.
8. Step 4 and 7 are in contradiction of each other. Our assumption must therefore be false.
9. *$\sqrt{2}$ cannot be expressed as a fraction. (And it then follows that the side and the diagonal of a square cannot be expressed as a whole number ratio; they are not commensurable).*

More regarding irrational numbers

What does it mean to not be commensurable?

- If the length of the square's diagonal is copied side-by-side infinitely many times, and the square's side is also copied side-by-side infinitely many times, then there will *never* be a place where the two arrive at the same exact spot. (See below.)

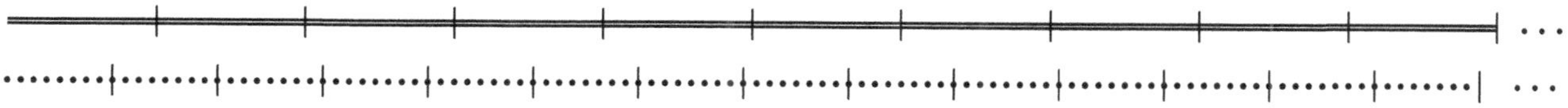

Another irrational number: π

- π is the ratio between the diameter and circumference of the circle.
- π answers the question: the circumference is how many times longer than the diameter?
- Archimedes was the first person to determine a method for calculating π to as much accuracy as desired.
- Here are some fractional approximations for π:
  - $\frac{22}{7} = 3^1/_7$ (Archimedes' upper-bound); $\frac{223}{71} = 3\frac{10}{71}$ (Archimedes' lower-bound)
  - $\frac{355}{113} = 3\frac{16}{113}$ was known by the Chinese mathematician, Zu Chongzhi in the 5th century.

    This is incredibly accurate – a better one can't be found until $\frac{52163}{16604}$

The key ideas of irrational numbers:

- An irrational number cannot be expressed as an exact fraction, or as a decimal which repeats or ends. (Recall that any rational number (fraction) is *exactly* equal to a decimal that either repeats or ends.)
- An irrational number does have an exact value, but you cannot say exactly what it is.
- A calculator gives an approximation of any irrational number, as would a computer that could calculate its value to a million decimal places.
- We can do exact calculations with irrational numbers, e.g., $3\sqrt{2} \cdot 5\sqrt{2} = 30$.
- π and $\sqrt{2}$ are irrational numbers. How do we know for sure that they are actually irrational? Perhaps they would end up repeating or ending after 2 million decimal places? How do we know this doesn't happen? Answer: there is a proof showing that it's impossible!

Archimedes

What follows is a selection of a few of Archimedes' achievements:

- Mechanical inventions (parabolic mirror, Archimedean screw, pulley system to move ships)
- Law of the Lever
- Archimedes Principle (Law of floating bodies)
- Spiral of Archimedes
- The area of a circle is equal to the area of a right triangle that has legs equal to the radius and the circumference of the circle.
- The surface of any right circular cylinder is equal to the area of the circle whose radius is equal to the geometric mean of the height and diameter of the cylinder.
- The surface area of a sphere is four times greater than the area of the greatest circle on it.
- The ratio of the volume of the Cone to the Sphere to the Cylinder is 1 : 2 : 3.
- The area of a parabolic segment is $^4/_3$ the area of the triangle having the same base and height.
- A method for calculating π to as much accuracy as desired. His algorithm was not essentially improved upon for 2000 years. This proof can be a highlight of the tenth grade track class. (See "Tenth Grade Proofs" for details.)

Euclid's *Elements* as the centerpiece

All of what has been mentioned above sets the stage for us to study Euclid's book, *The Elements*, which is the largest topic of the main lesson block. This impressive work has served the world of mathematics as the quintessential example of an axiomatic system – a collection of theorems building upon one another systematically. *The Elements* was the model of perfect truth and certainty for more than 2000 years.

During this main lesson, we give a brief overview of the whole of *The Elements* (all 13 "books"). However, the majority of the attention is placed on Book I (the first "chapter"), which serves as the foundation for the rest of the work. The intention is for the students to study selected proofs from Book I so that they begin to get a sense of how one can write a proof.

Biography of Πυθαγόρας (Pythagoras)

One day (ca. 570BC) a merchant from Samos named Mnesarchus was traveling and found himself in Delphi. Before making the long dangerous journey home, Mnesarchus decided to consult with the oracle about when the best time would be to begin his journey home. Instead, she told him that his wife was about to give birth to a boy, and this son would grow up to "exceed all others in beauty and wisdom." Mnesarchus's son was named Pythagoras.

As a young man, Pythagoras had three main teachers who influenced his interest in mathematics, geometry, astronomy, and music – one of whom was an old man, Thales. Thales advised Pythagoras to travel to Egypt to learn more. When Pythagoras was around 35 years old, he traveled to Egypt. Pythagoras was refused admission to all the temples except the one where he was accepted into the priesthood after completing the rites necessary for admission. This was unheard of for a foreigner to be accepted into the Egyptian priesthood. Pythagoras remained in Egypt for ten years.

At that time, the Persian empire had quickly expanded to include much of Central Asia, Babylonia, and the Middle East. Egypt was next; when Pythagoras was about 45 years old, Persia invaded Egypt. Pythagoras was taken to Babylon as a prisoner. But the Babylonians quickly realized Pythagoras's talents, and so instructed him in their sacred rites, and shared with him their knowledge of arithmetic, music, and other mathematical sciences.

At the age of 50, Pythagoras was released as a prisoner from Babylon and returned to Samos, which was by then also overtaken by the Persians. Pythagoras tried to form a school, but he was not accepted as a prophet in his own land. So after two years, he left Samos and went to Croton, in southern Italy. In Croton, he quickly became influential among the people, and gained many followers. His sermons inspired many to abandon their sinful ways and lead a purer life.

Word soon traveled about Pythagoras's teachings. Many came to believe that he was a divine being, sent by the gods to lead them. Soon a school was founded based upon the teachings of Pythagoras. It was a synthesis of a brotherhood, university, monastery, and commune. It was very secretive; the members were bound by a sacred vow to Pythagoras and to each other. In their ethical practices, the Pythagoreans were famous for their unselfishness, honesty, and mutual friendship. Mathematically speaking, the School of Pythagoras was most famous for two important reasons: the discovery of the Pythagorean Theorem and the discovery of irrational numbers.

(For more details about the School of Pythagoras, see the next page.)

When Pythagoras was nearly 100 years old, Cylon, who was a wealthy nobleman from Croton, petitioned to join the School. However, Pythagoras rejected Cylon because he was greedy and selfish. Cylon was furious and soon incited others in Croton who were also envious of the Pythagoreans, and together they attacked the School. Pythagoras and some of his followers fled and took refuge in a building outside the town. The attackers burned the building, and many died in the flames, including Pythagoras himself.

For almost half a century, the school thrived under Pythagoras's leadership. Even after Pythagoras's death, the Pythagorean Society flourished for many years, and spread to many other cities. For centuries to come, Pythagoras had a tremendous influence on many of the great mathematical and philosophical thinkers, especially Plato. Perhaps above all else, Pythagoras left a legacy of how to live a pure life, and taught us how to look at the world through a new philosophical and mathematical lens.

Pythagoras and his School

Quotes

- "Every man has been made by God in order to acquire knowledge and contemplate."
- "Numbers rule the universe."
- "Were it not for number and its nature, nothing that exists would be clear to anyone. You can observe the power of number not only in the affairs of the gods, but in all the acts and thoughts of people."

Aphorisms

- Walk on unfrequented paths.
- Govern your tongue before all other things, following the gods.
- Do not poke the fire with a sword.

Their Practices

- Communal living
- Egalitarianism; inclusive of women
- Strict diet
- Strict secrecy

The Four Subjects of Study

- *Arithmetic*: Number in Itself.
- *Geometry*: Number in Space
- *Music*: Number in Time
- *Astronomy*: Number in the Heavens

Central Beliefs

- That at its deepest level, reality is mathematical in nature.
- That philosophy can be used for spiritual purification.
- That the soul can rise to union with the divine.
- That certain symbols have mystical significance.

The Characteristics of Numbers (Listed here is just one of several characteristics for each.)

- *One*: Harmony
- *Two*: Balance
- *Three*: Wisdom
- *Four*: Justice
- *Five*: Nature
- *Six*: Perfection
- *Seven*: Fate
- *Eight*: Love
- *Nine*: Compassion
- *Ten*: God
- *Even numbers*: Feminine
- *Odd numbers*: Masculine

The Golden Verses of Pythagoras

First honor the immortal gods, as the law demands;
Then reverence thy oath, and then the illustrious heroes;
Then venerate the divinities under the earth,
due rites performing;
Then honor your parents, and all of your kindred.

Among others, make the most virtuous thy friend!
Love to make use of his soft speeches,
and learn from his deeds that are useful;
But alienate not the beloved comrade for trifling offences,
Bear all you can, what you can,
for power is bound to necessity.

Take this well to heart:
you must gain control of your habits;
First over stomach, then sleep, and then luxury, and anger.
What brings you shame, do not unto others,
nor by yourself.
The highest of duties is honor of self.

Let justice be practiced in words as in deeds;
Then make the habit, never inconsiderately to act;
Neither forget that death is appointed to all;
That possessions here gladly gathered, here must be left.

Think, before you act, so that nothing stupid results;
To act inconsiderately is part of a fool;
Yet whatever later will not bring you repentance,
that you should carry through.
Do nothing beyond what you know,
Yet learn what you may need:
thus shall your life grow happy.

Do not neglect the health of the body;
Keep measure in eating and drinking,
and every exercise of the body.
By measure, I mean what later will not induce pain.
Follow clean habits of life, but not the luxurious;
Avoid all things which will arouse envy.

Father Zeus, O free them all from sufferings so great,
Or show unto each the Genius, who is their guide!

Yet, do not fear, for the mortals are divine by race,
To whom holy Nature everything will reveal
and demonstrate;
Whereof if you have received, so keep what I teach you;
Healing your soul,
you shall remain insured from manifold evil.

Avoid foods forbidden;
reflect that this contributes to the cleanliness
And redemption of your soul. Consider all things well:
Let reason, the gift divine, be thy highest guide;
Then should you be separated from the body,
and soar in the aether,
You will be imperishable, a divinity, a mortal no more.

A sonnet by Edna St. Vincent Millay

Euclid alone has looked on Beauty bare.
Let all who prate of Beauty hold their peace,
And lay them prone upon the earth and cease
To ponder on themselves, the while they stare
At nothing, intricately drawn nowhere
In shapes of shifting lineage; let geese
Gabble and hiss, but heroes seek release
From dusty bondage into luminous air.
O blinding hour, O holy, terrible day,
When first the shaft into his vision shone
Of light anatomized! Euclid alone
Has looked on Beauty bare. Fortunate they
Who, though once only and then but far away,
Have heard her massive sandal set on stone.

Timeline for Greek Mathematics

(Each step is 25 years; all dates are approximate)

1200BC – Trojan war

1000BC –

800BC – Homer and the *Iliad* and the *Odyssey*
776BC – First Olympiad
753BC – Founding of Rome

560BC – Thales states the first simple theorems.

500BC – Pythagoras and his school: Pythagorean Theorem; discovery of irrational numbers.

450BC – Zeno states his paradoxes.
435BC – Hippocrates squares the lune, and writes the first *Elements*.
399BC – Death of Socrates
387BC – Plato founds the *Academy* in Athens.
365BC – Eudoxus develops his theory on proportions and irrational numbers.
336BC – Alexander becomes king of Macedonia; Aristotle founds the *Lyceum* in 335BC; Founding of Alexandria in 331BC.
300BC – Euclid writes *The Elements*.

255BC – Archimedes determines a method for calculating π.
220BC – Eratosthenes calculates the size of the earth; Archimedes killed by a Roman soldier in 212BC.
200BC – Apollonius writes *Conics*; **End of the "Golden Age" of Greek Mathematics**.

146BC – Greece conquered by Rome.

44BC – Death of Julius Caesar

0AD – Birth of Jesus

60AD – Heron writes *Metrica*, a book mostly on mensuration.

150AD – Ptolemy writes *Almagest*, a book mostly on astronomy, which includes some of the first trigonometry tables.

286AD – Split of the Roman Empire

320AD – Pappus writes *Mathematical Collections*.

415AD – Hypatia, the last great Greek mathematician, and a woman, is killed by a Christian mob.

476AD – Fall of Rome

529AD – Closing of Plato's *Academy* by Justinian

Six Proofs of the Pythagorean Theorem

These six proofs give students a taste of how different proofs can be. It may be best to give them a "blank" version, which doesn't include the wording. This allows them to look at the drawing and try to discover the thinking behind each proof. The blank version appears after this version.

1. *A paper cutout puzzle proof*

With any right scalene (non-isosceles) triangle, draw a square coming off each of the three sides. Extend two lines from the sides of the largest square so that they cut through the other two squares, in each case dividing the squares into a triangle and a trapezoid. Now, draw a line perpendicular to the line that divided the second largest square, by starting at the intersection point on the edge of that square. The second largest square has now been cut into three pieces: two triangles and a quadrilateral having two right angles. With scissors, cut the pieces (numbered 1 to 5 in the drawing) out of the two smaller squares. Place the five pieces on top of the large square so that they fit perfectly. This shows that the sum of the areas of the two smaller squares equals the area of the largest square. (If this was done in seventh grade, then we can now simply remind the students of this "experiential" proof.)

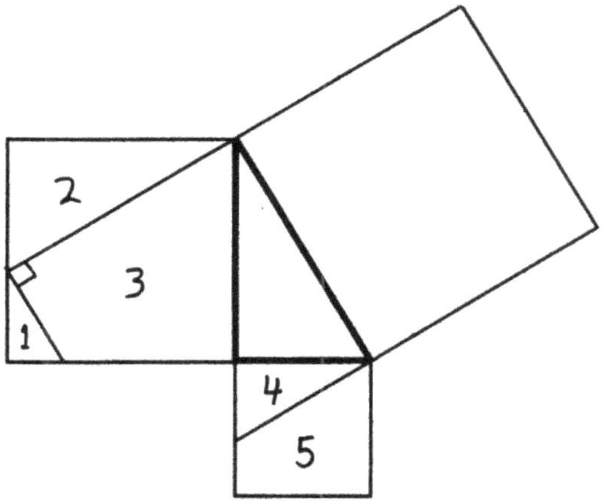

2. *Baravalle's proof using the Shear and Stretch.* (Often covered in 8th grade)

Hermann von Baravalle was a math teacher in the first Waldorf school, and this is a proof that utilizes the shear and stretch. The "Shear and Stretch" states that if two parallelograms (or, in the case of this drawing, a parallelogram and a rectangle) with the same length base lie between two parallel lines, then the two areas are equal. This is a beautiful visual proof, but tenth graders should be questioning whether the figure truly fits into place going from the second step to the third step.

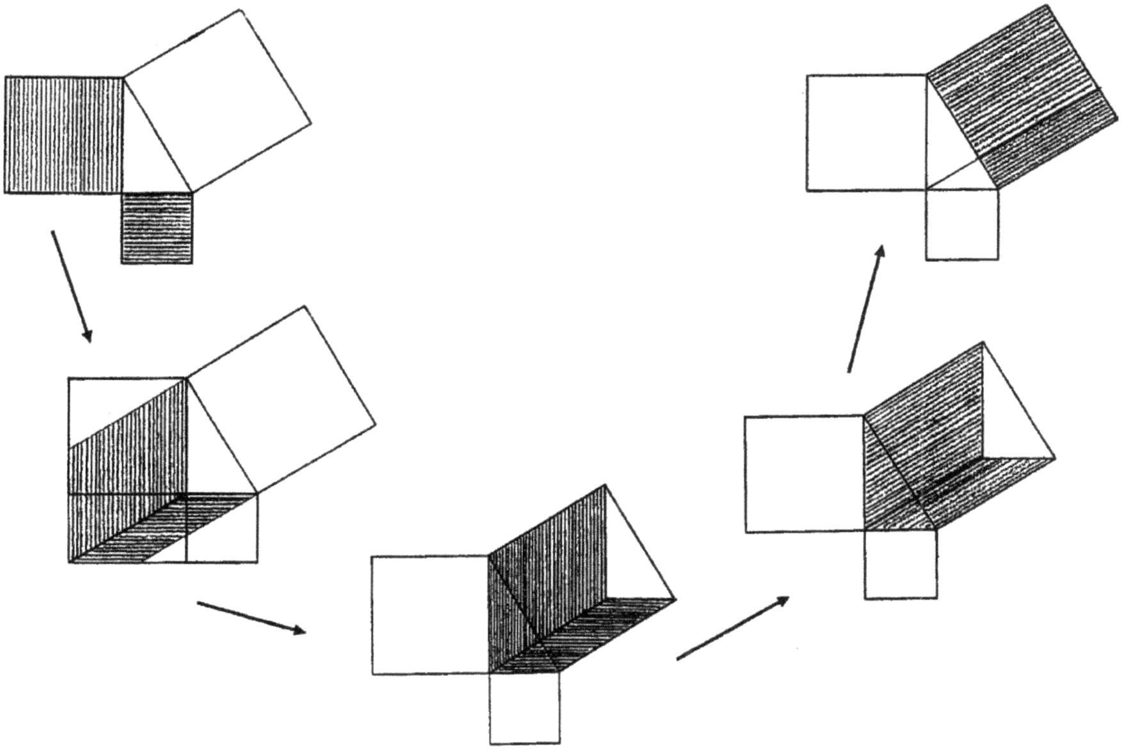

Six Proofs of the Pythagorean Theorem (Continued.)

3. *Rearranging the Triangles.* This is, perhaps, similar to what Pythagoras did.

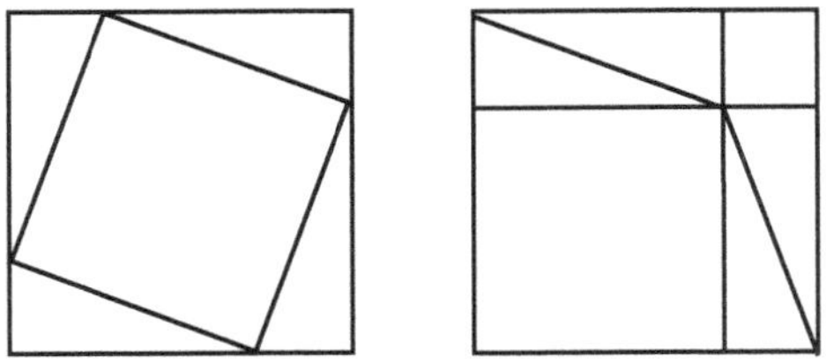

With the two figures on the right, each triangle is equal to the right triangle in the original configuration. The left figure contains the square (with length c) that is attached to the side of the triangle's hypotenuse, and the right figure contains the squares (with lengths a and b) that are attached to the triangle's short and medium sides. Since each figure is bounded by a larger square with sides of length a+b, the total areas of the two figures must be equal. And if we subtract (cut out and discard) the four equal triangles from the two figures (which we just said were equal), then we must be left with two equal areas. This means that the largest square must be equal in area to the sum of the areas of smallest square and the medium square.

4. *From Tabit ibn Qorra* (ca. 870AD)
This proof becomes obvious if you color in the small and medium-sized squares (as shown below), and then visualize moving the triangles that are outside the largest square and place them on top of the triangles that are inside the largest square. This shows that the areas of the two smaller squares combine to equal the area of the largest square. His only clue to the reader was: *Behold!*

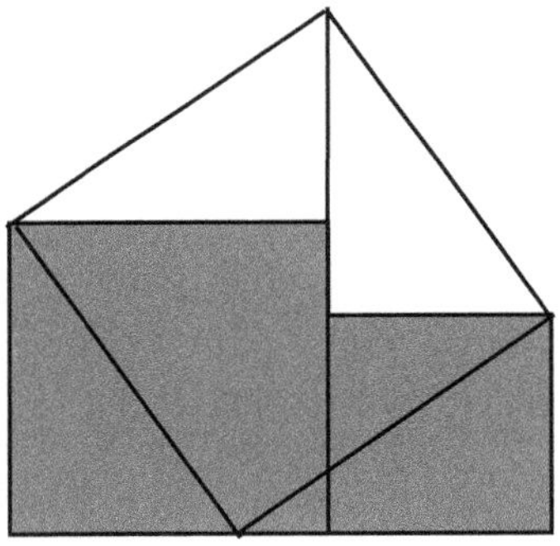

5. *From Bhaskara* (ca. 1150AD)
This proof requires a bit of algebra. The inner square's side has length (b-a), so its area is $(b-a)^2$. We simply set up the equation and then simplify it.

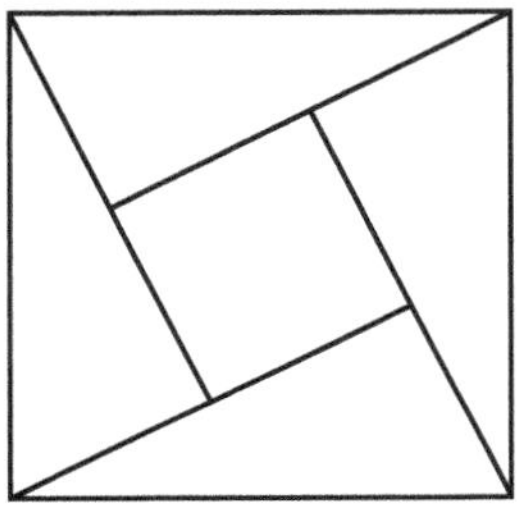

Outer Square = Inner Square + 4 Triangles

$$c^2 = (b-a)^2 + 4(\tfrac{1}{2}ab)$$
$$c^2 = b^2 - 2ab + a^2 + 2ab$$
$$\therefore \mathbf{c^2 = b^2 + a^2}$$

6. *Proportion Proof.* This proof is found in many modern high school geometry books, and it is the only one of the six proofs that doesn't involve areas of squares. Euclid wouldn't have liked it because it relies on ratios and proportions, which he didn't cover in *The Elements* until Books V and VI.

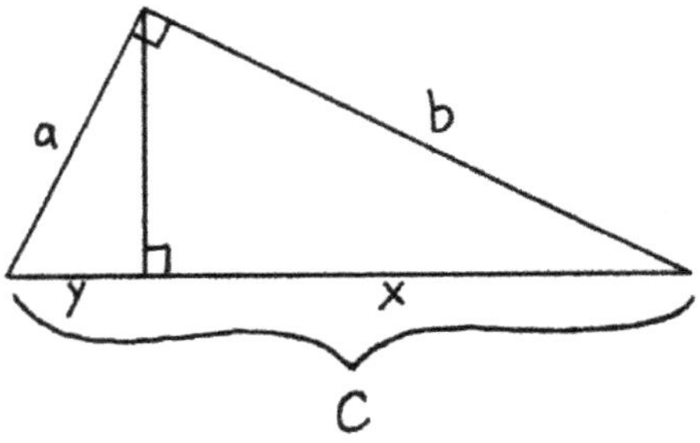

$a/y = c/a$ therefore $a^2 = cy$
$b/x = c/b$ therefore $b^2 = cx$

$$a^2 + b^2 = cy + cx$$
$$a^2 + b^2 = c(y + x)$$
$$\therefore \mathbf{a^2 + b^2 = c^2}$$

Six Proofs of the Pythagorean Theorem

1. *A paper cutout puzzle proof*

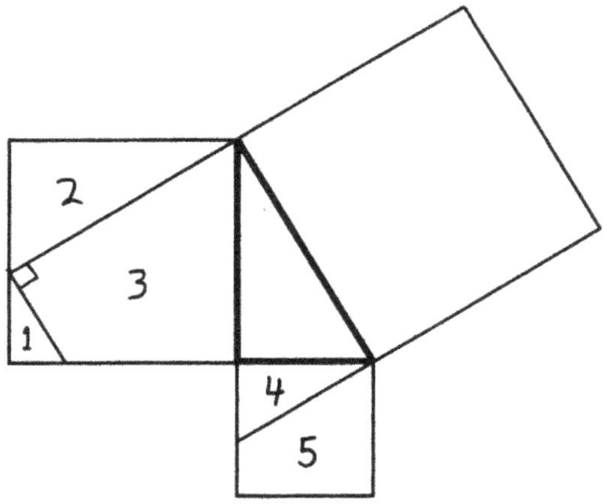

2. *Baravalle's proof using the Shear and Stretch.*

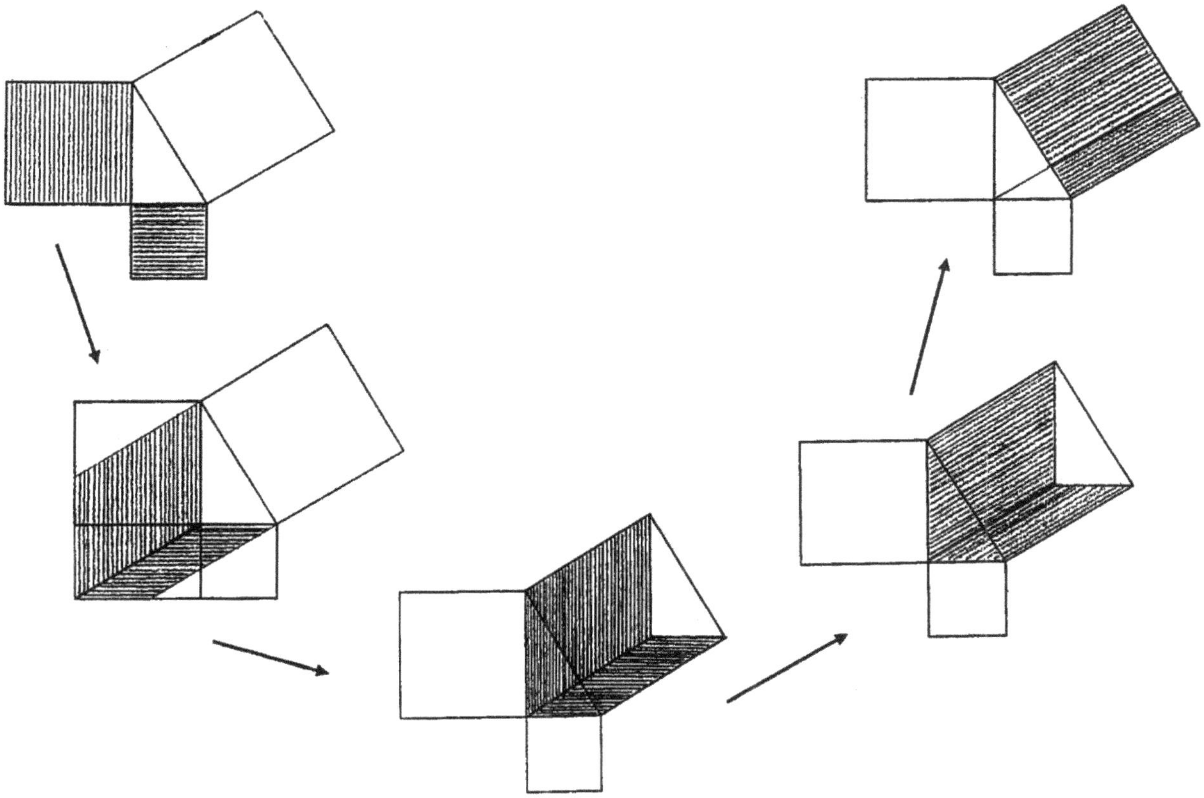

Six Proofs of the Pythagorean Theorem (Continued.)

3. *Rearranging the Triangles.* This is, perhaps, similar to what Pythagoras did.

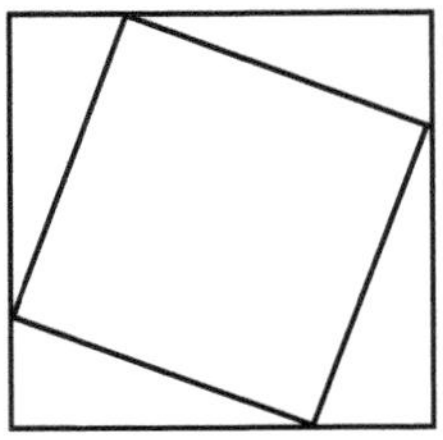

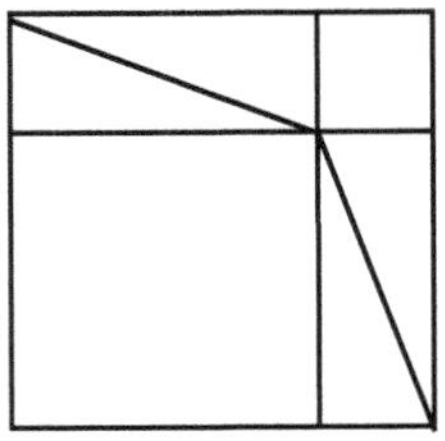

4. *From Tabit ibn Qorra* (ca. 870AD)
Behold!

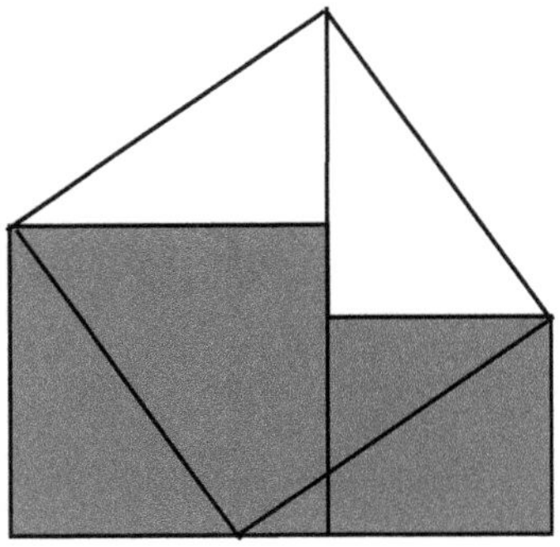

5. *From Bhaskara* (ca. 1150AD) This proof requires a bit of algebra.

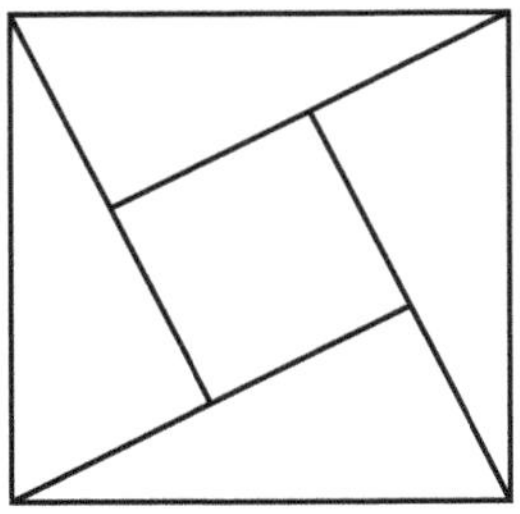

6. *Proportion Proof.* This proof is found in many modern high school geometry books, and it is the only one of the six that doesn't involve squares or area.

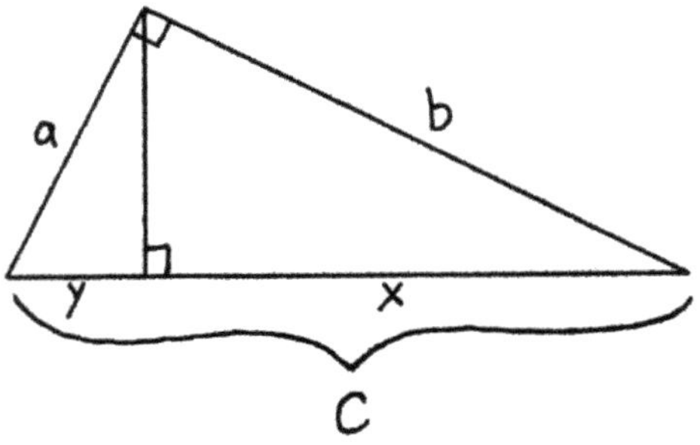

—— *Euclid's Elements* (10th Grade) ——

The role of Euclid's *Elements*

Euclid's book, *The Elements*, is the main topic of study in the Greek Geometry block. This massive work has served the world of mathematics as the quintessential example of an axiomatic system – a collection of theorems building upon one another systematically. *The Elements* was the model of perfect truth and certainty for more than 2000 years.

Background and key ideas

- *The Elements* contains 465 theorems, with a proof for each theorem.
- It was the textbook of geometry and mathematics until the 19th century, and is still the basis for geometry books today. It became the model for logic and mathematical rigor.
- *The Elements* contains more than just geometry. It was a textbook of almost all the mathematics known at the time of Euclid, including proportions, number theory, and irrational numbers.
- It contained few original ideas or theorems, but had many original proofs.
- It did not include the concept of infinity (e.g., a line always had finite length).

Method and style

- Contrary to popular belief, Euclid did not write two column proofs. His proofs were written in paragraph form. He did not even write down what the justifications were for each step. For the proof of any particular theorem, he expected that the reader was familiar enough with all of the previous theorems and definitions – so familiar that it wasn't necessary to state the justifications for the steps – the reader supposedly just knew them.

Euclid's five postulates

- The postulates (or axioms) are the foundation of a mathematical axiomatic system.
- All of *The Elements'* 465 theorems were built upon his five postulates.
- **The fifth postulate.** *If a straight line falling on two straight lines makes the interior angles on the same side less than two right angles, then the two straight lines, if produced indefinitely, meet on that side on which the angles are less than two right angles.*
  - Often, the fifth postulate is said to be: "*Two parallel lines never intersect*". However that is the definition of parallel lines.
  - This was the only postulate that was not "self-evident".
  - Mathematicians tried for centuries to prove it by using the first four postulates as a basis. The search for a proof of the fifth postulate lead, finally, in 19th century, to the discovery of *non-Euclidean* and projective geometry (which is an eleventh grade main lesson block).
  - Much later, mathematicians concluded that the fifth postulate could have been replaced by the following statement (without affecting the rest of the theorems):

    Through a given point, there can be drawn only one line parallel to a given line.

Some curiosities

- Euclid avoids using the fifth postulate and referring to the word "parallel" as long as possible – which was for 26 theorems. After that, theorems 27-48 all include the concept of parallel.
- He *defines* "parallel" lines as two lines that never meet.
- Note that squares, oblongs (rectangles), rhombuses, and rhomboids are all types of parallelograms, where a rhomboid is a parallelogram, as we normally think of it, that is guaranteed not to be any of the other three types. He never uses the terms oblong, rhombus, or rhomboid after defining them.
- He doesn't define a parallelogram anywhere, and sometimes uses the term "parallelogrammic area" (a four-sided figure bounded by parallel lines) instead. A "parallelogrammic area" has the advantage over a rhomboid in that it could also be a square, a rectangle, or a rhombus.

My "translation" of *The Elements*

Reading Euclid directly can be quite formidable for the students. In the pages that follow, I have reworked and summarized the content in an effort to make it more understandable for the students.

The Foundation of Euclid's Elements

The 34 Definitions (some of the names of the terms have been changed from Heath's translation.)

1. A **point** is that which has no part.
2. A **curve** is breadthless length.
3. The **extremities of a curve** are points.
4. A **line** is a curve which lies evenly with the points on themselves.
5. A **surface** is that which has length and breadth only.
6. The **extremities of a surface** are curves.
7. A **plane** is a surface which lies evenly with the lines on themselves.
8. A plane **angle** is the inclination to one another of two curves in a plane which meet one another and do not lie in a straight line.
9. When the sides of an angle are straight lines, then the angle is called **rectilineal**.
10. When a line stood up on another line makes the adjacent angles equal to one another, each of the angles is **right**, and the line standing on the other is called a **perpendicular** to that on which it stands.
11. An **obtuse angle** is greater than a right angle.
12. An **acute angle** is less than a right angle.
13. A **boundary** is that which is an extremity of anything.
14. A **figure** is that which is contained by any boundary or boundaries.
15. A **circle** is a plane figure contained by one curve such that all the lines falling upon it from one point among those lying within the figure are equal to one another.
16. And the point is called the **center** of the circle.
17. A **diameter** of the circle is any line drawn through the center and terminated in both directions by the circumference of the circle, and such a line also bisects the circle.
18. A **semi-circle** is the figure contained by the diameter and the circumference cut-off by it. The center of the semi-circle is the same as that of the circle.
19. **Rectilineal figures** are those contained by lines. **Triangles** are those contained by three lines, **quadrilaterals** are those contained by four lines, and **multilaterals** are those contained by more than four lines.
20. Of triangles, an **equilateral triangle** has three equal sides; an **isosceles triangle** has two of its sides alone equal; a **scalene** triangle has its three sides unequal, and…
21. A **right triangle** has a right angle; an **obtuse triangle** has an obtuse angle; and an **acute triangle** has its three angles acute.
22. Of quadrilaterals, a **square** is both equilateral and right-angled; an **oblong** is right-angled but not equilateral [i.e., a rectangle, which is not a square]; a **rhombus** is equilateral but not right-angled; and a **rhomboid** has its opposite sides and angles equal to one another, but is neither equilateral nor right-angled [i.e., a parallelo-gram, which is neither a rhombus nor a rectangle]. Let all other quadrilaterals be called **trapezia.**
23. **Parallel** lines are lines which, being in the same plane and being produced indefinitely in both directions, do not meet one another in either direction.

The Five Common Notions

1. <u>Transitive Property</u>. Things which are equal to the same thing are also equal to each other.
2. <u>Addition Property</u>. If equals are added to equals, then the sums are equal.
3. <u>Subtraction Property</u>. If equals are subtracted from equals, then the differences are equal.
4. Things (i.e., figures or solids) that coincide with one another are congruent.
5. The whole is greater than the part.

The Five Postulates

1. A line can be drawn between any two given points.
2. Any line can be extended.
3. A circle can be drawn with any center and any distance [as its radius].
4. All right angles are equal to one another.
5. <u>The Parallel Postulate</u>. If a line falling on two lines makes the interior angles on the same side less than two right angles, the two lines, if produced indefinitely, meet on that side on which the angles are less than two right angles.

A Summary of

The 13 Books of Euclid's Elements

Book I Basic constructions and theorems involving angles, triangles, parallelograms, etc.

Th. 1: To construct an equilateral triangle
Th 4: SAS triangle congruency theorem
Th 5: Isosceles Triangle Theorem
Th 8: SSS triangle congruency theorem
Th 13: Supplementary Angle Theorem
Th 15: Vertical Angle Theorem
Th 26: AAS, AAS triangle congruency
Th 29: (a) Corresponding angles are equal
(b) Alternate interior angles are equal
(c) Same-side interior angles are equal
Th 32: The angles in a triangle add to 180°
Th 35-38, 41: Shear and Stretch theorems
Th 46: To construct a square given one side
Th 47: Pythagorean Theorem

Book II "Geometrical Algebra" and theorems regarding equal area

Th. 4: "*If a straight line be cut at random, the square on the whole is equal to the squares on the segments and twice the rectangle contained by the segments.*" This is the geometric equivalent of the identity $(a+b)^2 = a^2 + 2ab + b^2$.
Th. 5: Geometric equivalent of the identity $(a+b)(a-b) = a^2 - b^2$, and used as solution to $ax - x^2 = b^2$.
Th. 11: The Golden Section. "*How to cut a given straight line so that the rectangle contained by the whole and one of the segments is equal to the square on the remaining side.*"
Th. 12, 13: Variation of the Pythagorean Theorem for acute and obtuse triangles (Law of Cosines)
Th 14: Construction of a square with an area equal to a given polygon

Book III Circle geometry

Th. 1: Finding the center of a given circle
Th 17: Constructing a tangent line through a given point on a circle
Th 20: Inscribed Angle Theorem
Th 21: "*Inscribed angles that are subtended by the same arc are equal to one another.*"
Th 22: Inscribed Quadrilateral Theorem
Th 31: Theorem of Thales
Th 32: Chord-Tangent Theorem
Th 35: Chord-Segment Theorem
Th 36: Secant-Tangent Theorem
Th. 37: Secant-Tangent Theorem converse

Book IV Constructions of polygons

Th. 1: To draw a chord inside a given circle equal to a given line
Th 2,3: To inscribe or circumscribe in or about a given circle a triangle similar to a given triangle
Th 4,5: To inscribe or circumscribe a circle in or about a given triangle
Th 6-9: To inscribe or circumscribe a square in or about a given circle, and vice versa
Th 10: To inscribe a *golden triangle* (the triangle found in a regular pentagon) in a given circle
Th 11-14: To inscribe or circumscribe a regular pentagon in or about a given circle, and vice versa
Th 15: To inscribe a regular hexagon in a given circle
Th 16: To inscribe a regular 15-gon in a given circle

Book V The "algebra" of proportions. (Eudoxus' theory of proportion)

Th. 1: States $ma+mb+mc+... = m(a+b+c...)$
Th. 4: States that if $a:b = c:d$ then $ma:nb = mc:nd$
Th. 5: States $ma-mb = m(a-b)$
Th. 9: States that if $a:c = b:c$ then $a=b$
Th. 10: States that if $a:c > b:c$ then $a>b$
Th. 11: States that if $a:b = c:d$ and $c:d = e:f$ then $a:b = e:f$
Th. 12: States that $a:a' = b:b' = c:c'.... = (a+b):(a'+b') = (a+b+c...):(a'+b'+c'...)$
Th. 15: States $a:b = ma:mb$
Th. 16: States that if $a:b = c:d$ then $a:c = b:d$
Th. 17: States that if $a:b = c:d$ then $(a-b):b = (c-d):d$
Th. 18: States that if $a:b = c:d$ then $(a+b):b = (c+d):d$ [also $a:(a+b) = c:(c+d)$]
Th. 19: States that if $a:b = c:d$ then $a:b = (a-c):(b-d)$
Th. 25: States that if $a:b = c:d$ and a is the greatest and d is the least, then $a+d > b+c$

Book VI Proportions relating to geometry

Th. 2: Triangle proportionality theorem
Th 3: Triangle angle-bisector theorem
Th 4: Similar triangles have their sides in equal proportions
Th 5: SSS similarity theorem
Th 6: SAS similarity theorem
Th 7: HL similarity theorem
Th 8: Altitude of the hypotenuse theorem
Th 11: To construct the third term in a geometric progression (Given x and y, find z so x:y = y:z)
Th 12: Given a, b, c to construct X such that a:b = c:x
Th 13: To construct the geometric mean (Given x and z, find y such that x:y = y:z)
Th 16: *"If four lines are proportional, then the rectangle contained by the extremes is equal to the rectangle contained by the means [and vice versa]."* Algebraically: if $a:b = c:d$ then $a\cdot d = b\cdot c$
Th. 25: To construct a polygon similar to one polygon and equal in area to another polygon
Th. 28, 29: Geometric solution to a general quadratic equation
Th. 31: Generalization of the Pythagorean Theorem: *"If a right triangle has similar figures drawn in the same orientation off each of its three sides, then the area of the largest figure equals the sum of the areas of the other two figures."*
Th. 33: With two equal circles, angles have the same ratio as the arcs that subtend them, whether they stand at the centers or at the circumferences.

Book VII, VIII, IX Elementary number theory

Th VII-2: To find the greatest common factor of two numbers
Th VII-16: Commutative property of multiplication $a\cdot b = b\cdot a$
Th VII-32: Any number is either prime or has some prime number as its factor
Th VII-34: To find the least common multiple of two numbers
Th VIII-14: If a^2 is a factor of b^2, then a is a factor of b, and vice versa
Th VIII-16: If a^2 is *not* a factor of b^2, then a is *not* a factor of b, and vice versa
Th VIII-24: If $a:b = c^2:d^2$ and a is a square, then b is also a square
Th VIII-25: If $a:b = c^3:d^3$ and a is a cube, then b is also a cube
Th IX-14: *The Fundamental Theorem of Arithmetic*, which says that any integer greater than one can be expressed as the product of primes in only one way. (e.g., $24 = 2^3\cdot 3$)
Th. IX-20: States that the number of primes is infinite
Th IX-35: The equivalent of a formula for the sum of the numbers in a geometric progression
Th IX-36: *Euclid's Perfect Number Theorem:* If $2^n - 1$ is prime, then $2^{n-1}(2^n - 1)$ is perfect.

Book X On Irrational Numbers (115 theorems!)

Th. X-3: Given two commensurable magnitudes, to find their common measure (common multiple)
Th X-28: A method for determining Pythagorean triples
Th X-42: The equivalent of saying if $a+\sqrt{b} = x+\sqrt{y}$ then a=x and b=y
Th X-112: The equivalent of rationalizing the denominator of a fraction – e.g., $\frac{3}{\sqrt{7}+\sqrt{5}}$

Book XI XII, XIII Solid geometry

Th. XII-2: *(The Basis for the Method of Exhaustion)* The areas of two circles have the same ratio as the areas of the squares of their diameters.
Th. XII-7,10: The formula for the volume of a *pyramid* and a *cone*
Th XIII-10: A triangle whose sides are respectively the sides of an equilateral pentagon, hexagon, and decagon, all inscribed in the same circle, is a right triangle.
Th. XIII-13,14,15,16,17: The ratio of the edges of a tetrahedron to an octahedron to a cube to an icosahedron to a dodecahedron to the diameter of the sphere that circumscribes them all is:

$$T:O:C:I:D:S = \sqrt{2/3} : \sqrt{1/2} : \sqrt{1/3} : \sqrt{\frac{5-\sqrt{5}}{10}} : \sqrt{\frac{\sqrt{5}-1}{2\sqrt{3}}} : 1$$

Th. XIII-18: There are only five possible regular [Platonic] solids.

A Summary of **Book I** of Euclid's Elements

<u>Note</u>: Some of the theorems have been reworded for clarity.

I-1 *Construction* of an equilateral triangle, given one side.

I-2 *Construction:* To place at a given point (as an extremity) a line[1] equal to a given line.[2]

I-3 *Construction:* Given two unequal lines, cut off from the greater line a piece equal to the lesser line.[3]

I-4 <u>SAS Congruency Theorem</u>. If the two sides and the included angle of one triangle are congruent to the two sides and the included angle of another triangle, then the third sides are equal, the remaining angles are equal, and the two triangles are congruent.

I-5 <u>Isosceles Triangle Theorem</u>. In an isosceles triangle, (a) the base angles are equal to one another, and (b) if the two sides are extended, then the angles under the bases will be equal to one another.

I-6 (Converse of #5) If the two base angles of a given triangle are equal, then the sides are also equal.

I-7 Given two lines, drawn from the ends of a third line, and meeting together in a point, there cannot be constructed, on the same third line and on the same side of it, two other lines, with the same lengths and placed on the same extremities as the first two lines, such that they meet at a different point. [This theorem is used to prove I-8.]

I-8 <u>SSS Congruency Theorem</u>. If the three sides of a given triangle are equal, respectively, to the three sides of a second triangle, then all of the angles will be equal, respectively, to one another.

I-9 *Construction:* Bisection of an angle.

I-10 *Construction:* Bisection of a line.

I-11 *Construction* of a line perpendicular to a given line from a point on that line.

I-12 *Construction* of a line perpendicular to a given line from a point NOT on that line.

I-13 <u>Supplementary Angle (Y) Theorem</u>. If two adjacent angles form a straight line, then the sum of the angles is equal to two right angles.

I-14 (Converse of #13) If two adjacent angles add to two right angles, then a straight line is formed.

I-15 <u>Vertical Angle (X) Theorem</u>. Vertical angles are equal.

I-16 In any triangle, the exterior angle is greater than either of the opposite interior angles.

I-17 In any triangle, the sum of any two angles is less than two right angles.

I-18 In any triangle, the greater side subtends the greater angle.

I-19 (Converse of #18) In any triangle, the greater angle is subtended by the greater side.

I-20 In any triangle, any two sides added together are greater than the remaining side.

I-21 If two lines are drawn from the ends of the base of a triangle, such that the point of intersection of the two lines is within the triangle, then the sum of the two lines will be less than the sum of the two sides of the original triangle, and it will contain a greater angle.

I-22 *Construction* of a triangle given three lines.

I-23 *Construction:* Copying a given angle onto a given line.

I-24 If the two sides of one triangle are equal to two sides of a second triangle, then the triangle with the greater included angle has the greater remaining side.

I-25 (Converse of #24) If the two sides of one triangle are equal to the two sides of a second triangle, then the triangle with the greater remaining side has the greater included angle.

I-26 <u>ASA, AAS Congruency Theorem</u>. If two angles and a side of one triangle are equal to two angles and a side of a second triangle, then the triangles are congruent.

---

[1] A *line* is what we call today a *line segment.*

[2] With Euclidean constructions, it is technically assumed that a compass collapses whenever it is lifted off the page, so that it may not be directly used to transfer distances. This theorem allows us to get around this problem, by showing how to construct a circle of a given radius, centered at any given point on the plane.

[3] Essentially, this means to copy a given distance from one line to another, e.g., to measure off AB equal to CD.

I-27 (Converse of #29a) If two lines are cut by a transversal, and alternate interior angles are equal, then the lines are parallel.

I-28 (Converse of #29b and c) If two lines are cut by a transversal, and corresponding angles are equal or the same-side interior angles add to two right angles, then the lines are parallel.

I-29 If two parallel lines are cut by a transversal, then:
- (a) Alternate Interior Angle (Z) Theorem. The alternate interior angles are equal.
- (b) Corresponding Angle (F) Theorem. The corresponding angles are equal.
- (c) Same-Side Interior Angle (C) Theorem. The same-side interior angles add to two right angles.

I-30 Two lines that are parallel to the same line are parallel to each other.

I-31 *Construction* of a line parallel to a given line, through a point not on that line.

I-32 In any triangle:
- (a) Triangle Exterior Angle Theorem. Any exterior angle is equal to the sum of the two opposite interior angles.
- (b) Triangle Interior Angle Theorem. The three interior angles add to two right angles.

I-33 Two lines that join two equal, parallel lines, are themselves parallel and equal.

I-34 In a parallelogram:
- (a) Opposite sides and angles are equal.
- (b) A diagonal divides the parallelogram into two congruent triangles.

I-35 **Parallelograms lying on the same base and between the same two parallel lines have equal area.

I-36 **Parallelograms having the same length base and lying between the same two parallel lines have equal area.

I-37 **Triangles lying on the same base and lying between the same two parallel lines have equal area.

I-38 **Triangles having the same length base and lying between the same two parallel lines have equal area.

I-39 Two congruent triangles sharing the same base, and lying on the same side of that base, [but perhaps a mirror image of each other] lie between the same two parallel lines.

I-40 Two congruent triangles having the same length base, and lying on the same side of the same line, lie between the same two parallel lines.

I-41 **If a triangle and parallelogram have the same length base and lie between the same two parallel lines, then the area of the parallelogram is twice that of the triangle.

I-42 *Construction* of a parallelogram given an angle and with an area equal to a given triangle.

I-43 If, in any parallelogram, two lines are drawn parallel to two adjacent sides of the parallelogram, such that they intersect on a diagonal of the parallelogram, then the two smaller parallelograms formed on opposite sides of the diagonal have equal area.

I-44 *Construction* of a parallelogram given an angle, a side, and with an area equal to a given triangle.

I-45 *Construction* of a parallelogram given an angle and with an area equal to a given polygon.

I-46 *Construction* of a square with a given side.

I-47 Pythagorean Theorem. In right triangles, [the area of] the square on the side subtending the right angle is equal to [the sum of the areas of] the squares on the other two sides.

I-48 (Converse of #47) In a triangle, if [the area of] the square on one of the sides is equal to [the sum of the areas of] the squares on the remaining two sides of the triangle, then the angle contained by the remaining two sides of the triangle is a right angle.

** These are Euclid's "shear and stretch" theorems.

Selected Proofs[1] from ***The Elements, Book I***

Theorem 1 *Construction of an equilateral triangle, given one side.*

Proof:

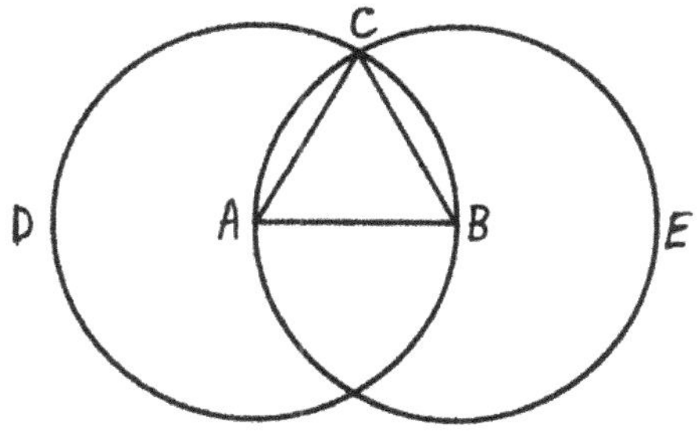

1. Given line AB.
2. With A as center and using AB as the radius draw circle BCD (see drawing). With B as center and using AB as the radius draw circle ACE. (Post. 3)
3. From point C, where the two circles intersect, draw lines to both points A and B. (Post. 1).
4. Since point A is the center of circle BCD, AC ≅ AB
   Since point B is the center of circle ACE, BC ≅ AB
   (Def. of a circle)
5. AC ≅ BC (C.N. 1)
6. AC ≅ AB ≅ BC ∴ΔABC is equilateral. (Definition of equilateral) Q.E.D.

Theorem 5 *In an isosceles triangle, (a) the base angles are equal to one another, and (b) if the two sides are extended, then the angles under the bases will be equal to one another.*

Proof:

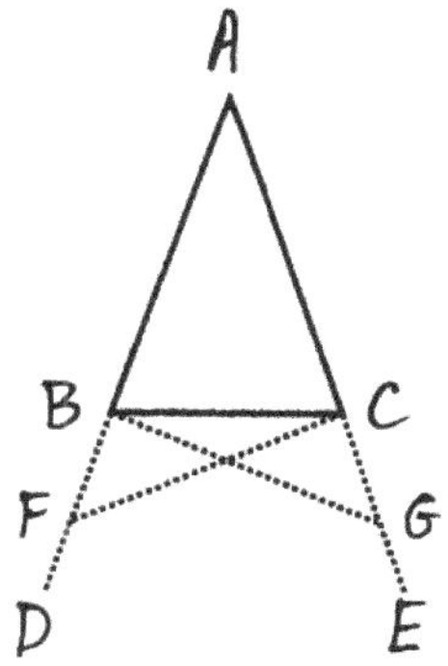

1. Given ΔABC is an isosceles triangle. Let AB and AC be the equal sides. (Def. of isosceles triangle)
2. Extend sides AB and AC to D and E, respectively. (Post. 2)
3. Choose point F at random on BD. Cut off AE at G, such that AG ≅ AF. (Th. I-3)
4. Join the lines FC and GB. (Post. 1)
5. Regarding ΔAFC and ΔAGB :
   they share ∠GAF; AF ≅ AG (step 3); AB ≅ AC (step 1)
   ∴ΔAFC ≅ ΔAGB; FC ≅ BG; ∠ACF ≅ ∠ABG;
   and ∠AFC ≅ ∠AGB (Th. I-4)
6. Since AF ≅ AG and AB ≅ AC then BF ≅ CG (C.N. 3)
7. Regarding ΔBFC and ΔCGB :
   ∠BFC ≅ ∠CGB (same as ∠AFC ≅ ∠AGB, step 5)
   BF ≅ CG (step 7) and FC ≅ BG (step 5)
   ∴ ΔBFC ≅ ΔCGB, ∠BCF ≅ ∠CBG, and
   ∠CBF ≅ ∠BCG (Th. I-4) Q.E.D. (for part b)
8. Since ∠ACF ≅ ∠ABG (step 5) and in these angles ∠BCF ≅ ∠CBG (step 7)
   Then the remaining angles are equal (C.N. 3):
   ∴∠ABC ≅ ∠ACB Q.E.D. (for part a)

[1] All of the proofs listed here are the result of me rewording T. L. Heath's translation of *The Elements* (Dover Publications, 1956).

Selected Proofs from *The Elements, Book I* (continued)

Theorem 9 *Construction of an angle bisector.*

Proof:

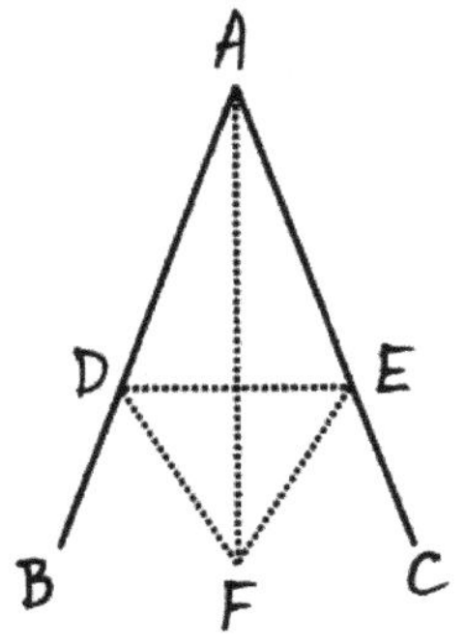

1. Given $\angle BAC$ (to be bisected) with point D randomly on AB.
2. Let AC be cut off at E, such that $AD \cong AE$ (Th. I-3)
3. Draw DE. (Post. 1)
4. Draw equilateral ΔDEF on DE. (Th. I-1)
5. Draw AF. (Post. 1)
6. $DF \cong EF$ (Def. of Equilateral Triangle)
7. $\angle DAF \cong \angle EAF$ (Th. I-8 SSS)
8. $\therefore \angle BAC$ has been bisected. (Def. of Bisect) Q.E.D.

Theorem 10 *Bisection of a line.*

Proof:

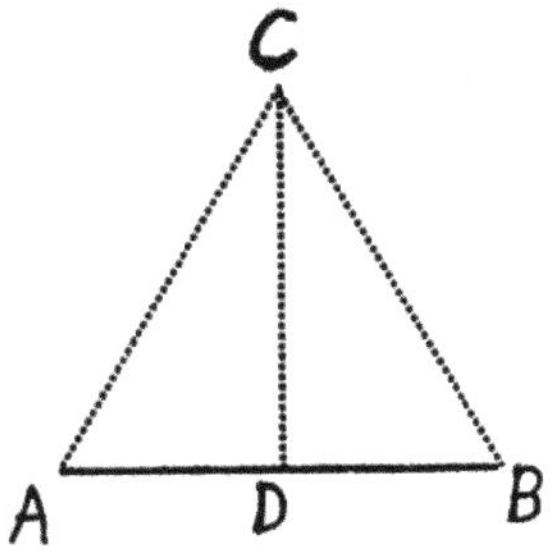

1. Given line AB to be bisected.
2. Draw equilateral ΔABC on AB (Th. I-1)
3. Draw the bisector CD of $\angle ACB$ (Th. I-9)
4. $\angle ACD \cong \angle BCD$ (Def. Angle Bisector)
5. $AC \cong BC$ (Def. of Equilateral Triangle)
6. $\Delta ACD \cong \Delta BCD$ and $AD \cong BD$ (Th. I-4)
7. $\therefore$ AB has been bisected. (Def. of Bisect) Q.E.D.

Theorem 13 *Supplementary Angle Theorem* (Y Theorem). *If two adjacent angles form a straight line, then the sum of the angles is equal to two right angles.*

Proof:

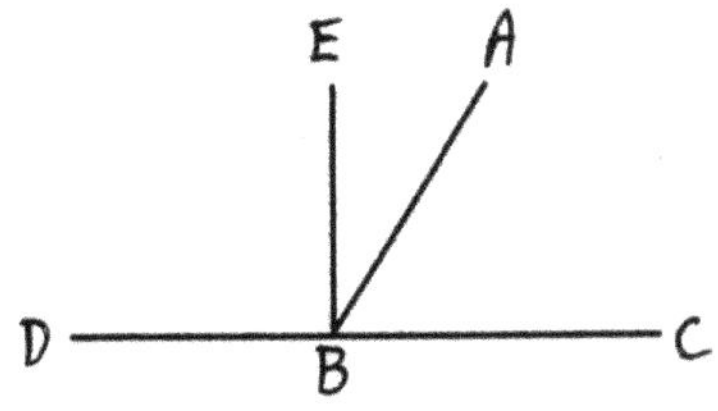

1. Given line AB set up on line DC.
2. If $\angle CBA \cong \angle ABD$, then they are two right angles. (Definition of Right Angles)
3. If these two angles are not equal, then draw BE from point B and perpendicular to line DC. (Th. I-11)
4. $\angle CBE$ and $\angle DBE$ are right angles. (Def. of Perpendicular)
5. $m\angle CBE = m\angle ABC + m\angle ABE$ (from drawing: No reason stated)
6. $m\angle CBE + m\angle DBE = m\angle DBE + m\angle ABC + m\angle ABE$ (C.N. 2)
7. $m\angle DBA = m\angle DBE + m\angle ABE$ (from drawing: No reason stated)
8. $m\angle DBA + m\angle ABC = m\angle DBE + m\angle ABE + m\angle ABC$ (C.N. 2)
9. $m\angle CBE + m\angle DBE = m\angle DBA + m\angle ABC$ (steps 6 & 8, C.N. 1)
10. Because $\angle CBE$ and $\angle DBE$ are both right angles (step 4), $\angle DBA$ and $\angle ABC$ together form two right angles [they are supplementary]. (C.N. 1) Q.E.D.

Selected Proofs from *The Elements, Book I* (continued)

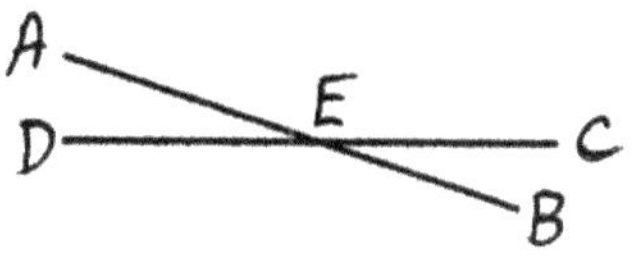

Theorem 15 (X Theorem) *Vertical angles are equal.*

Proof:

1. Given lines AB and CD intersecting at E.
2. The sum of ∠CEA and ∠AED is equal to two right angles. (Th. I-13)
3. The sum of ∠CEA and ∠CEB is equal to two right angles. (Th. I-13)
4. The sum of ∠CEA and ∠AED is equal to the sum of ∠CEA and ∠CEB (Post. 4 and C.N. 1)
5. ∠AED ≅ ∠CEB (C.N. 3) (Similarly, it can be proven that ∠CEA ≅ ∠BED) Q.E.D.

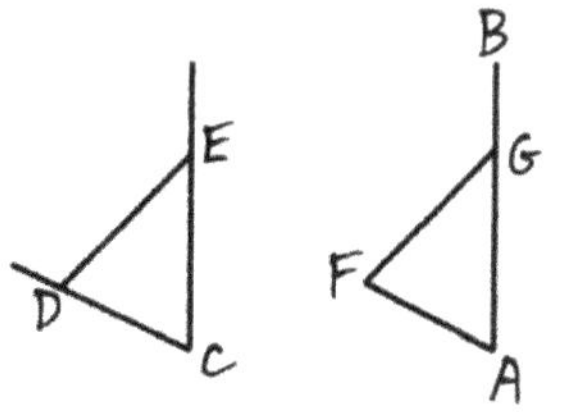

Theorem 23 *Copying an angle.*

Proof:

1. Given angle DCE to be copied to point A on the line AB.
2. Let DE be drawn. (Post. 1)
3. By using the three lines CD, DE, and CE construct the triangle AFG such that CD = AF, CE = AG, and DE = FG. (Th. I-22)
4. Since the three sides of the triangle AFG are equal to the three sides of the triangle CDE, then the angle DCE is equal to the angle FAG. (Th. I-8) *Q.E.D.*

Theorem 27 *If two lines are cut by a transversal, and alternate interior angles are equal, then the lines are parallel.*

Proof:

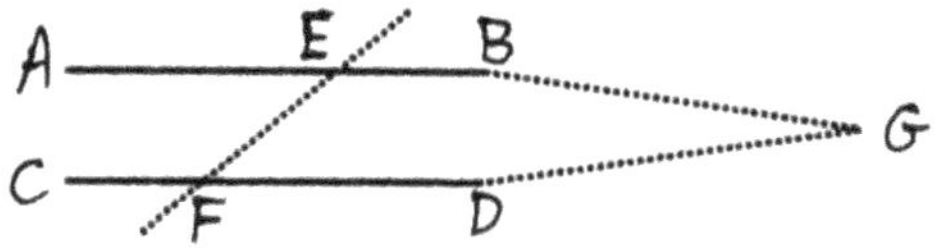

1. Given that EF falls on AE and CD, and ∠AEF ≅ ∠EFD
2. Assume that AB and CD meet at point G, in the direction of B, D.
3. Then in ΔEFG, the exterior angle (∠AEF) is equal to an interior and opposite angle (∠EFG), which is impossible. (Th. I-16)
4. ∴ the assumption (step 2) is false. AB and CD cannot meet in the direction of B, D.
5. Similarly, it can be shown that AB and CD cannot meet in the direction of A, C.
6. AB and CD do not meet in either direction, therefore they are parallel. (Def. of parallel) Q.E.D.

Selected Proofs from *The Elements, Book I* (continued)

Theorem 29 *If two parallel lines are cut by a transversal, then the alternate interior angles are equal, the corresponding angles are equal,* and *the same-side interior angles add to two right angles.*

[Note: This is the first theorem where Euclid uses the fifth postulate.]

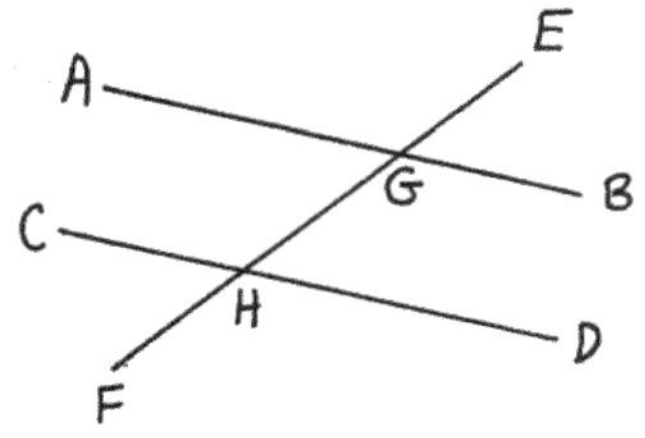

Proof:

1. Given parallel lines AB and CD, with line EF falling on them.
2. Assume that $\angle AGH$ and $\angle GHD$ are not equal, and that $\angle AGH$ is larger. So, $\angle AGH > \angle GHD$.
3. $\angle AGH + \angle BGH > \angle GHD + \angle BGH$ (C.N.2 for inequalities)
4. $\angle AGH + \angle BGH =$ two right angles (Th. I-13)
5. two right angles $> \angle GHD + \angle BGH$ (C.N.1 for inequalities)
6. Because the sum of $\angle GHD$ and $\angle BGH$ is less than two right angles, lines AB and CD must meet. (Postulate 5)
7. But lines AB and CD cannot meet. (Def. of Parallel Lines)
8. Steps 6 and 7 are in contradiction, so our assumption (step 2) must be false, and $\therefore$ $\angle AGH \cong \angle GHD$ [*alternate interior angles are equal*].
9. $\angle AGH \cong \angle EGB$ (Th. I-15)
10. $\therefore$ $\angle EGB \cong \angle GHD$ (C.N.1) [*corresponding angles are equal*]
11. $\angle EGB + \angle BGH = \angle GHD + \angle BGH$ (C.N.2)
12. $\angle EGB + \angle BGH =$ two right angles (Th. I-13)
13. $\therefore$ $\angle GHD + \angle BGH =$ two right angles (C.N.1) [*same-side interior angles add to two right angles*] Q.E.D.

Theorem 32 *In any triangle, (a) Any exterior angle is equal to the sum of the two opposite interior angles, and (b) The three interior angles add to two right angles.*

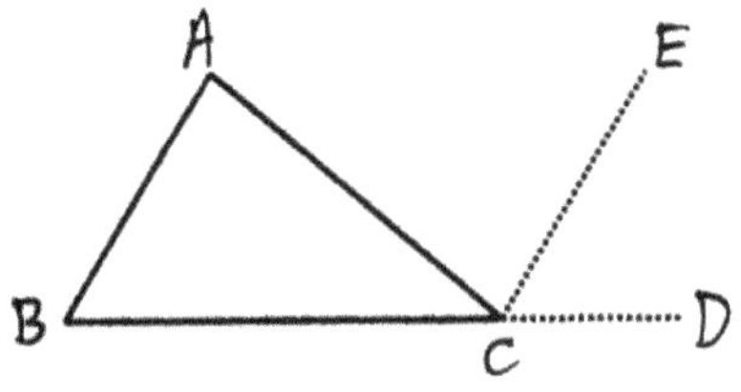

Proof:

1. Given ΔABC
2. Extend BC to D (Post. 2)
3. Draw CE parallel to AB (Th. I-31)
4. Since AB is parallel to CE, and AC transverses both of them, $\angle ACE \cong \angle BAC$ (Th. I-29) and $\angle ECD \cong \angle ABC$ (Th. I-29)
5. $\angle ACE + \angle ECD = \angle BAC + \angle ABC$ (C.N. 2)
6. $\angle ACE + \angle ECD = \angle ACD$ (from drawing)
7. $\boldsymbol{\angle ACD = \angle BAC + \angle ABC}$ (C.N. 1) Q.E.D. (for part a)
8. Adding $\angle ACB$ to both sides of the equation: $\angle ACD + \angle ACB = \angle BAC + \angle ABC + \angle ACB$ (C.N. 2)
9. But $\angle ACD$ and $\angle ACB$ are adjacent angles and form the straight line BD, therefore they are equal to two right angles. (Th. I-13)
10. $\therefore$ **$\angle BAC + \angle ABC + \angle ACB$ is also equal to two right angles.** (C.N. 1) Q.E.D. (for part b)

Selected Proofs from *The Elements, Book I* (continued)

Euclid's Proof of the Pythagorean Theorem

(Theorem I-47)

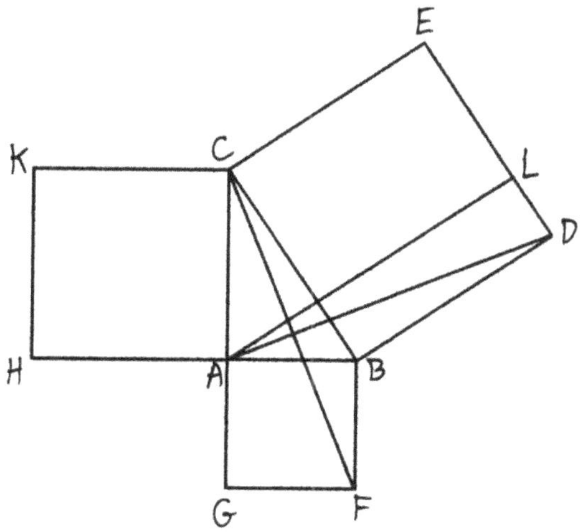

1. Given: ΔABC is a right triangle, with $\angle BAC$ a right angle.
2. Construct a square on each of the 3 sides of ΔABC. (Th. I-46)
3. Draw AL parallel to BD. (Th. I-31)
4. Draw lines AD and FC. (Post. 1)
5. (a) $\angle DBC$ & $\angle FBA$ are both right angles. (Def. of Square)
   (b) $\angle DBC \cong \angle FBA$ (Post. 4)
   (c) $\angle DBC + \angle ABC = \angle FBA + \angle ABC$ (C.N. 2)
   (d) $\angle ABD \cong \angle FBC$ (from drawing)
6. (a) $BD \cong BC$ and $AB \cong FB$. (Def. of Square)
   (b) $\Delta ABD \cong \Delta FBC$ because $BD \cong BC$ and $AB \cong FB$ and $\angle ABD \cong \angle FBC$ (step 6). (Th. I-4)
7. (a) $\angle BAG$ is a right angle. (Def. of Square)
   (b) $\angle BAC$ and $\angle BAG$ are adjacent and both right angles, so CA is in a straight line with AG. (Th. I-14)
   (c) $\angle BAC \cong \angle FBA$ (Post. 4)
   (d) CG is parallel to FB. (Th. I-27)
   (e) [The area of] square GB is twice [the area of] ΔFBC, because they have the same base FB and lie between the same parallels FB and GC. (Th. I-41)
8. [The area of] parallelogram BL is twice [the area of] ΔABD, because they have the same base BD and they lie between the same parallels BD and AL. (Th. I-41)
9. $\Delta FBC \cong \Delta ABD$, therefore twice [the area of] ΔFBC is equal to twice [the area of] ΔABD. (C.N. 1)
10. [The area of] square GB is equal to [the area of] parallelogram BL. (C.N. 1)
11. Similarly, if lines AE and BK are drawn, parallelogram CL can be proven equal to square HC.
12. The sum of [the areas of] squares HC and GB is equal to the sum of [the areas of] parallelograms CL and BL. (C.N. 2)
13. [The area of] the square BE is equal to the sum of [the areas of] parallelograms CL and BL. (from drawing)
14. $\therefore$ **[The area of] the square BE is equal to the sum of [the areas of] the squares GB and HC.** (C.N. 1) *Q.E.D.*

Theorem X-1 from *The Elements*[1]

In the Original Greek

Δύο μεγεθῶν ἀνίσων ἐκκειμένων, ἐὰν ἀπὸ τοῦ μείζονος ἀφαιρεθῇ μεῖζον ἢ τὸ ἥμισυ καὶ τοῦ καταλειπομένου μεῖζον ἢ τὸ ἥμισυ, καὶ τοῦτο ἀεὶ γίγνηται, λειφθήσεταί τι μέγεθος, ὃ ἔσται ἔλασσον τοῦ ἐκκειμένου ἐλάσσονος μεγέθους.

Ἔστω δύο μεγέθη ἄνισα τὰ ΑΒ, Γ, ὧν μεῖζον τὸ ΑΒ· λέγω, ὅτι ἐὰν ἀπὸ τοῦ ΑΒ ἀφαιρεθῇ μεῖζον ἢ τὸ ἥμισυ καὶ τοῦ καταλειπομένου μεῖζον ἢ τὸ ἥμισυ, καὶ τοῦτο ἀεὶ γίγνηται, λειφθήσεταί τι μέγεθος, ὃ ἔσται ἔλασσον τοῦ Γ μεγέθους.

Τὸ Γ γὰρ πολλαπλασιαζόμενον ἔσται ποτὲ τοῦ ΑΒ μεῖζον. πεπολλαπλασιάσθω, καὶ ἔστω τὸ ΔΕ τοῦ μὲν Γ πολλαπλάσιον, τοῦ δὲ ΑΒ μεῖζον, καὶ διῃρήσθω τὸ ΔΕ εἰς τὰ τῷ Γ ἴσα τὰ ΔΖ, ΖΗ, ΗΕ, καὶ ἀφῃρήσθω ἀπὸ μὲν τοῦ ΑΒ μεῖζον ἢ τὸ ἥμισυ τὸ ΒΘ, ἀπὸ δὲ τοῦ ΑΘ μεῖζον ἢ τὸ ἥμισυ τὸ ΘΚ, καὶ τοῦτο ἀεὶ γιγνέσθω, ἕως ἂν αἱ ἐν τῷ ΑΒ διαιρέσεις ἰσοπληθεῖς γένωνται ταῖς ἐν τῷ ΔΕ διαιρέσεσιν.

Ἔστωσαν οὖν αἱ ΑΚ, ΚΘ, ΘΒ διαιρέσεις ἰσοπληθεῖς οὖσαι ταῖς ΔΖ, ΖΗ, ΗΕ· καὶ ἐπεὶ μεῖζόν ἐστι τὸ ΔΕ τοῦ ΑΒ, καὶ ἀφῄρηται ἀπὸ μὲν τοῦ ΔΕ ἔλασσον τοῦ ἡμίσεως τὸ ΕΗ, ἀπὸ δὲ τοῦ ΑΒ μεῖζον ἢ τὸ ἥμισυ τὸ ΒΘ, λοιπὸν ἄρα τὸ ΗΔ λοιποῦ τοῦ ΘΑ μεῖζόν ἐστιν. καὶ ἐπεὶ μεῖζόν ἐστι τὸ ΗΔ τοῦ ΘΑ, καὶ ἀφῄρηται τοῦ μὲν ΗΔ ἥμισυ τὸ ΗΖ, τοῦ δὲ ΘΑ μεῖζον ἢ τὸ ἥμισυ τὸ ΘΚ, λοιπὸν ἄρα τὸ ΔΖ λοιποῦ τοῦ ΑΚ μεῖζόν ἐστιν. ἴσον δὲ τὸ ΔΖ τῷ Γ· καὶ τὸ Γ ἄρα τοῦ ΑΚ μεῖζόν ἐστιν. ἔλασσον ἄρα τὸ ΑΚ τοῦ Γ.

Καταλείπεται ἄρα ἀπὸ τοῦ ΑΒ μεγέθους τὸ ΑΚ μέγεθος ἔλασσον ὂν τοῦ ἐκκειμένου ἐλάσσονος μεγέθους τοῦ Γ· ὅπερ ἔδει δεῖξαι—ὁμοίως δὲ δειχθήσεται, κἂν ἡμίση ᾖ τὰ ἀφαιρούμενα.

Translated into English

Two unequal magnitudes being set out, if from the greater there be subtracted a magnitude greater than the half, and from the remainder a magnitude greater than its half, and so on continually, there will be left some magnitude which will be less than the lesser magnitude set out.

Let AB, Γ be the two unequal magnitudes, of which AB is the greater ; I say that, if from AB there be subtracted a magnitude greater than its half, and from the remainder a magnitude greater than its half, and so on continually, there will be left some magnitude which will be less than the magnitude Γ.

For Γ, if multiplied, will at some time be greater than AB [see v. Def. 4]. Let it be multiplied, and let ΔE be a multiple of Γ, greater than AB, and let ΔE be divided into the parts ΔZ, ZH, HE equal to Γ, and from AB let there be subtracted BΘ greater than its half, and from AΘ let there be subtracted ΘK greater than its half, and so on continually, until the divisions in AB are equal in multitude to the divisions in ΔE.

Let, then, AK, KΘ, ΘB be divisions equal in multitude with ΔZ, ZH, HE ; now since ΔE is greater than AB, and from ΔE there has been subtracted EH less than its half, and from AB there has been subtracted BΘ greater than its half, therefore the remainder HΔ is greater than the remainder ΘA. And since HΔ is greater than ΘA, and from HΔ there has been subtracted the half, HZ, and from ΘA there has been subtracted ΘK greater than its half, therefore the remainder ΔZ is greater than the remainder AK. Now ΔZ is equal to Γ ; and therefore Γ is greater than AK. Therefore AK is less than Γ.

There is therefore left of the magnitude AB the magnitude AK which is less than the lesser magnitude set out, namely, Γ ; which was to be proved—and this can be similarly proved even if the parts to be subtracted be halves.

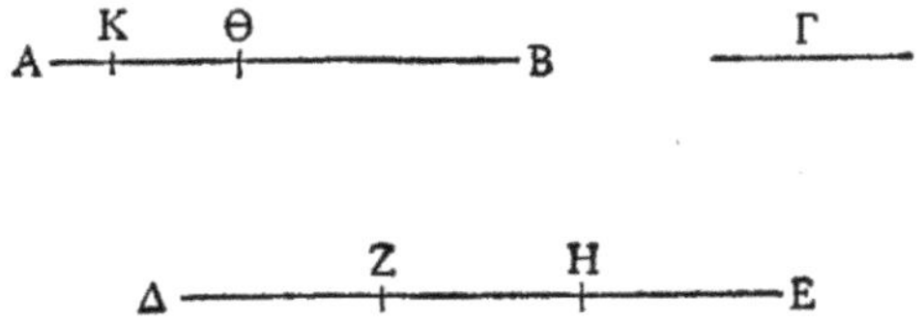

[1] Ivor Thomas, *Greek Mathematical Works*. Harvard University Press, 1998. pp 453-5

—— *Euclidean Constructions* (10th Grade) ——

Handouts and worksheets. A handout on *Basic Euclidean Constructions* is found in the following pages. Additionally, Euclidean construction worksheets can be downloaded from our website.

The Greek Geometric Game

- *The rules of the game.*
  1. A *straightedge* can only be used to draw a line through two chosen points. (Postulate #1)
  2. A *compass* can be used to draw a circle (or a part of a circle) with a chosen point as its center and a determined distance (the width of the compass) as its radius. (Postulate #3)
  3. The width of a *compass* can be set equal to the distance between two given points.[1]
  4. No other tools (e.g., a ruler, a protractor, drawing triangle, etc.) may be used.
- *Why compass and straightedge only?* According to the ancient Greek mathematicians, all geometric constructions were to be done using only two tools: a compass and a straightedge (without any marks for the purpose of measurement). Marked rulers, protractors, and right-angled drawing triangles were not allowed. For the Greeks, this was a challenging mental game. The objective was to come up with theoretically perfect methods to do certain constructions using only these two tools. Some constructions turn out to be very simple, such as bisecting an angle, or putting a hexagon in a circle. Some constructions were fairly complicated, such as constructing a pentagon, or constructing a square that is equal in area to a given polygon. Some construction puzzles were never solved by the Greeks, such as the construction of a 7-gon, the construction of a 17-gon, and the trisection of an angle. Some two thousand years later, a few of the solutions (e.g., the 17-gon) were discovered, but most were proven to be impossible (e.g., the 7-gon, and the trisection of an angle).

Methods for doing constructions

- There are four types of methods for doing constructions:
  1. *Euclidean constructions with compass and straightedge.* These are the theoretically exact, Euclid-approved constructions. *In practice*, nobody can construct a *perfect* square. However, there is a theoretically perfect method for constructing a square.
  2. *Measurement constructions.* These constructions allow the use of a protractor, a drawing triangle, or a ruler (as opposed to just a straightedge), and can be, *in practice*, very accurate. However, these constructions are not *theoretically perfect* according to the Euclidean rules.
  3. *The guess and check method.* Here we use a compass (or perhaps something else) as a tool for *guessing* how big a length should be, see how much error results, and then adjust the compass and redo the construction. We keep *guessing, checking, and adjusting* until we get satisfactory results. This method is not theoretically perfect (and not Euclid-approved), but can be in practice as close to perfect as we would like. Any regular polygon can be done quite accurately this way.

     Example: To construct a 15-gon inside a circle, we first *guess* what the length of a side of the 15-gon will be, and set the compass width equal to that. Mark a point on the circle, place the compass needle on that point, and then make a mark on the circle with the compass. Using that same compass width, we step around the circle marking one point at a time. If the results are good, then the 15th step should come out very close to the point that we started at. If the results aren't satisfactory, then we simply adjust the compass slightly and try it again. Usually the third guess produces very accurate results.
  4. *Approximate constructions.* These constructions are done mostly for Euclidean impossible constructions, and are useful because they are a specific method that can quickly produce very accurate constructions. They are not theoretically perfect, but they have little error.

     Example: Many different approximate constructions are used for cases that are impossible by Euclidean means. One such case is the construction of a regular 7-gon inside a given circle, which uses the fact that the length of the side of the 7-gon (A in the left figure) is *almost* equal to the radius of a circle inscribed in a hexagon (B in the right figure). This has, in theory, only 0.2% error!

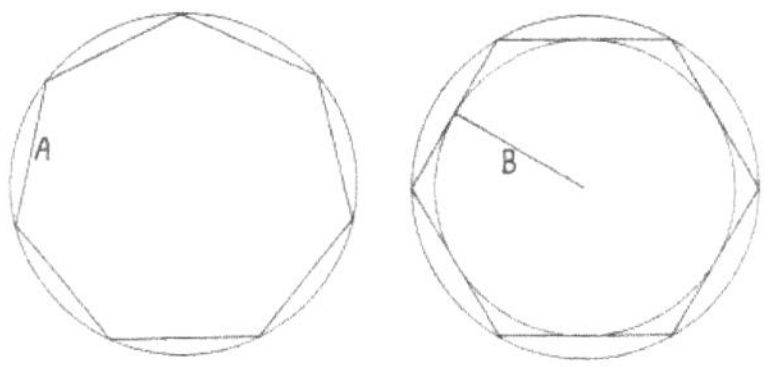

[1] Technically, it is assumed that a compass collapses whenever it is lifted off the page. Theorems I-2 and I-3 allow us to get around this problem so that we can use a compass to copy a given length.

Which regular polygons are possible?

Gauss's 17-gon and other "prime number" polygons.

- In 1796, at the age of 19, Carl Friedrich Gauss proved that all regular n-gons where $n = 2^{(2^n)}+1$ are constructible. By letting n = 0, 1, 2, 3, 4 we get polygons with 3, 5, 17, 257, and 65537 sides. This discovery supposedly convinced Gauss that he should dedicate his life to mathematics.
- Gauss did not provide a method for constructing the 17-gon; he just proved that it was possible. In 1800, Johannes Erchinger provided the first method for constructing the 17-gon. (See instructions for *Construction of a 17-gon*, in the pages that follow.)

Combinations of prime number polygons.

- By using only the "prime number" polygons of 3, 5, and 17, we can also do the following Euclidean constructions:
  - 15-gon (15 = 5·3). We create a 15-gon by first drawing a pentagon in the circle, and then placing equilateral triangles at each of the vertices of the pentagon. Likewise, we can do the ones below.
  - 51-gon (51 = 3·17)
  - 85-gon (85 = 5·17)
  - 255-gon (255 = 3·5·17)
  - Notice that a factor may only appear once (no exponents allowed). Therefore a 9-gon ($9 = 3^2$) or a 25-gon ($25 = 5^2$) is not constructible.

Doubling the number of sides.

- If we know that a certain regular n-gon is possible to construct, then it is also possible to construct a regular n-gon with twice the number of sides. Therefore the following regular n-gons are possible:
  - 3 → 6, 12, 24, 48, etc.
  - 4 → 8, 16, 32, 64, etc.
  - 5 → 10, 20, 40, 80, etc.
  - 15 → 30, 60, 120, etc.
  - 17 → 34, 68, 136, etc.
  - 51 → 102, 204, 408, etc.
  - 85 → 170, 340, 680, etc.
  - 255 → 510, 1020, 2040, etc.
  - 257 → 514, 1028, 2056, etc.
  - and so on...

Polygons with fewer than 300 sides.

- In a paper he wrote published in 1801, Gauss listed all 37 possible regular polygons with fewer than 300 sides that can be constructed by Euclidean methods. The number of sides of these polygons is:
  3, 4, 5, 6, 8, 10, 12, 15, 16, 17, 20, 24, 30, 32, 34, 40, 48, 51, 60, 64, 68, 80, 85, 96, 102, 120, 128, 136, 160, 170, 192, 204, 240, 255, 256, 257, 272. The rest are impossible!

Equal area transformations

Try the following sequence:

1. *The Equal-Area Transformation of a 7-gon to a Triangle*
   The Construction: For a non-regular 7-gon, label the vertices, in order, as A,B,C,D,E,F,G. Draw a line *k* through point A such that it is parallel to the diagonal GB. Line *m* is side BC extended. Point X is the intersection of lines *k* and *m*. Have the students *imagine* the vertex A of ΔGAB sliding from A along line *k* to X. ΔGAB therefore has the same area as ΔGXB, and the 7-gon ABCDEFG has the same area as the hexagon XCDEFG. (Point A has been slid to X, and point B has been eliminated as a vertex.) The same process shall now be done to construct a pentagon with the same area by sliding point C (parallel to diagonal XD) to point Y. The desired quadrilateral and triangle are created in the same way.

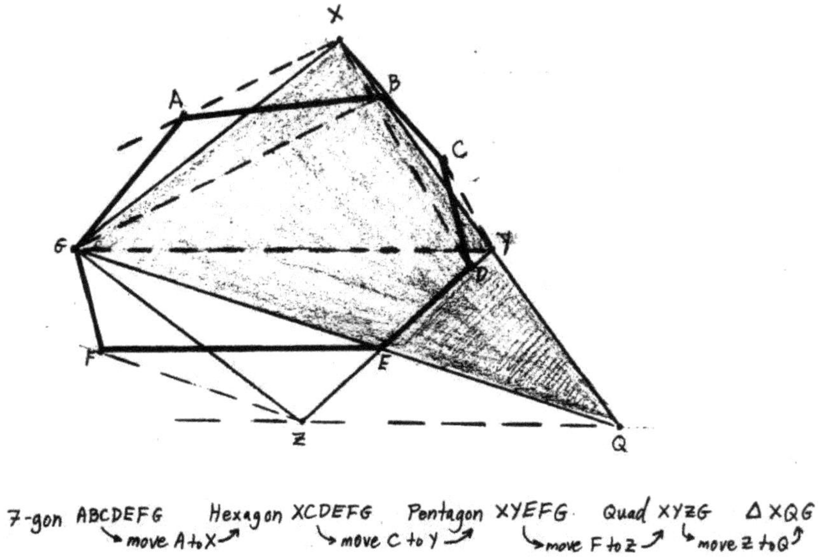

2. *The Equal-Area Transformation of a Quadrilateral into a Rectangle.*

Given quadrilateral ABCD, draw line *m* through D such that it is parallel to diagonal AC, and draw line *n* through C such that it is parallel to AB. Label the intersection of lines *n* and *m* as point X. Trapezoid ABCX has an area equal to quadrilateral ABCD. Through the midpoints of BC and AX, draw perpendiculars to line AB (extending side AB, if necessary) thereby producing the desired (shaded) rectangle. The shaded rectangle has an area equal to the original quadrilateral ABCD.

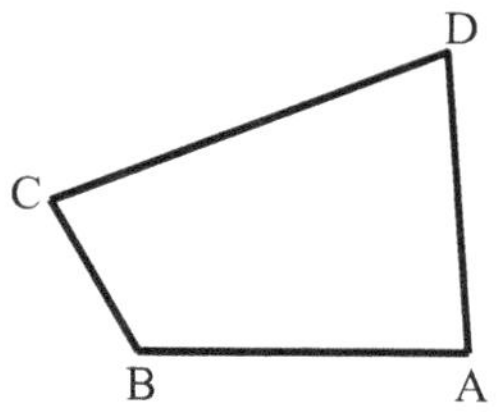

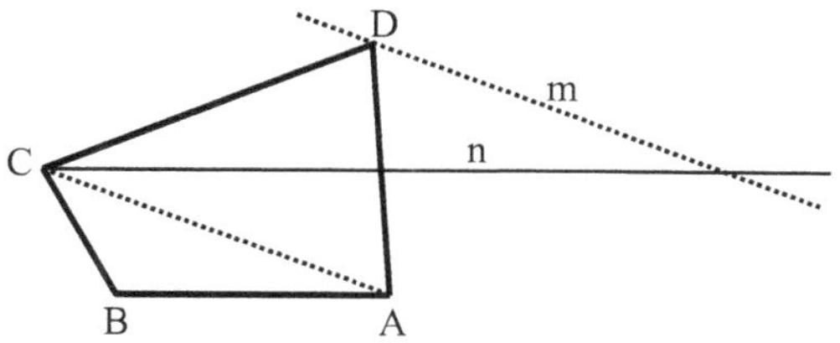

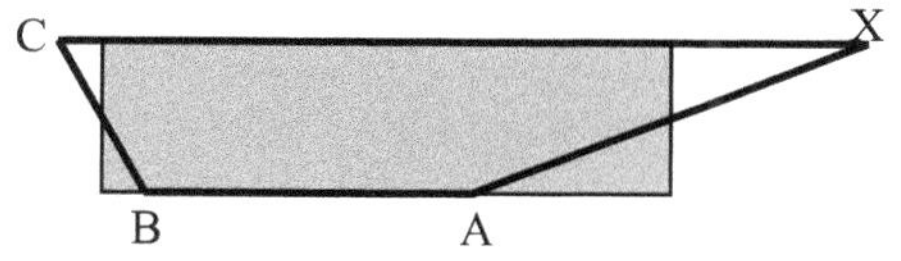

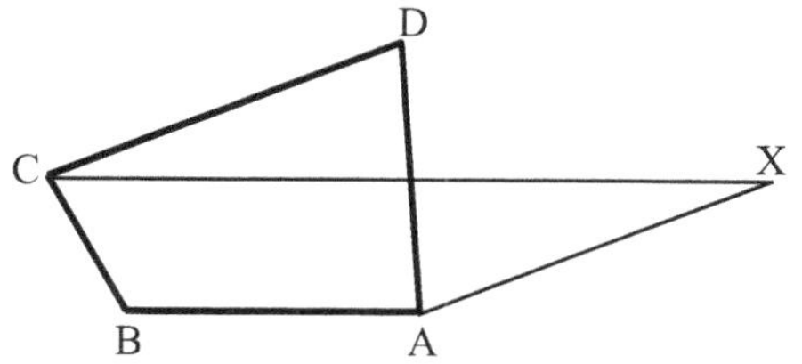

3. *The Equal-Area Transformation of a Rectangle into a Square.*
Given rectangle ABCD, with AB as the base, extend side AB beyond point A to a point Q such that AQ = AD (the height). Bisect QB in order to locate the midpoint, M. Draw a circle with center at M and radius MB. (The circle also passes through point Q.) Extend side AD past D to the edge of the circle, at point X. Length AX is the length of the side of the desired square that has an area equal to the original rectangle's area.

We may now ask: how we can be sure that this is correct? If we consider the triangle QXB, the Theorem of Thales tells us it is a right triangle. This triangle has the altitude AX, and using the Altitude of the Hypotenuse Theorem we know that:

$AX^2 = QA \cdot AB$ and because QA = AD, we get:

$$\mathbf{AX^2 = AD \cdot AB}$$

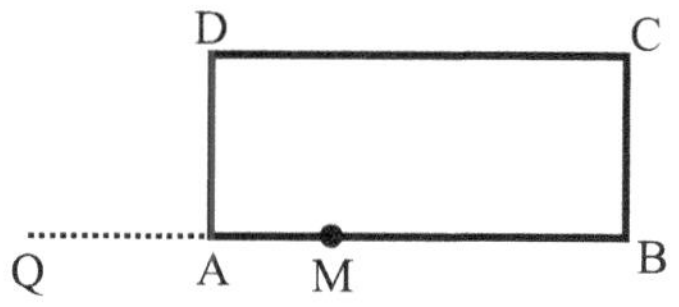

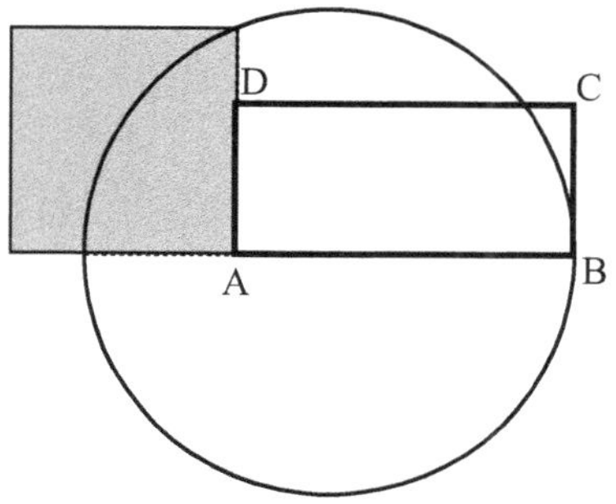

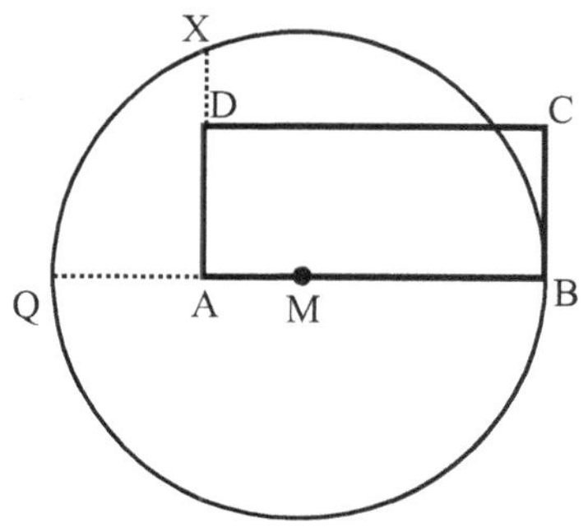

The three classic problems of Greek geometry (All were proven impossible in the 19th cent.)

1. *Trisecting an Angle.* How to construct the trisection of an angle.
2. *Squaring the Circle.* How to construct a square having an area equal to a given circle. Perhaps discuss Archimedes' ("illegal") solution using the spiral of Archimedes (see Eves, p.89).
3. *Doubling the Cube.* How to construct the edge of a cube having twice the volume of a given cube. (Of course, we do know how to construct a square with twice the area of a given square.)

Triangle constructions

The instructions given here for each drawing are intended for the teacher only. Mostly, the students should be guided to discover it for themselves.

- *SSS (side-side-side): Constructing a triangle given 3 line segments.*
  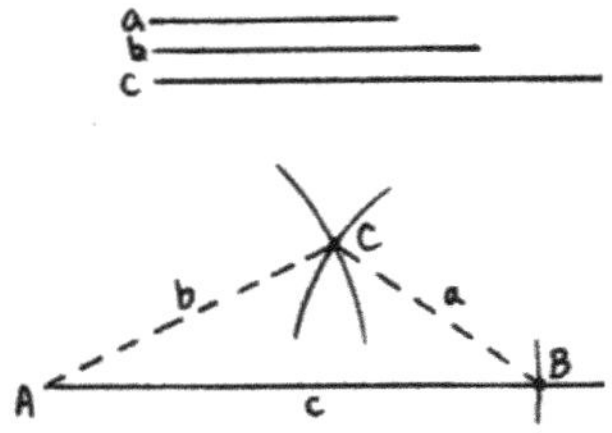

  Instructions: We are given three line segments (a, b, c). Our objective is to construct a triangle that has its sides equal to the length of these three segments. Start by drawing a horizontal line segment that is somewhat longer than segment c. Using a compass, copy the length of c onto this line segment. This is now the base of our triangle. Set the width of the compass equal to the length of segment a, and by placing the compass needle on the right end of the base of the triangle (point B), draw a short arc close to where the apex of the triangle will end up. Now set the width of the compass equal to the length of segment b, place the compass needle on the left end of the base of the triangle (point A), and draw an arc that passes through the arc previously drawn. These two arcs pass through the third point (the apex, or point C) of the triangle. Check, by using your compass, to see if the three sides of the triangle ABC are indeed equal in length to the original three given line segments.
  Note: This construction will not work if the longest given line segment is equal to, or longer than, the sum of the other two given line segments.

- *SAS (side-angle-side): Constructing a triangle given two sides and an in-between angle.*
  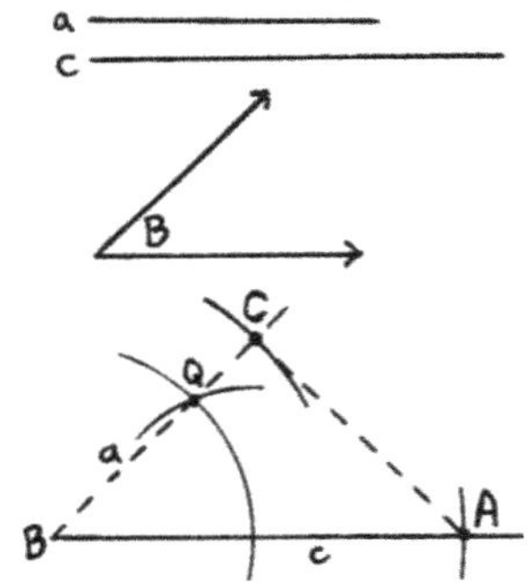

  Instructions: We are given two line segments (a and c) and an angle (B). Our objective is to construct a triangle that has two of its sides equal in length to these two given sides, and that has an angle *in-between* these two sides that is equal to the given angle. Start by drawing a horizontal line segment that is somewhat longer than segment c. Using a compass, copy the length of c onto this line segment. This is now the base of our triangle. Now copy angle B so that its vertex falls on the left side of the base of the triangle. In the drawing here, this is shown as the two arcs intersecting at point Q. Draw a line segment from point B through and beyond point Q, making sure that it is longer than the line segment a (the original given line segment). Now copy line segment a onto the line segment BQ, so that the length from B to C is equal to the given line segment a. Lastly, draw a line connecting points A and C. Triangle ABC is the desired triangle.
  Note: This construction will work for any angle and any two line segments.

- *ASA (angle-side-angle): Constructing a triangle given two angles and an in-between side.*
  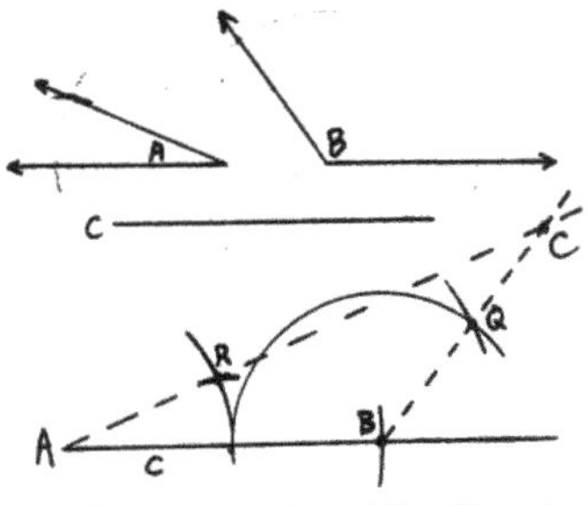

  Instructions: We are given one line segment (c) and two angles (A and B). Our objective is to construct a triangle that has a side equal in length to the given side (c), and that has the two angles that are adjacent to that side and equal to the two given angles (A and B). This construction is very similar to the SAS construction done above. Start by using the same steps given with the SAS construction to draw side c with angle A constructed onto its left end. Then copy the second angle (B) onto the other end of side c. The drawing here shows that points R and Q are used to copy angles A and B to the triangle. We then extend the lines AR and BQ until they intersect at point C, which is the third point of the triangle. We finish by drawing a line that connects points A and C, and then a line that connects points B and C. Triangle ABC is the desired triangle.
  Note: This drawing will not work if the two angles combine to 180° or more.

- *SSA (side-side-angle). Constructing a triangle given two sides and a non-in-between angle.*
  Instructions: As with the SAS construction, we are given two sides and an angle. The thinking involved is, however, much more complicated. Of the two given line segments, one (b) is intended to be adjacent to the triangle's given angle (A), and the other line segment (a) is then attached to the other end of side b. Since the angle in-between these two sides is not given, we can imagine that there is a hinge between sides a and b that swings open or closed until it finds the proper moment when the desired triangle is found. The actual construction is not very complicated. As with the SAS construction, we simply copy line segment b onto the base of the triangle (with endpoints A and C), and then copy angle A (by finding point Q) so that angle A lies on the right side of side b. Now extend AQ well beyond Q. Then set the compass to the length of given segment a, and by placing the compass needle at point C, draw an arc. Depending on the sizes of the given angle and sides, this arc may end up crossing the extended line AQ in one or two places, or not at all. In the drawing shown, the arc crosses line AQ in two places. This means that for this drawing there are two possible shapes for the desired triangle ABC, since B could be in either of two places (as shown in the drawing).

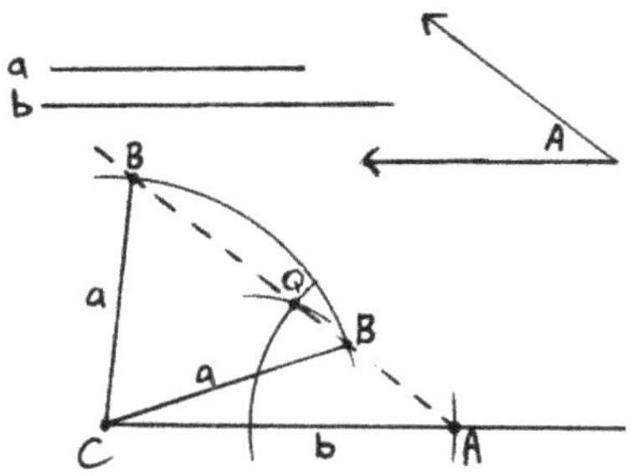

  Note: In general, there are 6 possibilities for this SSA construction, depending on the sizes of the two sides and the given angle:
  1. The angle is acute, and side a (the "swinging" side) is shorter than side b and crosses the line AQ in two places. This results in two possible triangles as the solution. (This case is shown in the above drawing.)
  2. The angle is acute, and side a is shorter than side b but barely reaches the line AQ, thereby forming a right angle. The result is one right triangle as a solution.
  3. The angle is acute, and side a is shorter than side b, and is not long enough to reach line AQ. The result is an impossible triangle; there is no solution.
  4. The angle is acute, and side a is longer than side b, therefore crossing line AQ in just one place. This results in one solution.
  5. The angle is either right or obtuse, and side a is longer than side b. This results in one solution.
  6. The angle is either right or obtuse, and side a is shorter than side b. This triangle is impossible because side a cannot reach the line AQ; there is no solution.
- *(optional) AAS (angle-angle-side): A triangle given two angles and a non-in-between side.*
  Instructions: This is the most complicated construction. We are given two of the three angles in a triangle and a side that is not in-between them. We start by copying line segment a to the base of the triangle, and angle B adjacent to it, as we did with the SAS construction. We then label the endpoints of this base as C and B. Next, we extend the other side of angle B (in the drawing, this is segment BQ) well beyond Q and label its endpoint as point M. Then, we copy angle A to point M (by finding point R). We now need to construct the third side of the triangle, which passes through point C and is parallel to MR. We do this by first extending segments BC and MR to meet at point E. Now, copy angle CEF to DCT. (We could have instead copied angle CEM to angle BCA.) We have now located point A and have therefore determined the third side (AC) of the desired triangle ABC.

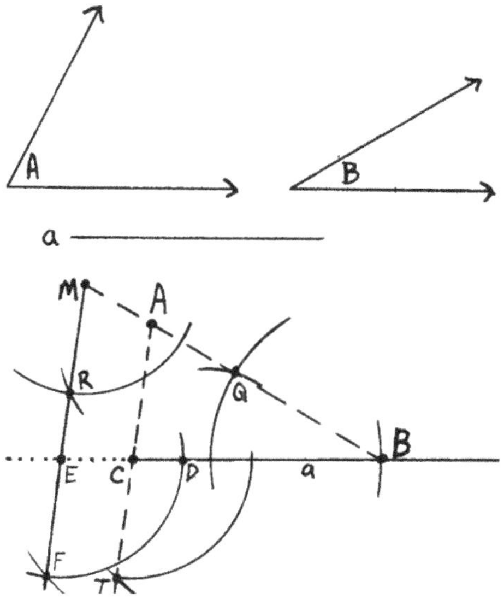

Basic Euclidean Constructions

Copying a line segment

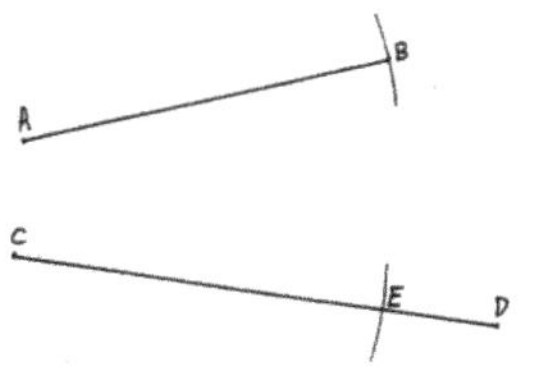

Instructions: *The intention is to copy line segment AB onto line CD.* Make sure that CD is longer than AB. Set the compass's width equal to AB. Put the needle of the compass on C, and mark an arc that passes through line CD at point E. CE is now equal in length to AB.

Copying an angle

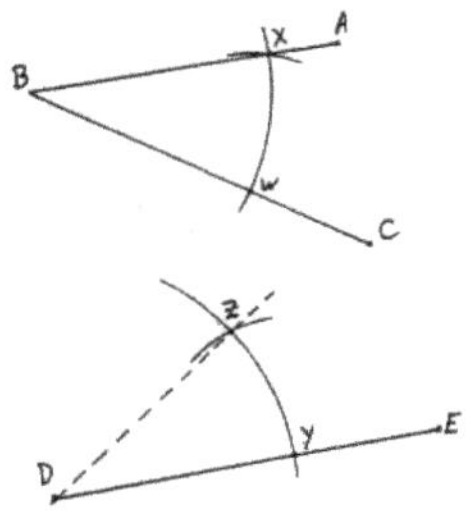

Instructions: *The intention is to copy angle ABC onto line DE.* Set the compass at a width that is a bit less than the shortest of the line segments AB, BC, and DE. Using this width of the compass, draw an arc with the needle at B that passes through both AB (at X) and BC (at W), and then draw an arc with the needle at D that passes through DE at Y. Place the needle at W and adjust the compass so that it reaches to X, and then draw a short arc through X. Keeping this width of the compass, draw an arc, with the needle at Y, that crosses through the previously drawn arc at point Z. Angle ZDY is now equal to angle ABC.

Bisecting a line segment (and construction of the perpendicular bisector)

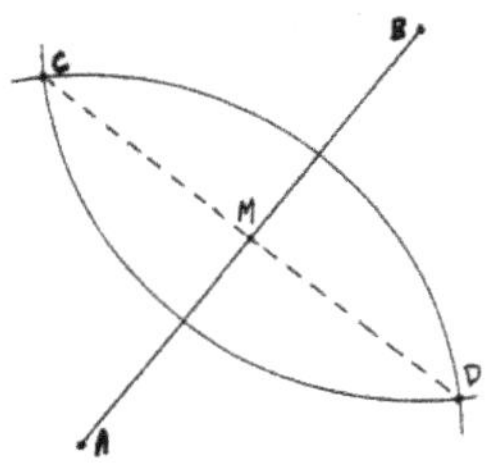

Instructions: *The intention is to bisect the line segment AB, and to draw a perpendicular bisector* through *it.* Set the compass width so that it is a bit more than half the length of AB. Using this compass width, draw two arcs, one with the needle at A and the other with the needle at B, so that they cross one another in two places – at points C and D. CD is the perpendicular bisector of AB, and M is the midpoint of AB.
Note: This same technique is used to bisect an arc.

Bisecting an angle

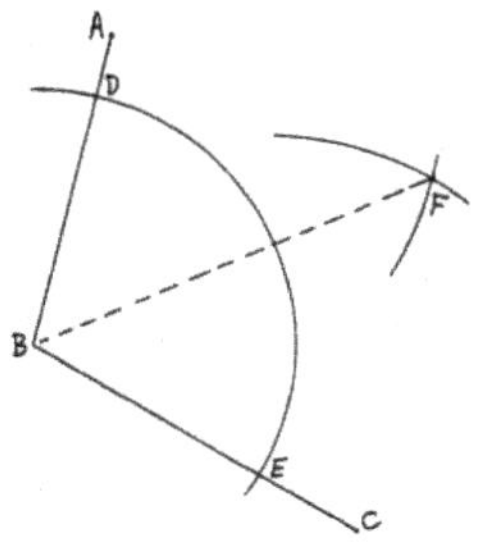

Instructions: *The intention is to bisect angle ABC.* Set the compass width a bit less than both AB and BC. Draw an arc, with the needle at B, that passes through AB at D, and passes through BC at E. Now draw two arcs, both with the same compass width, with the needle at D and then at E, so that the two arcs cross inside angle ABC at point F. The line BF is the desired bisector of the angle ABC. Notice that this will still work if the two arcs are made to intersect "outside" (in this case, to the left of) the angle.

Constructing a perpendicular line through a point on that line

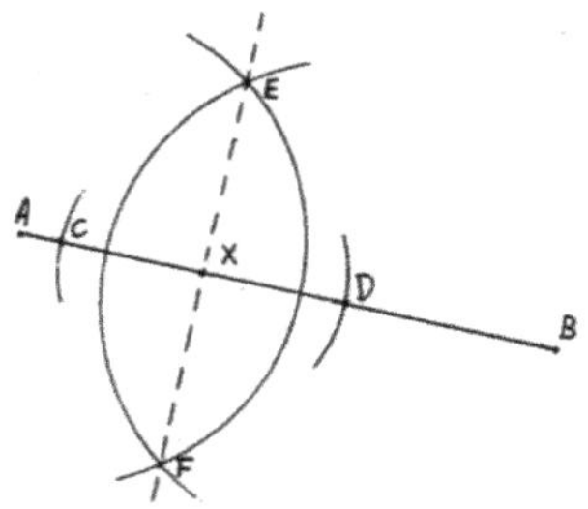

Instructions: *The intention is to construct a line perpendicular to AB that passes through X, which is a point on AB.* First, draw two arcs, each one using the same compass width and with the needle at X – one arc passing through AX at C and the other passing through XB at D. Now lengthen the compass somewhat and draw two long arcs – one with the needle at C and the other with the needle at D, such that they cross each other at points E and F. Line EF is the desired line; it passes through X and is perpendicular to AB.

Constructing a perpendicular line through a point *not* on that line

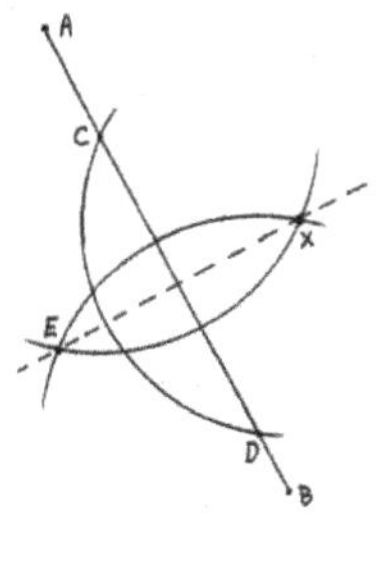

Instructions: *The intention is to construct a line perpendicular to AB that passes through X, which is NOT on AB.* First, set the compass width a bit longer than the distance that X is from line AB, and then draw an arc, with the needle at X that passes through AB in two points, C and D. Now draw two long arcs using the same compass width, one with the needle at C and the other with the needle at D. They should cross each other at X and at another point E, which is on the other side of AB from X. Line EX is the desired line – it passes through X and is perpendicular to AB.

Basic Euclidean Constructions (p2)

Constructing a parallel line

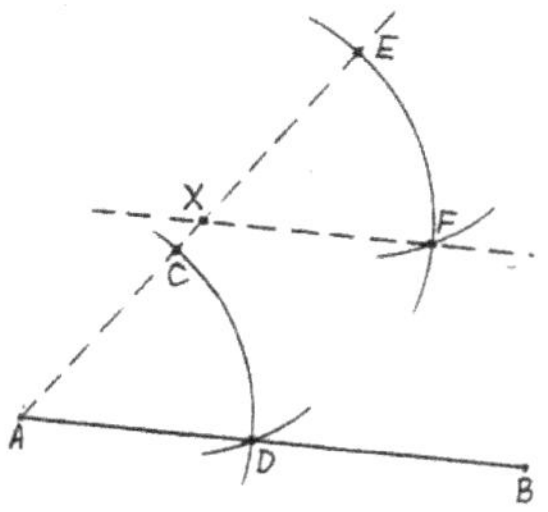

Instructions: *The intention is to construct a line that is parallel to AB and that passes through X, which is not on AB.* Draw line AX significantly beyond X. Set the compass width so that it is a bit shorter than AX, and draw an arc, with the needle at A, that passes through both AB at D and AX at C. Using that same compass width, draw an arc, with the needle at X, that passes through both the extended line AX (at E) and the line (not yet drawn) that passes through X and is parallel to AB. Now, adjusting the compass width, draw a short arc, with the needle at C, that passes through D, and then using the same compass width, draw an arc, with the needle at E that crosses, at point F, the arc that was drawn earlier that passed through E. The line XF is the desired line – it passes through X and is parallel to AB.

Constructing a square, given one side

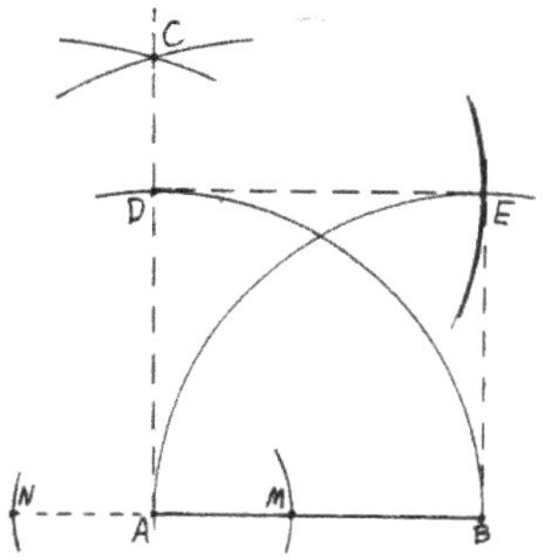

Instructions: *The intention is to construct a square that has each side equal in length to AB.* Extend AB past A to N, and then mark point M on AB such that the length of NA is equal to the length of AM. Adjust the compass so that it is somewhat wider than AB and draw two arcs – one with the needle at N, and the other with the needle at M, so that they intersect vertically above A, at point C. Line AC is now perpendicular to AB. Set the compass width equal to AB and draw an arc, with the needle at A, so that it crosses line AC at point D. Using the same compass width, draw two more arcs: one that is horizontally to the right of D, with the needle at D, and a second arc that is above B, with the needle at B. These two arcs cross at point E. Finish the square by connecting the four points ABED.

Constructing a hexagon, inside a given circle

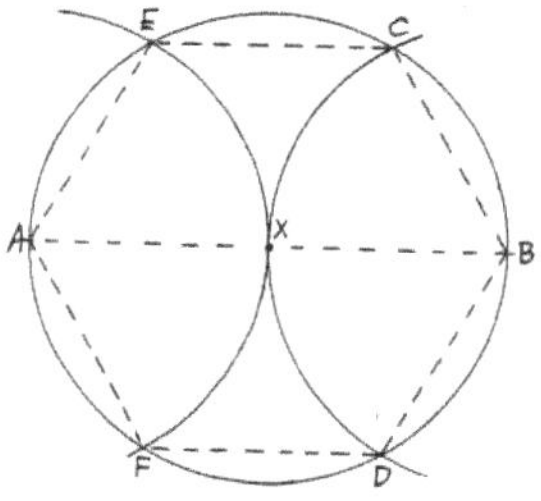

Instructions: *The intention is to construct a regular hexagon inside the given circle.* Draw diameter AB passing through the center of the circle, X. Then set the width of the compass equal to the radius of the circle, and draw one arc with the needle at B, which crosses the circle at points C and D, and another arc, with the needle at A, which crosses the circle at points E and F. The desired hexagon is AFDBCE.

Constructing a pentagon, inside a given circle

Instructions: *The intention is to construct a regular pentagon inside the given circle.*

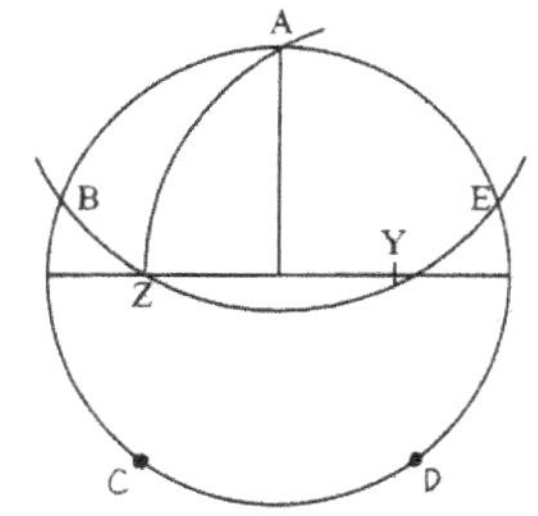

- *Method #1.* Draw a diameter and then find the midpoint, Y, of the radius. Point A is located vertically above the center. Placing the needle of the compass at Y, draw an arc through A to point Z on the diameter. The distance A to Z is the desired length of the sides of the pentagon. Copy the length AZ around the perimeter of the circle to get the five points of the pentagon: A, B, C, D, E.

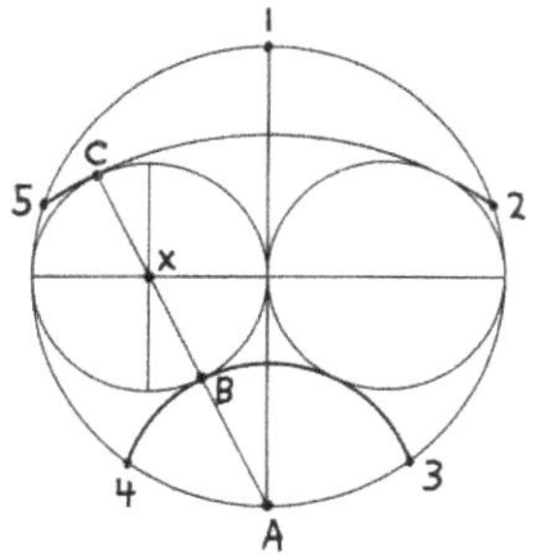

- *Method #2.* Draw horizontal and vertical diameters of the circle. Draw two half-sized circles along the diameter of the original circle. Draw line AX so that it intersects one of the half-sized circles at points B and C. Place the compass needle at point A and draw an arc using AB as the radius, which locates points 3 and 4 on the original circle. Now draw a second arc using AC as the radius (keeping the needle on point A), which locates points 2 and 5 on the original circle. The desired pentagon has points 1, 2, 3, 4, 5 equally spread out on the circle.

Construction of a 17-gon[1]

1. Construct a circle with diameter AB and center C.
2. Construct a radius, perpendicular to AB, with point D on that radius such that $\overline{CD} = \frac{1}{4}\,\overline{CA}$.
3. Find point E on BC such that $\angle EDC = \frac{1}{4}\angle BDC$.
4. Find point H on AC such that $\angle EDH$ is half a right angle (45°).
5. Draw a circle with BH as diameter, labeling its center as X and its intersection with line CD extended as K.
6. Draw a circle with E as its center and EK as its radius. Label this circle's intersection with BC as Y, and its intersection with AC as Z. (Note: X and Y are close, but do not actually coincide.)
7. Draw a line perpendicular to AB from Y and label where it crosses the original circle as P_4. Draw a line perpendicular to AB from Z and label where it crosses the original circle as P_6 (on the same side of AB as P_4).
8. Points P_4 and P_6 are the 4th and 6th vertices of the desired 17-gon. Find P_5 by bisecting $\angle P_4CP_6$.
9. Find the remaining vertices of the 17-gon by marking off the distance $\overline{P_4P_5}$ around the perimeter of the circle. If done perfectly, point B will be the first vertex (P_1), and the radius CA bisects a side of the 17-gon.

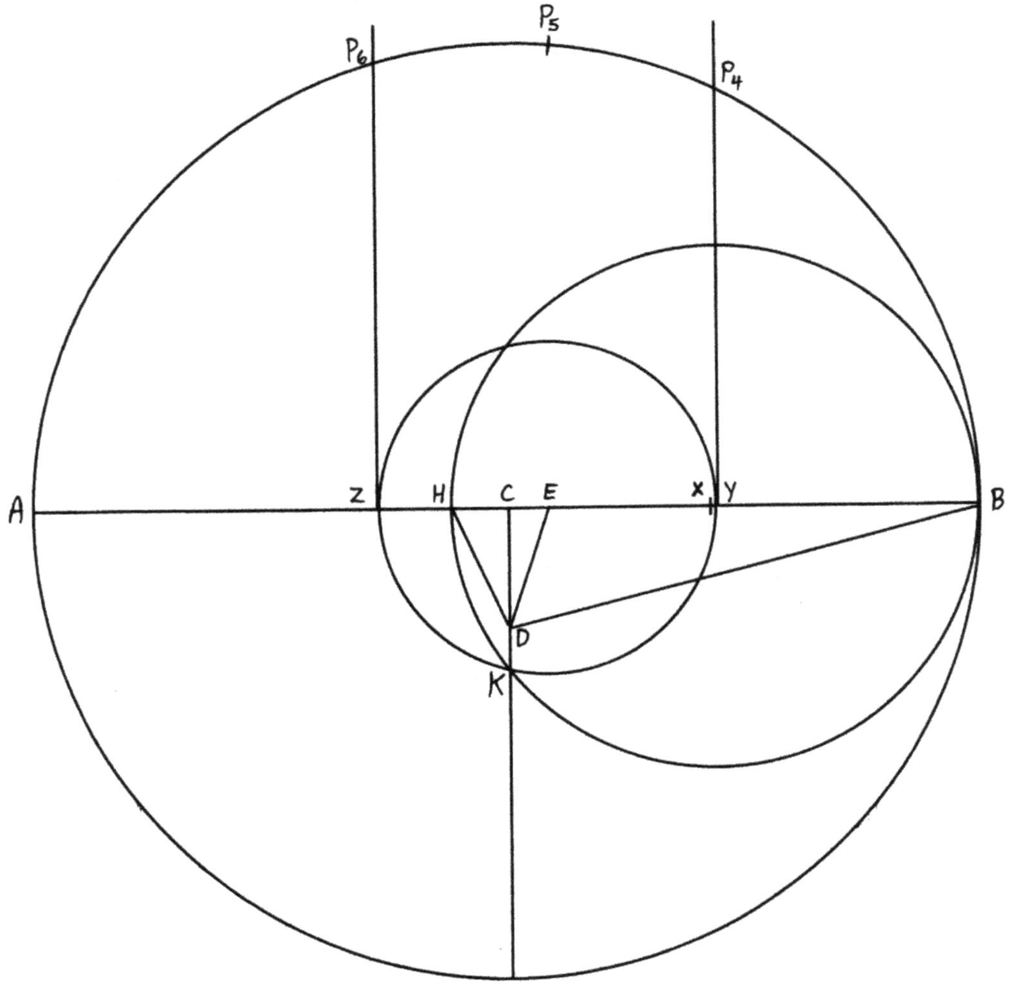

[1] This particular construction is by H.W. Richmond (*Mathematische Annalen*, volume 67, 1909). In 1796, Carl Friedrich Gauss proved that the 17-gon was constructible, but he did not provide a method for doing it. In 1800, Johannes Erchinger provided the first method for constructing the 17-gon.

Standard Proofs for
The Inscribed Angle Theorem
and
The Intersecting Chord Theorem

Standard Proof of the <u>Inscribed Angle Theorem</u>:

"An angle inscribed in a circle is half the subtended arc."

- **All three of these cases need to be proven:**

Case #1 A side of the angle is a diameter of the circle.

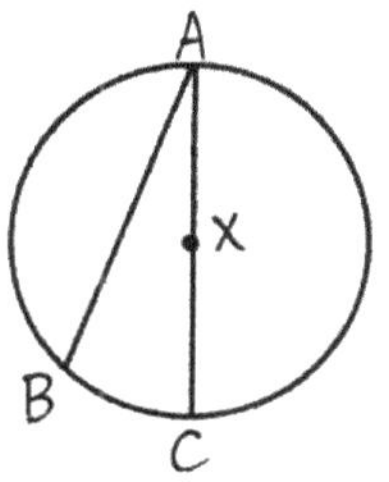

1. Draw segment BX.
2. $BX \cong AX$
3. $\angle BXC = \angle XAB + \angle XBA$ (Δ exterior angle Th.)
4. $\angle XAB \cong \angle XBA$
5. $\angle BXC = 2\angle XAB$
6. $\angle XAB = \frac{1}{2}\angle BXC$
7. $\therefore \angle BAC = \angle XAB = \frac{1}{2}\angle BXC = \frac{1}{2}\text{arc}BC$

Case #2 The center lies in the interior of the angle.

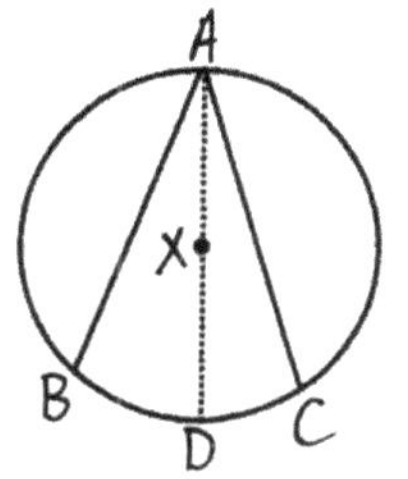

1. Draw diameter from A through X to point D.
2. $\angle BAC = \angle BAD + \angle DAC$
3. $\angle BAD = \frac{1}{2}\angle BXD$; $\angle DAC = \frac{1}{2}\angle DXC$
4. $\angle BAC = \frac{1}{2}\angle BXD + \frac{1}{2}\angle DXC$
5. $\angle BAC = \frac{1}{2}(\angle BXD + \angle DXC)$
6. $\angle BXC = \angle BXD + \angle DXC$
7. $\therefore \angle BAC = \frac{1}{2}\angle BXC = \frac{1}{2}\text{arc}BC$

Case #3 The center lies outside of the angle.

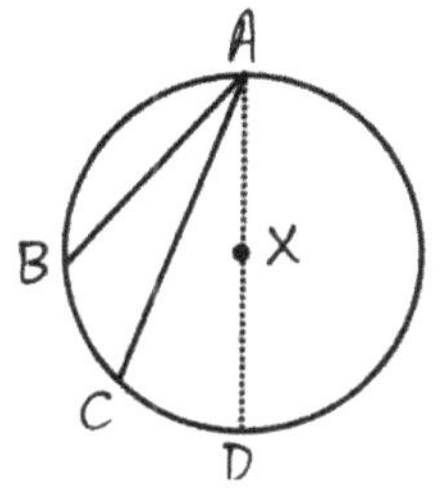

1. Draw diameter from A through X to point D.
2. $\angle BAD = \angle BAC + \angle DAC$
3. $\angle BAD = \frac{1}{2}\angle BXD$; $\angle DAC = \frac{1}{2}\angle DXC$
4. $\frac{1}{2}\angle BXD = \angle BAC + \frac{1}{2}\angle DXC$
5. $\angle BAC = \frac{1}{2}(\angle BXD - \angle DXC)$
6. $\angle BXC = \angle BXD - \angle DXC$
7. $\therefore \angle BAC = \frac{1}{2}\angle BXC = \frac{1}{2}\text{arc}BC$

Standard Proof of the <u>Intersecting Chord Theorem</u>

"The angle formed by two intersecting chords is equal to the average of the two subtended arcs."

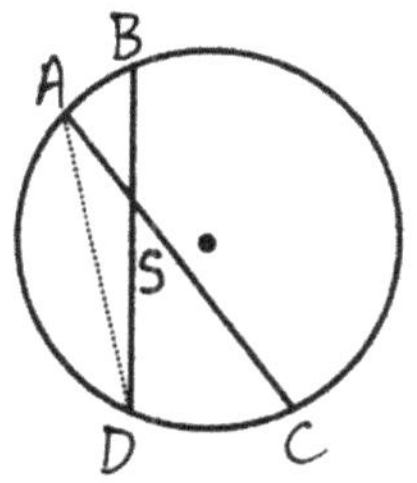

1. Draw chord AD
2. $\angle A = \frac{1}{2}\text{arc}DC$
3. $\angle D = \frac{1}{2}\text{arc}AB$
4. $\angle S = \angle A + \angle D$ (Δ exterior angle Th.)
5. $\angle S = \frac{1}{2}\text{arc}DC + \frac{1}{2}\text{arc}AB$
6. $\angle S = \frac{1}{2}(\text{arc}DC + \text{arc}AB)$

Movement Proofs for
The Inscribed Angle Theorem
and
The Intersecting Chord Theorem

Intersecting Chord Theorem

"The angle formed by two intersecting chords is equal to the average of the two subtended arcs."

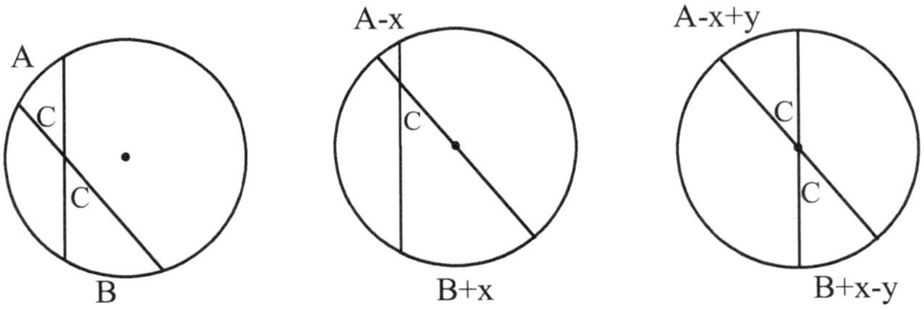

Proof:

1. Given two intersecting chords, which form angle C and the two subtended arcs A and B.
2. Slide one chord over to the center of the circle such that the new position of the chord is parallel to the original. One arc shrinks by the same amount (x) that the other arc grows (parallel chord theorem). The two new arcs may now be labeled $A-x$ and $B+x$. Note also that angle C has not changed (corresponding angle theorem).
3. Slide the other chord also over to the center in the same manner, thereby shrinking and enlarging the two arcs by the same amount (y). The two arcs are now $A-x+y$ and $B+x-y$. (Note that if angle C subtends the center of the circle then the two arcs would instead be: $A-x-y$ and $B+x+y$)
4. Since angle C is now a central angle, both of the resulting arcs are now equal to angle C. Therefore we can write two equations and then add them together to get:

$$C = A-x+y$$
$$C = B+x-y$$

Added together gives: $2C = A + B$ or $\longrightarrow$ $C = \frac{1}{2}(A + B)$

Inscribed Angle Theorem

"The measure of an inscribed angle is half the measure of its intercepted arc."

Proof: Simply imagine two intersecting chords where the point of intersection moves to the edge of the circle. One of the two arcs has now become zero. Using the intersecting chord theorem, we now get: $C = \frac{1}{2}(A + B) \longrightarrow C = \frac{1}{2}(A + 0) \longrightarrow C = \frac{1}{2}A$

- *Corollary:* Inscribed angles that intercept equal arcs are congruent.
- *Corollary:* Theorem of Thales. An angle inscribed in a semicircle is a right angle. (Review from Greek geometry main lesson).

Proof of the Parallel Chord Theorem

"Two arcs that lie between two parallel chords are congruent."
(This should be proven before proving the Intersecting Chord Theorem.)

Proof: (Case #1: Both chords to the same side of the center.)

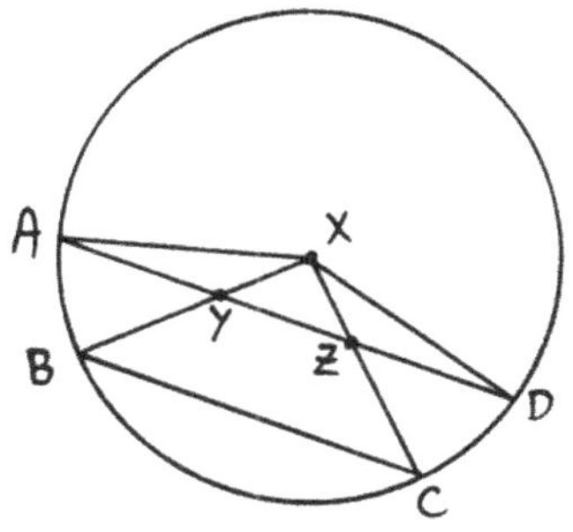

1. Given 2 parallel chords, draw radii to the 4 points of the intersection.
2. $\angle XBC \cong \angle XCB$ (Isosceles Δs)
   $\angle XYZ \cong \angle XBC$ and $\angle XZY \cong \angle XCB$ (Corresponding $\angle$s)
   $\angle XYZ \cong \angle XZY$ (Transitive)
3. $\angle XAY \cong \angle XDZ$ (Isosceles Δs)
4. $\angle XYZ = \angle XAY + \angle AXB$ (Exterior $\angle$s)
   $\angle XZY = \angle XDZ + \angle DXC$ (Exterior $\angle$s)
5. $\angle AXB = \angle XYZ - \angle XAY$
   $\angle DXC = \angle XZY - \angle XDZ = \angle XYZ - \angle XAY$ (subst.)
6. $\angle AXB \cong \angle DXC$ and $\therefore$ **arcAB ≅ arcCD**

Proof of the Outside Angle Theorem

"The measure of an angle formed by two secants that intersect each other outside the circle is equal to half the difference of the measures of the intercepted arcs."

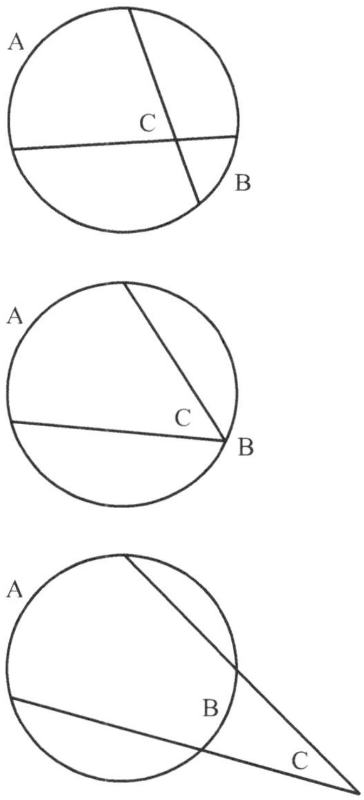

Movement Proof: We will do the same as with our movement proof for the inscribed angle theorem. Start with the case of the angle formed by two intersecting chords. The formula for this angle is $C = ½(A + B)$. Now imagine that the vertex of this angle (see top drawing) moves away from the center of the circle until it lies on the edge of the circle. Arc B is now zero and the formula is $C = ½A$. (Now the tricky part!) Allow the vertex of the angle to continue to move away from the center of the circle, thereby creating the intersection of two secants that intersect outside the circle. Arc B had a positive value when the vertex was inside the circle and then a value of zero when it was on the circle. Now that the vertex is outside the circle, it can be imagined that *arc B has a negative value*. The formula for an outside angle is therefore:

$$C = ½(A-B)$$

Standard Proof: One secant crosses a circle at points A and B, and another secant crosses the circle at points C and D, such that the two secants intersect each other outside the circle, and the arcs BC and AD lie between the two secants. Draw chord AC.

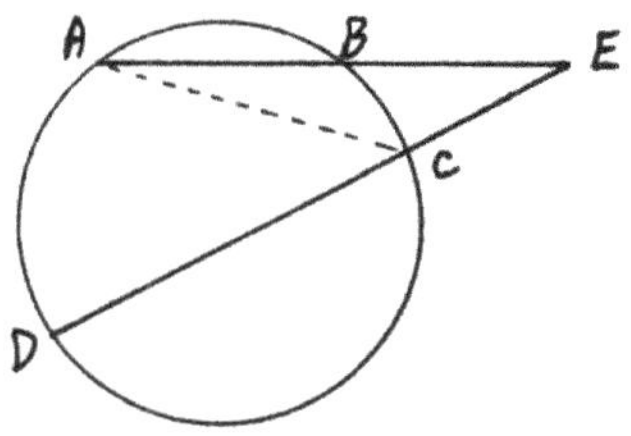

$$\angle ACD = \angle BAC + \angle E.$$

$$½\text{arcAD} = ½\text{arcBC} + \angle E.$$

$$\therefore \angle E = ½(\text{arcAD} - \text{arcBC})$$

Inscribed Quadrilateral Theorem.

"The opposite angles of a quadrilateral inscribed inside a circle are supplementary."

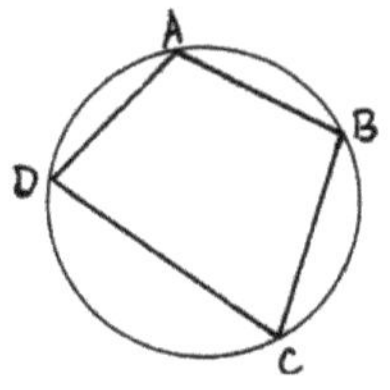

Proof:
1. Draw quadrilateral ABCD inside a circle.
2. ∠A = ½arcBCD; ∠C = ½arcBAD
3. arcBCD + arcBAD = 360° (The whole circle!)
4. ∠A + ∠C = ½(arcBCD + arcBAD) = ½(360°) = 180°
5. ∴∠A and ∠C are supplementary.

Chord Segment Theorem

"When two chords intersect inside a circle, the product of the segments of one chord equals the product of the segments of the other chord."

Proof:

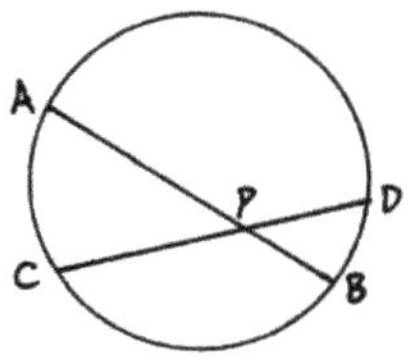

1. Given: circle with chords AB, CD intersecting at P.
2. Draw chords AD and BC.
3. ∠A ≅ ∠C and ∠D ≅ ∠B
4. ΔAPD ~ ΔCPB
5. AP:PD = CP:PB
6. ∴AP·PB = CP·PD

Secant Segment Theorem

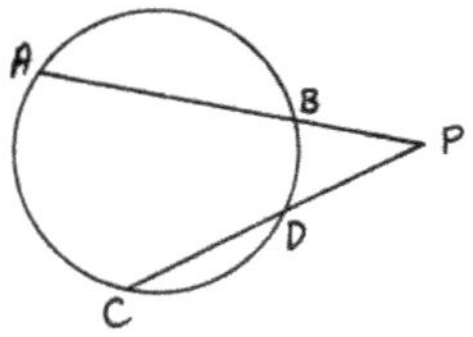

"When two secant segments[1] are drawn from a point outside the circle, the product of one secant segment and its external portion equals the product of the other secant segment and its external portion."

Once again: AP·PB = CP·PD

Secant-Tangent Theorem

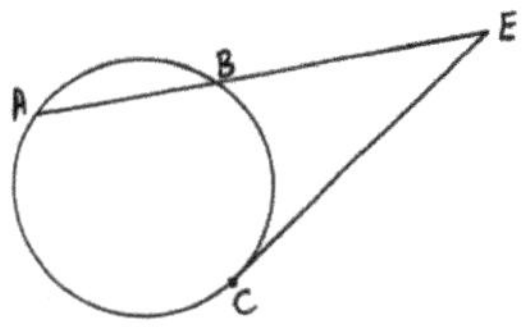

"When a tangent segment and a secant segment are drawn from a point outside a circle, the product of the secant segment and its external portion is equal to the square of the tangent segment."

In this case: AE·BE = CE^2

Circumscribed Quadrilateral Theorem.

"The sums of the lengths of opposite pairs of sides of a circumscribed quadrilateral are equal."

Proof.

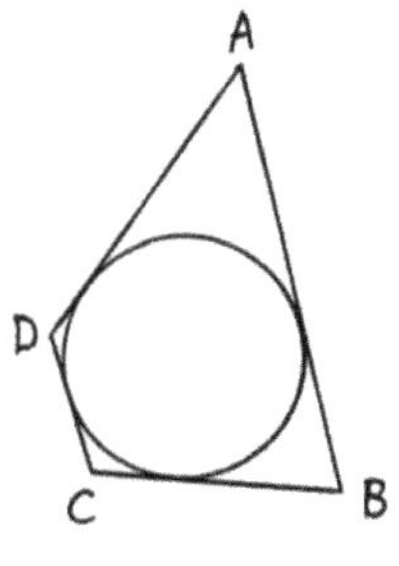

1. Draw quadrilateral ABCD, circumscribed (all four sides are tangent) about a given circle.
2. Color the two line segments (with the same color) from point A, along the side of the quadrilateral, to the two tangent points. Use different colors to color each pair of tangent line segments from the other three vertices.
3. Each pair of same-colored tangent line segments has equal lengths. (Intersecting tangent theorem.)
4. Any two opposite sides of the quadrilateral include one segment of each of the four differently colored line segments.
5. ∴The sums of the lengths of opposite pairs of sides are equal.

Required reading

In order to gain a deeper understanding of this *Circle Geometry* unit, the teacher should read the commentary found in the *Teacher's Edition of our 10th Grade Workbook* and also work through the *Circle Geometry* problem sets found in the workbook.

---

[1] A *secant segment* is a chord that has been extended in one direction to a point outside the circle.

—— *Triangle Geometry* (10th Grade) ——

Overview

In many ways, this unit has the flavor of a geometric drawing main lesson. Mostly with only a compass and straightedge, the students are led to discover several fascinating theorems that only relatively recently came to light in the world of mathematics. In terms of necessary skills for further mathematical studies, this unit has no value. One can then understand why this topic is so neglected in our skills-dominated mainstream mathematics curriculum. The real value of this brief unit is how it cultivates a sense of wonder in the students. There are moments when the students complete a drawing, and then look with awe at the beauty and lawfulness of what lies before them.

Required reading

In order to gain a deeper understanding of this unit, the teacher should read the commentary found in the *Teacher's Edition of our 10th Grade Workbook* and also work through the drawings as described in the *Triangle Geometry* unit in the workbook.

The Four Centers of a Triangle

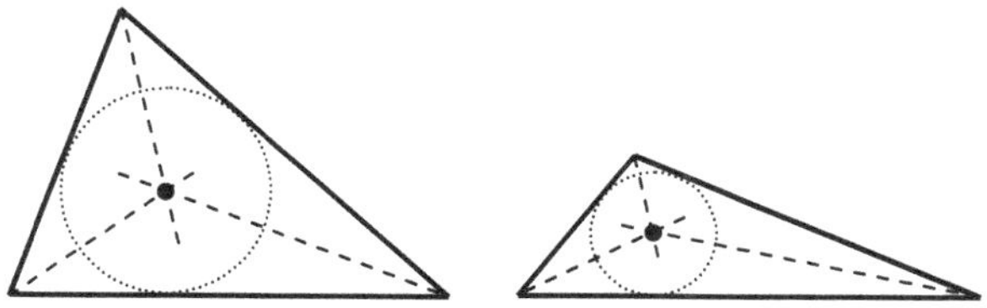

Incenter
The incenter is the intersection of the three angle bisectors, and the center of the inscribed circle.

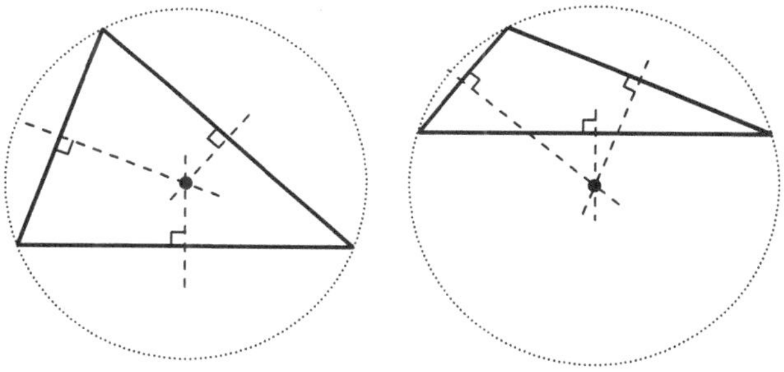

Circumcenter
The circumcenter is the intersection of the three perpendicular bisectors, and the center of the circumscribed circle.

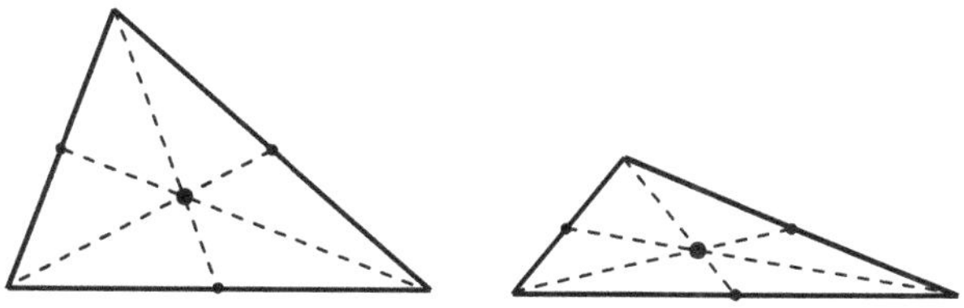

Centroid
The centroid is the intersection of the three medians, and the center of gravity (balance point) of the triangle.

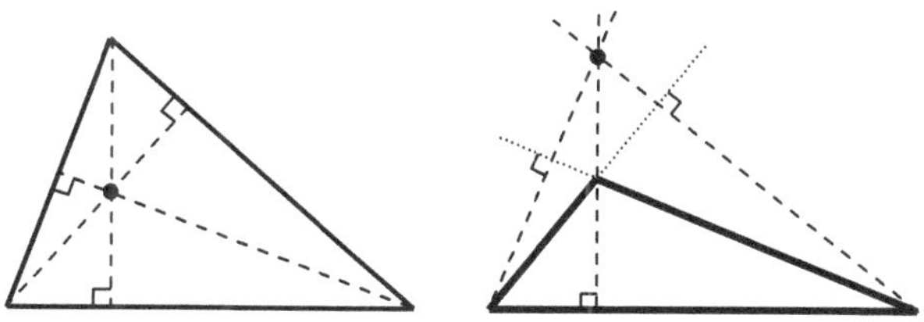

Orthocenter
The orthocenter is the intersection of the three altitudes.

The Four Centers of a Triangle in Movement

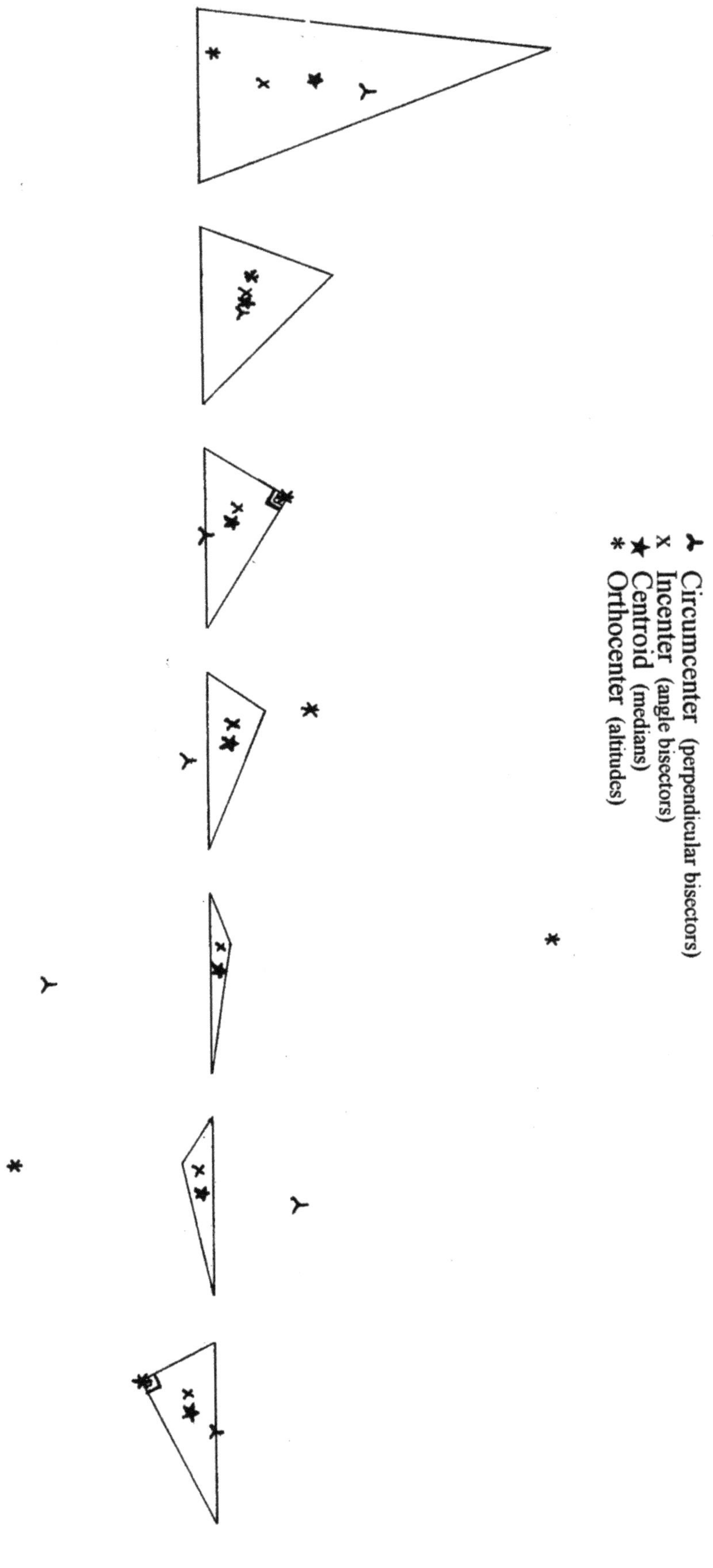

Proofs of the Four Centers of a Triangle

1. <u>The Incenter</u>. *The center of the inscribed circle* (angle bisectors)
The bisectors of the angles of a triangle intersect in a point that is equidistant from the three sides of the triangle. A circle can then be drawn tangent to all three sides.

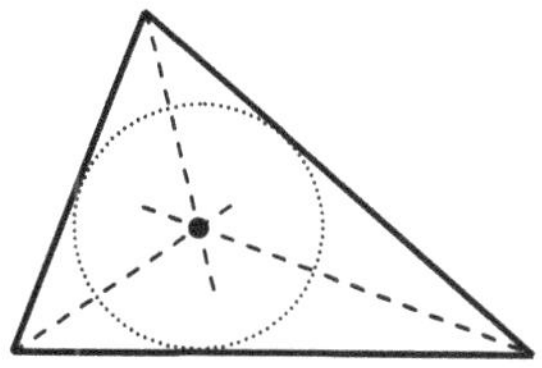

Proof:

Given ΔABC, point I is the intersection of the bisectors of ∠A and ∠B. Draw perpendiculars from I intersecting AB, BC, and AC at points R, S, and T respectively. ΔATI ≅ ΔARI and ΔBSI ≅ ΔBRI (AAS). ∴TI ≅ RI ≅ SI and a circle can be drawn with center I and radius TI. Draw segment CI. ΔCSI ≅ ΔCTI (HL). ∠TCI ≅ ∠SCI.
∴CI bisects ∠C.

2. <u>The Circumcenter</u>. *The center of the circumscribed circle* (perpendicular bisectors)
The perpendicular bisectors of the sides of a triangle intersect in a point that is equidistant from the three vertices of the triangle. A circle can therefore be drawn which passes through the three vertices.

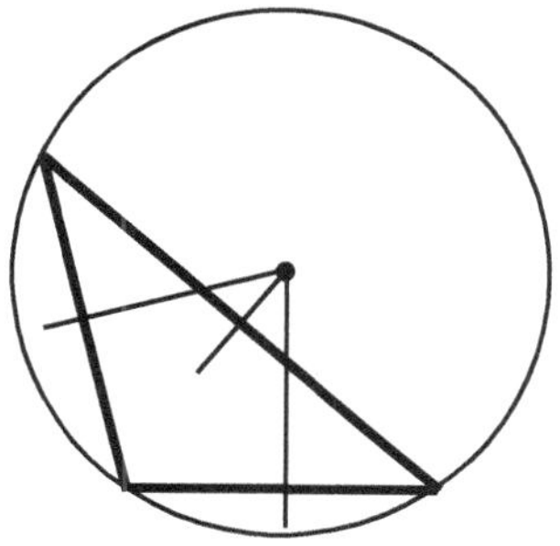

Proof:

Given ΔABC, let R, S, and T be the midpoints of the three sides AB, BC, AC. Point O is the intersection of the perpendicular bisectors of AC and BC. Draw OA, OB, and OC. ΔATO ≅ ΔCTO and ΔBSO ≅ ΔCSO (SAS). ∴OA ≅ OC ≅ OB and a circle can be drawn with center O and radius OC.
Draw segment RO. ΔARO ≅ ΔBRO (SSS). ∠ARO ≅ ∠BRO.
∠ARO + ∠BRO = 180°. ∠ARO is a right angle.
∴RO is the perpendicular bisector of AB.

- *Corollary:* The area of any triangle is given by $\frac{abc}{4R}$, where R is radius of the circumcircle.

3. <u>Orthocenter</u>. (altitudes)
The altitudes of any triangle intersect in one point.

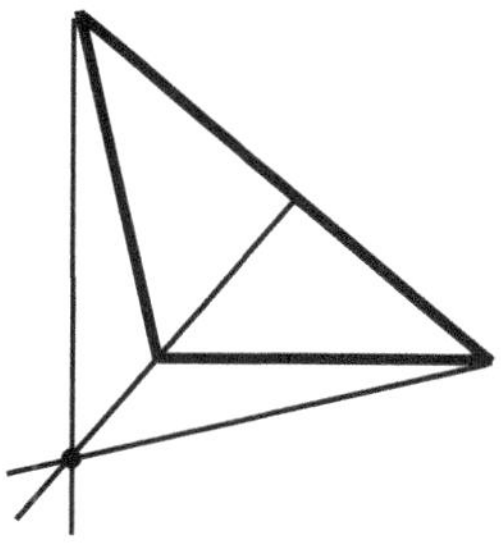

Proof:

Given ΔABC, draw through each vertex a line parallel to its opposite side, thereby forming three points of intersection, labeled R, S, and T falling closest to AB, BC, and AC, respectively. From opposite interior angles, corresponding angles, and the fact that each outer small triangle shares a side with the original triangle, all four triangles are congruent. Therefore A, B, and C are midpoints of the sides of ΔRST. The perpendicular bisectors for RS, ST, and TR must meet in a single point (the circumcenter), and they form right angles with AC, AB, and BC, respectively.
∴The three altitudes of ΔABC meet in a point.

4. <u>Centroid</u>. *Center of gravity* (medians)
There are four theorems involving the centroid.

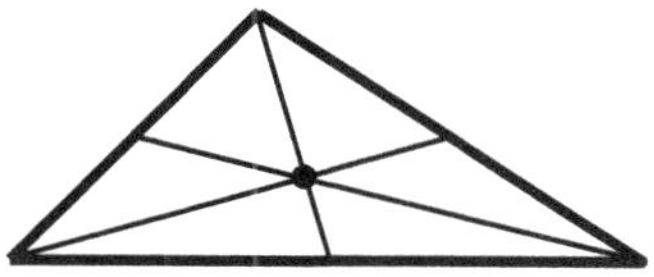

- Two medians of a triangle divide each other at ⅓ of their lengths.
- The three medians of any triangle intersect at one point.
- The three medians of a triangle divide the triangle into 6 smaller triangles of equal area.
- The centroid is the center of gravity of the triangle – the point where the triangle may be balanced.

See the proofs of these four theorems on the next page.

Four Theorems involving the Centroid

I. Two medians of a triangle divide each other at $\frac{1}{3}$ of their lengths.

Proof:

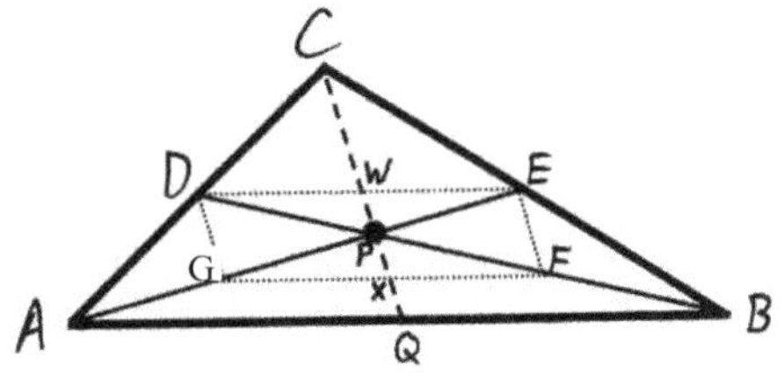

1. Sides AC and BC (of ΔABC) have midpoints D and E respectively.
   Draw medians BD and AE, which intersect at P.
   F and G are midpoints of BP and AP.
2. $DE \parallel AB$ and $DE = \frac{1}{2}AB$ (triangle midpoint Th.)
   $GF \parallel AB$ and $GF = \frac{1}{2}AB$ (triangle midpoint Th.)
   $DE \parallel GF$ and $DE \cong GF$
   $\therefore$ quadrilateral DEFG is a parallelogram.
3. $DP \cong FP$ and $GP \cong EP$ (Parallelogram Diagonal Th.)
   $FB \cong FP$ and $GP \cong AG$ (Def. of midpoint)
4. **$\therefore DP:BP = 1:2$** and **$EP:AP = 1:2$** and **$DP = \frac{1}{3}BD$** and **$EP = \frac{1}{3}AE$** *Q.E.D.*

II. The three medians of any triangle intersect at one point.

Proof:

1. Continuing with the drawing from the first proof, draw CP, extending it to meet AB at Q, and label the intersection of this newly drawn line with DE as W, and with GF as X.
2. Using ΔBPC, because $PF \cong FB$ and $CE \cong EB$ then $EF \parallel PC$ (also QC) (Δ Midpoint Th.)
3. Quad XWEF is a parallelogram, so $WE \cong XF$. Also, $\Delta DWP \cong \Delta FXP$ (AAS); $DW \cong XF$
   $\therefore$ **$WE \cong DW$**
4. Using ΔABC, we know that $DE \parallel AB$ (see above proof), therefore:
   $\Delta ECW \sim \Delta BCQ$ and $\Delta DCW \sim \Delta ACQ$
5. Since $BC = 2 \cdot EC$ and $AC = 2 \cdot DC$ then $QB = 2 \cdot WE$ and $AQ = 2 \cdot DW$.
6. $\therefore AQ \cong QB$ (substitution using steps 3 & 5), and therefore *CQ is a median of the triangle and passes through the point of intersection (P) of the other two medians. Q.E.D.*

III. The 3 medians of a triangle divide the triangle into 6 triangles of equal area.

Proof:

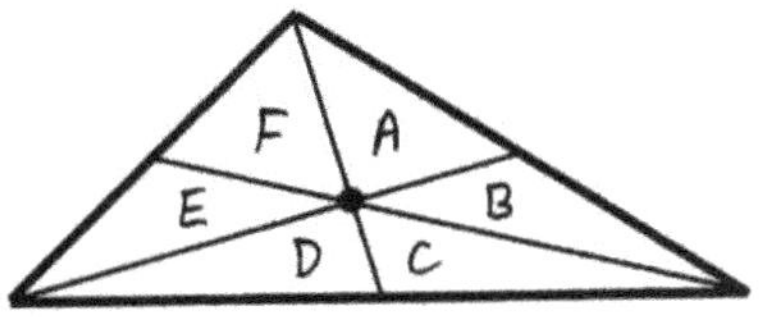

1. Given a triangle with all three of its medians drawn, thereby dividing the triangle into 6 smaller triangles.
2. Triangles C and D have equal area because their bases and altitudes are equal. Likewise triangles A and B have equal area as do triangles E and F.
3. Considering now the large, original triangle, we can say that the left half of it (which is a combination of triangles F, E, and D) is equal in area to the right half (which is a combination of triangles A, B, and C). In terms of the areas of these triangles, we can therefore say:
   $A + B + C = D + E + F$.
4. Since $C = D$, $A = B$, and $E = F$, we can conclude that areas of A and F equal. Similarly, we can conclude that $B = C$ and that $D = E$. $\therefore$ *All six* triangles *have equal areas. Q.E.D.*

IV. The centroid is the point where the triangle may be balanced.

Proof:

Given ΔABC with the midpoint E of BC, draw AE. Draw lines m and n through the vertices B and C, respectively, such that they are parallel to AE. C and B are equidistant from line AE. Leaving points A and E fixed, slide point C along line n and point B along line m until each triangle becomes isosceles. The distance of points B and C to line AE remains constant as they slide along their respective lines. Once they have both become isosceles triangles, they become congruent and therefore can balance along line AE. As B and C are slid back to their original position, all points within the boundary of the triangle remain at a constant distance from AE, therefore the triangle remains in balance. If this is repeated for all three lines, we have the three "lines of balance" forming a single balance point, or center of gravity.

A Moving Triangle's Orthocenter forms a Parabola!

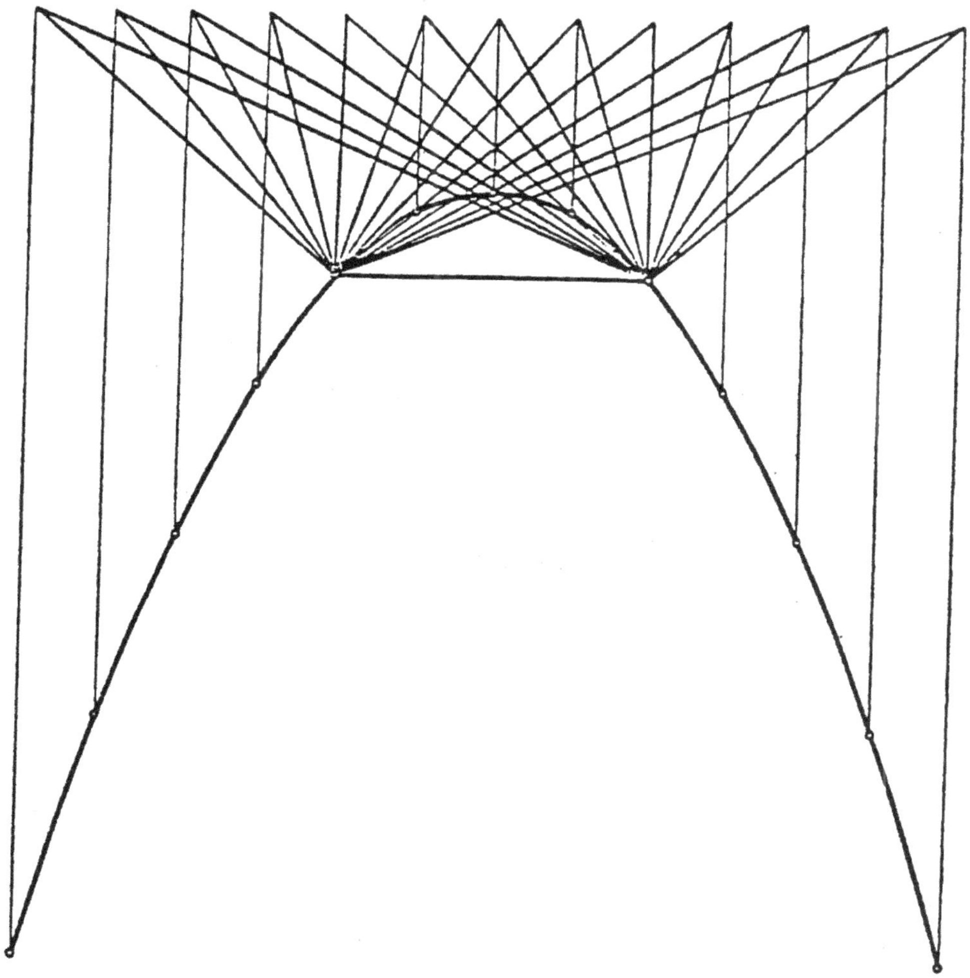

Instructions:

1. Draw a small equilateral triangle near the top of the page such that the base is horizontal.
2. Find and mark the orthocenter.
3. Draw a line through the apex that is parallel to the base.
4. Mark points on this newly draw line that are about equally spaced and on both sides of the apex.
5. Draw new triangles, where the points along this line are used as the new apex and the base remains the same as the original triangle.
6. Find and mark the orthocenters of these newly formed triangles.
7. Draw a parabola by connecting all the orthocenters.

A Proof of Euler's Line[1]

Prerequisite Knowledge

1) *The Four Centers of a Triangle*: *Circumcenter* (perpendicular bisectors); *Centroid* (medians); *Incenter* (angle bisectors); *Orthocenter* (altitudes).
2) *Centroid Theorem.* The centroid of a triangle divides each median in a ratio of 2:1.
3) *Parallelogram Diagonal Theorem Converse.* If the diagonals of a quadrilateral bisect each other, then it is a parallelogram.
4) *Triangle Midpoint Theorem.* Connecting the midpoints of two sides of a triangle creates a triangle similar to the original. The two triangles' bases are parallel. The ratio of the sides is 2:1.

To prove[2]: The orthocenter, centroid and circumcenter are collinear; the ratio of their distances is 2:1.

1) Given (scalene) triangle ABC, with AC as the base.
2) The construction:
   a) Locate D as the midpoint of AC.
   b) Construct the circumcenter P, and the centroid M.
   c) Locate K as the midpoint of MB.
   d) Locate points F and G on the line PM (extended) such that GF = FM = MP.
   e) Connect FD, KP, BG, BK, KM, MD, KF, PD.
   f) Extend line BG to meet line AC at point Q.

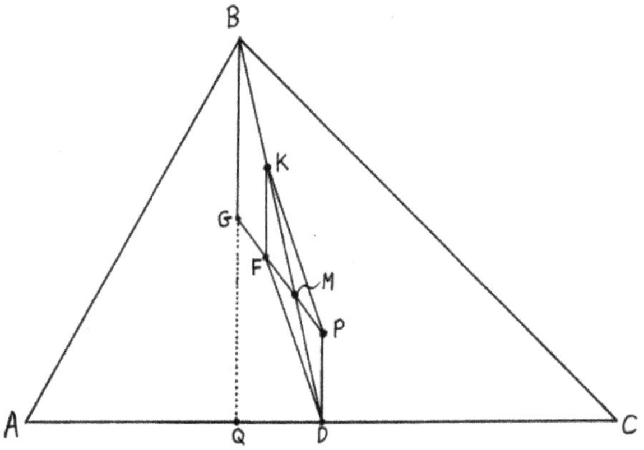

3) F and K are midpoints of ΔBGM. (def. of midpoint)
4) KM = ½BM (Triangle Midpoint Theorem)
5) DM = ½BM (Centroid Theorem)
6) KM = DM (C.N. 1)
7) KFDP is a parallelogram. (Parallelogram Diagonal Theorem Converse)
8) PD is parallel to KF. (def. of parallelogram)
9) BG is parallel to KF. (Triangle Midpoint Theorem)
10) PD is parallel to BG. (*Euclid Th. I-30*: "Two lines parallel to the same line are parallel to each other")
11) PD ⊥ AC. (by construction)
12) ∠BQC ≅ ∠PDC; BQ ⊥ AC. (Corresponding Angle Th.; def. perpendicular)
13) G lies on an altitude. If we repeat the above steps from all sides of the triangle, we can show that G lies on all three of the altitudes. Therefore, G is the orthocenter. Also the points G, M, P are collinear (as constructed). ∴ **The Orthocenter, Centroid and Circumcenter are collinear.**
14) MG:MP = 2:1 (by construction).
    ∴ **The Orthocenter is twice as far from the Centroid as the Circumcenter is.**

---

[1] This proof is modeled after a proof by Kenneth Lein, courtesy of Sarah Heirman.

[2] In proving this to students, it may be best not to state the outcome at the beginning, but let it emerge as a surprise.

The Nine-Point Circle

With ΔRST:

- L, M, P are the midpoints of its sides.
- O and C are its orthocenter and circumcenter.
- A, B, E are the feet of its altitudes.
- H, G, I are the midpoints of RO, SO, TO, respectively.
- N is the midpoint of OC and the center of the nine-point circle.

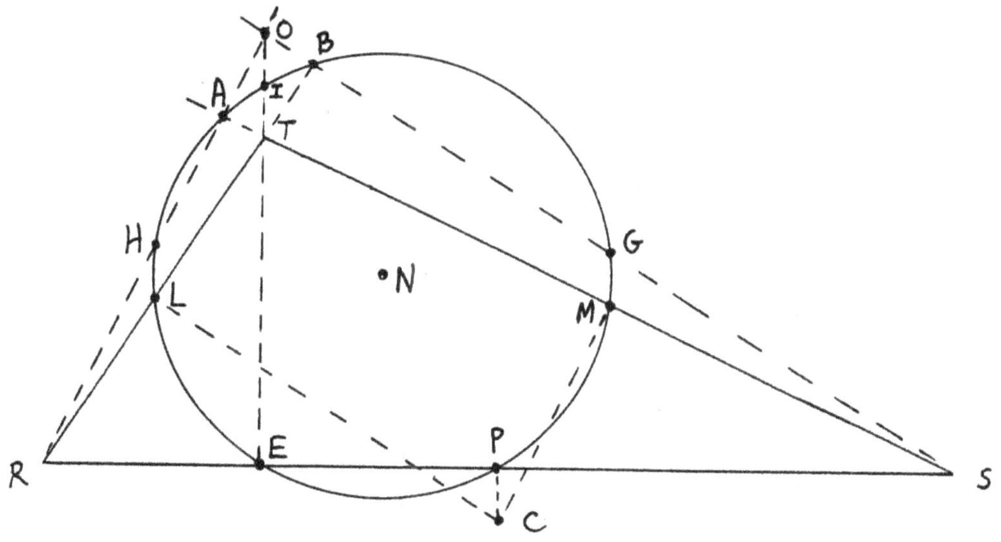

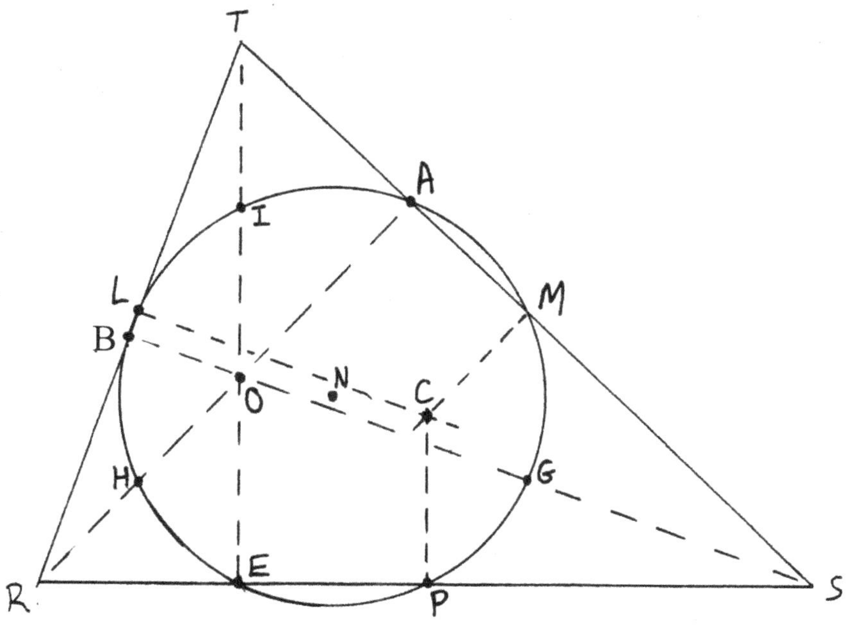

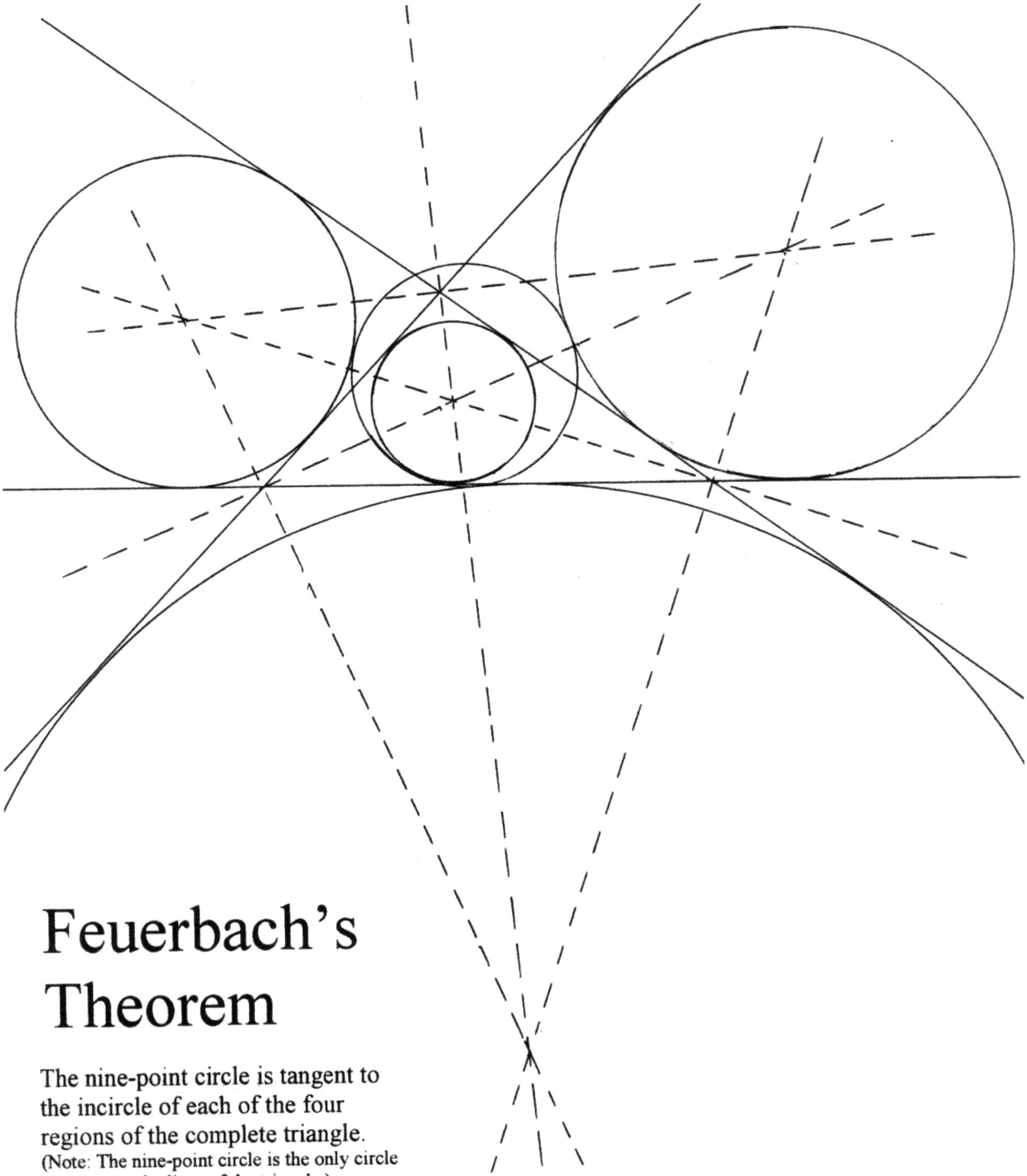

Feuerbach's Theorem

The nine-point circle is tangent to the incircle of each of the four regions of the complete triangle.
(Note: The nine-point circle is the only circle that crosses the lines of the triangle.)

Steiner's Hypocycloid

The Simson lines* of any triangle form a hypocycloid, which is tangent to both the nine-point circle and the original triangle, and has the reverse orientation from its Morley's Triangle.

* To draw a Simson line, choose a point on the circumcircle. From that point, locate the three feet of the perpendicular lines drawn to the sides of the triangles. These three feet will lie upon a line known as a Simson Line.

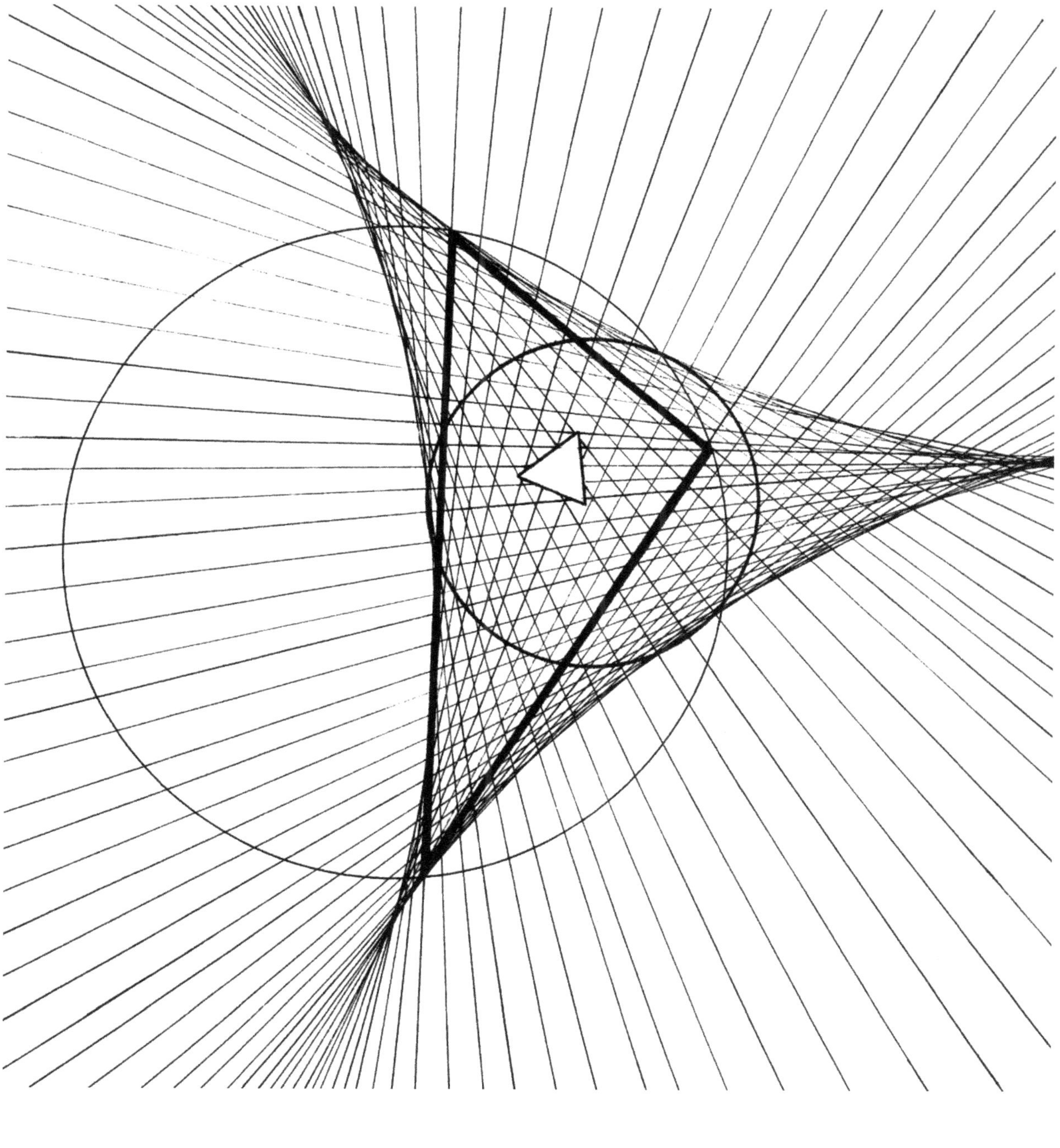

—— *Theorems and Proofs* (10th Grade) ——

Overview

Ideally, during the Greek Geometry main lesson, the students have seen proofs of historical significance and leave the block understanding truly what a proof is, and its importance in the world of mathematics. Now, after a short break following the main lesson, it is time for the students to learn to write their own proofs. This is the purpose of the *Proofs* unit in our workbook.

For many students, this unit is the most challenging unit of the year – but it is a good challenge. This unit should be done thoroughly; it is important to take the time needed, so that the students can walk away from this challenge feeling successful.

Required reading

Some of the highlights of the *Proofs* unit are given below, but for a complete picture of the unit it is important for the teacher to carefully read both the commentary on the *Proofs* unit in the *Teacher's Edition of our 10th Grade Workbook*, and the entire *Proofs* unit in the workbook, including the "notes" for the students found at the start of the unit.

Prerequisites for the unit

The students need to be familiar with the following topics before beginning the *Proofs* unit:

- Euclid's Postulates and Common Notions
- Segment Addition Postulate
- Angle Addition Postulate
- Substitution Property (of algebra)
- Reflexive Property
- All of the constructions from Euclid's *Elements, Book I*
- Triangle congruency theorems (SSS, SAS, ASA, AAS, HL)
- Triangle similarity theorems (SSS, SAS, AA, HL)
- Pythagorean Theorem (and its converse)
- Isosceles Triangle Theorem (and its converse)
- Triangle Interior Angle Th. (Angles in a triangle add to 180°)
- Triangle Exterior Angle Th. (The exterior angle of a triangle equals the sum of the two opposite interior angles.)
- Angle theorems (supplementary, vertical, corresponding, alternate interior, same-side interior)

Book V from *The Elements*

- The following laws of ratios and proportions from *Book V* of the *The Elements* are covered:
  - *Th. V-12:* $a:a' = b:b' = c:c' .... = (a+b):(a'+b') = (a+b+c...):(a'+b'+c'...)$
  - *Th. V-16:* If $a:b = c:d$ then $a:c = b:d$
  - *Th. V-17:* If $a:b = c:d$ then $(a-b):b = (c-d):d$
  - *Th. V-18:* If $a:b = c:d$ then $(a+b):b = (c+d):d$
  - *Th. V-19:* States that if $a:b = c:d$ then $a:b = (a-c):(b-d)$.
- For more details, read the commentary on the *Proofs* unit in the *Teacher's Edition of our 10th Grade Workbook.*

New simple theorems

Here is a list of new simple theorems that appear in this unit:

- Parallelogram Side Theorem
- Parallelogram Angle Theorem
- Parallelogram Diagonal Theorem
- Rectangle Side Theorem
- Rectangle Diagonal Theorem
- Rhombus Diagonal Theorem
- Triangle Midpoint Theorem
- General Pythagorean Theorem

Challenge proofs and topics

Here is a list of the most challenging theorems and proofs:
- Polygon Exterior Angle Theorem
- Triangle Proportionality Theorem
- Triangle Angle–Bisector Theorem
- Eratosthenes' Measurement of the Earth
- Ptolemy's Quadrilateral Theorem
- Midpoint of the Hypotenuse Theorem
- Parallelogram Angle-Bisector Theorem
- The Pentagon & the Golden Triangle
- A "Pythagorean Curiosity"

More details on the above topics appear in the following pages and in the commentary on the *Proofs* unit in the *Teacher's Edition of our 10th Grade Workbook.*

The Altitude of the Hypotenuse Theorem. (Th. VI-8 from *The Elements)*

If the altitude to the hypotenuse of a right triangle is drawn, then the two triangles formed are similar to the original triangle and to each other, and the square of the length of the altitude is equal to the product of the lengths of the two segments of the hypotenuse.

$$\mathbf{Z^2 = X \cdot Y}$$

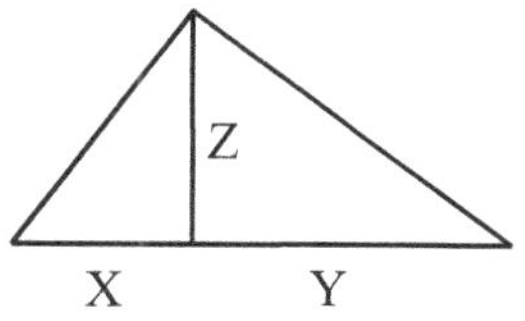

The Polygon Exterior Angle Theorem.

The sum of the exterior angles in a convex polygon is equal to 360°.

Movement Proof: Draw a small random polygon where all of the sides are extended in a counter-clockwise direction. Imagine that the polygon shrinks to a point, or, alternatively, imagine that your eye moves further and further away from the polygon. It then becomes clear that the sum of all of the exterior angles is 360°.

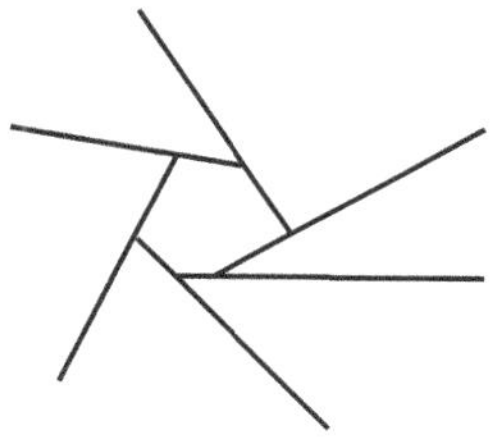

Triangle Angle-Bisector Theorem. (Th. VI-3 from The Elements)

The angle bisector of an angle in a triangle divides the opposite side into segments proportional to the other two sides. This can also be expressed as: AB:AC = BD:DC or AB:BD = AC:DC

Proof:
1. Given: AD bisects ∠BAC in triangle ABC.
2. Draw a line through C that is parallel to AD, such that it intersects line AB (extended) at point Q.
3. ∠DAB ≅ ∠DAC (Def. of bisector)
   ∠DAC ≅ ∠ACQ (Alternate interior angles)
   ∠CQA ≅ ∠DAB (Corresponding angles)
   ∠CQA ≅ ∠ACQ (Transitive)
   AC ≅ AQ (Isosceles Δ th. converse)
4. BD:DC = BA:AQ (Triangle proportionality th.)
   ∴**BD:DC = BA:AC** (Substitution)

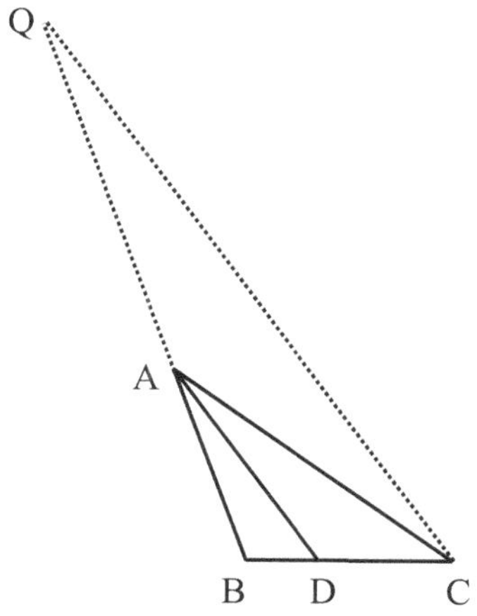

Ptolemy's Quadrilateral Theorem

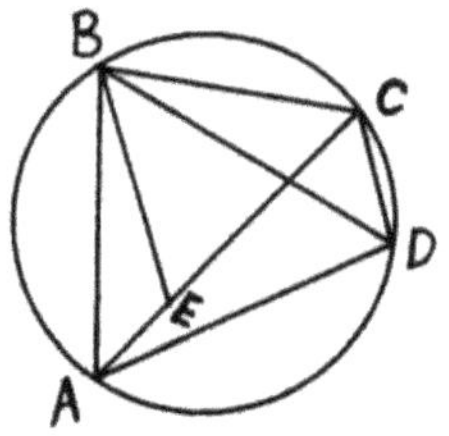

"The [area of the] rectangle contained by the diagonals of any quadrilateral inscribed in a circle is equal to the sum of [areas of the] the rectangles contained by the pairs of opposite sides."

With the given drawing, this means: AC·BD = AB·CD + BC·AD
To understand this, it is best to ignore line BE (which is used in the proof), and to picture that AC·BD means the area of the rectangle formed using AC as the base and BD as the height. AB·CD and BC·AD also represent areas of rectangles.

(Most justifications are from Euclid's *Elements*.)

1. Given quad ABCD, with its two diagonals, all inscribed in a circle.
2. Place E on AC such that ∠ABE ≅ ∠DBC. (Th. I-23)
3. ∠BAC ≅ ∠BDC (Th. III-21)
4. ∠BEA + ∠BAC + ∠ABE = ∠BCD + ∠BDC + ∠DBC (Th. I-32b)
5. ∠BEA ≅ ∠BCD (C.N.3 – note: Euclid does not have an AA ~ theorem)
6. ΔABE ~ ΔDBC (def. of equiangular or similiar)
7. AB:AE = BD:DC (Th. VI-4)
8. AB·DC = BD·AE (Th. VI-16)
9. ∠ABE + ∠DBE =∠DBC + ∠DBE (C.N.2)
10. ∠ABD ≅ ∠EBC (from drawing or angle addition postulate)
11. ∠BDA ≅ ∠BCA (Th. III-21)
12. ∠BAD + ∠BDA + ∠ABD = ∠BEC + ∠BCA + ∠EBC (Th. I-32b)
13. ∠BAD = ∠BEC (C.N.3)
14. ΔABD ~ ΔEBC (def. of equiangular or similiar)
15. BC:CE = BD:AD (Th. VI-4)
16. AD·BC = BD·CE (Th. VI-16)
17. AB·DC + AD·BC = BD·AE + BD·CE (C.N.2 – steps 8 & 16)
18. AB·DC + AD·BC = BD(AE + CE) (Th. V-1)
19. **∴AB·DC + AD·BC = BD·AC** (from drawing or segment addition postulate)

Construction of a Golden Triangle

- This is theorem IV-10 from *The Elements*. It is used in theorem IV-11, where Euclid shows how to inscribe a pentagon inside a circle.
- The *Golden Triangle* is the tall isosceles triangle that is found within the pentagon. Each of its base angles is equal to 72°, which is twice the apex angle (36°).
- This is a particularly good proof to do with the students as it calls upon theorems from Books I, II, III, and IV as justification for its steps.
- See the *Proofs* unit, problem set #5 of our *10th Grade Workbook* (and Answer Key), for the full proof.

Heron's Formula for the area of a triangle

- Heron's formula states: Area ΔABC $= \sqrt{s(s-a)(s-b)(s-c)}$, where $s = ½(a + b + c)$
- This proof can be one of the highlights of the year. This "super-proof" is a great way to review many of the theorems that were covered earlier in the year.
- See the proof of Heron's formula in the pages later in this section.
- There exists a simpler formula that uses trigonometry, which Heron, of course, did not have access to.
- We use Heron's formula when we can't easily determine the height of a triangle.
  Example: Using Heron's formula with the triangle here, the perimeter is 72 feet, so the semi-perimeter (S) is half of 72, which is 36. The area of the triangle is then:

  $\text{Area} = \sqrt{36\cdot(36\text{-}28)\cdot(36\text{-}24)\cdot(36\text{-}20)} \rightarrow \sqrt{36\cdot8\cdot12\cdot16} \rightarrow 96\sqrt{6}$ or $\sqrt{55296} \approx$ <u>235.1 ft²</u>
- Area of a Cyclic Quadrilateral
  - $\text{Area} = \sqrt{(s-a)(s-b)(s-c)(s-d)}$, where $s = ½(a + b + c + d)$
  - Brahmagupta (ca. 630AD) discovered this, but thought it worked for any quadrilateral.

A Pythagorean Curiosity[1]

Construction:

Starting with the right triangle ABC, draw squares off each of the three sides. Connect the corners of those three squares (line segments LD, IE and MH) and then draw three more squares (NH, EJ and LG) off those line segments. Draw lines that connect the corners of these squares and extend the lines in order to form the triangle PQR.

Questions:

1) Which of the figures within the diagram (e.g., triangles, squares, etc.) are congruent? Which are similar?
2) Prove that PR is parallel to AC. (Likewise, it follows that CB is parallel to RQ.)
3) Find the area of each figure in terms of a and b, where a=CB and b=AC:
   a) ΔABC, ΔCHM, ΔADL and ΔIBE.
   b) The trapezoids HIJK, LMNO and DEFG.
   c) The squares drawn onto NO, FG, and KJ.
   d) The squares NH, EJ and LG.
   e) ΔJFQ and ΔOGP.
4) a) What is the relationship between the areas of the squares drawn onto ON, KJ, and FG?
   b) What is the relationship between the areas of the squares NH, EJ, and LG?
5) Comparing ΔABC and ΔPQR…
   a) Find a formula for the lengths of RQ and RP, in terms of a and b.
   b) Find the ratios of CB:RQ, AC:PR, and AB:PQ.
   c) Find the ratio of the area of ΔPQR to the area of ΔABC.

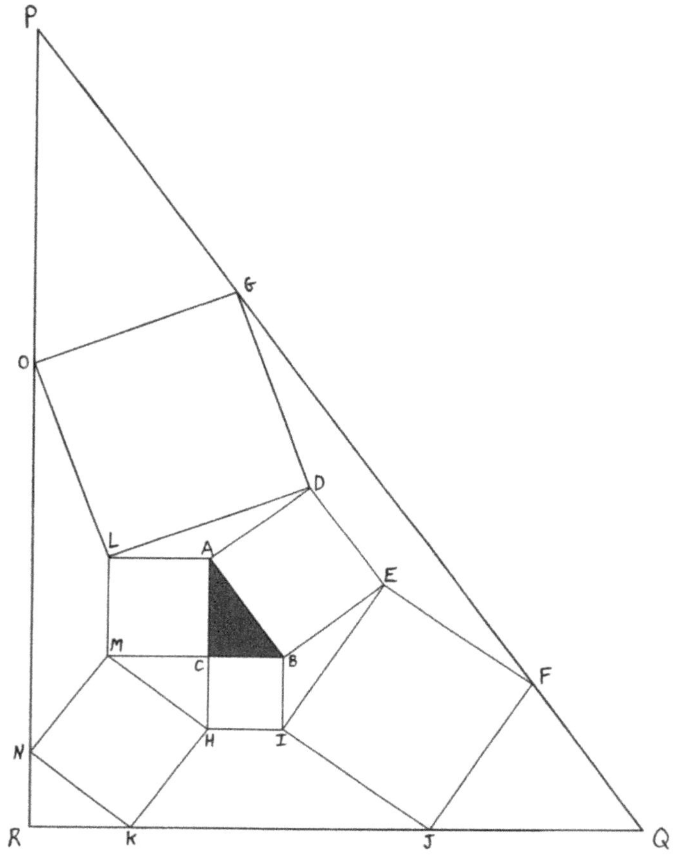

[1] This construction is from page 252 of *The Pythagorean Proposition* by Elisha Loomis (NCTM, 1972). It is said to have first appeared in print in a New York newspaper in 1899. Many of the questions are my own.

A Pythagorean Curiosity (continued)

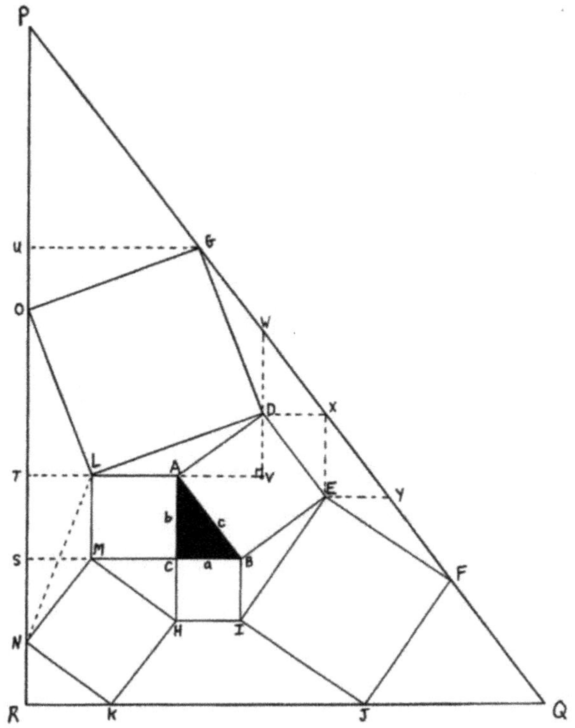

Solutions:

1) Squares AE and NH are congruent. Triangles ABC, MHC and KNR are all congruent, and similar to ΔPQR. All the squares are similar to one another.

2) *To prove LM is parallel to ON:*
First, we draw line LN. Considering the four angles that meet at point A (and ignoring the dotted line), we can say that m∠LAD = 180° – m∠CAB. Likewise, m∠LMN = 180° – m∠CMH. Since ∠CMH ≅ ∠CAB, we now know ∠LAD ≅ ∠LMN. And because squares AE and MK are congruent, we can say that ΔLAD ≅ ΔLMN (SAS). It then follows that OL ≅ LN and ∠NOL ≅ ∠ONL, which we will call θ. Letting α = ∠MLN (=∠ALD), and considering the angles surrounding point L, we can say that ∠OLN = 180° – 2α. Considering ΔOLN, we get ∠OLN = 180° – 2θ, which allows us to say that α = θ. It follows that the alternate interior angles ∠MLN and ∠ONL are equal and LM is parallel to ON.

3) a) All of these triangles have an area equal to the area of ΔABC, which is ½ab. The reasoning is as follows. Since ΔMHC is congruent to ΔABC, their areas are equal. To find the area of ΔADL extend line LA and drop a perpendicular line down from D to point V. This creates ΔADV, which is congruent to ΔABC. Therefore ΔADL also has an area of ½ab. Similarly, it can be shown that ΔIBE also has an area equal to ½ab, as well.

b) Points T and S come from extending LA and CM to the left. It can be shown that TS = SN = b, that OT = 2b, and that TL = a. Therefore, trapezoid LMNO has an area of $^5/_2$ab, which is five times the area of ΔABC. Similarly, it can be shown that trapezoid HIJK has the same area. In order to show that trapezoid DEFG has again that same area, we extend horizontal and vertical lines from points D and E, thereby dividing the trapezoid into five triangles. These five triangles have equal area because ΔDWG ≅ ΔLAD, ΔIBE ≅ ΔEYF, and the remaining three triangles (ΔWXD, ΔEDX, ΔXYE) are all congruent to ΔABC.

c) Since NO, KJ, and FG are four times longer, respectively, than b, a, and c, the areas of the squares drawn off NO, KJ, and FG are $16a^2$, $16b^2$ and $16c^2$, respectively.

d) Surprisingly, the squares NH, EJ and LG do not follow the typical Pythagorean relationship. In fact, if ΔABC is isosceles, then square EJ is congruent to square LG. Since square NH is congruent to square AE, its area is c^2. By using ΔLVD to calculate the length of LD, we can determine that the area of square LG is $4b^2 + a^2$. Similarly, the area of square EJ turns out to be $4a^2 + b^2$.

e) By drawing a horizontal line from point G, we create ΔGUO, which is congruent to ΔOTL. We therefore know that UG = 2b. Since ΔPUG is similar to ΔABC, we can say that PU = $2b^2/a$, and that the area of ΔOGP is $\frac{1}{2}(2b^2/a + a)(2b)$, which works out to $(2b^3 + a^2b)/a$. Similarly, the area of ΔJFQ is $(2a^3 + b^2a)/b$.

4) a) These squares follow the normal Pythagorean relationship: $ON^2 + FG^2 = KJ^2$

b) This one is a pleasant surprise. Using our answer from 3d we can say that $EJ^2 + LG^2 = 5NH^2$.

5) a) Using our work from 3e, we get RQ = $2b + 4a + 2a^2/b$, which works out to $\frac{2}{b}(a+b)^2$. RP = $\frac{2}{a}(a+b)^2$.

b) Of course, all of these ratios must be equal. It can be expressed as $\frac{2}{ab}(a+b)^2:1$ or as $2(a+b)^2:ab$.

c) The ratio of the areas is the square of the ratio of the lengths. The answer is:
$\frac{4}{a^2b^2}(a+b)^4:1$ or $4(a+b)^4:a^2b^2$.

Archimedes' Proof of the Formula for the Volume of a Sphere

View looking slightly downward

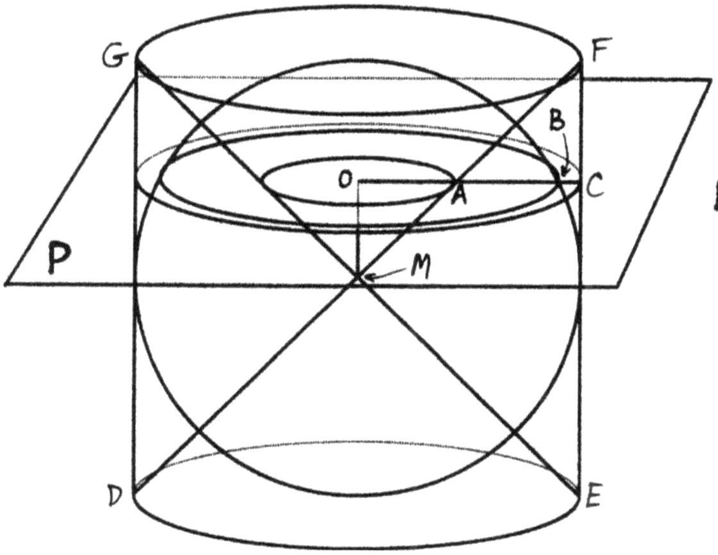

A vertical cross section through center,
<u>or</u> a frontal view with eyes placed along plane P

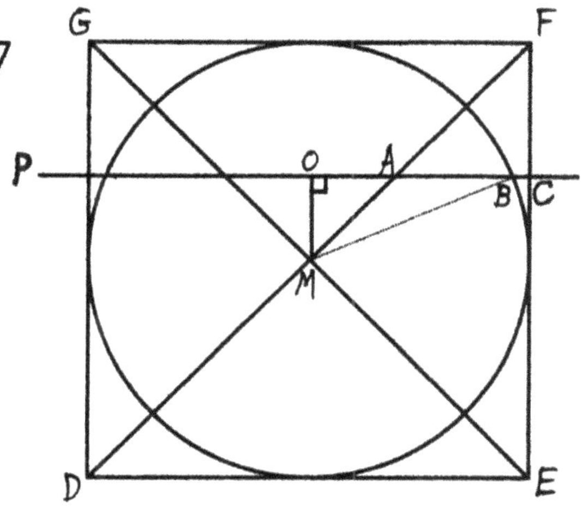

Proof:

1. Each figure shows the same cylinder, which has identical diameter and height. Inside the cylinder, sits a sphere with the same diameter, and also a double cone, again with the same height and diameter. The sphere and cone interpenetrate one another.
   (Note: Volume of double cone = volume of regular cone)
2. Plane P cuts horizontally through the cylinder creating three circles, which are the cross sections of the cylinder, sphere, and cone. Depending on where plane P cuts through the cylinder (in other words, how close plane P is to M), the circle formed by the cross section of the sphere (on plane P) may be larger or smaller than the cross section formed by the cone. The radii of the three circles are:
   - $\mathbf{r_1 = OA}$ (radius of the circle formed by cross section of the cone)
   - $\mathbf{r_2 = OB}$ (radius of the circle formed by cross section of the sphere)
   - $\mathbf{r_3 = OC}$ (radius of the whole cylinder, or of its cross section)
3. Radius of the *whole* sphere = the radius of the cylinder. Therefore:
   $OC = \mathbf{MB = r_3}$
   $\angle OMA = \angle OAM = 45°$; $OA = \mathbf{OM = r_1}$
   We now have a right triangle: ΔOMB.
   $MB^2 = OB^2 + OM^2 \rightarrow r_3^2 = r_2^2 + r_1^2 \rightarrow \boldsymbol{\pi r_3^2 = \pi r_2^2 + \pi r_1^2}$
   $\therefore$ The sum of the areas of the two smaller circles is equal to the area of the largest circle.
4. Consider a second plane P_1, parallel to P, and separated from P by a very small distance Δx. Three cross-sectional disks are now formed between the two planes - one each for the cone, sphere, and the cylinder. We can say that the sum of the volumes of the disks from the cone and the sphere is equal to the volume of the disks from the cylinder.
5. Consider that the cone, sphere, and cylinder are all a stack of such thin disks. Then the volume of the whole cone plus the volume of the whole sphere is equal to the volume of the whole cylinder. And since the volume of the cone is ⅓ of the cylinder, the volume of the sphere is then ⅔ of the cylinder.

   Archimedes expresses this as a ratio of the volumes: **Cone:Sphere:Cylinder = 1:2:3**

Archimedes' Calculation of π – as Archimedes did it[1]

Circumscribed Polygons

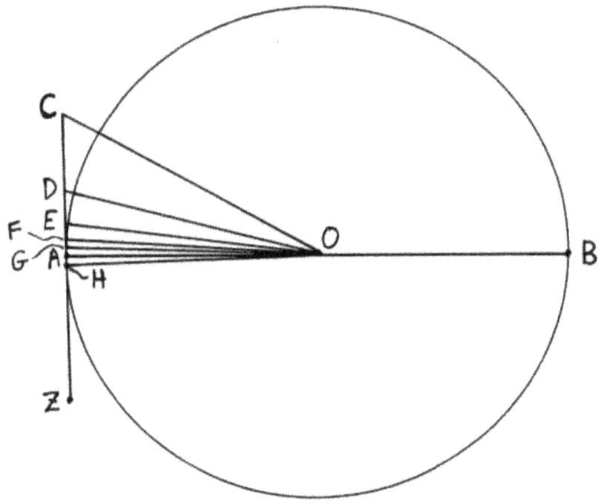

Getting Started

- With the above drawing, AC, AD, AE, AF, and AG are the half-sides of the circumscribed 6-gon, 12-gon, 24-gon, 48-gon, 96-gon, respectively.
- AB is a diameter of the circle, and O is the center. OA is perpendicular to CZ.
- Our goal is to find the ratio of OA:AG. We can then find the ratio of the perimeter of the 96-gon to the diameter of the circle.

Calculating the 6-gon (hexagon)

- Because ΔAOC is a 30°-60°-90° triangle, we know that $OA:AC=\sqrt{3}:1$ and $OC:AC=2:1$
- Archimedes approximates $\sqrt{3}$ as $\frac{265}{153}$, which is too small by 0.0014%. We can then say:

OA:AC > 265:153 and **OC:AC = 306:153**

Calculating the 12-gon

- With ΔOAC, $\angle AOC$ is bisected by OD.
- OC:OA = CD:AD [$\Delta\ \angle$ Bisector Th.; *Elem.* VI-3]
- (OC+OA):OA = (CD+AD):AD [*Elements* V-18]
- (OC+OA):OA = AC:AD
- (OC+OA):AC = OA:AD [*Elements* V-16]
- OA:AD = (OC+OA):AC
- By using the ratios from the 6-gon, we get: OA:AD > (306+265):153

OA:AD > 571:153

(The 12-gon is continued on next column…)

- $OD^2 = OA^2 + AD^2$ [Pythagorean Theorem]
- $OD^2 : AD^2 = (OA^2 + AD^2) : AD^2$
- $OD^2 : AD^2 > (571^2 + 153^2) : 153^2$
- $OD^2 : AD^2 > 349450 : 23409$

OD:AD > $591\frac{1}{8}$: 153

Calculating the 24-gon

- We repeat the same process, but leave out the smaller steps this time.
- With ΔOAD, $\angle AOD$ is bisected by OE.
- OD:OA = DE:AE [$\Delta\ \angle$ Bisector Th.; *Elem.* VI-3]
- OA:AE = (OD+OA):AD > $(591\frac{1}{8} + 571) : 153$

OA:AE > $1162\frac{1}{8}$: 153

- $OE^2 : AE^2 = (OA^2 + AE^2) : AE^2$
  $OE^2 : AE^2 > (1162\frac{1}{8}^2 + 153^2) : 153^2$
  $OE^2 : AE^2 > 1350534\frac{33}{64} : 23409$

OE:AE > $1172\frac{1}{8}$: 153

Calculating the 48-gon (with even fewer steps!)

- OA:AF = (OE+OA):AE > $(1172\frac{1}{8} + 1162\frac{1}{8})$:

OA:AF > 2334¼ : 153

- $OF^2 : AF^2 = (OA^2 + AF^2) : AF^2$, which leads to:

OF:AF > 2339¼ : 153

Calculating the 96-gon (finally!)

- OA:AG = (OF+OA):AF > (2339¼ + 2334¼) : 153

OA:AG > 4673½ : 153 Our Goal!!

Calculating an Upper Bound for π

- Let P = Perimeter of 96-gon, and
  Let D = Diameter of circle.
- From above: AG:OA < 153 : 4673½
- $\pi:1 < P:D = 192\cdot AG : 2\cdot OA = 96\cdot AG : OA$
- $\pi:1 < 96\cdot 153 : 4673\frac{1}{2} = 14688 : 4673\frac{1}{2} < 3\frac{1}{7} : 1$

$$\pi < 3\tfrac{1}{7}$$

[1] Heath, T.L., *The Works of Archimedes*. New York: Dover Publications, 2002. pp 93-98.
This is the famous third theorem from Archimedes' work titled, *The Measurement of a Circle*.

Archimedes' Calculation of π – as Archimedes did it

Inscribed Polygons

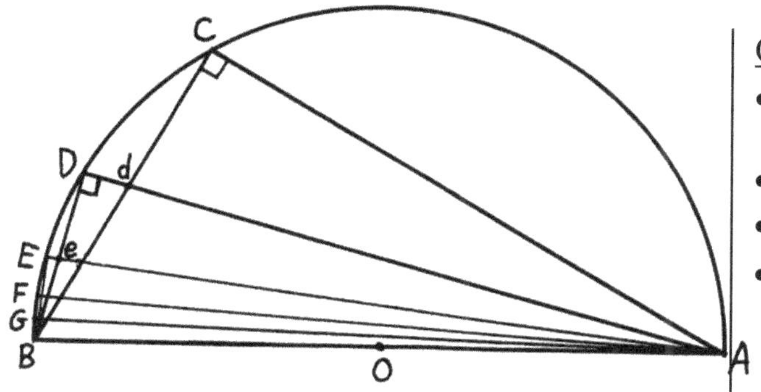

Getting Started

- With the above drawing, the sides of the inscribed polygons, where the number of sides is 6, 12, 24, 48, 96, are given by BC, BD, BE, BF, BG, respectively.
- AB is a diameter of the circle, and O is the center.
- Our primary goal is to find the ratio of AB:BG. We can then find the ratio of the perimeter of the 96-gon to the diameter of the circle.

Calculating the 6-gon (hexagon)

- Because ΔABC is a 30°-60°-90° triangle, we know that $AC:BC = \sqrt{3}:1$ and $AB:BC = 2:1$
- Archimedes approximates $\sqrt{3}$ as $\frac{1351}{780}$, which is too large by 0.000027%. We can then say:

AC:BC < 1351:780 and **AB:BC = 1560:780**

Calculating the 12-gon

- With ΔABC, $\angle BAC$ is bisected by AD.
- AC:Cd = AB:Bd [Δ $\angle$ Bisector Th.; *Elem.* VI-3]
- AC:Cd = AB:Bd = (AC+AB):(Cd+Bd) [*Elements* V-12]
- AC:Cd = AB:Bd = (AC+AB):BC
- AC:Cd = AD:BD [because $\Delta ACd \sim \Delta ADB$]
- AD:BD = (AB+AC):BC [from above steps]
- By using the ratios from the 6-gon, we get: AD:BD < (1560 + 1351) : 780

AD:BD < 2911 : 780

- $AB^2 = AD^2 + BD^2$ [Pythagorean Theorem]
- $AB^2 : BD^2 = (AD^2 + BD^2) : BD^2$
  Using the above ratio, we get:
  $AB^2 : BD^2 < (2911^2 + 780^2) : 780^2$
  $AB^2 : BD^2 < 9082321 : 608400$

AB:BD < 3013¾ : 780

Calculating the 24-gon

- We repeat the same process, but leave out the smaller steps this time.
- With ΔABD, $\angle BAD$ is bisected by AE.
- AD:De = AB:Be [Δ $\angle$ Bisector Th.; *Elem.* VI-3]
- AE:BE = (AB+AD):BD < (3013¾ + 2911) : 780
  AE:BE < 5924¾ : 780, which reduces to:

AE:BE < 1823 : 240

- $AB^2 : BE^2 = (AE^2 + BE^2) : BE^2$
  $AB^2 : BE^2 < (1823^2 + 240^2) : 240^2$
  $AB^2 : BE^2 < 3380929 : 57600$

AB : BE < $1838\frac{9}{11}$: 240

Calculating the 48-gon (with even fewer steps!)

- With ΔABE, $\angle BAE$ is bisected by AF.
- AF:BF = (AB+AE):BE < ($1838\frac{9}{11}$ + 1823) : 240
  AF:BF < $3661\frac{9}{11}$: 240, which reduces to:

AF:BF < 1007 : 66

- $AB^2 : BF^2 < (1007^2 + 66^2) : 66^2$
  $AB^2 : BF^2 < 1018405 : 4356$

AB : BF < $1009\frac{1}{6}$: 66

Calculating the 96-gon (finally!)

- With ΔABF, $\angle BAF$ is bisected by AG.
- AG:BG = (AB+AF):BF < $2016\frac{1}{6}$: 66

AG:BG < $2016\frac{1}{6}$: 66

- $AB^2 : BG^2 < (2016\,{}^1/_6{}^2 + 66^2) : 66^2$
  $AB^2 : BG^2 < 4069284\frac{1}{36} : 4356$

AB : BG < 2017¼ : 66 Our goal!!

Calculating a Lower Bound for π

- Let P = Perimeter of 96-gon, and
  Let D = Diameter of circle.
- From above: BG : AB > 66 : 2017¼
- π:1 > P : D = 96·BG : AB
- π:1 > 96·66 : 2017¼ = 6336 : 2017¼ > $3\frac{10}{71}$: 1

$$\pi > 3\frac{10}{71}$$

Archimedes' Calculation of π – a Modern Version

Circumscribed Polygons

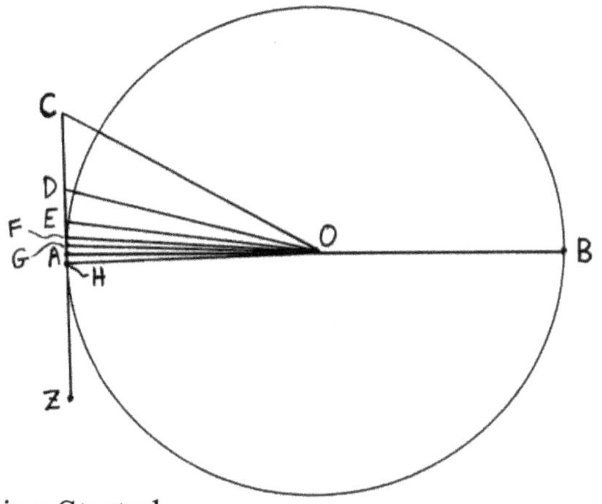

Getting Started

- With this drawing, AC, AD, AE, AF, and AG are the half-sides of the circumscribed 6-gon, 12-gon, 24-gon, 48-gon, 96-gon, respectively.
- AB is a diameter of the circle, and O is the center. OA is perpendicular to CZ.
- OD bisects ∠AOC; OE bisects ∠AOD
  OF bisects ∠AOE; OG bisects ∠AOF
- If we let AB = 1, then the circumference of the circle is equal to π.
- The goal is to calculate the perimeter of the 96-gon, which is 192 times the length of AG.

His "Formula" for Circumscribed Polygons

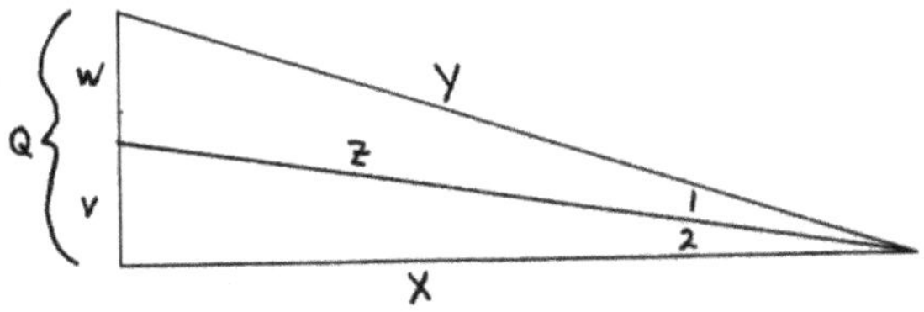

- Given any triangle with sides Q, x, y, where Z is an angle bisector, such that ∠1 ≅ ∠2.
- v:w = x:y [Δ ∠ Bisector Th.; *Elem.* VI-3]
- v:(v+w) = x:(x+y) (*Elements* V-18)
- v:Q = x:(x+y)

$$\mathbf{v = \frac{Q \cdot x}{(x+y)}}$$

- Note: The above formula can be used when we know the lengths of the sides of the larger triangle and want to know the lengths of the sides of the smaller (lower) triangle. This allows us to calculate the perimeters of the circumscribed polygons.

Table for Calculating the Perimeters of the Circumscribed Polygons

# sides	**Δ name**	**medium side**	**formula for short side**	**value for short side**	**hypotenuse**	**perimeter**
6-gon	ΔAOC	AO=0.5	30-60-90 Δ	AC ≈ 0.28867514	CO ≈ 0.57735027	3.4641016
12-gon	ΔAOD	AO=0.5	$AD = \frac{AC \cdot AO}{AO + CO}$	AD ≈ 0.13397460	DO ≈ 0.51763809	3.2153903
24-gon	ΔAOE	AO=0.5	$AE = \frac{AD \cdot AO}{AO + DO}$	AE ≈ 0.06582625	EO ≈ 0.50431448	3.1596599
48-gon	ΔAOF	AO=0.5	$AF = \frac{AE \cdot AO}{AO + EO}$	AF ≈ 0.03277173	FO ≈ 0.50107283	3.1460862
96-gon	ΔAOG	AO=0.5	$AG = \frac{AF \cdot AO}{AO + FO}$	AG ≈ 0.01636831	Not needed	**3.1427146**

- Archimedes' value for the perimeter of the 96-gon was $96 \cdot \left(\frac{153}{4673\frac{1}{2}}\right)$. He said this was about $3\frac{1}{7}$, which is only off by about 0.0000306. This final value for π is only off by about 0.00126.

Archimedes' Calculation of π – a Modern Version

Inscribed Polygons

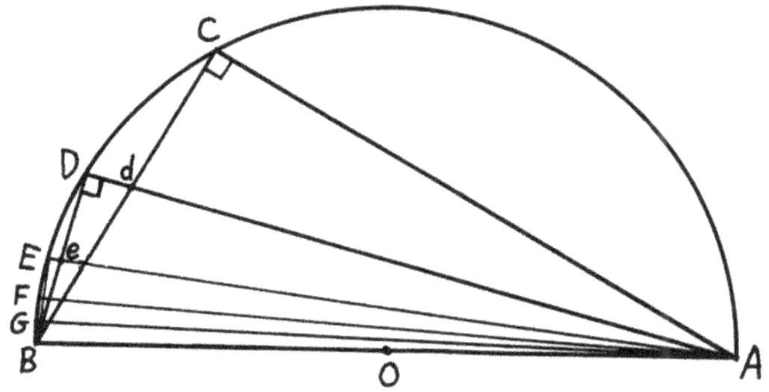

Getting Started

- With the above drawing, the sides of the inscribed polygons, where the number of sides is 6, 12, 24, 48, 96, are given by BC, BD, BE, BF, BG, respectively.
- If the diameter (AB) of the circle be equal to 1, then the circumference of the circle is equal to π.
- ΔABC is a 30°-60°-90° triangle. AC = $\sqrt{3}/_2$. BC = ½. Therefore, the perimeter of the 6-gon is exactly 3.
- The goal is to find the perimeter of the inscribed 96-gon, which is 96 times the length of BG.

His "Formula" for Inscribed Polygons

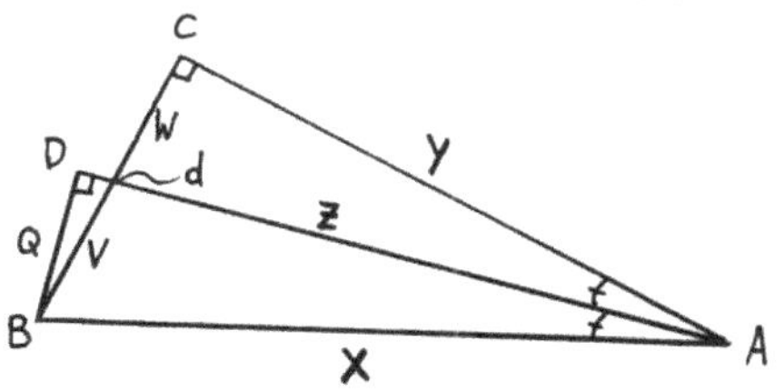

1. Given right ΔABC and ΔABD, where ∠BAC has been bisected by AD (side Z).
2. y:x = w:v [Δ ∠ Bisector Th.; *Elem.* VI-3]
3. y:w = x:v [*Elements* Th. V-16]
4. y:w = x:v = (y+x):(w+v) [*Elem.* Th. V-12]
5. y:w = z:Q [because ΔACd ~ ΔADB]
6. **∴ z:Q = (y+x):(w+v)** [Steps 4 & 5]

- Note: The above formula can be used when we know the length of the side of an inscribed polygon, and we want to calculate the length of the side of a new polygon that has twice the number of sides.

Table for Calculating the Perimeters of the Inscribed Polygons

# sides	Δ name	hypotenuse	formulas	short side	medium side	perimeter
6-gon	ΔABC	1	Not needed	BC = 0.5	AC ≈ 0.86602548	3.0
12-gon	ΔABD	1	AD:BD = (AB+AC):BC $AB^2 = BD^2 + AD^2$	BD ≈ 0.25881905	AD ≈ 0.96592583	3.1058285
24-gon	ΔABE	1	AE:BE = (AB+AD):BD $AB^2 = BE^2 + AE^2$	BE ≈ 0.13052619	AE ≈ 0.99144486	3.1326286
48-gon	ΔABF	1	AF:BF = (AB+AE):BE $AB^2 = BF^2 + AF^2$	BF ≈ 0.06540312	AF ≈ 0.99785892	3.1393502
96-gon	ΔABG	1	AG:BG = (AB+AF):BF $AB^2 = BG^2 + AG^2$	BG ≈ 0.03271908	Not needed	**3.1410320**

The Final Conclusion

The circumference of the circle lies between the perimeters of the circumscribed and inscribed 96-gons. We can therefore conclude that **3.1410320 < π < 3.1427146**

Archimedes concluded that $3\frac{10}{71} < \pi < 3\frac{1}{7}$

Proof of Heron's Formula

for the Area of a Triangle

Area ΔABC = $\sqrt{s(s-a)(s-b)(s-c)}$, where the semi-perimeter, s = ½(a + b + c).

Background theorems:

- *Inscribed Quadrilateral Theorem* (Elements Th. III-22). The opposite angles of a quadrilateral inscribed inside a circle are supplementary.
- *Proportionality Laws*
  - *Elements Th. V-16.* If a:b = c:d then a:c = b:d.
    Example: If 6:9 = 8:12 then 6:8 = 9:12
  - *Elements Th. V-18.* If a:b = c:d then (a+b):b = (c+d):d [also a:(a+b) = c:(c+d)].
    Example: If 6:9 = 8:12 then 15:9 = 20:12
- *The Altitude of the Hypotenuse Theorem* (Elements Th. VI-8).
  If the altitude to the hypotenuse of a right triangle is drawn, then the two triangles formed are similar to the original triangle and to each other, and the square of the length of the altitude is equal to the product of the lengths of the two segments of the hypotenuse.
- **Theorem A:** In a quadrilateral, if the two diagonals and two opposite sides form two angles that are equal, then the quadrilateral is *cyclic* (all four vertices lie on a circle).
  Proof:
  1. Given quadrilateral ABCD where ∠ABD ≅ ∠ACD, draw a circle through points A, B, D (the circumcenter of ΔABD).
  2. *Assume point C is NOT on the circle.* Point E is the intersection of line AC and the circle.
  3. ∠AED≅∠ABD (Elements Th. III-21: "*Inscribed angles that are subtended by the same arc are equal to one another.*")
  4. ∠ACD≅∠AED (C.N. 1; Transitive Property)
  5. If ∠ACD ≅ ∠AED, then CD is parallel to ED (Corresponding Angle Th.)
  6. If CD is parallel to ED then they don't intersect. (Def of parallel)
  7. But CD *does* intersect ED at point D, so we have a contradiction.
  8. ∴Our assumption is false; therefore point C must also lie on the circle. The quadrilateral is cyclic.
- **Theorem B:** Area of a triangle = r · s; where r is the radius of the inscribed circle, and s is the semi-perimeter of the triangle.

  Proof: Draw angle bisectors through all three angles of the triangle. Using the point where the three bisectors intersect as the center, draw the circle that is inscribed in the triangle. From the center (I) of the circle, draw lines to the vertices of the triangle, and to the points of tangency. This creates six small triangles. Since the vertices of the original triangle are bisected, and the newly drawn lines to the tangent points form right angles, then the small triangles that share hypotenuses are congruent. Six of the sides of these triangles are segments of the sides of the original triangle. These segments are equal in three pairs, and these three lengths we shall call d, e, and f. The area of the original triangle is therefore:

  Area = 2(½d·r) + 2(½e·r) + 2(½f·r)
  Area = r (d + e + f)
  Area = r . s, where s is the semi-perimeter.

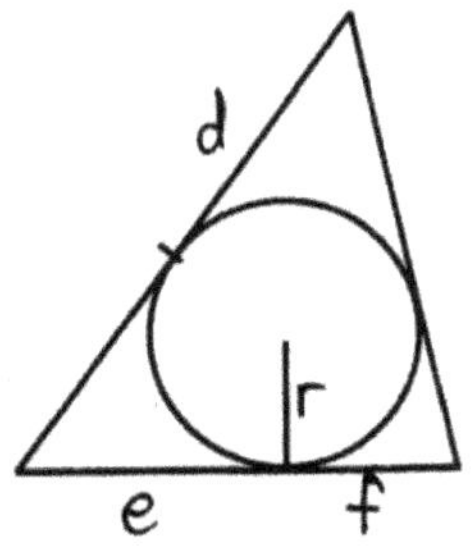

Heron's Formula[1] (continued)

The proof of Heron's Formula:

Given any triangle ABC, having three sides with lengths a, b, c…

1. **The drawing:** Draw the inscribed circle of ΔABC with I as center. Label tangent points along sides BC, CA, AB as D, E, F, respectively. Draw lines from I to A, B, C, D, E, and F. Extend side BC past C to point G, such that CG = AE. Draw a line perpendicular to BI from I, and another line perpendicular to BC from C, and label their intersection as H. Draw BH. Label the intersection of BC and IH as J.

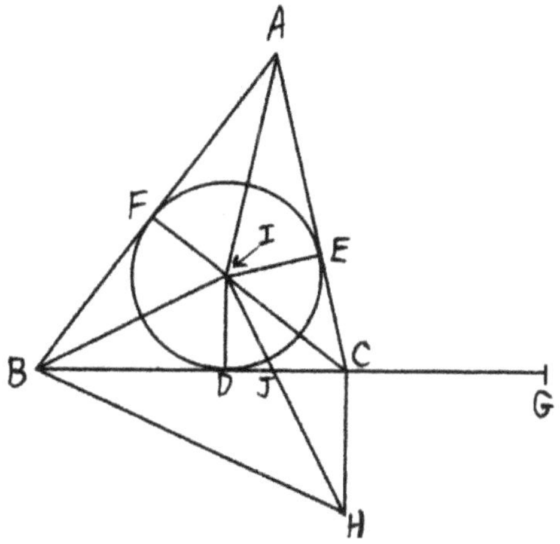

2. IF ⊥ BA; IE ⊥ AC; ID ⊥ BC (Diameter-Tangent Th.)
   ΔBID≅ΔBIF ; ΔCIE≅ΔCID ; ΔAIE≅ΔAIF (AAS)
   ∠BIF+∠BID+∠CID+∠CIE+∠AIE+∠AIF = 360°
   ∠BIF = ∠BID ; ∠CID = ∠CIE ; ∠AIE = ∠AIF
   ∠BID+∠BID+∠CID+∠CID+∠AIE+∠AIE = 360°
   ∠BID + ∠CID + ∠AIE = 180°
   ∠BIC = ∠BID + ∠CID
   ∴∠BIC + ∠AIE = 180°
3. ∠BIH = ∠HCB = 90°. (as constructed)
   BICH is a cyclic quadrilateral; (Theorem A)
   ∠BIC + ∠BHC = 180° (Inscribed Quad. Th.)
   ∠BIC + ∠BHC = ∠BIC + ∠AIE (Transitive)
   ∠BHC = ∠AIE (Subtraction)
4. ∠HCB = ∠IEA = 90° (as constructed)
   ΔBHC ~ ΔAIE (AA theorem)
   BC:CH = AE:IE (def. of similar triangles)
   ∴BC:AE = CH:IE (Proportionality Law - Elements Th. V-16).
5. ΔIDJ ~ ΔHCJ (AA theorem)
   CH:CJ = ID:DJ (def. of similar triangles)
   ∴CH:ID = CJ:DJ (Proportionality Law - Elements Th. V-16).
6. But since ID = IE then CH:ID = CH:IE = **BC:AE = CJ: DJ** (from steps 5 and 6 above)
   And CG = AE therefore BC:**CG** = CJ:DJ (Transitive Property)
   ∴BG:CG = CD:DJ (Proportionality Law - Elements Th. V-18).
7. Multiplying the left side by $\frac{BG}{BG}$ and the right by $\frac{BD}{BD}$, we get: $\mathbf{\frac{BG^2}{BG \cdot CG} = \frac{BD \cdot CD}{BD \cdot DJ}}$
8. ΔBIJ has altitude ID → **∴BD·DJ = ID²** (The altitude of the hypotenuse theorem)
9. Using steps 7 and 8 and substituting, we get:
   $\frac{BG^2}{BG \cdot CG} = \frac{BD \cdot CD}{ID^2}$ → $BG^2 \cdot ID^2 = BG \cdot CG \cdot BD \cdot CD$ → $\mathbf{BG \cdot ID = \sqrt{BG \cdot CG \cdot BD \cdot CD}}$
10. BF = BD ; CE = CD ; AE = AF = CG (congruent triangles, step 2)
    Perimeter of ΔABC = 2s = CE + CD + BD + BF + AF + AE
    = CD + CD + BD + BD + CG + CG
    ∴ s = CD + BD + CG = BG, where s is the semi-perimeter of ΔABC, and s = ½(a+b+c)
11. Area ΔABC = BG · ID (Theorem B), and using step 9, we can substitute $\sqrt{BG \cdot CG \cdot BD \cdot CD}$ in for BG·ID: **Area ΔABC** = $\mathbf{\sqrt{BG \cdot CG \cdot BD \cdot CD}}$
12. Since CD + BD + CG = s
    CD = s − (CG + BD) = s − (AF + BF) = s − c
    BD = s − (CG + CD) = s − (AE + CE) = s − b
    CG = s − (BD + CD) = s – a
13. **∴Area ΔABC** = $\mathbf{\sqrt{s(s-a)(s-b)(s-c)}}$ (From step 11 and 12)

---

1. The key steps are from *an Introduction to the History of Mathematics* by Howard Eves, page 172. I have used algebra in places in order to make it more understandable; this algebra came into being well after Heron's day.

Proof of the Half-Angle Formula

This proof is largely modeled after Ptolemy's proof of his half-angle formula.

The purpose of the proof

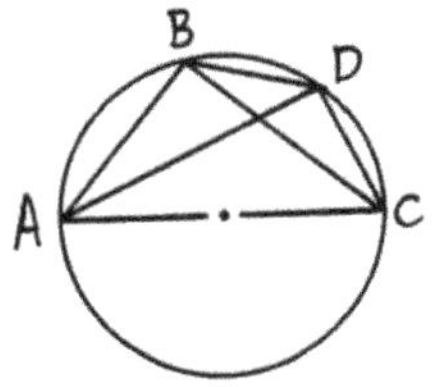

- We are given angle α (in the drawing, $\alpha = \angle BAC$), and we start off knowing the value of $sin(\alpha)$ and $cos(\alpha)$. Also, AD bisects α. Our goal is to find the *sine* of half of α. This means that in the drawing we aim to find the *sine* of $\angle DAC$.

The Proof

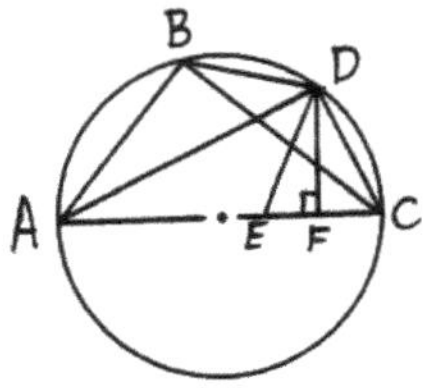

1) Place F on AC such that $DF \perp AC$.
   Place E on AC such that $AB \cong AE$.
2) $\Delta BAD \cong \Delta EAD$; $BD \cong DE$; $BD \cong CD$;
   $DE \cong CD$
3) ΔCDE is isosceles; $EF \cong CF$
4) $AC = AE + EF + CF$;
   $AC = AB + CF + CF$;
   $CF = \frac{1}{2}(AC - AB)$
5) $CD^2 = CF^2 + DF^2$;
   $DF^2 = AF \cdot CF$;
   $CD^2 = CF^2 + AF \cdot CF$;
   $CD^2 = CF(CF+AF)$;
   $CD^2 = CF \cdot AC$;
   $CD^2 = AC(\frac{1}{2}(AC - AB))$
   $CD^2 = \frac{1}{2}AC(AC - AB)$
6) $sin(^{\alpha}/_{2}) = \frac{CD}{AC}$; $CD = AC\ sin(^{\alpha}/_{2})$;
   $cos(\alpha) = \frac{AB}{AC}$; $AB = AC\ cos(\alpha)$
7) Combining steps 5 and 6 gives us:
   $[AC\ sin(^{\alpha}/_{2})]^2 = \frac{1}{2}AC(AC - AC\ cos(\alpha))$;
   $AC^2\ [sin(^{\alpha}/_{2})]^2 = \frac{1}{2}AC^2 - \frac{1}{2}AC^2\ cos(\alpha)$;
   $[sin(^{\alpha}/_{2})]^2 = \frac{1}{2} - \frac{1}{2}\ cos(\alpha)$;

$$sin(^{\alpha}/_{2}) = \sqrt{\tfrac{1}{2} - \tfrac{1}{2}\ cos(\alpha)}$$

Proof of the Difference Formula

This proof is largely modeled after Ptolemy's proof of his difference formula.

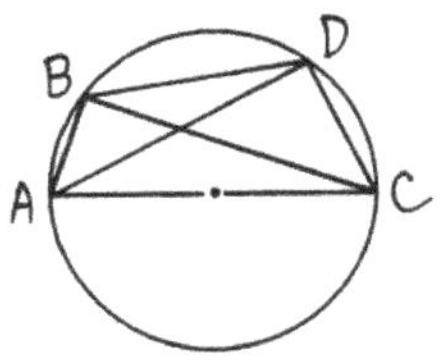

The purpose of the proof

- We are given two angles: α and β (in the drawing $\alpha = \angle BAC$ and $\beta = \angle DAC$). We also know the values of both the sine and cosine of these two angles. Our goal is to find $sin(\alpha - \beta)$. This means that in the drawing we aim to find the *sine* of $\angle BAD$.

The Proof

1) From Ptolemy's quadrilateral theorem we get $AC \cdot BD + AB \cdot CD = AD \cdot BC$
which then becomes $AC \cdot BD = AD \cdot BC - AB \cdot CD$
2) $cos(\beta) = \frac{AD}{AC} \rightarrow AD = AC\ cos(\beta)$; Likewise, we get $BC = AC\ sin(\alpha)$; $AB = AC\ cos(\alpha)$;
$CD = AC\ sin(\beta)$; $BD = AC\ sin(\alpha - \beta)$;
3) Substituting the values from #2 into the equation from #1 gives us:
$AC[AC\ sin(\alpha - \beta)] = [AC\ cos(\beta)] \cdot [AC\ sin(\alpha)] - [AC\ cos(\alpha)] \cdot [AC\ sin(\beta)]$
Dividing both sides by AC^2 we get:

$$\boxed{sin(\alpha - \beta) = cos(\beta) \cdot sin(\alpha) - cos(\alpha) \cdot sin(\beta)}$$

Proof of the Sum Formula

This proof is largely modeled after Ptolemy's proof of his sum formula.

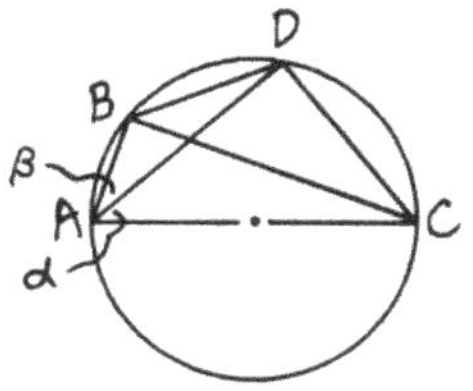

The purpose of the proof

- We are given two angles: α and β. We also know the values of both the sine and cosine of these two angles. Our goal is to find $cos(\alpha + \beta)$. This means that in the drawing we aim to find the *cosine* of $\angle BAC$.

The Proof

1) We begin by placing point E on the circle such that $BE \perp BD$, and then drawing DE and AE.
2) Using Ptolemy's quadrilateral theorem with ABDE we get $DE \cdot AB + AE \cdot BD = AD \cdot BE$
which then becomes $DE \cdot AB = AD \cdot BE - AE \cdot BD$
3) $\Delta ADE \cong \Delta ADC$; $AE \cong CD$; $AC \cong DE$
4) $\angle BED \cong \angle BAD = \beta$;

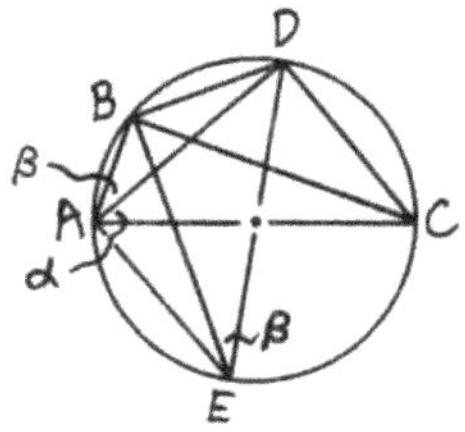

5) $cos(\alpha) = \frac{AD}{AC} \rightarrow AD = AC\ cos(\alpha)$;
$sin(\beta) = \frac{BD}{DE} \rightarrow BD = DE\ sin(\beta) \rightarrow BD = AC\ sin(\beta)$;
$cos(\beta) = \frac{BE}{DE} \rightarrow BE = DE\ cos(\beta) \rightarrow BE = AC\ cos(\beta)$
$sin(\alpha) = \frac{CD}{AC} \rightarrow CD = AC\ sin(\alpha); \rightarrow AE = AC\ sin(\alpha)$;
$cos(\alpha + \beta) = \frac{AB}{AC} \rightarrow AB = AC\ cos(\alpha + \beta)$
6) Substituting the values from #5 into the equation from #2 gives us:
$AC \cdot AC\ cos(\alpha + \beta) = [AC\ cos(\alpha)] \cdot [AC\ cos(\beta)] - [AC\ sin(\alpha)] \cdot [AC\ sin(\beta)]$
Dividing both sides by AC^2 we get:

$$\boxed{cos(\alpha + \beta) = cos(\alpha) \cdot cos(\beta) - sin(\alpha) \cdot sin(\beta)}$$

—— *Two-Dimensional Symmetry* (10th Grade) ——

Overview

This optional topic does not appear in our workbook. It can fit in track class or part of a main lesson.

Background

We begin this fascinating topic with the question: how many types of symmetry are there for tiling a floor? Of course there are infinitely many ways to tile a floor, but what we are interested in is tiling a floor such that there is a symmetry which extends infinitely in all directions on the plane, without any central point (or finite number of points) having any special status. After serious consideration, one can conclude there are three general types of symmetry: translation, rotation, and reflection.

Translational symmetry means that if we slide the whole floor a certain distance in a certain direction, then everything "clicks" into the same place that it started; translational symmetry must be present for all tilings. Rotational symmetry can only be of order 2, 3, 4, or 6. A rotational symmetry of order 5 cannot exist for the same reason that regular pentagons cannot fill the plane. Reflective symmetry comes in two varieties. The normal case consists of when we simply flip the whole floor (temporarily coming into 3-D space) about the axis of symmetry, which allows everything to click back into place. A "glide reflection" is more complicated. In this case we need to flip the whole floor about the glide reflection line and then translate (i.e., slide up) the whole floor until it clicks into place.

In all, there are 17 unique two-dimensional symmetry groups. The teacher should first study the next two pages, which clearly show what they are and how they can be indentified. It is a great exercise for the students (and teacher!) to look at a variety of tilings and drawings and identify what kind of symmetry is present. Even more challenging would be to guide the students to discover as many of the symmetry groups as possible. I will now explain a few of the below drawings.

Figure 1: It clearly has rotational symmetry of order 2, and reflective symmetry. Some of the points of rotational symmetry have reflective lines through them, and some don't. Therefore it is C2mm.

Figure 2: This Escher drawing has no rotational symmetry, but does have reflective symmetry along the vertical lines that run through the middle of the beetles. If we look carefully, we can see lines of glide refection using the vertical lines that I have drawn in. Just rotate and slide up until it clicks into place.

Figure 3: This Escher drawing has no rotational symmetry, and no lines of reflection. But if we look carefully, we see lines of glide reflection: we flip the drawing along a vertical line through the horses' back leg and then slide it upward until the black horse clicks into the white, and vice versa. So it's Pg.

Figure 4: This window is from a mosque in Cairo. It is P6mm. The stars clearly have rotational symmetry of order 6, but if you look closely, you can also see rotational symmetry of order 3 (where there is a small triangle) and order 2 (the diamond halfway between two stars). Reflective symmetry is easy to see, but the glide reflection lines are harder to locate.

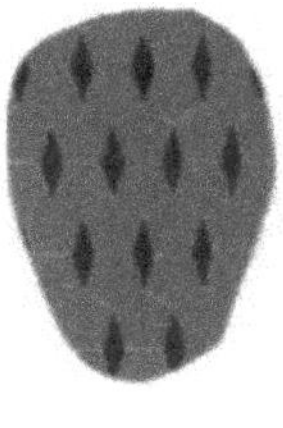

Fig. 1 (C2mm)

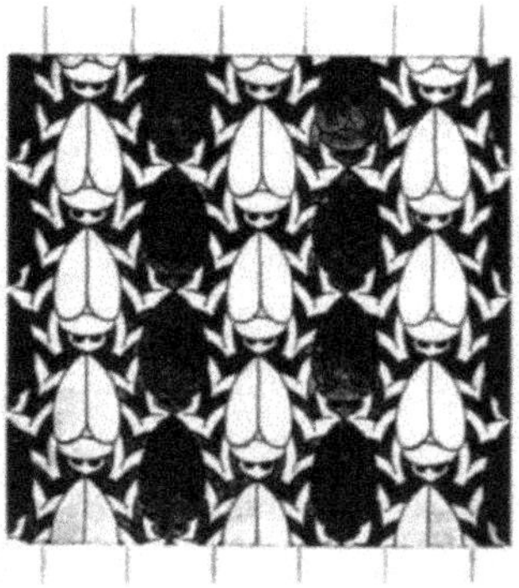

Fig. 2 (Cm)

Fig. 3 (Pg)

Fig. 4 (P6mm)

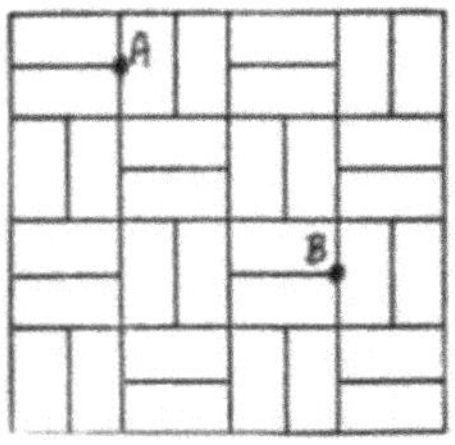

Fig. 5 (P4gm)

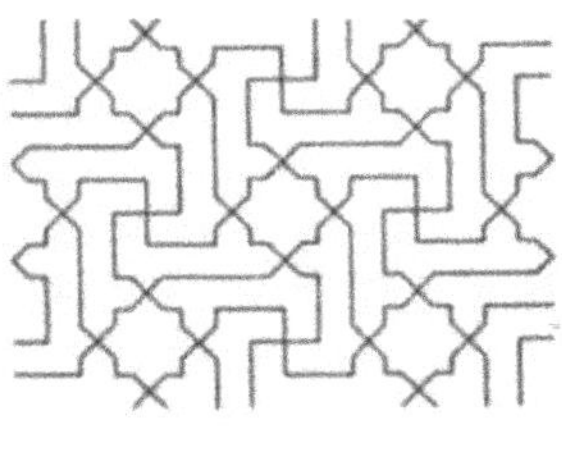

Fig. 6 (P4)

Fig. 7 (P4gm)

Fig. 8 (P4gm)

The 17 Two-Dimensional Symmetry Groups

with Unit Cells

═ reflection
--- glide reflection
⬬,▲,■,⬣ rotational axis of order 2, 3, 4, 6

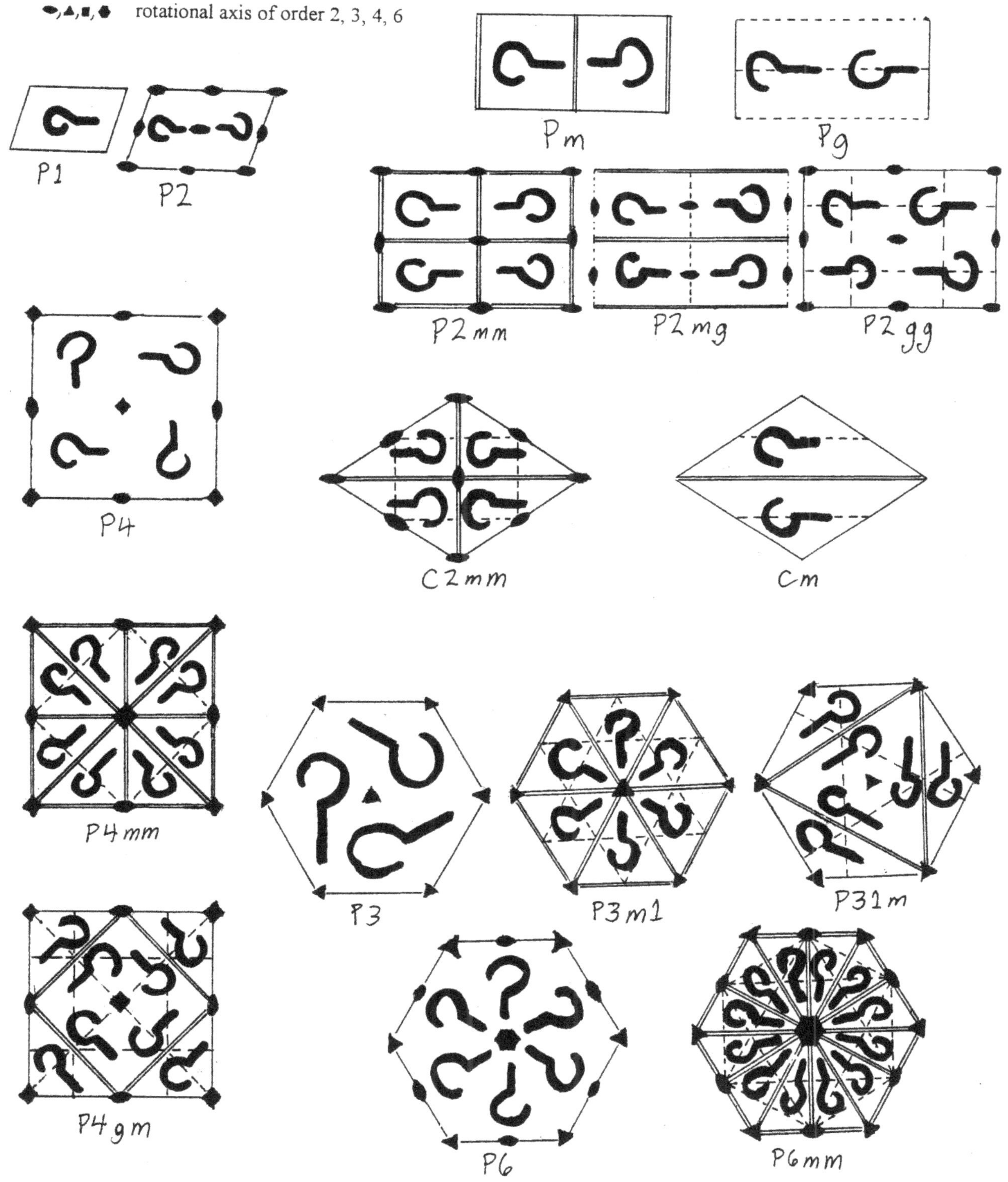

Patterns from the 17 Two-Dimensional Symmetry Groups

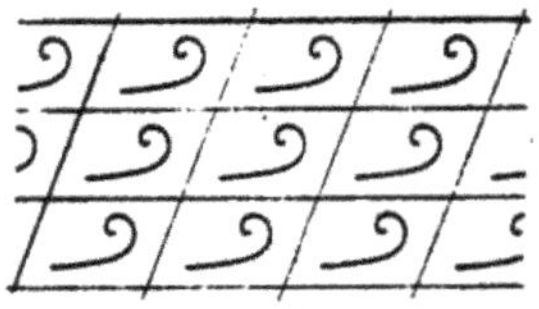

P1

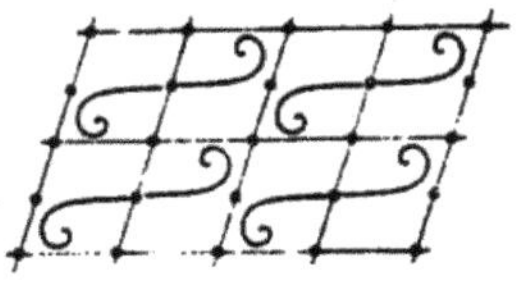

P2

Pm

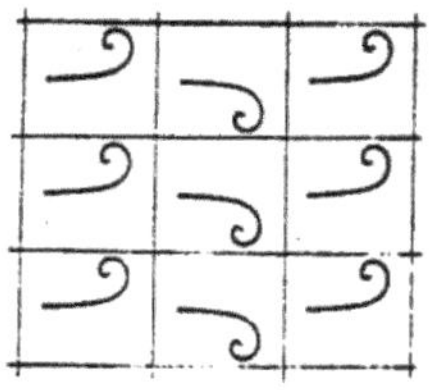

Pg

P2mm

P2mg

P2gg

P4

C2mm

Cm

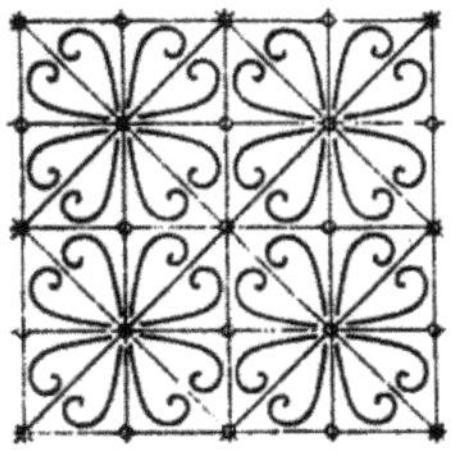

P4mm

P3

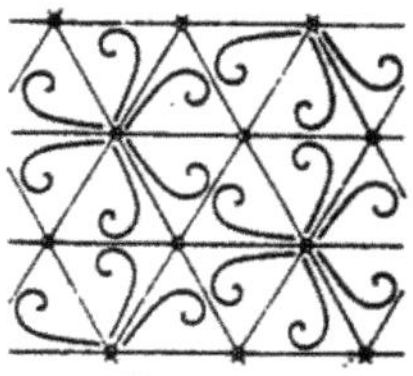

P3m1

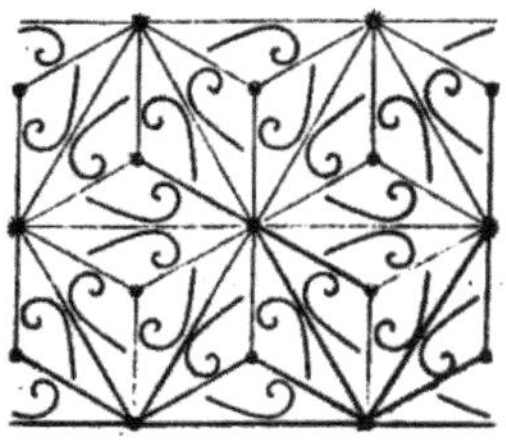

P31m

P4gm

P6

P6mm

—— *Mensuration* (10th Grade) ——

Overview

Mensuration is a subject within geometry focused on the calculation of lengths, areas, and volumes. In comparison to the previous unit in the workbook, *Proofs*, this unit is much shorter (only five problem sets), yet it has its own challenges. The whole unit weaves in a review of topics covered in our *8th Grade Workbook*, especially volumes. Additionally, ratios are once again highlighted.

Required reading

In order to gain a deeper understanding of this unit, the teacher should read the commentary found in the *Teacher's Edition of our 10th Grade Workbook* and also work through the *Mensuration* problem sets found in the workbook.

A word about volume formulas

In order to calculate volume, many textbooks encourage students to memorize a separate formula for each possible solid. This quickly becomes an exercise in performing blind procedures. Instead, we encourage our students to work primarily with two general formulas, which they can easily have an intuitive understanding of:

$\mathbf{V = A_{base} \cdot H}$ for solids where the top and bottom are the same

$\mathbf{V = \frac{1}{3} A_{base} \cdot H}$ for solids where the top is a point

The only formula that really needs to be memorized is for the volume of a sphere: $\mathbf{V = \frac{4}{3} \pi \cdot r^3}$

Scale factors and dimension

- If the scale factor of two similar figures is a:b then the ratio of their areas is $a^2:b^2$.
- If the scale factor of two similar solids is a:b then the ratio of their volumes (or weight) is $a^3:b^3$.

Example: If one circle has a radius 3 times as long as a second circle, then how much greater is its area? (Answer: 9 times greater.)

Example: If a rectangle's length and width is enlarged in a photocopier by 50%, then how much greater is its area? (Answer: $1.5^2 = 2.25$ times as great, or enlarged by 125%.)

Example: If the edge of one cube is 5 times longer than the edge of another, then how much greater is its volume? (Answer: The volume is 125 times greater.)

Example: If one log is 60% longer and 60% thicker than another log, then how much greater is its weight? (Answer: The weight of the first log is $1.6^3 = 4.096$ times greater.)

Challenge problems (Each problem appears in our *10th Grade Workbook* and *Answer Key*)

- *The Conical Drinking Glass*

  Question: How much water is in a conical drinking glass that is filled halfway to the top, if it has a capacity of 12 fl. oz.?

  Solution: The cone formed by the water is half the size of the whole glass, therefore it is $\frac{1}{8}$ full, which amounts to 1½ fl. oz.

- *Nested Cube, Tetrahedron, and Octahedron*

  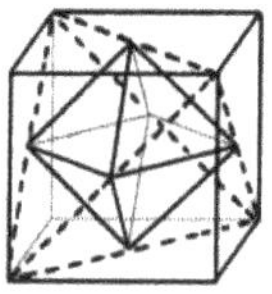

  Question: If you have a cube with a octahedron and a tetrahedron (shown in dotted lines) inside it, then what is the ratio of their volumes?

  Solution: The ratio of the volume of the cube to the tetrahedron to the octahedron is 1:2:6.

- *Derivation of the Volume Formula for a Tetrahedron*

  Question: What is the formula for the volume of a tetrahedron given only the length of an edge (E)?

  Solution: The trickiest part of this problem is realizing that the center of the base (as shown in the diagram) is ⅓ of the way along the altitude of the triangular face.

  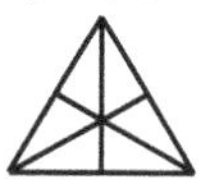

  We then imagine a triangle that goes from the apex down to the center of the base, out to the midpoint of the edge, and then up along the altitude of the face, back to the apex. The hypotenuse of this triangle, which is the length of the altitude of a face, is $\frac{\sqrt{3}}{2} \cdot E$, and the short leg of this triangle is ⅓ of this, which is $\frac{\sqrt{3}}{6}\cdot E$. Using the Pythagorean Theorem to find the third side of this triangle, which is the height of the whole tetrahedron, we get $\frac{\sqrt{6}}{3}\cdot E$. The area of the base of the tetrahedron is then $\frac{\sqrt{3}}{4}\cdot E^2$, and by using the formula $V = \frac{1}{3} A_{Base} \cdot H$, we find that the formula for the volume of a tetrahedron is: $V = \frac{\sqrt{2}}{12}\cdot E^3$

- Derivation *of the Volume Formula for an Octahedron*
  Question: What is the formula for the volume of an octahedron given only the length of an edge (E)?
  Solution: Solved in a manner similar to that used for the formula for the volume of a tetrahedron (above), we arrive at a result that is exactly 4 times the tetrahedron: $V = \frac{\sqrt{2}}{3}\cdot E^3$

- Leonardo *da Vinci's Lunes*
  Question: What is the combined area of the two lunes (areas A & E)?
  Solution: From the generalization of the Pythagorean Theorem, we know that the largest semi-circle (B+C+D) has an area equal to the sum of the areas of the two smaller semi-circles. This means that the combined areas of the regions B+C+D = (A+B)+(D+E). Subtracting B and D from both sides of this equation, we get: C = A+E. The areas of the two lunes combined are always equal to the area of the triangle!

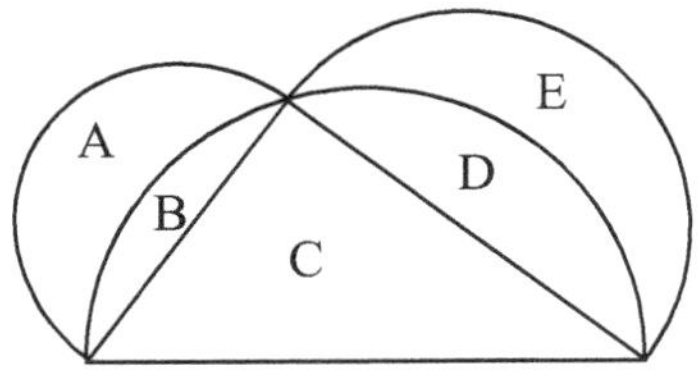

  Interesting side-note: If the triangle is an isosceles right triangle, and the length of each of the legs of the triangle is 1, then each lune has an area of exactly ¼. It is surprising that we have a figure made from circles that has an area independent of π.

- *Ratios of Solids* (Each problem appears in our *10th Grade Workbook* and *Answer Key*)
  Question: What is the ratio of the volume of a cube to a cone that fits perfectly in it? (Answer is $12{:}\pi$)
  Question: What is the ratio of the surface area of a cube to a cone that fits in it? (Answer is $24 : (\sqrt{5}+1)\pi$)
  Question: What is the ratio of the volume of a cube to a sphere that fits in it? (Answer is $6{:}\pi$)
  Question: What is the ratio of the surface area of a cube to a sphere that fits in it? (Answer is $6{:}\pi$)

- *The tetrahedron and two-sphere problem*
  Question: In the drawing shown here, we have a tetrahedron with inscribed and circumscribed spheres. Find the ratio of the radii of the two spheres.

  Solution:
  1. Let X be the center, and A, B, C, D be the vertices of the tetrahedron, where A, B, and C are "sitting on the floor", and D is the "peak" of the tetrahedron. Let M be the center of the triangular face that sits on the floor. Let the edge of the tetrahedron be equal to 1.
  2. Imagine the tetrahedron sits inside a cube such that each of the edges of the tetrahedron are a diagonal of a face of the cube. We know that the ratio of the edges of the tetrahedron to the cube is $\sqrt{2} : 1$. The edge of the cube is therefore $\sqrt{2}/2$.
  3. AB and CD are opposite edges of the tetrahedron. Draw a line between the midpoints of these two edges. This line has a length equal to the edge of the square, and its midpoint is at the center of the tetrahedron (and is also the center of the two spheres). Therefore, if we let Y be the midpoint of AB, $XY = \sqrt{2}/4$.
  4. Now consider the triangle XAY. $\angle XYA$ is right. $YA = \frac{1}{2}$, and $XY = \sqrt{2}/4$.
  5. $YA^2 + XY^2 = XA^2$, which leads to $XA = \sqrt{6}/4$ (= DX), which the radius the larger sphere.
  6. $YD = \sqrt{3}/2$. $YM = \frac{1}{3}YD = \sqrt{3}/6$. DM is the height of the whole tetrahedron. $DM^2 = YD^2 - YM^2$ This leads to $DM = \sqrt{6}/3$. This height is also equal to the sum of the radii of the two spheres.
  7. DX is the radius of the larger sphere (which is $\sqrt{6}/4$). Therefore, the radius of the smaller sphere is: $MX = DM - DX \rightarrow \sqrt{6}/3 - \sqrt{6}/4 \rightarrow \sqrt{6}/12$.
  8. The ratio of the radii of the two spheres is $DX : MX = \sqrt{6}/4 : \sqrt{6}/12 \rightarrow$ **3:1.**

—— ***Surveying*** (10th Grade Main Lesson) ——

by Jeff O'Brien

Overview

Tenth grade is often the year of "How?" Surveying fits beautifully with this theme. How are maps made? How does one go about collecting the data needed to make a map? How are maps created with specific uses in mind?

Surveying can be taught in any high school grade, but it fits best in tenth grade. Tenth graders are often trying to find their place in the world. They see the eleventh and twelfth graders preparing themselves for life after high school and know that they will soon be embarking on that road. They are young enough to still need the "care and feeding" of living at home, but are wise enough to know that they will be "on their own" quite soon. Surveying can have a grounding effect just as they are beginning to feel "ungrounded."

On a practical level, surveying teaches the need for accuracy, teamwork, careful planning and seeing a project through from beginning to end. It is a practical use of the mathematics that they know.

Lesson plans

Detailed day-by-day lesson plans can be downloaded from our website: **www.JamieYorkPress.com**.

Prerequisites and timing

In order to successfully complete a surveying course, the students should be familiar with the following:

- Basic ninth grade algebra
- The Pythagorean theorem, including solving for missing sides of a right triangle
- Basic right triangle trigonometry – specifically the ability to solve for sides and angles. This requires at least a working knowledge of sine.
- The properties of parallelograms
- Experience in finding the locus points that meet a certain criteria is also helpful, but not essential.

Given all of the above, it is best to schedule the surveying block during the spring.

Surveying trip or in school project?

Many Waldorf schools in Europe make the surveying block into a class trip. For some schools, the surveying trip becomes a community service project – they complete a fairly professional surveying project for a community in need. This kind of trip requires professional equipment and the expertise of someone who can guide such a project.

Whether the surveying block includes a class trip or not, our approach (as described in the following pages) incorporates simple hand-made instruments, and culminates with the students creating their own hand-drawn topographical maps.

An introduction to maps

Typically, some students in the class have a good deal of experience with maps, but likely others have surprisingly little experience with maps. It is therefore good to begin the course looking at different maps. This is best done with actual maps to roll out on a large table with the class standing around, but it can also be easily done with a media projector and accessing maps online. (It may be best to check a local university for a variety of old maps.)

Presenting an introduction to maps in the following order takes the class from a large to a small focus:

- Old maps of the world (the more inaccurate the better)
- Different projections of the world map (Peterson projection and the Mercator projection)
- Political and physical world maps
- Old and modern maps of the "new world" (physical and political)
- Old and modern maps of your state or region (physical and political)
- Old and modern maps of your town
- A map or blueprint of your school campus
- A blueprint of the building you are in
- A plan of the room you are in

At each stage you can discuss the purpose of each map, what is it used for? Who would find this map useful? Are the older maps a work of art, meant for hanging on a wall, or meant to be used? What liberties were taken in creating the map (e.g., the equator in the Mercator projection is not in the middle and Europe is much larger than is should be). Discuss the information that each map gives. What are the "pros" and "cons" of each map? How are the legends different in each map? How are they the same?

Topographical maps

Hand out a topographical map to each group of students (or project a map onto the screen for the class to see.) Discuss the same questions as with the other maps. After talking about the legend and uses of the map, focus on the contour lines. What do the contour lines mean? Talk about how this attempts to give information of three dimensions in two dimensions. Does it succeed in doing so? What are the advantages of this kind of map? What are the shortcomings? What information would you need to create such a map?

Map practice sheets (See the three practice sheets in the following pages.)

These practice sheets allow the students to practice drawing contour lines on maps with given elevation data. The teacher needs to decide on what interval to draw the contour lines.

The teacher needs to carefully go over the results of the practice sheets. Did all the students arrive at the same set of contour lines? Is it possible to have more than one correct set of contour lines for a set of given data? Can contour lines ever intersect? Must they always be "circles" or go off the page? Challenge groups of students to come up with another set of contour lines from the same data, different from the one they arrived at.

Then the teacher should give the students a challenging data set to create contour lines. Is it better to have more data? You can replicate data from a topographical map from your area to give students. It is especially good to use a place that the students know. Is there a mountain or lake that they all climb or go to for recreation?

An important question

Here is an important question to discuss, preferably at the end of class, leaving it with the students for the night: If you wanted to create a topographical map, how would you go about gathering the data required to create contour lines?

This discussion can and will go in many directions. Eventually, the students will realize that they need a way to determine the exact location of a set of points in space from a reference point. Students will likely first go with an x-y-z coordinate system. Students may come up with spherical coordinates. They often come up with their own unique 3-dimensional coordinate systems. After discussing them all, there should be one thing in common with all of them: *they all require three measurements*. Isn't this what 3-dimensional space means?

So we will need to agree on one system that we will all work with. And it will be this one: Going from point A to point B in space can be defined using, the distance from A to B, the compass bearing from A to B, and angle of elevation from A to B (from the horizontal).

A method for describing the position of two points in space

Doing distance first, if point B is 50 feet from point A, then you can imagine that point B is a locus of points on a sphere of radius 50 feet with point A as its center (see figure 1).

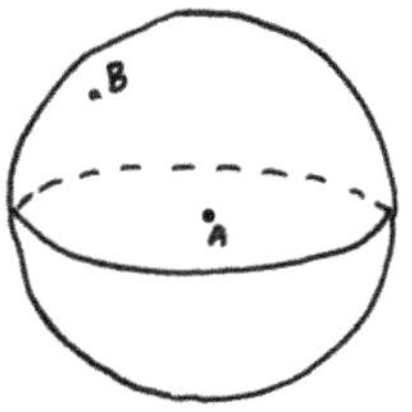

figure 1

If you do compass bearing next, you can imagine a plane intersecting the sphere at the compass bearing, creating a locus of points that is a semi-circle. If the compass bearing is 330°, then a semi-circle describes the set of all points 50 feet from A and at a compass bearing of 330° (see figure 2).

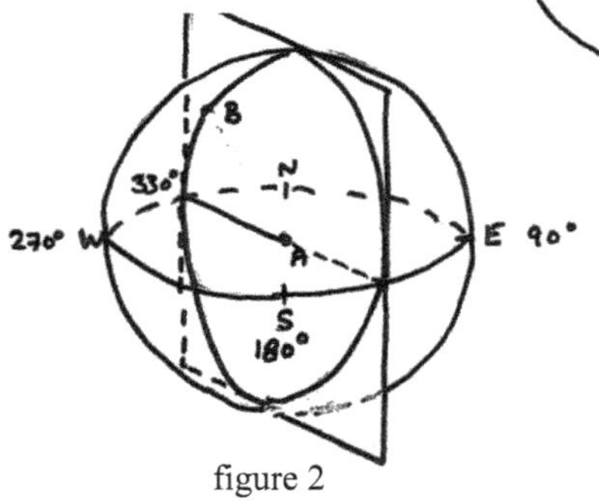

figure 2

Lastly, the angle of elevation will locate point B on the semi-circle (see figure 3) thereby locating point B in space, relative to point A.

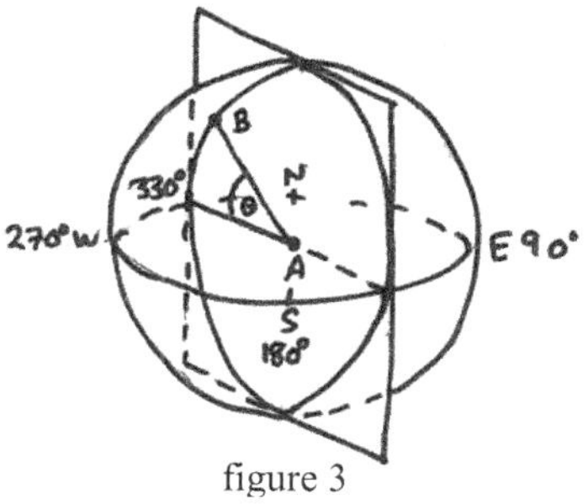

figure 3

Some students find it interesting that the order does not matter. We could just as easily start with the compass bearing, which creates a plane from point A in which point B must lie (see figure 4). Let's say we take the angle of elevation next. This will create a ray from point A on which point B must lie (see figure 5). Lastly the distance from A to B will reveal where on the ray point B is (see figure 6).

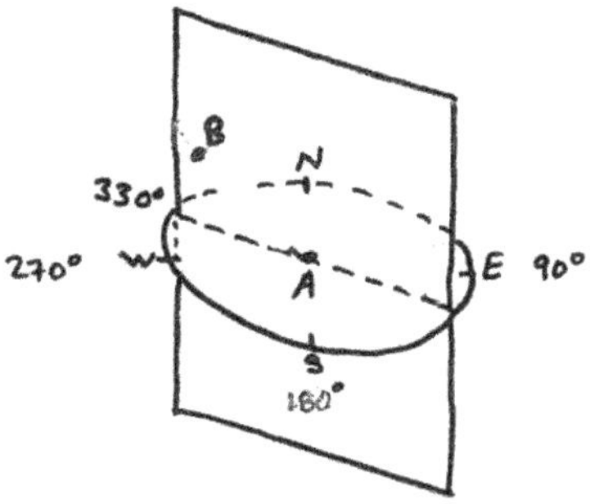

figure 4

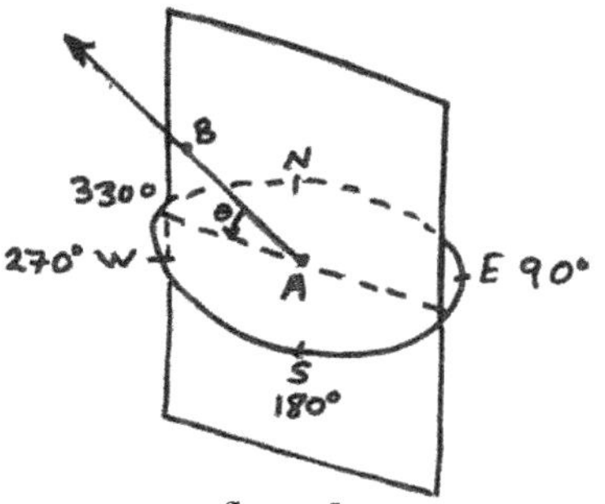

figure 5

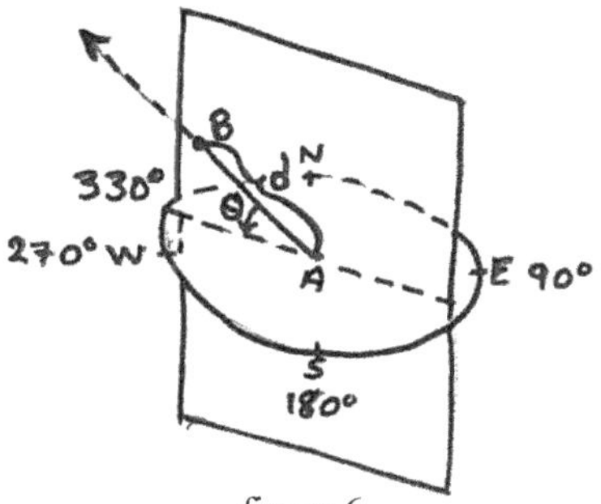

figure 6

The teacher could now ask the students how many different permutations there are of the three measurements, thereby recalling their ninth grade *Possibility and Probability* main lesson.

Required tools

Now we ask the students: what tools are needed to take the measurements for all of this work? Two of the three tools are obvious: a tape measure for long distances, and a compass (not for drawing circles!) to determine a bearing of direction. Measuring the angle of elevation is more complicated. There are tools that can do this, including a surveyor's transit, but we will use a clinometer. This can be purchased, but instead we will first make a simple one from a protractor, a pierce of string, and a small weight (a hex nut works well), as shown below.

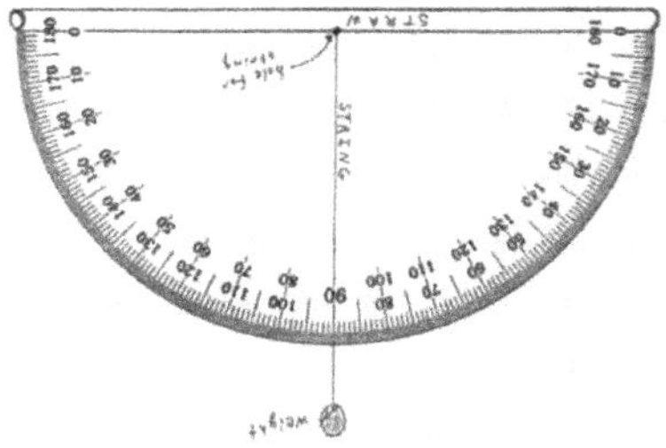

You can make a simple clinometer by gluing a drinking straw to the edge of a protractor, and then threading a string though the protractor's hole. At the other end of the string we hang a weight (e.g., a hex nut). Alternatively, you can purchase a clinometer from an online retailer, such as www.enasco.com.

<u>Important</u>: The students must understand that taking these three measurements from a reference point to multiple points in the field will produce the data necessary to draw contour lines. Using this method, we can create a page of data similar to that found on the *Map Practice Sheets.*

Our surveying parallelogram

Students need to realize that there is a parallelogram created with every set of measurements. This parallelogram gives us the data.

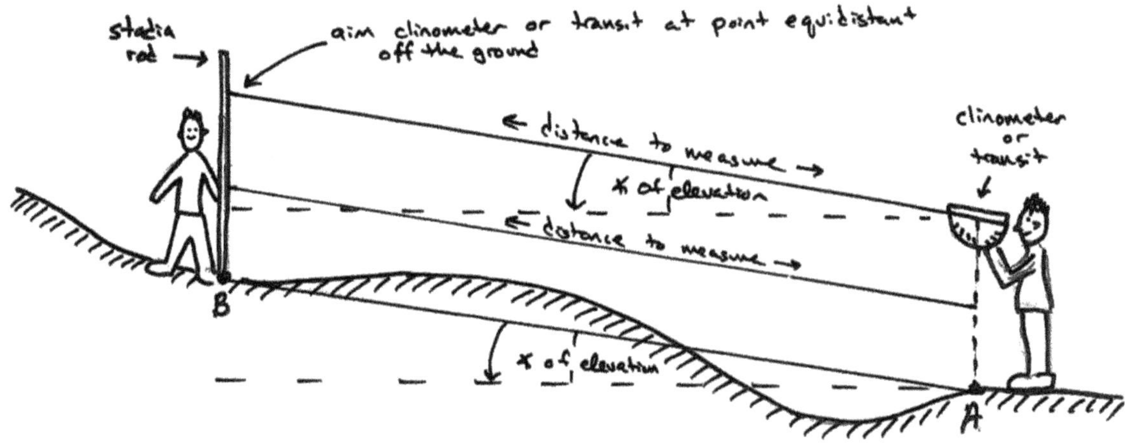

Practicing taking measurements

Although students probably have experience with a tape measure, we still need to discuss how and what we are measuring. Do you put the tape measure along the ground? Do you hold it up? If you hold it up, then is it important that both ends be at the same height above the ground.

It may be necessary to have the students practice using a tape measure, clinometer, and compass before we start surveying.

Activity #1: *Practice with distance*

Create a scale drawing of the classroom. Have the students measure the classroom and create a scale drawing. Key skill: If the room is 25 feet by 15 feet what scale do I need to use to fit the room nicely on an 8.5 inch by 11 inch piece of paper? I would like the scale drawing to fill the page, but I don't want it to be too crowded since I need room for a legend, title, and comments.

Activity #2: *Practice with angle of elevation*

Students may have done this when they learned trigonometry. Find the height of a flagpole, tall tree, or building. Use the clinometer to find the angle of elevation. Use a tape measure to find the distance from the base of the flagpole (or other object) to the observation point. Use trigonometry to calculate the height of the object. Confirm your results by repeating this from another vantage point.

Activity #3: *Practice with bearing (direction)*

Have the students work in small groups. The goal is for students to realize how accurate they need to be especially when dealing with long distances. This is best done in a playground or large parking lot. Prior to class create a "scavenger" hunt. Place pieces of brightly covered wool (a different color for each team) in various place in the forest (or playground) and give the bearings from a starting point to first one, from the first one to the second one, etc. For example, one group might have a list that says: Your first piece of yellow wool is located on a bearing of 170° from the starting point. The second piece of yellow wool is located on a bearing of 25° from where the first piece of yellow wool is.

Making our first topographical map

You should now be ready to survey your first plot of land. Chose your spot carefully. This first attempt ideally is...

- Right outside the classroom, or a short walk.
- A slope with a 5% grade, or steeper, is best.
- The total area should be smaller than a square with 100-foot sides.
- For this first time, it is easiest for the reference point to be at the very bottom of the hill.

Before going into the field, it is important to discuss the role of the stadia rods. If the ground is not smooth, then when measuring the distance from point A to point B it is important to measure the distance from points equidistantly above points A and B. Likewise, for the angle of elevation, if the clinometer is held 66 inches above the ground, it needs to "aim" for a point 66 inches above the ground. Stadia rods help with this. Students need to measure the height at which they hold a clinometer and aim for that height on a stadia rod. Stadia rods can be easily made by marking planks with a sharpie pen at regular intervals. It may be best to have a plumb bob attached to the edge of each stadia rod in order to ensure that the stadia rod is held exactly vertically.

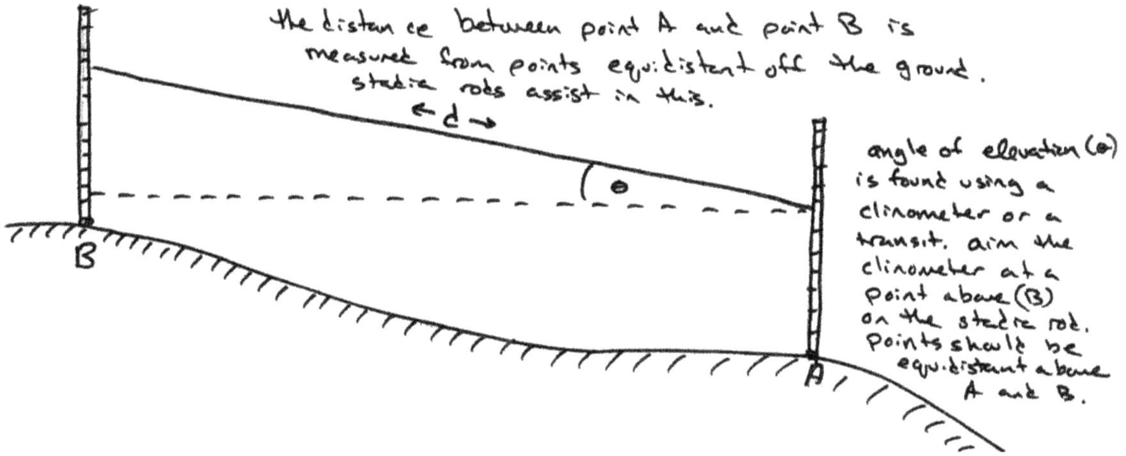

The pair of students at the reference point is responsible for confirming the three measurements (distance, bearing, angle of elevation) with the pair at the point being measured.

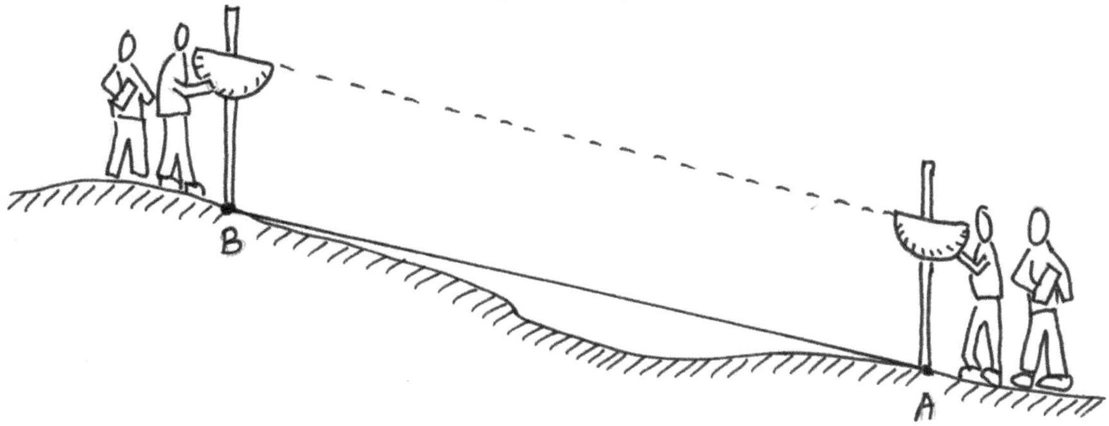

Working in groups of four is ideal, two students at each end. Each pair has a clinometer, tape measure, stadia rod, and compass. They should confirm each other's measurements. If they are different they should take an average of the two. Stadia rods at each end will make it easy for both groups to be working equidistant off the ground.

There are also pros and cons for each group using (approximately) the same reference point. If it is important to you that all of your groups to have similar data, then have them all work from the same reference point to a set of predetermined points on the field. Giving students a data table to fill out (see further below) can be helpful.

Points B to Z can be predetermined, labeled and marked with stakes and surveyor's tape in the field by the teacher (in order to make all the data the same) or students can randomly choose 25 points. If you choose the points for the students, ask them why you chose the ones you did? If you let the students choose the points, ask them what would be a good set of points. The key is that you want a variety of points, some close to the reference point, some further away, some to the left, and some to the right.

Once students have the data, it is a good idea to go over the "parallelogram" again. Then ask them: is the distance from the reference point to each point, the distance that is represented on the map? Students should be able to conclude that it is not the distance from the reference point to each data point that is needed but the horizontal distance. The map is "projected" onto a "page". If looking from above the horizontal distance from A to B is what would be "projected" onto the map. This can be found using the cosine of the angle. Try to have them derive the following formula for themselves:

horizontal distance = (distance) x (cosine of the angle of elevation)

The horizontal distance will need to be scaled down to fit on the page. What is a good scale? Look at your largest numbers and the size of your paper to help you decide on the scale. The activity in mapping the classroom is helpful for this.

And how do we get the vertical height from the data? The students should derive this formula:

vertical distance = (distance) x (sine of the angle of elevation)

Everything thus far is nicely summarized with this diagram:

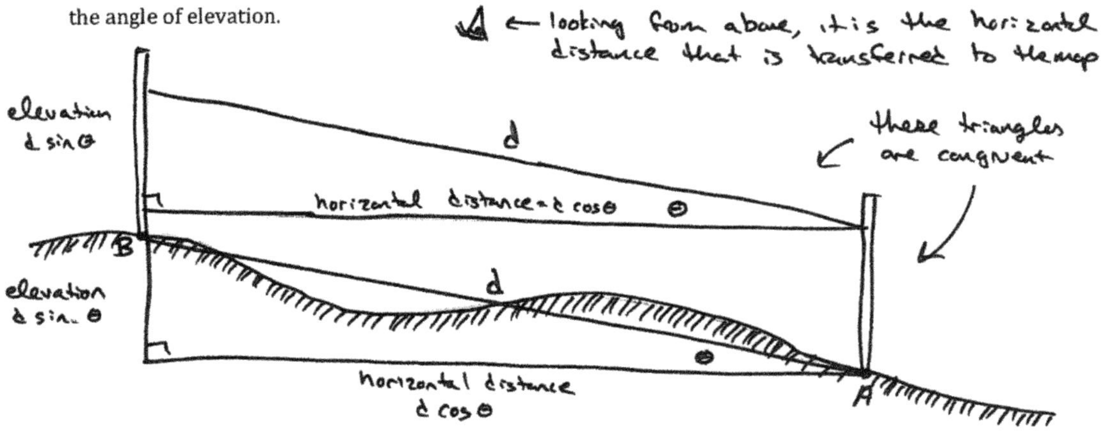

After some discussion and instruction, the students should realize that they have enough data to draw contour lines for a topographical map. All of the collected data can be consolidated on this table:

From Reference Point	To Point in the field	Distance Measured on Tape Measure from A to point Convert to Inches (D)	Angle of Elevation from A to point (θ)	Bearing from A to point	Horizontal Distance (in inches) Dcosθ	Elevation (in inches) Dsinθ
A	B					
A	C					
A	D					
A	E					
⋮	⋮					
A	Y					
A	Z					

Using this data, we can create the data similar to that found on the *Map Practice Sheets*. Starting at a random reference point on the page and choosing a random direction as magnetic north, we measure the scaled distance and compass bearing from the reference point to the first data point using a protractor and a ruler, and mark the result spot with a dot. At that location on the page, we then write a number which indicates the vertical height. We then repeat this for every data point. The page should now look similar to the *Map Practice Sheets*. Lastly, we draw in the contour lines to complete the topological map.

In some ways, this first map is a planned disaster. This will re-enforce the need for accuracy and care with our measurements, as well as the importance of confirming our measurements with others. All of these lessons will be applied to our work on our second map.

Making our second topographical map

If the map is lacking due to accuracy, it is good to ask: which instrument was the least accurate? The homemade clinometers are usually the culprit. For the second map, I allow my students to use a transit if they are available. For price and availability, I recommend the Northwest Instrument Transit Level NSLP500B Package from Engineer Supply, www.engineersupply.com. This kit includes a transit, tripod and stadia rod.

Also, transits can often be borrowed from a surveying company. Most surveying companies use GPS models now and have older equipment that they might be willing to lend. Local surveying companies also sometimes get very excited about teaching surveying and will offer other help/expertise.

Construction firms also sometime have transits. If transits are not available, then doing the second map with the more primitive equipment is fine.

For the second map, it is best to go to a remote location and spend a few nights. The surveying field trip is a highlight with tenth grades at many schools. Again choosing a good spot is very important. This time it needs to be near or at a place where you can camp. Doing work in the field is a great experience for all. This second map is a joy, perhaps the best few days of my teaching year. The students need very little help and guidance. They are on a field trip away from home and with their buddies.

I have always thought that the goal of a teacher is to become unneeded. This is my goal for the second map, that I sit back and watch the students collect the data in the field. We return home after a few days and spend some time in the classroom creating the second map. I am available to help, but none is really needed. Almost a whole week goes by where I don't do any teaching; the students are acting on what they have learned as they create a topographical map from scratch on their own.

Here are two examples of student work (my apologies that they are missing the legend for each map).

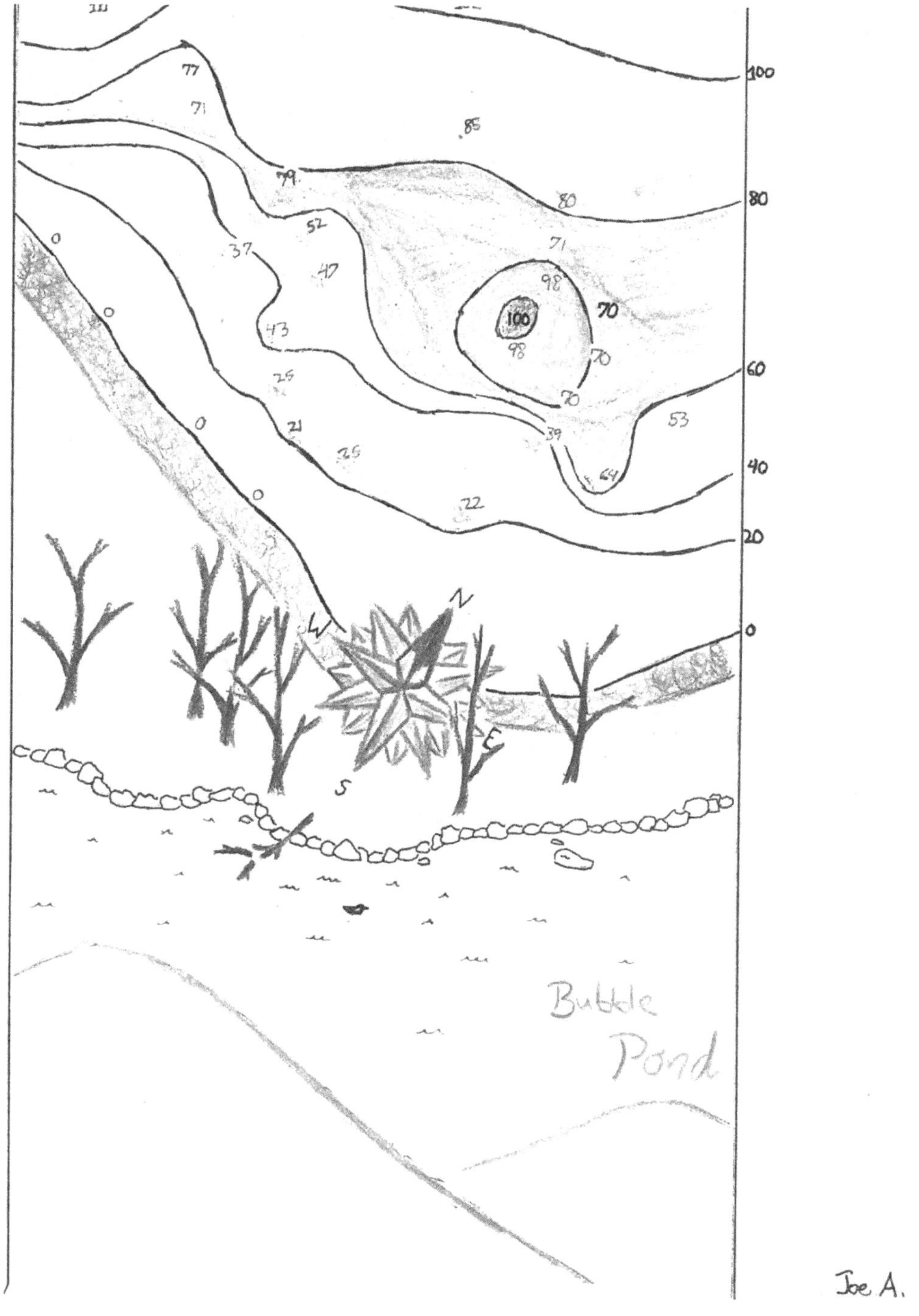

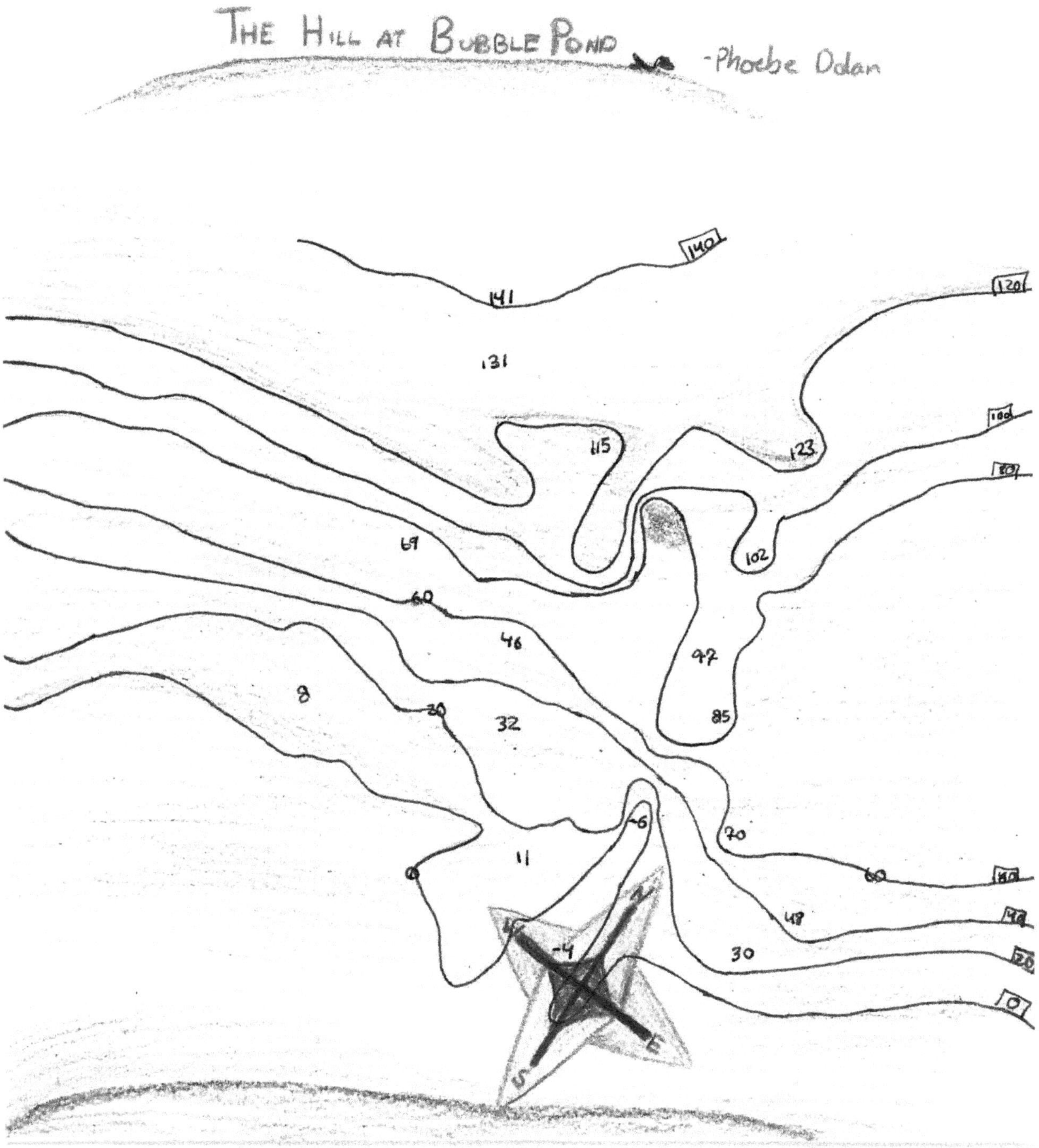
THE HILL AT BUBBLE POND
-Phoebe Odan
140
141
120
131
100
115
123
80
69
102
60
46
97
8
30
32
85
-6
70
11
0
60
40
48
N
W
-4
30
20
0
E
S

Poems for the surveying main lesson

The Map
by Elizabeth Bishop

Land lies in water; it is shadowed green.
Shadows, or are they shallows, at its edges
showing the line of long sea-weeded ledges
where weeds hang to the simple blue from green.
Or does the land lean down to lift the sea from under,
drawing it unperturbed around itself?
Along the fine tan sandy shelf
is the land tugging at the sea from under?

The shadow of Newfoundland lies flat and still.
Labrador's yellow, where the moony Eskimo
has oiled it. We can stroke these lovely bays,
under a glass as if they were expected to blossom,
or as if to provide a clean cage for invisible fish.
The names of seashore towns run out to sea,
the names of cities cross the neighboring mountains
-the printer here experiencing the same excitement
as when emotion too far exceeds its cause.
These peninsulas take the water between thumb and finger
like women feeling for the smoothness of yard-goods.

Mapped waters are more quiet than the land is,
lending the land their waves' own conformation:
and Norway's hare runs south in agitation,
profiles investigate the sea, where land is.
Are they assigned, or can the countries pick their colors?
-What suits the character or the native waters best.
Topography displays no favorites; North's as near as West.
More delicate than the historians' are the map-makers' colors.

Spring Morning
by A.A. Milne

Where am I going? I don't quite know.
Down to the stream where the king-cups grow,
Up on the hill where the pine-trees blow,
Anywhere, anywhere. I don't know.

Where am I going? The clouds sail by,
Little ones, baby ones, over the sky.
Where am I going? The shadows pass,
Little ones, baby ones, over the grass.

If you were a cloud, and sailed up there,
You'd sail on water as blue as air,
And you'd see me here in the fields and say:
"Doesn't the sky look green today?"

Where am I going? The high rooks call:
"It's awful fun to be born at all."
Where am I going? The ring-doves coo:
"We do have beautiful things to do."

If you were a bird, and lived on high,
You'd lean on the wind when the wind came by,
You'd say to the wind when it took you away:
"That's where I wanted to go today!"

Where am I going? I don't quite know.
What does it matter where people go?
Down to the wood where the blue-bells grow,
Anywhere, anywhere. I don't know.

Map Practice Sheet #1

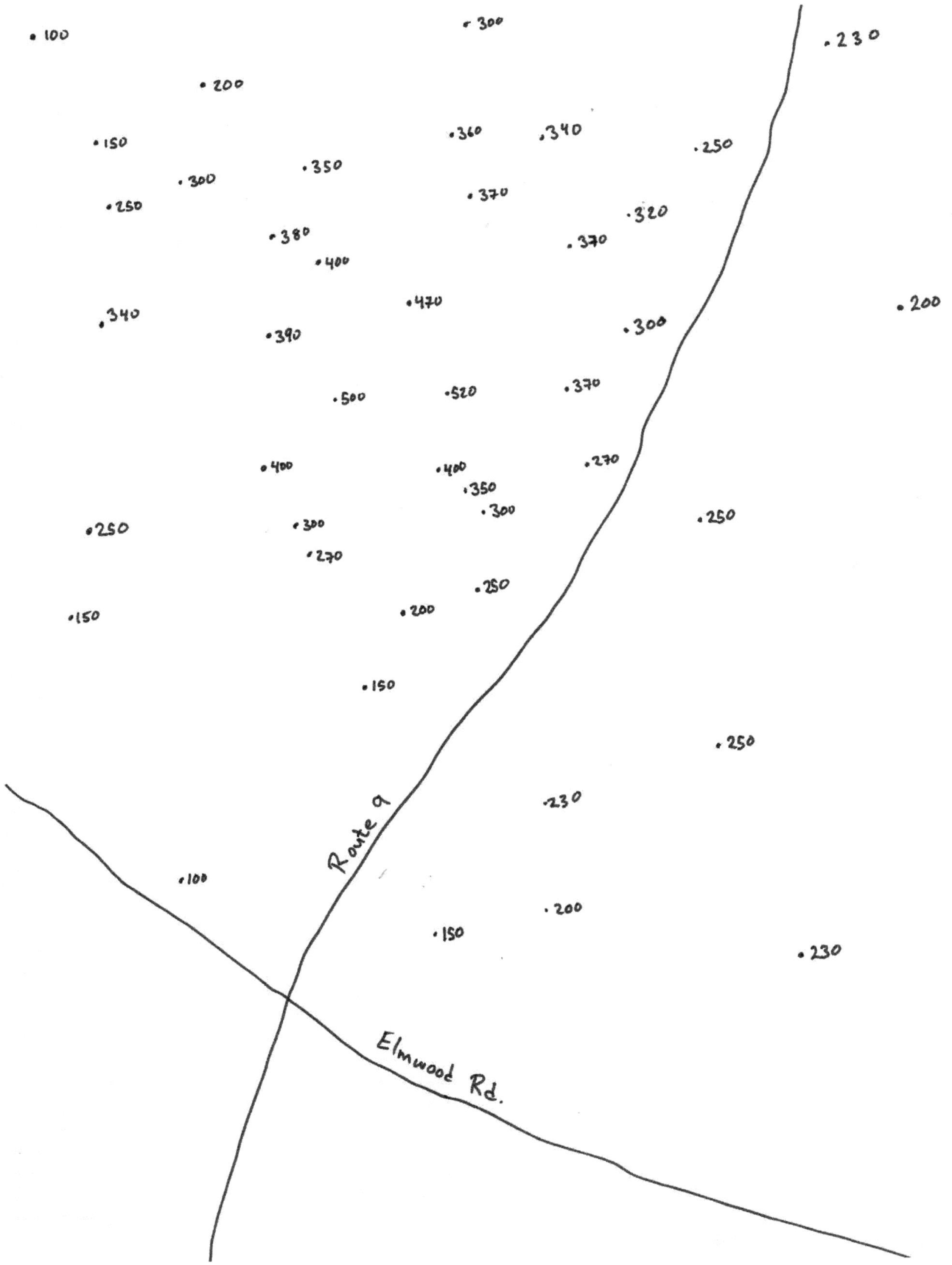

Map Practice Sheet #2

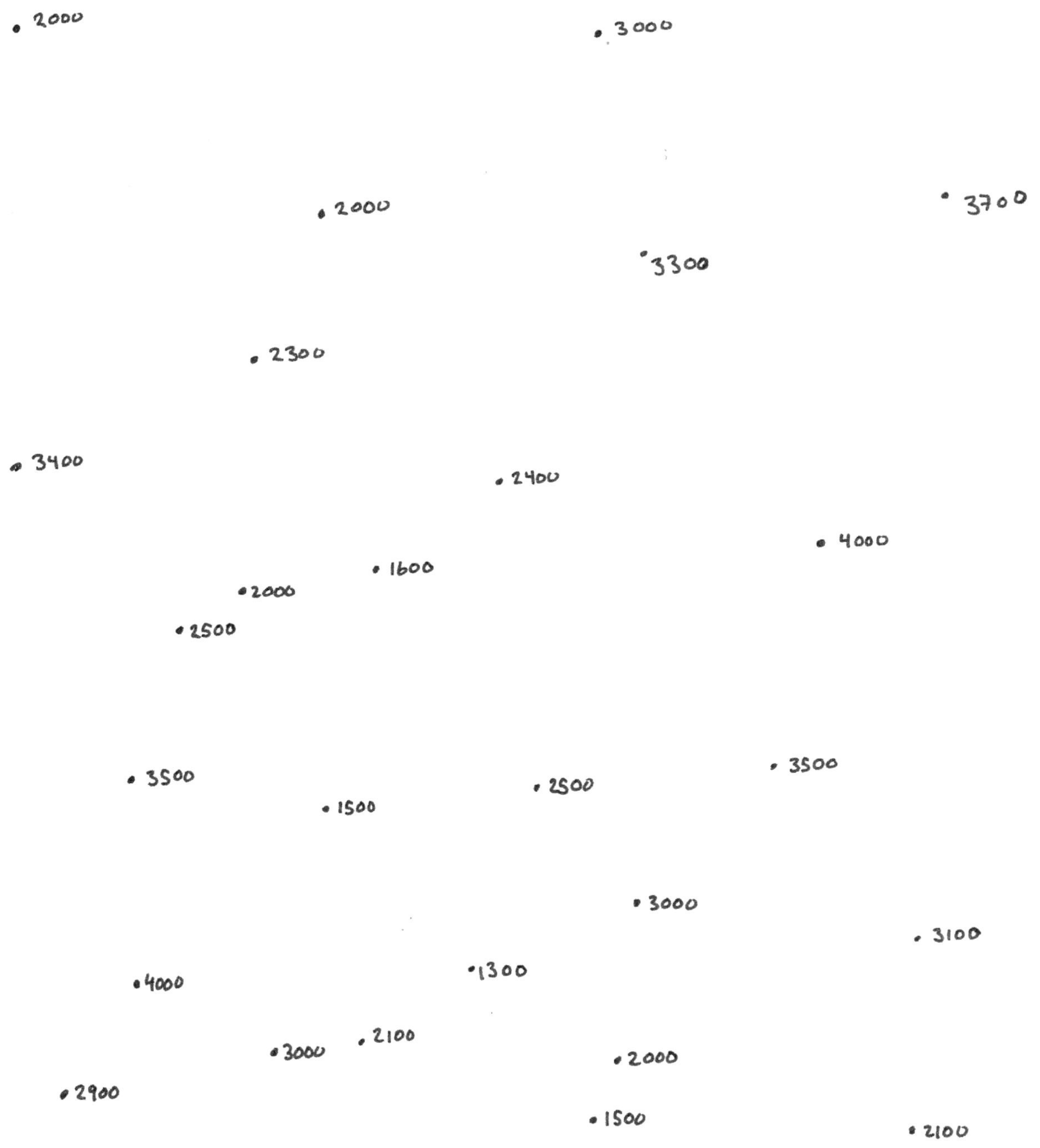

Map Practice Sheet #3

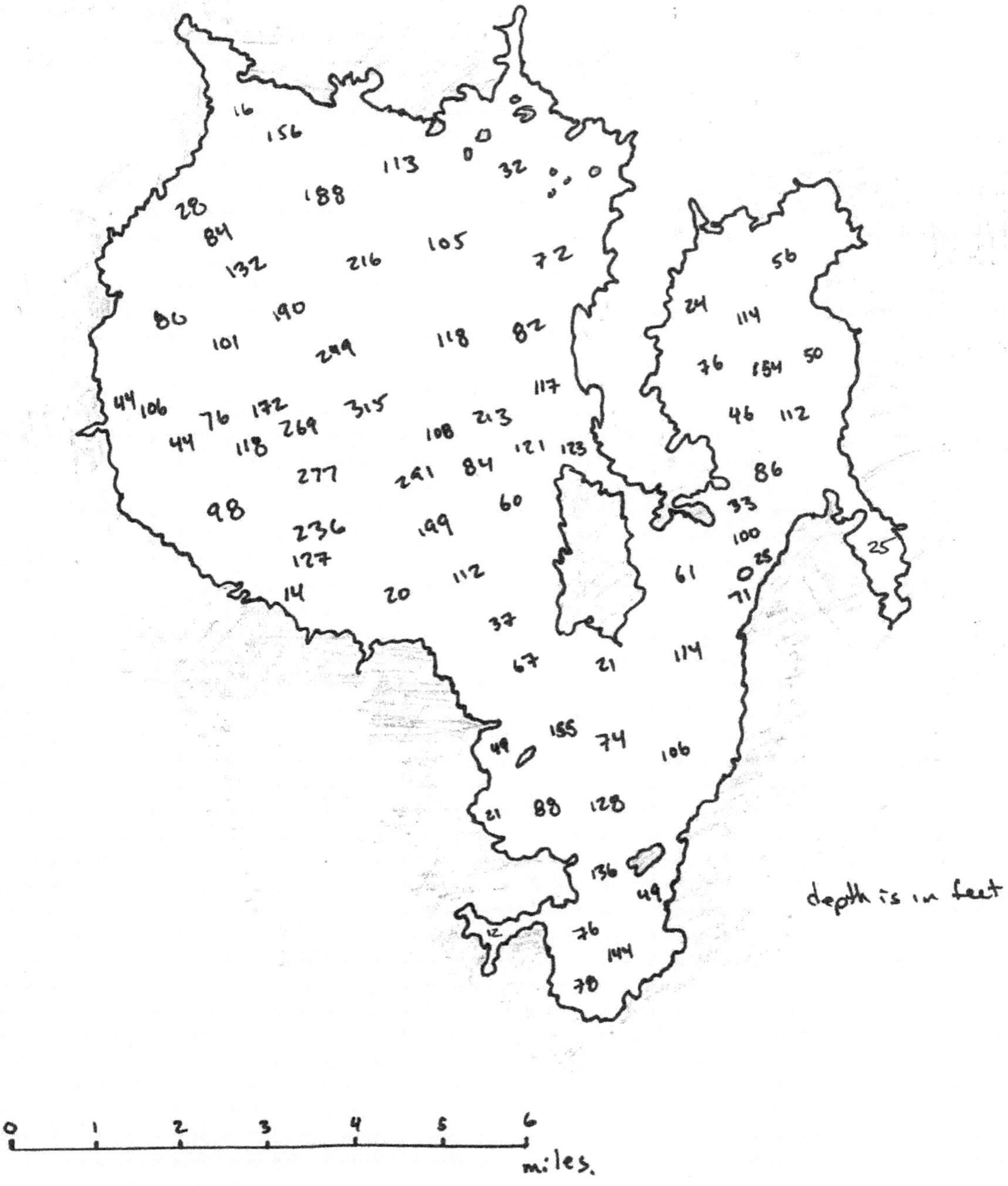

—— *Logarithms* ——

A Lesson Plan for the First Day of Logarithms (in 9th grade)

(This 4-step sequence can be done in one 45-minute track class.)

1. *Subtraction as the Inverse of Addition*
   - Write the three's addition table on the board in the same way that the two's power table is written. The left column is labeled N and has the values 1,2,3, etc. The right column is labeled N+3 and has the values 4, 5, 6, etc.
   - We can view this table as the values of the left column posing the questions, and the right column giving the answers. The question from the 4th row is then:
     Question: What is 4 plus 3?
     Answer: 7
   - Alternatively, we can view this table as the values of the right column posing the questions, and the left column giving the answers. The question from the 4th row is then:
     Question for subtraction (posed in terms of addition): What plus 3 is 7?
     Answer: 4
2. *Division as the Inverse of Multiplication*
   - Write the three's multiplication table on the board, with the right column labeled $N \cdot 3$ and with the values 3, 6, 9, 12, etc.
   - We can view this table as the values of the left column posing the questions, and the right column giving the answers. The question from the 4th row is then:
     Question: What is 4 times 3?
     Answer: 12
   - Alternatively, we can view this table as the values of the right column posing the questions, and the left column giving the answers. The question from the 4th row is then:
     Question for division (posed in terms of multiplication): What times 3 is 12?
     Answer: 4
3. *Cube Rooting as the Inverse of Cubing*
   - Write the cubing table on the board, with right column labeled N^3, with values 1, 8, 27, 64, etc.
   - We can view this table as the values of the left column posing the questions, and the right column giving the answers. The question from the 4th row is then:
     Question: What is 4 cubed?
     Answer: 64
   - Alternatively, we can view this table as the values of the right column posing the questions, and the left column giving the answers. The question from the 4th row is then:
     Question for cube rooting (posed in terms of cubing): What cubed is 64?
     Answer: 4
4. *Logarithms as the Inverse of an Exponential Function*
   - Write the three's power table, with the right column labeled 3^N, with values 3, 9, 27, 81, etc.
   - By this point, the students should be able to see what this is leading to.
     Simply ask them at this point "What's the question to be asked for logarithms?"
     Many of the students should be able to come up with everything listed below on their own.
   - We can view this table as the values of the left column posing the questions, and the right column giving the answers. The question from the 4th row is then:
     Question: What is 3 to the 4?
     Answer: 81
   - Alternatively, we can view this table as the values of the right column posing the questions, and the left column giving the answers. The question from the 4th row is then:
     Question for the logarithm (posed in terms of exponents)**: Three to the what is 81?**
     Answer: 4 **Point out that we write this as: $\log_3 81$**

—— *Logarithms* (10th Grade) ——

Overview

In ninth grade, the class should have had a brief introduction to logarithms. Now, in tenth grade, we review what was covered in ninth grade, and then take it further with more advanced topics and problems. It is important for the students to have at least an exposure to logarithms for three consecutive years so that they leave high school feeling comfortable with the topic.

Required reading

In order to gain a deeper understanding of this unit, the teacher should read the commentary found in the *Teacher's Edition of our 10th Grade Workbook* and also work through the *Logarithms* problem sets found in the workbook.

The Laws of Logarithms

In the Logarithms unit of our *10th Grade Workbook*, the students are led to discover the laws of logarithms for themselves. Here they are:

- $\log_b M\cdot N \leftrightarrow \log_b M + \log_b N$
- $\log_b ({}^{M}/_{N}) \leftrightarrow \log_b M - \log_b N$
- $\log_b N^k \leftrightarrow k \cdot \log_b N$
- $\log_b ({}^{1}/_{N}) \leftrightarrow -\log_b N$
- $\frac{1}{\log_b a} \leftrightarrow \log_a b$
- $\log_b (b^k) \rightarrow k$
- $b^{\log_b N} \rightarrow N$

Two approaches to solving for a variable in the exponent

Example: How long does it take to triple your money at an interest rate of 6.4%?

Solution: Using the formula $P_t = P_0(1+r)^t$ we get $3 = (1.064)^t$

The two approaches for solving this are:

1. Converting into log form. This gives:
   $\log_{1.064} 3 = t$ for an answer of $t \approx 17.7$ years.
2. Take the log base 1.064 of both sides. This gives:
   $\log_{1.064} 3 = t \cdot \log_{1.064} 1.064$, which leads to the same answer as above.

Change of base formula $\quad \log_a x = \frac{\log_b x}{\log_b a}$

Proof: Let $\log_a x = c$ therefore $a^c = x$ Now taking the log base-b of both sides…

$\log_b (a^c) = \log_b x \rightarrow c\cdot\log_b a = \log_b x \rightarrow c = \frac{\log_b x}{\log_b a}$

subbing back into the original equation gives us $\log_a x = \frac{\log_b x}{\log_b a}$

Two approaches to simplifying a "tricky" log problem

Example: Simplify $\log_8 32$

1. The *intuitive* approach: Ask "8 to the what is 32" or $8^x = 32$. Taking the cube root of 8 (which is $8^{1/3}$), yields 2, and then taking that to the 5th makes 32. So the answer is ${}^{5}/_{3}$.
2. Use the *change of base formula* to change to an easier base (base 2):
   $\log_8 32 \rightarrow \frac{\log_2 32}{\log_2 8} \rightarrow \frac{5}{3}$

Why isn't $\log_2 6 = 2.5$?

Students often think that since $\log_2 4 = 2$ and $\log_2 8 = 3$, and because 6 is halfway between 4 and 8, that $\log_2 6 = 2.5$. This isn't true because if we look at the base 2 power's table (see appendix), then we see that the left column is an arithmetic progression while the right column is a geometric progression.

A half-step for the left column is then adding ½, while a half-step for the right column is multiplying by $2^{1/2}$, or $\sqrt{2}$. Therefore, a half-step beyond the 4 in the right column is really 4 times $\sqrt{2}$. Therefore, we can conclude that $\log_2(4\sqrt{2}) = 2.5$

Using the common log table

The *common log table* (see the appendix) can be used to find the logarithms of large or small numbers. In order to use the table, we need to translate the problem so that we are taking log base-10 of a number between 1 and 10.

Example: $\log_{10} 270000 \rightarrow \log_{10}(2.7 \cdot 10^5) \rightarrow \log_{10}(10^5) + \log_{10} 2.7 \rightarrow \underline{5.4314}$

Example: $\log_{10} 0.00563 \rightarrow \log_{10}(5.63 \cdot 10^{-3}) \rightarrow \log_{10}(10^{-3}) + \log_{10} 5.63 \rightarrow -3 + 0.7507 \rightarrow -\underline{2.2495}$

Using logarithms to make calculations by hand easier

Historically, logarithms were used to make difficult calculations easier. This saved engineers, scientists, astronomers, and mathematicians much time in their work. The following problems are examples of using logarithms to do difficult calculations. (Note that this requires a *Common Log Table*. Underlined digits are guesses.)

- Estimate 218^8 by using logarithms.

$x = 218^8$

$\log x = \log 218^8$ (Note that if there is no base, then it is assumed to be base 10)

$\log x = 8 \cdot \log 218$

$\log x = 8 \cdot \log(2.18 \cdot 10^2)$

$\log x = 8 \cdot (2 + 0.3385)$

$\log x = 18.708$

$x \approx 5.10\underline{5} \cdot 10^{18}$ (The actual answer is $\approx 5.101 \cdot 10^{18}$)

- Estimate $5372 \cdot 857$ by using logarithms.

$x = 5372 \cdot 857$

$\log x = \log(5372 \cdot 857)$

$\log x = \log(5372) + \log(857)$

$\log x = \log(5.372 \cdot 10^3) + \log(8.57 \cdot 10^2)$

$\log x = 0.730\underline{1} + 3 + 0.9330 + 2$

$\log x = 6.6631$

$x = \text{antilog}(6.6631)$

$x = 10^6 \cdot 10^{0.6631}$

$x = 10^6 \cdot 4.60\underline{4}$

$x = 4{,}604{,}000$ (Less than $^1/_{100}$% error!)

- Estimate $54.1 \div 5809$ by using logarithms.

$x = 54.1 \div 5809$

$\log x = \log(54.1 \div 5809)$

$\log x = \log(5.41 \cdot 10^1) - \log(5.809 \cdot 10^3)$

$\log x = 1.7332 - 3.764\underline{1}$

$\log x = -2.0309$

$\log x = -3 + 0.9691$

$x = 10^{-3} \cdot 10^{0.9691}$

$x \approx 0.009313\underline{1}$ (The actual answer is ≈ 0.0093135)

- Estimate the 8th root of 5200 by using logarithms.

$x = 5200^{1/8}$

$\log x = {}^1/_8 \log(5200)$

$\log x = {}^1/_8 [\log(5.2) + \log(10^3)]$

$\log x = {}^1/_8 (3.716)$

$x = 10^{0.4645}$

$x = 2.91\underline{4}$ (The actual answer is 2.9140729...)

—— *Sequences and Series* (10th Grade) ——

Overview

Sequences and series is a fascinating glimpse into a new world of mathematics. At first glance it seems fairly concrete, but quickly it gets very abstract. There is certainly enough great material here to form a wonderful main lesson. If it is done in track class, then the *Sequences & Series* unit in our *10th Grade Workbook* should work nicely, but be warned – it is very challenging.

Required reading

In order to gain a deeper understanding of this unit, the teacher should work through the *Sequences and Series* problem sets found in the workbook.

Three averages

Most people would quickly say the average of 8 and 18 is 13. And that would be correct if we were talking about points scored at a basketball game. This is the *arithmetic mean.* But we get a different average if we ask this question: "A town with constant percentage growth has a population of 18 thousand. Ten years ago, its population was 8 thousand. What was its population five years ago?" The answer is not 13 thousand, but, surprisingly, 12 thousand. This is the *geometric mean.* And we get yet another perspective of average with the following problem. "Jeff rides up a hill at 8 mph, and then comes down (the same route) at 18mph. What is his average speed?" The answer here is ≈ 11.08 mph. This is the *harmonic mean.* With the below problems, x and y are the two given numbers, and x > y.

- *Arithmetic Mean* (A).
  "With the *arithmetic mean* (A) the difference between the mean and the smaller given number is equal to the difference between the larger given number and the mean." This leads to:

  $A-y=x-A \quad \rightarrow \quad \mathbf{A}=\frac{x+y}{2}$

- *Geometric Mean* (G).
  "With the *geometric mean* (G), the proportion that the mean is greater than the smaller given number is equal to the proportion that the larger given number is greater than the mean." This leads to:

  $\frac{G-x}{x}=\frac{y-G}{G} \quad \rightarrow \quad \mathbf{G}=\sqrt{xy}$

- *Harmonic Mean* (H). Three Persepctives
  "With the *harmonic mean* (H), the proportion that the mean is greater than the smaller given number is equal to the proportion that the mean is less than the larger given number." This leads to:

  $\frac{H-y}{y}=\frac{x-H}{x} \quad \rightarrow \quad \mathbf{H}=\frac{2xy}{x+y}$

  "With the harmonic mean, the ratio of the two differences created by placing the mean (H) between the two given numbers (x and y) is equal to the ratio of the two given numbers." This leads to:

  $(x-H):(H-y)=x:y \quad \rightarrow \quad \mathbf{H}=\frac{2xy}{x+y}$

  "The reciprocal of the harmonic mean is equal to the arithmetic mean of the reciprocals of the two given numbers." This leads to:

  $\frac{1}{H}=\frac{1}{2}\left(\frac{1}{x}+\frac{1}{y}\right) \quad \rightarrow \quad \mathbf{H}=\frac{2xy}{x+y}$

Example: Find the three means of 10 and 40
Solution: A = 25; G = 20; H = 16

Constructing the three means given two lengths: x, y.

Given y = EB and x = BC, and ∠EBD = ∠DFB = 90°.

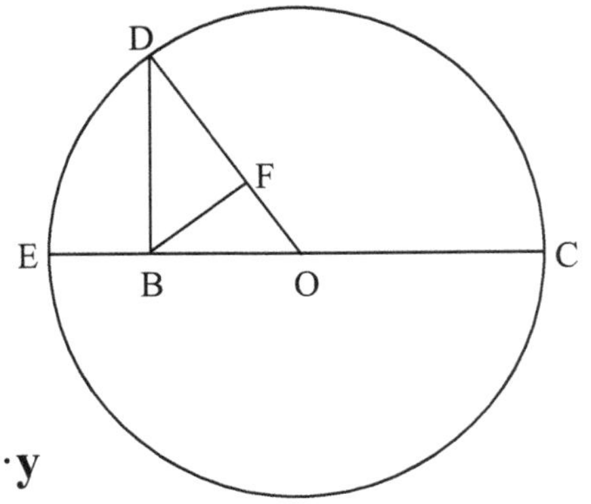

- The *arithmetic mean* $A=\frac{x+y}{2}$ is DO (or EO) in drawing.
- The *geometric mean* $G=\sqrt{xy}$ is DB in drawing.
- The *harmonic mean* $H=\frac{2xy}{x+y}$ is DF in drawing.
- We can see that ΔDBF ~ ΔDBO. Therefore DF : DB = DB : DO, which tells us that $\mathbf{H:G=G:A}$ and leads to $\mathbf{G^2=H\cdot A=x\cdot y}$

Three sequences

- *Arithmetic Sequence.*

  General formula: $x_n = x_0 + n(x_1 - x_0)$ or $x_n = x_0 + n \cdot d$ (where d is the common difference)

  Recursive formula: $x_n = x_{n-1} + d$

  Question: If 45 and 60 are two consecutive terms in an arithmetic sequence, then give the six terms before and after. Describe what happens if we go far in both directions.

  Solution: …-45, -30, -15, 0, 15, 30, **45, 60,** 75, 90, 105, 120, 135, 145…
  The arithmetic infinite sequence passes quickly through zero and approaches infinity slowly on both the positive and negative side, but never gets to or passes through infinity.

- *Geometric Sequence.*

  General formula: $x_n = x_0\left(\frac{x_1}{x_0}\right)^n$ or $x_n = x_0 \cdot r^n$ (where r is the common ratio)

  Recursive formula: $x_n = r \cdot x_{n-1}$

  Question: If 45 and 60 are two consecutive terms in a geometric sequence, then give the six terms before and after. Describe what happens if we go far in both directions.

  Solution: …≈8.01, ≈10.68, ≈14.24, ≈18.98, 25.3125, 33.75, **45, 60,** 80, $106\frac{2}{3}$, $142\,^{2}/_{9}$, ≈189.63, ≈252.84, ≈337.12…The geometric infinite sequence approaches infinity increasingly quickly on the positive side (but never passes through), but on the "other" side it slowly approaches zero, but never gets to or passes through zero.

- *Harmonic Sequence.*

  General formula: $x_n = \frac{x_0 \cdot x_1}{x_1 - n(x_1 - x_0)}$ **Recursive formula:** $x_n = \frac{x_{n-1} \cdot x_{n-2}}{2x_{n-2} - x_{n-1}}$

  Question: If 45 and 60 are two consecutive terms in a harmonic sequence, then give the six terms before and after. Describe what happens if we go far in both directions.

  Solution: …18, 20, $22\frac{1}{2}$, $25\,^{5}/_{7}$, 36, **45, 60,** 90, 180, ∞, -180, -90, -60, -45…
  The harmonic infinite sequence passes quickly through infinity and approaches zero *very* slowly on both sides, but never gets to or passes through zero. (This is the opposite of the arithmetic sequence.)

The Golden Section and Φ (Also found in *The Elements*, Theorem II-11)

- The golden section is the place where you can cut a line segment such that the ratio of the lengths of the two pieces is equal to the ratio of the whole to the larger piece.

$$\text{whole} : \text{larger} = \text{larger} : \text{smaller} \;\rightarrow\; JL : JK = JK : KL \;\rightarrow\; \Phi : 1$$

Alternatively, we can see this as: the square on JK equals the rectangle formed by JL and KL.

Proof: Let KL = 1, and Φ (as a variable) = JK. JL : JK = JK : KL → $(1+\Phi):\Phi = \Phi:1$ → $\Phi^2 = 1 + \Phi$

→ $\Phi^2 - \Phi - 1 = 0$ Using the quadratic formula $\mathbf{\Phi = \frac{1+\sqrt{5}}{2} \approx 1.61803398874989485...}$

The Golden Ratio and the pentagon

- The ratio of the diagonal to the side of a regular pentagon is Φ : 1.
- For more details, see *The Pentagon & the Golden Triangle* from Problem Set #5 of the *Proofs* unit of our *10th Grade Workbook.*
- Note that all of the triangles within the drawing are isosceles and all angles are 36°, 72°, or 108°.
- The Golden Ratio $\Phi = \frac{1+\sqrt{5}}{2}$

  Proof:
  1. We wish to find the ratio of the diagonal to the side of the pentagon. Let the side BC = 1, and the diagonal DB = Φ.
  2. ΔIBC is isosceles; IB = BC = 1; DI = Φ − 1
  3. ΔDCB ~ ΔDIC
  4. DB : DC = DC : DI → Φ : 1 = 1:(Φ − 1)
  5. $\Phi^2 - \Phi - 1 = 0 \rightarrow \Phi = \frac{1+\sqrt{5}}{2}$

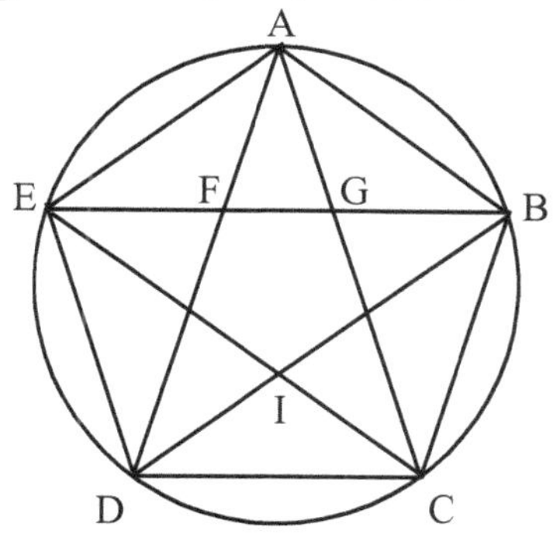

The wonders of the Golden Ratio

- The reciprocal of Φ is 0.6180... the same as $\Phi - 1$. Also Φ^2 is 2.6180... the same as $\Phi + 1$.
- $\Phi = \frac{\sqrt{5}+1}{2}$; $\Phi^2 = \frac{\sqrt{5}+3}{2}$; $\frac{1}{\Phi} = \frac{\sqrt{5}-1}{2}$;
- Take any number (except zero), take the reciprocal, add one, take the reciprocal, add one, and continue. The more you do this, the closer you get to Φ.
- Take any number (not negative), take the square root, add one, take the square root, add one, and continue. The more you do this, the closer you get to Φ.
- A regular decagon with sides = 1 has outer radius = Φ.

The Fibonacci Sequence

- *Fibonacci Sequence* (1, 1, 2, 3, 5, 8, 13, 21, 34...)
  - In 1225, Leonardo de Pisa (known as Fibonacci) posed the following problem, which appears in the *Sequences and Series* of our *10th Grade Workbook*:
    "Beginning with a single pair of baby rabbits, if every month each productive pair bears a new pair, how many pairs of rabbits will there be after each month?" (Assume that each pair becomes productive when one month old, and that they remain alive and productive indefinitely.)
  - Before the students go too far, you should give the sequence up to 34, and then ask:
    (1) How many numbers in the sequence are less than 100? (Answer: 11)
    (2) How many numbers in the sequence are between 100 and 1000? (Answer: 5)
    (3) How many numbers in the sequence are between 1000 and 10,000? (Answer: 4)
  - 1, 1, 2, 3, 5, 8, 13, 21, 34, 55, 89, 144, 233, 377, 610, 987, 1597, 2584, 4181, 6765, 10946, 17711, 28657, 46368, 75025, 121393, 196418, 317811, 514229, 832040, 1346269, 2178309, 3524578, 5702887, 9227465, 14930352, 24157817, 39088169, 63245986, 102334155, 165580141, 267914296...
- Have students discover that the ratio (using division) of two consecutive numbers in the Fibonacci sequence approaches 1:Φ the further up the list you go.
- The same ratio (1:Φ) is approached starting with *any* two numbers!! (i.e., 3,7,10,17,27,44...)
- Start a Fibonacci sequence with 1 and Φ and you get 1,Φ,1+Φ,1+2Φ,2+3Φ,3+5Φ... which is the same as $1,\Phi,\Phi^2,\Phi^3,\Phi^4, \Phi^5$.

Three types of spirals

1. The Archimedean Spiral ($r = a\cdot\theta$)

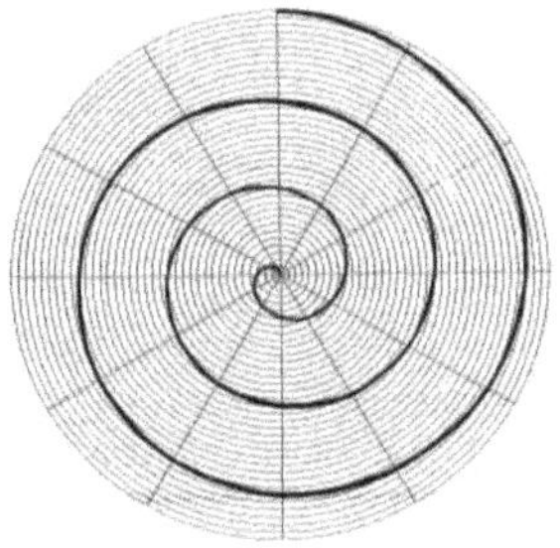

   - The defining property of the Archimedean spiral is that its growth follows an arithmetic progression. In other words, its radius increases by the same amount after each full rotation.
   - The Archimedean spiral clearly reaches the center, and can even be continued past the center point, which creates a "negative" spiral – the mirror reflection of the original spiral.
   - As with an infinite arithmetic sequence, the Archimedean spiral goes toward infinity very slowly, but gets to zero (the center) and easily moves past it.
   - The angle of approach (the direction of the tangent line) of an Archimedean spiral becomes directed more towards the center as it approaches the center, and becomes more perpendicular to the radius line as it moves away from the center.

2. The Logarithmic (or Equiangular) Spiral ($r = a^{\theta}$)

   - The golden spiral is a logarithmic spiral. As it approaches the center, every 90° segment decreases in size by a factor of Φ.
   - The defining property of the logarithmic spiral is that its growth follows a geometric progression. In other words, its radius increases by the same factor (or ratio) after each full rotation.
   - As with an infinite geometric sequence, the logarithmic spiral goes toward infinity increasingly quickly, but never gets there or passes through it.
   - The logarithmic spiral also never gets to zero (the center) – if we think of it as the number of rotations needed to get to the center.
   - However, from any point on a logarithmic spiral, the distance to the center is finite. (See below, where the length of the spiral is calculated.)
   - The angle of approach of a logarithmic spiral is constant – the same from any point on the spiral.

3. The Hyperbolic (or Reciprocal) Spiral $(r = {}^{a}/_{\theta})$
   - The hyperbolic spiral is the opposite of the Archimedean spiral.
   - (I believe that) the hyperbolic spiral follows a harmonic progression.
   - The hyperbolic spiral goes rapidly toward infinity, while approaching an asymptote, passing through infinity and then returns from the other direction, thereby creating a second branch of the spiral. It approaches zero (the center) very slowly – never getting there.
   - The hyperbolic spiral has two branches which are mirror reflections of each other. The two branches are symmetric about the line passing through the center and perpendicular to the asymptote.
   - As a hyperbolic spiral moves further away from the center, the angle of approach is directed more toward the center of the circle. The angle of approach becomes more perpendicular to the radius line as it moves towards the center.
   - From any point on a hyperbolic spiral, the distance to the center is infinite.

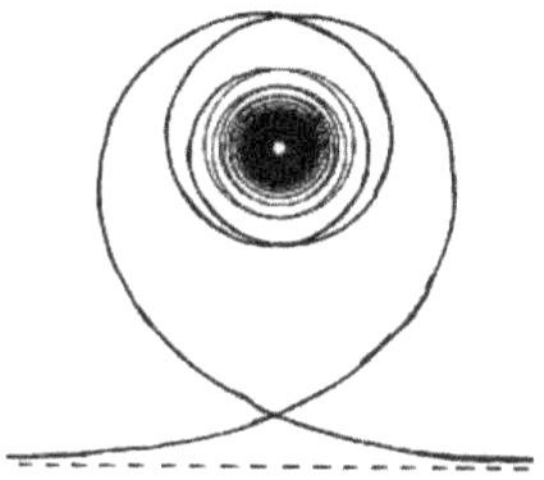

Special spirals

- *The Golden Spiral.* The golden spiral (logarithmic) is produced by starting with a *golden rectangle* (which has a ratio of Φ:1) and then cutting off a square from one end. The remaining piece is another (smaller and rotated) golden rectangle. We continue cutting squares off each rectangle thereby forming a spiral of infinitely many increasingly smaller squares.
- Spirals also appear in nature in shells, plants, and cloud formations as shown with the below drawings.
- In various plants (as shown in the drawings), the number of spirals in each direction is a consecutive pair of Fibonacci numbers!

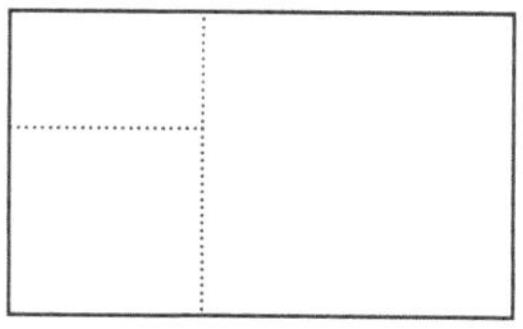

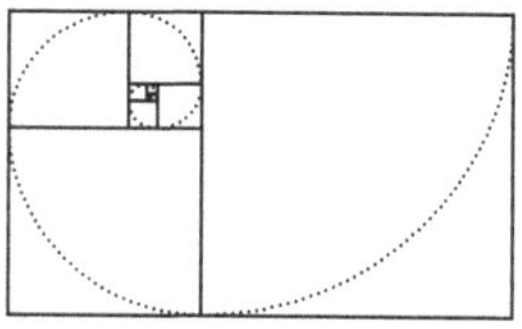

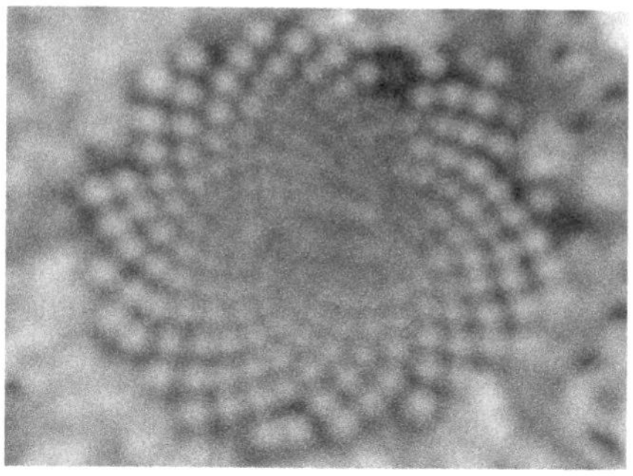

Sunflower
Blurry photo showing 21 spirals in one direction and 34 in the other.

Hurricane Sandy's Golden Spiral

Pine Cone
8 spirals in one direction and 13 in the other direction.

Cactus
13 spirals in one direction and 21 in the other direction.

Chambered Nautilus

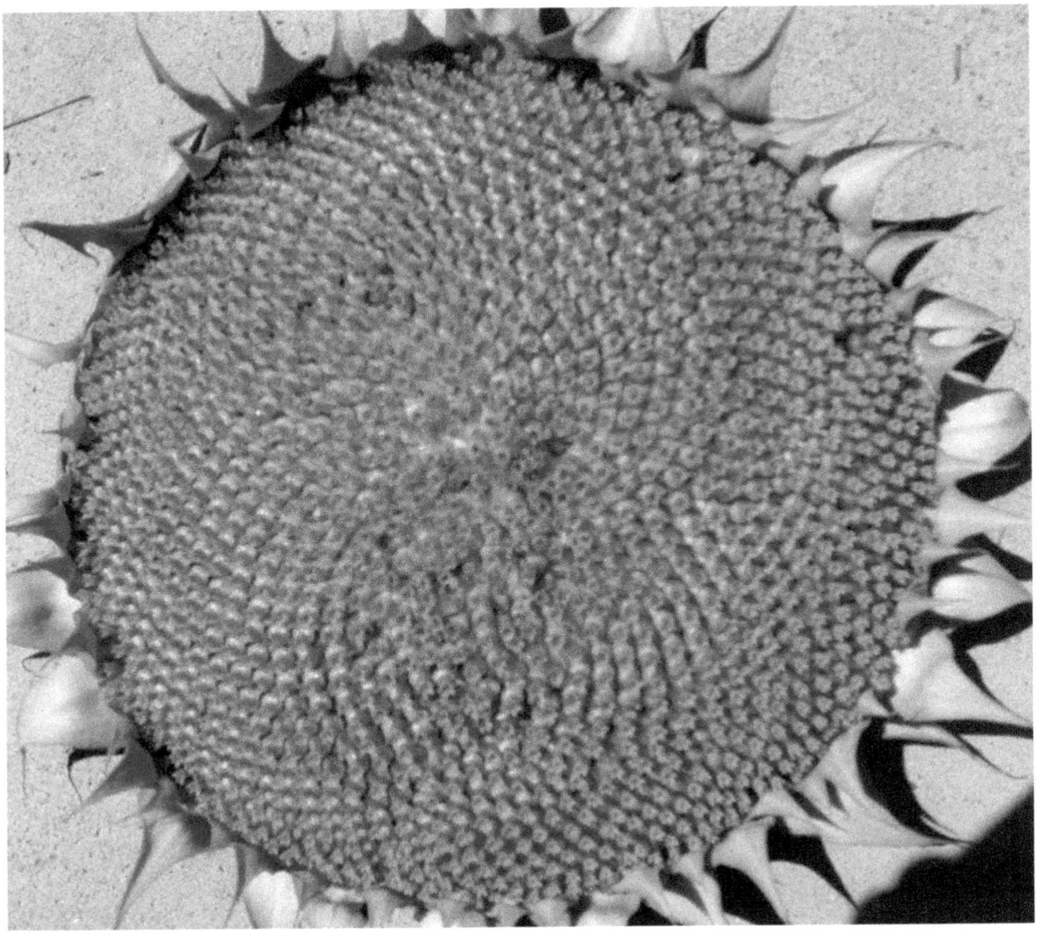

Giant Sunflower: 34 spirals in one direction and 55 in the other!

Summation formulas

(For proofs of these formulas see *Calculus main lesson*)

- For i = 1 to n $\Sigma\, c = c \cdot n$
- For i = 1 to n $\Sigma\, i = \frac{n(n+1)}{2}$ This is Gauss's formula.
- For i = 1 to n $\Sigma\, i^2 = \frac{n(n+1)(2n+1)}{2}$
- For i = 1 to n $\Sigma\, i^3 = \frac{n^2(n+1)^2}{4} = (\Sigma\, i)^2$
- For i = 1 to n $\Sigma\, i^4 = \frac{n(n+1)(2n+1)(3n^2+3n-1)}{30}$

The Power Series Formula

We build up to this formula by leading the students along a path of discovery:

- $(x-1)(x+1) \rightarrow x^2 - 1$
- $(x-1)(x^2+x+1) \rightarrow x^3 - 1$
- $(x-1)(x^3+x^2+x+1) \rightarrow x^4 - 1$
- $(x-1)(x^6+x^5+x^4+x^3+x^2+x+1)$, which can also be written as $(x-1)\sum_{i=0}^{6} x^i \rightarrow x^7 - 1$

- $(x-1)\sum_{i=0}^{n} x^i \rightarrow x^{n-1} - 1$
- The power series formula: $\sum_{i=0}^{n} x^i = \frac{x^{n+1}-1}{x-1}$

Example: $1 + 3 + 3^2 + 3^3 = \sum_{i=0}^{3} 3^i = \frac{3^4 - 1}{3 - 1} = 40$

The Infinite Power Series Formula

This may be pushing the bounds of what the tenth graders are ready for; it may be best to wait until the twelfth grade calculus main lesson.

- If $y = x^n$ and $0 < x < 1$ then as n approaches infinity, y approaches zero.
- Using the *Power Series Formula* $\sum_{i=0}^{n} x^i = \frac{x^{n+1} - 1}{x - 1}$ and the above limit, we get the

  Infinite Power Series Formula, which states if $0 \le x < 1$, then $\sum_{i=0}^{\infty} x^i = \frac{1}{1 - x}$

Example: Evaluate the infinite series: $(\frac{3}{5}) + (\frac{3}{5})^2 + (\frac{3}{5})^3 + (\frac{3}{5})^4 + \ldots$

Solution: First of all, we notice that the infinite power series starts with $n = 0$, so we need to add the term $(\frac{3}{5})^0$, which equals 1. $\sum (\frac{3}{5})^i = \frac{1}{1 - \frac{3}{5}} = 2\frac{1}{2}$ Therefore our answer is **$1\frac{1}{2}$**.

Calculating the length of the *golden spiral.*

As stated above, the golden spiral is a logarithmic spiral. As it approaches the center, every 90° segment decreases in size by a factor of Φ (see drawing). If X_n is the length of the nth 90° segment of the spiral, and X_{n+1} is the length of the next segment (as we move toward the center), then $X_{n+1} = X_n / \Phi$. The total length of the spiral (S_n) from segment X_n in to the center of the spiral is then:

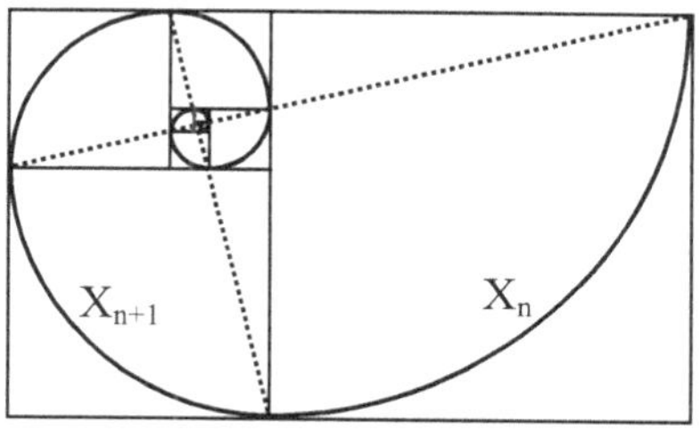

$$S_n = \sum X_n = X_n + X_{n+1} + X_{n+2} + \ldots + X_\infty$$
$$S_n = X_n + X_n/\Phi + X_n/\Phi^2 + X_n/\Phi^3 \ldots$$
$$S_n = X_n\,[1 + {}^1/\Phi + {}^1/\Phi^2 + {}^1/\Phi^3 \ldots]$$
$$S_n = X_n \cdot \frac{1}{1 - {}^1/\Phi} \rightarrow S_n = X_n \cdot \frac{\Phi}{\Phi - 1}$$

And we know that $\Phi - 1 = {}^1/\Phi$. Therefore $S_n = X_n \cdot \frac{\Phi}{{}^1/\Phi} = \Phi^2 X_n$

Furthermore $S_{n+2} = \Phi^2 X_{n+2} = X_n \quad \therefore \mathbf{S_{n+2} = X_n}$

This means that the length of any 90° spiral segment is equal to the total length of the spiral starting two segments toward the center and going all the way to the center – even though it takes infinitely many rotations to get to the center!

We can also say that a 90° segment of the spiral is equal to the sum of the next two smaller segments.

Proof:

We know these facts: $X_n = \Phi X_{x+1} = \Phi^2 X_{n+2}$; $X_{n+1} = \Phi X_{n+2}$; $1 + \Phi = \Phi^2$

$X_{n+1} + X_{n+2} = \Phi X_{n+2} + X_{n+2} \rightarrow X_{n+1} + X_{n+2} = X_{n+2}(\Phi + 1) \rightarrow X_{n+1} + X_{n+2} = \Phi^2 X_{n+2}$

$\therefore \mathbf{X_{n+1} + X_{n+2} = X_n}$ Which is the same recursive formula as the Fibonacci sequence!

Expressions and equations involving infinity – Irrational numbers and continued fractions

- Equations of the type: $x^{x^{x^{x\ldots}}} = 2$. These are interesting because it is an introduction, algebraically, to the paradox of infinity: to add to infinity just gives something more infinite! In this case, if $x^{x^{x^{x\ldots}}}$ on to infinity is equal to 2, then we could say that all the $x^{x^{x^{x\ldots}}}$ after the first one are equal to 2. Then our equation is simply $x^2 = 2$ and $x = \sqrt{2}$.
- Equations of the type: $x = \sqrt{5+\sqrt{5+\sqrt{5+\sqrt{5+\ldots}}}}$ By the same reasoning, all the $\sqrt{5+\sqrt{5+\sqrt{5+\sqrt{5+\ldots}}}}$ after the first one are equal to x, so we can say $x = \sqrt{5+x}$ which leads to the quadratic equation $x^2 - x - 5 = 0$. Therefore $x = \frac{1 \pm \sqrt{21}}{2} \approx 2.79$
- Many irrational numbers, including e, Φ, π, can be expressed as continued fractions, as shown on the following pages.

Irrational Numbers
expressed as
Continued Fractions

$$\sqrt{3} = 1 + \cfrac{1}{1 + \cfrac{1}{2 + \cfrac{1}{1 + \cfrac{1}{2 + \cfrac{1}{1 + \dots}}}}}$$

$$e = 1 + \cfrac{2}{1 + \cfrac{1}{6 + \cfrac{1}{10 + \cfrac{1}{14 + \cfrac{1}{18 + \dots}}}}}$$

$$\sqrt{5} = 2 + \cfrac{1}{4 + \cfrac{1}{4 + \cfrac{1}{4 + \cfrac{1}{4 + \cfrac{1}{4 + \dots}}}}}$$

$$e = 2 + \cfrac{1}{1 + \cfrac{1}{2 + \cfrac{1}{1 + \cfrac{1}{1 + \cfrac{1}{4 + \cfrac{1}{1 + \cfrac{1}{1 + \dots}}}}}}}$$

$$\sqrt{2} = 1 + \cfrac{1}{2 + \cfrac{1}{2 + \cfrac{1}{2 + \cfrac{1}{2 + \cfrac{1}{2 + \dots}}}}}$$

$$\pi = \cfrac{4}{1 + \cfrac{1^2}{2 + \cfrac{3^2}{2 + \cfrac{5^2}{2 + \cfrac{7^2}{2 + \dots}}}}}$$

$$\Phi = 1 + \cfrac{1}{1 + \cfrac{1}{1 + \cfrac{1}{1 + \cfrac{1}{1 + \cfrac{1}{1 + \dots}}}}}$$

$$\pi = 3 + \cfrac{1^2}{6 + \cfrac{3^2}{6 + \cfrac{5^2}{6 + \cfrac{7^2}{6 + \cfrac{9^2}{6 + \dots}}}}}$$

$$\pi = \cfrac{4}{1 + \cfrac{1^2}{3 + \cfrac{2^2}{5 + \cfrac{3^2}{7 + \cfrac{4^2}{9 + \dots}}}}}$$

π Equivalences

$$\pi = 2^{n} \cdot 3\sqrt{2-\sqrt{2+\sqrt{2+\sqrt{2+\ldots+\sqrt{2+\sqrt{3}}}}}}$$

- This formula is the equivalent of the lower bound from Archimedes' algorithm for calculating π.

$$\pi = \frac{2}{\sqrt{\tfrac{1}{2}}\cdot\sqrt{\tfrac{1}{2}+\tfrac{1}{2}\sqrt{\tfrac{1}{2}}}\cdot\sqrt{\tfrac{1}{2}+\tfrac{1}{2}\sqrt{\tfrac{1}{2}+\sqrt{\tfrac{1}{2}}}}\cdot\ldots}$$

- This formula was given by Viète in 1593.

$$\pi = 2\cdot\frac{2\cdot2\cdot4\cdot4\cdot6\cdot6\ldots}{1\cdot3\cdot3\cdot5\cdot5\cdot7\ldots}$$

- This formula was given by John Wallis in 1655.
- It is the first formula that gives π as a series without using roots.
- It converges extremely slowly: it takes 986 terms before it gets the second decimal place correct!

$$\pi = \cfrac{4}{1+\cfrac{1^2}{2+\cfrac{3^2}{2+\cfrac{5^2}{2+\cfrac{7^2}{2+\ldots}}}}}$$

- This formula was given by Brouncker around 1660.
- It converges very slowly: it takes 628 terms before it gets the second decimal place correct.

$$\pi = 4\left(\frac{1}{1}-\frac{1}{3}+\frac{1}{5}-\frac{1}{7}+\ldots\right)$$

- This formula was given by Gregory and Leibniz in 1674.
- It is derived from the series definition of arctan: $\arctan(x) = x - \frac{x^3}{3} + \frac{x^5}{5} - \frac{x^7}{7}\ldots$
- It converges very slowly: it takes 628 terms (also!) before it gets the second decimal place correct.

$$\pi = 6\left(\frac{1}{2}+\frac{1}{(2)(3\cdot2^3)}+\frac{1\cdot3}{(2\cdot4)(5\cdot2^5)}+\frac{1\cdot3\cdot5}{(2\cdot4\cdot6)(7\cdot2^7)}+\ldots\right)$$

- This formula was given by Newton in 1737.
- It converges very quickly. The fourth term yields 3.1412.

e

$$e = \lim_{n \to \infty} \left(1 + \frac{1}{n}\right)^n$$

$e \approx$

2.71828182845904523536028747135266249775724709369995957
4966967627724076630353547594571382178525166427427466391
9320030599218174135966290435729003342952605956307381323
2862794349076323382988075319525101901157383418793070215
4089149934884167509244761460668082264800168477411853742
3454424371075390777449920695517027618386062613313845830
0075204493382656029760673711320070932870912744374704723
0696977209310141692836819025515108657463772111252389784
4250569536967707854499699679468644549059879316368892300
9879312773617821542499922957635148220826989519366803318
2528869398496465105820939239829488793320362509443117301
2381970684161403970198376793206832823764648042953118023
2878250981945581530175671736133206981125099618188159304
1690351598888519345807273866738589422879228499892086805
8257492796104841984443634632449684875602336248270419786
2320900216099023530436994184914631409343173814364054625
3152096183690888707016768396424378140592714563549061303
1072085103837505101157477041718986106873969655212671546
8895703503540212340784981933432106817012100562788023519
3033224745015853904730419957777093...

$$e = \frac{1}{0!} + \frac{1}{1!} + \frac{1}{2!} + \frac{1}{3!} + \frac{1}{4!} + \ldots$$

$$e = 1 + \cfrac{2}{1 + \cfrac{1}{6 + \cfrac{1}{10 + \cfrac{1}{14 + \cfrac{1}{18 + \cfrac{1}{22 + \ldots}}}}}}$$

The "fly and the bicycle" problem

Two bicycles, initially 20 miles apart, ride toward each other at 10mph. A fly leaves one bike the instant they start, flies toward the other bike, and immediately turns around and flies back. He flies back and forth like this until the bicycles meet. If the fly travels at 30mph, how far does he fly?

To start with, it helps to realize that once the fly has reached the second bike (at the end of the first leg of the journey) the combined distance traveled by the fly and the second bike is equal to 20 miles. The ratio of the speeds of the fly to the bike (coming toward the fly) is 3:1. Therefore, the fly covers ¾ of the 20 miles on the first leg of the journey. So the fly turns around and heads toward the second bike. But how far away is the second bike at the start of the second leg of the journey? The two bikes have each gone ¼ of the whole distance, so half of the original distance is left. This means that the second leg will be half as long as the fist leg. The resulting infinite series is therefore:

$$\tfrac{3}{4}\cdot 20 + \tfrac{1}{2}\cdot\tfrac{3}{4}\cdot 20 + (\tfrac{1}{2})^2\cdot\tfrac{3}{4}\cdot 20 + (\tfrac{1}{2})^3\cdot\tfrac{3}{4}\cdot 20 + \ldots$$

$$= \tfrac{3}{4}\cdot 20\,(1 + \tfrac{1}{2} + (\tfrac{1}{2})^2 + (\tfrac{1}{2})^3 + \ldots) \;\rightarrow\; 15\,(1 + \tfrac{1}{2} + (\tfrac{1}{2})^2 + (\tfrac{1}{2})^3 + \ldots)$$

$$= 15\left(\sum_{i=0}^{\infty}(\tfrac{1}{2})^i\right) \;\rightarrow\; 15\left(\frac{1}{1-\tfrac{1}{2}}\right) \;\rightarrow\; 15\,(2) \;\rightarrow\; \underline{\mathbf{30}}$$ The fly travels a total of 30 miles.

The easier way to solve this problem would be to realize that the fly is in the air for a total of one hour (because that's how long it takes for the bikes to meet), so he must have traveled 30 miles. Apparently, this problem was given to John von Neumann at a cocktail party. He thought for a moment and answered correctly, after which the person presenting the puzzle remarked that most people don't think of the easy way to do the problem, and normally try to do an infinite series and get tangled up in it for a while, to which von Neumann responded, "But, that's what I did".

An example using fractals

Consider a square with sides of length 1. Divide the square into four regions and shade in the top left region. Now divide the remaining three squares into four and shade in the top left of each of them. Continue in this manner infinitely many times. The question is: after infinitely many iterations, how much of the original square is shaded in?

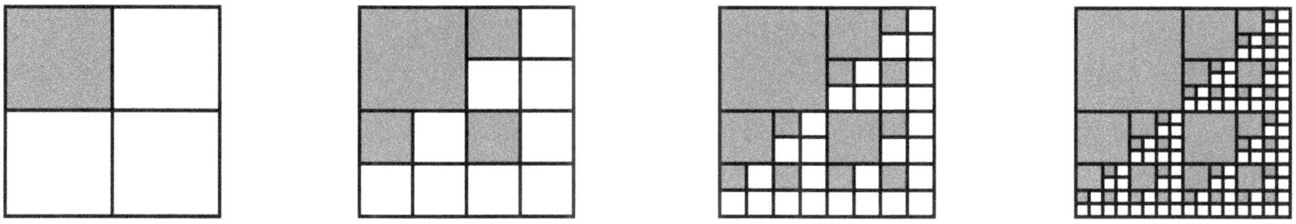

One way to proceed is to consider how much of the square has been shaded in after each step.

After step #1, the shaded-in area $= \tfrac{1}{4}$

After step #2, the shaded-in area $= \tfrac{1}{4} + 3\cdot(\tfrac{1}{4})^2$

After step #3, the shaded-in area $= \tfrac{1}{4} + 3\cdot(\tfrac{1}{4})^2 + 3^2\cdot(\tfrac{1}{4})^3$

After step #4, the shaded-in area $= \tfrac{1}{4} + 3\cdot(\tfrac{1}{4})^2 + 3^2\cdot(\tfrac{1}{4})^3 + 3^3\cdot(\tfrac{1}{4})^4$

If we allow this for infinitely many iterations and factor out ¼ from each term (which makes the exponents the same in each term), we get:

$$\tfrac{1}{4}\,[\,(1 + 3\cdot(\tfrac{1}{4}) + 3^2\cdot(\tfrac{1}{4})^2 + 3^3\cdot(\tfrac{1}{4})^3 + \ldots + 3^{\infty}\cdot(\tfrac{1}{4})^{\infty}\,]$$

$$\tfrac{1}{4}\,[\,1 + (\tfrac{3}{4}) + (\tfrac{3}{4})^2 + (\tfrac{3}{4})^3 + \ldots + (\tfrac{3}{4})^{\infty}\,]$$

$$\tfrac{1}{4}\left[\sum(\tfrac{3}{4})^i\right] \;\rightarrow\; \tfrac{1}{4}\left(\frac{1}{1-\frac{3}{4}}\right) \;\rightarrow\; \tfrac{1}{4}\,(4) \;\rightarrow\; \textcircled{1}$$

The entire square has been shaded in! And the result would have been the same if we had started by shading in one-hundredth of each square!

—— *Math and Music* (10th Grade) ——

Overview

This fun unit is a great way to end the tenth grade year in math class – but don't be fooled, there is a good amount of sophisticated math involved. We begin – as it began historically with the Pythagoreans – by investigating the ratios of various musical intervals. This leads to some surprising results, some troublesome difficulties, and ultimately to the realization that there is no possible way to construct the perfect scale. In the end, the students create their own equitempered scale and represent the data on a graph in order to judge whether it would be a pleasant sounding scale or not.

Required reading

In order to gain a deep understanding of this unit, the teacher should begin by reading the "Summary of some Key Ideas from Math and Music" (found on the next pages), and then read the commentary found in the *Teacher's Edition of our 10th Grade Workbook.* Lastly, but most importantly, the teacher should work through the *Math and Music* problem sets found in our *10th Grade Workbook.*

The three averages related to music

The three means are the *arithmetic mean, geometric mean*, and *harmonic mean.* All of these were covered in the previous unit, *Sequences and Series* (see above). In music, the significance is:

- The interval of the fifth produces the ratio of 3:2, which is 3½ whole steps up from the root note. The frequency of the fifth is the *arithmetic mean* of the frequencies of the root note and the octave above it.
- The interval of the fourth produces the ratio of 4:3, which is 2½ whole steps up from the root note. The frequency of the fourth is the *harmonic mean* of the frequencies of the root note and the octave above it.
- A diminished fifth (or augmented fourth) is 3 whole steps up from the root note (which is in between the fifth and the fourth). Its frequency is the *geometric mean* of the root note and the octave above it.
- **Example**: Using the notes C (256Hz) and C' (512Hz, an octave above C), we get the arithmetic mean of 384 Hz (G), the harmonic mean of is 341⅓ (F), and the geometric mean of 362Hz (F#).

The musical proportion $a : \frac{a+b}{2} = \frac{2ab}{a+b} : b$

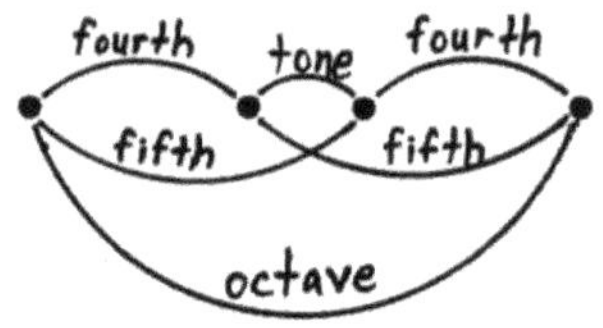

- a is the frequency of the root note, and b is the octave above it.
- $\frac{a+b}{2}$ is the fifth, which is the arithmetic mean of a and b.
- $\frac{2ab}{a+b}$ is the fourth, which is harmonic mean of a and b.
- The musical proportion says that the fifth above the fourth is the octave.

Ratios and frequencies of notes:

- Middle C is 261.6 Hz
- A typical piano has a range of **A** 27.50 Hz to **C** 4186 Hz
- Violin strings are tuned at: **G** 196 Hz, **D** 293.7 Hz, **A** 440 Hz, **E** 659.3 Hz
- Viola strings are tuned at: **C** 130.8 Hz, **G** 196 Hz, **D** 293.7 Hz, **A** 440 Hz
- Cello strings are tuned at: **C** 65.4 Hz, **G** 98 Hz, **D** 146.8 Hz, **A** 220 Hz
- Bass strings are tuned at: **E** 41.2 Hz, **A** 55 Hz, **D** 73.4 Hz, **G** 98 Hz
- The violin, viola, and cello have strings that increase in frequency by a fifth.
  The bass has strings (sometimes 5 strings) that increase in frequency by a fourth.
- The viola is a fifth lower than the violin.
  The cello is an octave lower than a viola.
  The bass is (roughly speaking) an octave lower than a cello.

- The note names of the bass strings (which increase in fourths: E, A, D, G) are the same as note names of the violin strings (which increase in fifths: G, D, A, E) – but reversed!
  - The E string on a bass (which is its lowest string) is four octaves lower than the E string on a violin (which is its highest string).
  - The A string on a bass is three octaves lower than the A string on a violin.
  - The D string on a bass is two octaves lower than the D string on a violin.
  - The G string on a bass (which is its highest string) is (only!) one octave lower than the G string on a violin (which is its lowest string).
- The ratios of the (major) intervals are as follows (in just intonation):
  - Second 2nd is 9:8
  - Major 3rd is 5:4
  - Fourth is 4:3
  - Fifth is 3:2
  - Major 6th is 5:3
  - Major 7th is 15:8
  - Octave is 2:1
- The ratios of the minor intervals are as follows (in just intonation):
  - Minor 2nd is 16:15
  - Minor 3rd is 6:5
  - Minor 6th is 8:5
  - Minor 7th is 9:5 (or 16:9)
- There are different "sevenths":
  - The *major seventh* interval has a ratio of 15:8 (in just intonation). Given an A string tuned at 440 Hz, the major seventh in an A major scale is G# (825 Hz).
  - The *minor seventh* interval has a ratio of 16:9 or 9:5 (in just intonation). Given an A string tuned at 440 Hz, the minor seventh is G (782.2 Hz).
  - The *harmonic seventh* (or septimal minor seventh) interval has a ratio of 7:4 (in just intonation). Given an A string tuned at 440 Hz, the harmonic seventh has a frequency of 770 Hz, which falls close to the middle of (an equitempered) G and F#. The harmonic seventh interval is fairly common with pieces that are written for a just intonation scale, particularly with musical pieces for barbershop quartets.

Alternatives to the 12-note equitempered scale

The 12-note equitempered scale is the dominant scale in the world of music today. An equitempered scale doesn't have to have 12 notes to the octave. In some ways, an equitempered scale might be better if it instead had 19, 22, 31, or 53 steps to the octave. For example, a 53-note equitempered scale hits all of the important intervals almost perfectly…but imagine playing a piano with nearly 400 keys!

Things could have evolved differently. Proponents of *Just Intonation* tuning (which advocates using only the pure Pythagorean ratios found in just intonation scales) feel that something important was lost when we adopted the equitempered scale. They would say the following about the equitempered scale:

> *By degrading the purity of each chord or interval, we have degraded the aesthetic appeal of music.* -- Giuseppe Tartini, an 18th century Venetian composer and violinist

Summary of some Key Ideas from

Math and Music

Pythagorean ratios

The Pythagoreans discovered a very important property – that the most pleasing musical intervals were those that had frequencies which could be reduced to simple whole number ratios. The simpler the ratio (e.g., 3:2), the more consonant, or harmonious, the interval. Intervals with more complex ratios (e.g., 16:15) would sound more dissonant to one's ear. A *Table of Intervals* (for any major scale) is shown here. These ratios can be used to build a *diatonic scale in just intonation* (which we will call a "just/diatonic scale").

Building upon the Pythagoreans' discovery, we know today that a string's length is inversely proportional to its frequency (measured in cycles per second, or Hertz, Hz). Therefore, if the A string of a violin is tuned to 440 Hz, we know that by pressing at $^{3}/_{5}$ of the string's length, the resulting frequency will be $440 \cdot {}^{5}/_{3}$, which is $733\frac{1}{3}$ Hz.

Table of Intervals

Name of Interval	Ratio of Interval	Example
Second	9:8	C → D
Major 3rd	5:4	C → E
Fourth	4:3	D → G
Fifth	3:2	A → E
Major 6th	5:3	C → A
Major 7th	15:8	C → B
Octave	2:1	B → B'

Overtones

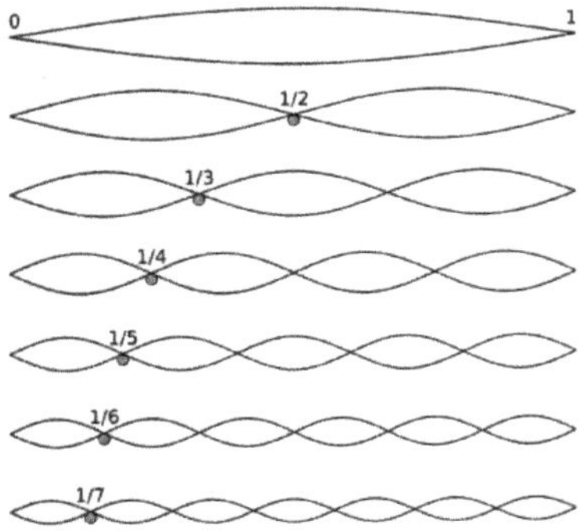

Usually, when we hear a note played on an instrument, there are several overtone notes that are also occurring simultaneously, each one less and less audible. With a string instrument, the string vibrates in a very complex pattern, as is shown at the right, except that they are all laid on top of each other. Each overtone has a frequency which is a multiple of the fundamental root note. For example, with the A string (440 Hz) the overtones are as follows:

- $2 \cdot 440 \rightarrow$ **A 880 Hz** (with ½ the wavelength of the full string)
- $3 \cdot 440 \rightarrow$ **E 1320 Hz** (with ⅓ the wavelength of the full string)
- $4 \cdot 440 \rightarrow$ **A 1760 Hz** (with ¼ the wavelength of the full string)
- $5 \cdot 440 \rightarrow$ **C# 2200 Hz** (with $^{1}/_{5}$ the wavelength of the full string)
- $6 \cdot 440 \rightarrow$ **E 2640 Hz** (with $^{1}/_{6}$ the wavelength of the full string)
- $7 \cdot 440 \rightarrow$ **G? 3080 Hz** (with $^{1}/_{7}$ the wavelength of the full string)

(The note of this last overtone is about halfway between a minor 7th and a major 7th.)

Again, all of the above notes are sounded (although less and less audibly) whenever we play an open A string! There are more (even less audible) overtones, as well, which correspond to $^{1}/_{8}$, $^{1}/_{9}$, $^{1}/_{10}$, etc.

Harmonics

Again, remember that when a string is being played, the string is vibrating in a complex pattern that results from having all different waves (in the above diagram) laid on top of each other. We will assume again that the string is a violin A string tuned at 440 Hz. If we place our finger one-third of the way down the string, pressing down will give us an E (660 Hz). In pressing down in this way, two-thirds of the string is vibrating (with the same, but shorter, complex wave pattern as shown in the above diagram), and the remaining one-third of the string is dead. However, if we instead barely touch the string at that same place, then the *full length* of the string will vibrate, but this time in a very different way. In this case, every overtone will be canceled if it doesn't have a node where the finger is touching. In other words, the only overtones that aren't canceled are the ⅓ (E 1320 Hz), the $^{1}/_{6}$ (E 2640 Hz), the $^{1}/_{9}$ (B 3960 Hz, which is not audible), etc. By canceling most of the overtones, the harmonic produces a more "pure" sounding tone.

Similarly, if we instead place our finger ¼ of the way down the A string, pressing down will result in a D (with all of its overtones), and touching the string there will result in a harmonic A (two octaves higher than the open A string).

Building a just/diatonic scale

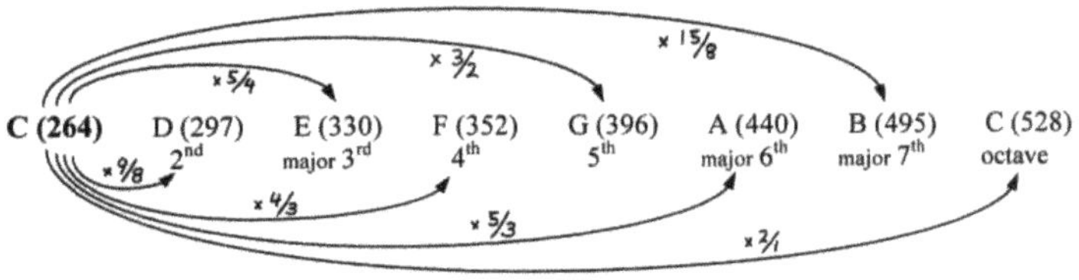

To simplify matters, we will build a C major scale, which is the only major scale that has no sharps or flats. Middle C 264 Hz is our root note. Given the *Table of Intervals* (see above), we can calculate the rest of the notes in the scale. For example, to get the fifth, we simply multiply $264 \cdot {}^{3}/_{2}$, which equals 396 Hz. We then complete the picture with the rest of the intervals. The result (shown in this diagram) is what we refer to as a *just/diatonic scale*.

Summary of Math and Music (continued)

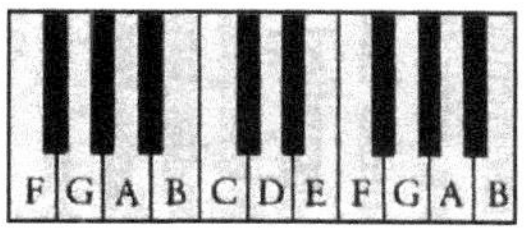

Major and minor scales

With the C major scale, there are no sharps or flats. So we can play the notes of a C major scale on the piano without hitting any of the black keys. This produces the notes C, D, E, F, G, A, B, C. Looking at the keys on a piano, we see that the half steps occur after the third note (E to F) and the seventh note (B to C). We can then conclude that, with every major scale, the whole step (w) and half step (H) sequence is w-w-H-w-w-w-H. This is what differentiates a minor and major scale. In short:

The sequence of interval sizes for a **major scale** is: **w-w-H-w-w-w-H**

The sequence of interval sizes for a **minor scale** is: **w-H-w-w-H-w-w**

The second, fourth and fifth intervals are the same with both a major and a minor scale. However, three of the intervals have lower frequencies with the minor scale (compared to a major scale). These different intervals are: the minor third (6:5), the minor sixth (8:5), and the minor seventh (16:9). For example, the major and minor (just/diatonic) scales using D as the root note are:

D major scale: D (297), E (334.1), F# (371.3), G (396), A (445.5), B (495), C# (556.9), D (594).

D minor scale: D (297), E (334.1), F (356.4), G (396), A (445.5), B_b (475.2), C (528), D (594).

The Trouble with Changing Keys and Scales

C major scale: C (264), D (297), E (330), F (352), G (396), A (440), B (495), C (528)

D major scale: D (297), E (334.1), F# (371.3), G (396), A (445.5), B (495), C# (556.9), D (594).

If we compare the above just/diatonic scales of C major and D major, then we notice that the notes D, G, and B all have the same frequencies in both scales. We also notice that two of the notes in the D major scale have sharps, which weren't in the C major scale. Most troublesome, however, is that the notes E and A should be the same, but their frequencies are significantly different. This is part of the difficulty with a just/diatonic scale – if an instrument (e.g., a piano) is tuned for a particular piece in a particular musical key, then the instrument has to be re-tuned for a new piece that is in a different key. Also, with the circles of fifths, going up by 7 octaves should be the same as going up by 12 fifths. This would mean that $(^3/_2)^{12}$ should be equal to 2^7, but it is, again, significantly off.

The Equitempered Scale

By the 18th century the need arose for a scale system which allowed composers and musicians to move easily from one musical key to another (e.g., without re-tuning a piano or "fixed" instrument). While the just/diatonic scale is built on the notion that each interval has a simple ratio, resulting in a pure sound, the equitempered scale is built on the notion that every step in the scale must be equal. In other words, the percentage increase in frequency between any two neighboring notes must be equal. If we are looking for 12 equal (half) steps between A 440 and A 880, then we must solve:

$$880 = 440 \cdot R^{12} \rightarrow \text{Solving this leads to } R = \sqrt[12]{2} \approx 1.0595$$

This means that each half step increases in frequency by about 5.95%. Starting at A 440 gives us the standard 12-note equitempered scale, which we shall compare to the just/diatonic scale (see above):

Equitempered Scale:

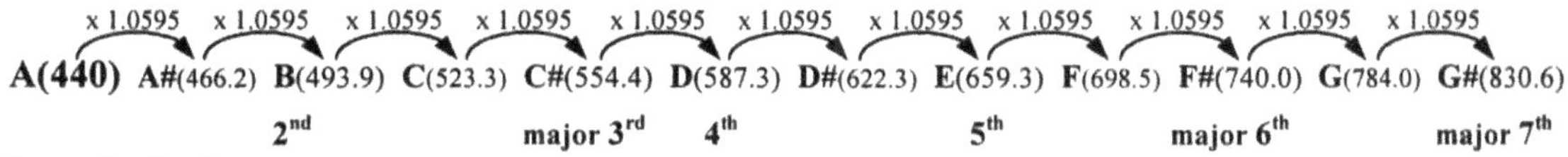

Just/diatonic Scale:

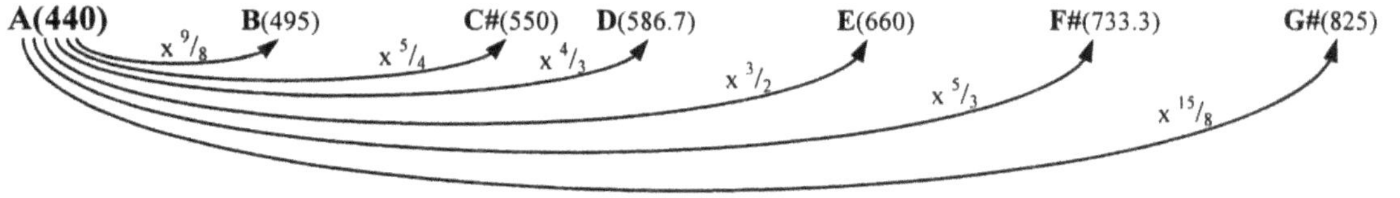

	Equitempered			Just/Diatonic		
Interval	F_E Freq	C_E Cents	Half-Steps	F_J Freq	C_J Cents	$C_E - C_J$ Error
Root (A)	440 Hz	0	0	440 Hz	0	0
mj. Third (C#)	554.4	400	4	550	386.3	+13.7%
Fourth (D)	587.3	500	5	586.7	498.0	+2.0%
Fifth (E)	659.3	700	7	660	702.0	-2.0%
mj. Sixth (F#)	740.0	900	9	733.3	884.4	+15.6%

"Cents" are used to compare two notes. a full octave is 1200 "cents". For example, to compare a "just" C# and A, we can solve $\frac{550}{440} = \sqrt[12]{2}^{C_J} \rightarrow C_J \approx 386.3$

This differs from an equitempered C# by 13.7 cents. Therefore, roughly speaking, the equitempered C# (third) is 13.7% of the way up to a D.

Frequencies of Notes of Various Equitempered Scales.

Note: The 12-note scale shown below is our standard equitempered scale, with the "ideal" frequencies of each of the 12 notes in the octave starting at A 440.

The Objective is to find a scale that "hits" the most important intervals: the fifth (3:2 ratio, 660Hz), the fourth (4:3 ratio, 586⅔Hz), the major third (5:4, 550Hz), and the major sixth (5:3 ratio, 733.3Hz). It can then be clearly seen that the 12-note and 19-note scales are best among the scales that divide the octave into less than 20 notes. It is interesting to note that the first nearly perfect scale requires the octave to be broken into 53 notes.

with 5 notes : 440.0 505.4 580.6 666.9 766.1 880.0

with 6 notes : 440.0 493.9 554.4 622.3 698.5 784.0 880.0

with 7 notes : 440.0 485.8 536.4 592.2 653.8 721.9 797.0 880.0

with 8 notes : 440.0 479.8 523.3 570.6 622.3 678.6 740.0 807.0 880.0

with 9 notes : 440.0 475.2 513.3 554.4 598.7 646.7 698.5 754.4 814.8 880.0

with 10 notes : 440.0 471.6 505.4 541.7 580.6 622.3 666.9 714.8 766.1 821.1 880.0

with 11 notes : 440.0 468.6 499.1 531.6 566.1 603.0 642.2 683.9 728.4 775.8 826.3 880.0

with 12 notes: 440.0 466.2 493.9 523.3 554.4 587.3 622.3 659.3 698.5 740.0 784.0 830.6 880.0

with 13 notes : 440.0 464.1 489.5 516.3 544.6 574.4 605.9 639.1 674.1 711.0 749.9 791.0 834.3 880.0

with 14 notes : 440.0 462.3 485.8 510.5 536.4 563.6 592.2 622.3 653.8 687.0 721.9 758.5 797.0 837.5 880.0

with 15 notes : 440.0 460.8 482.6 505.4 529.3 554.4 580.6 608.0 636.8 666.9 698.5 731.5 766.1 802.3 840.3 880.0

with 16 notes : 440.0 459.5 479.8 501.1 523.3 546.4 570.6 595.9 622.3 649.8 678.6 708.6 740.0 772.8 807.0 842.7 880.0

with 17 notes : 440.0 458.3 477.4 497.3 517.9 539.5 562.0 585.3 609.7 635.1 661.5 689.0 717.7 747.6 778.7 811.1 844.8 880.0

with 18 notes : 440.0 457.3 475.2 493.9 513.3 533.4 554.4 576.1 598.7 622.3 646.7 672.1 698.5 725.9 754.4 784.0 814.8 846.8 880.0

with 19 notes : 440.0 456.3 473.3 490.9 509.1 528.0 **547**.7 568.0 **589**.1 611.0 633.7 **657**.3 681.7 707.0 **733**.3 760.5 788.8 818.1 848.5 880.0

with 20 notes : 440.0 455.5 471.6 488.2 505.4 523.3 541.7 560.8 580.6 601.1 622.3 644.2 666.9 690.4 714.8 740.0 766.1 793.1 821.1 850.0 880.0

Comparison of Equitempered Scales

Percentage error from the ideal note is given in parentheses. (This is not "cents".)

# Notes in scale	Fifth 3:2 660Hz	Fourth 4:3 586.7Hz	Major Third 5:4 550Hz	Major Sixth 5:3 733.3Hz
12 notes	659.3Hz (0.11%)	587.3Hz (0.11%)	554.4Hz (0.80%)	740Hz (0.91%)
19 notes	657.3Hz (0.41%)	589.1Hz (0.41%)	547.7Hz (0.42%)	733.3Hz (0.00%)
22 notes	662.7Hz (0.41%)	584.3Hz (0.41%)	548.6Hz (0.26%)	728.4Hz (0.67%)
31 notes	658.0Hz (0.30%)	588.4Hz (0.30%)	550.2Hz (0.05%)	735.9Hz (0.35%)
53 notes	659.97Hz (0.0%)	586.69Hz (0.0%)	549.55Hz (0.08%)	732.8Hz (0.08%)

Note: The 53-note scale dates back to Ching Fang (78-37BC), a Chinese music theorist. This scale allows the most important intervals (including the second) to be nearly perfectly in tune for all keys. There are disadvantages to this 53-note scale, not the least of which is that a piano designed on this scale would need 53 notes to an octave, for a total of nearly 400 keys (as opposed to the standard 88-key piano). (See also http://en.wikipedia.org/wiki/53_equal_temperament.)

Musical Scale Graph for a 12-Step Equitempered Scale

Notes:

- This is the predominate scale in today's world of music.
- Instructions are found in Problem Set #5 from the Math & Music unit in our *10th Grade Workbook.*
- Notice how the fifth and fourth intervals fall right on the mark, and the third and sixth are slightly off.

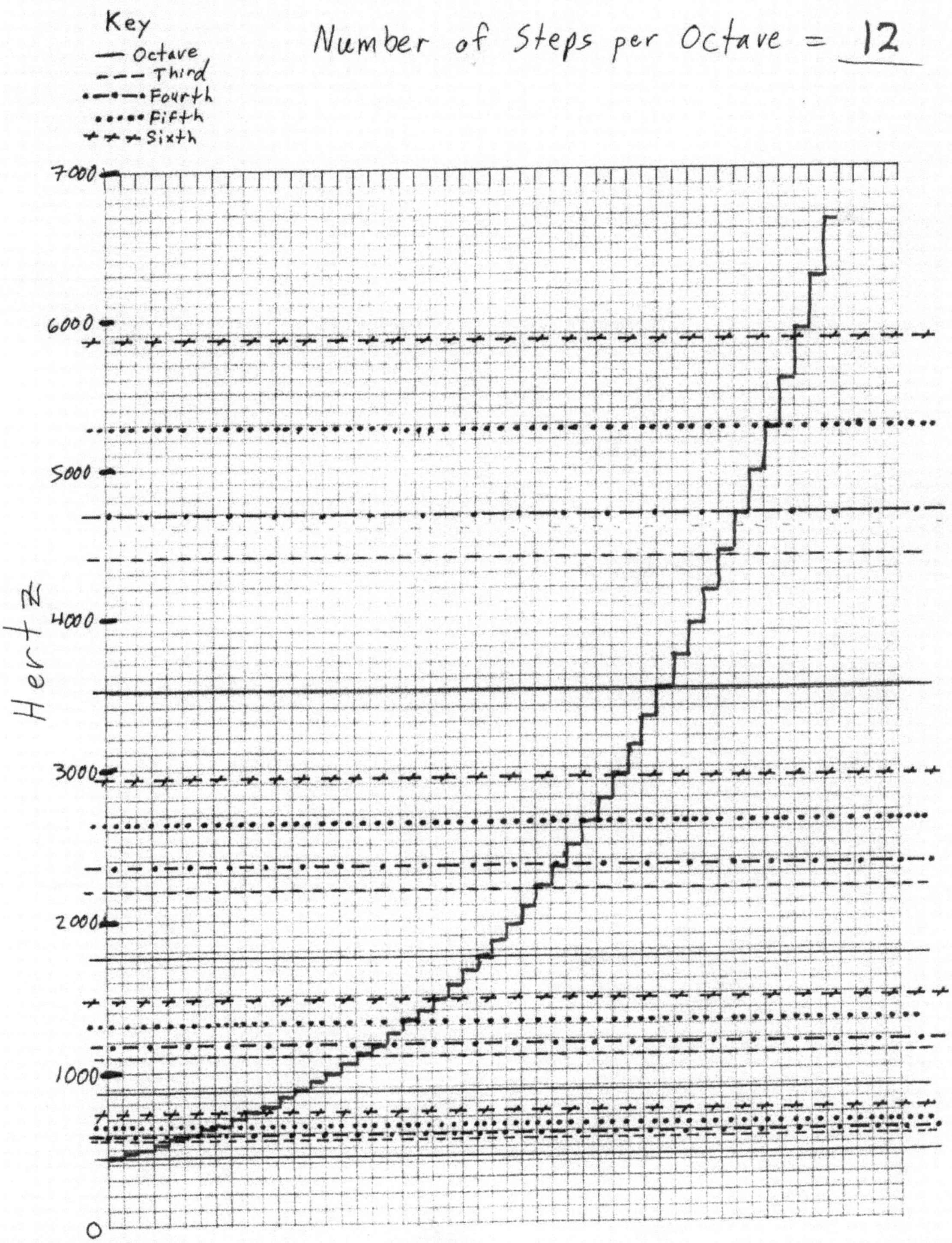

Musical Scale Graph for an 8-Step Equitempered Scale

Notes:

- Notice how every interval (except the octaves) badly misses the mark. This scale would sound awful.
- The instructions are found in Problem Set #5 from the Math & Music unit in our *10th Grade Workbook.*

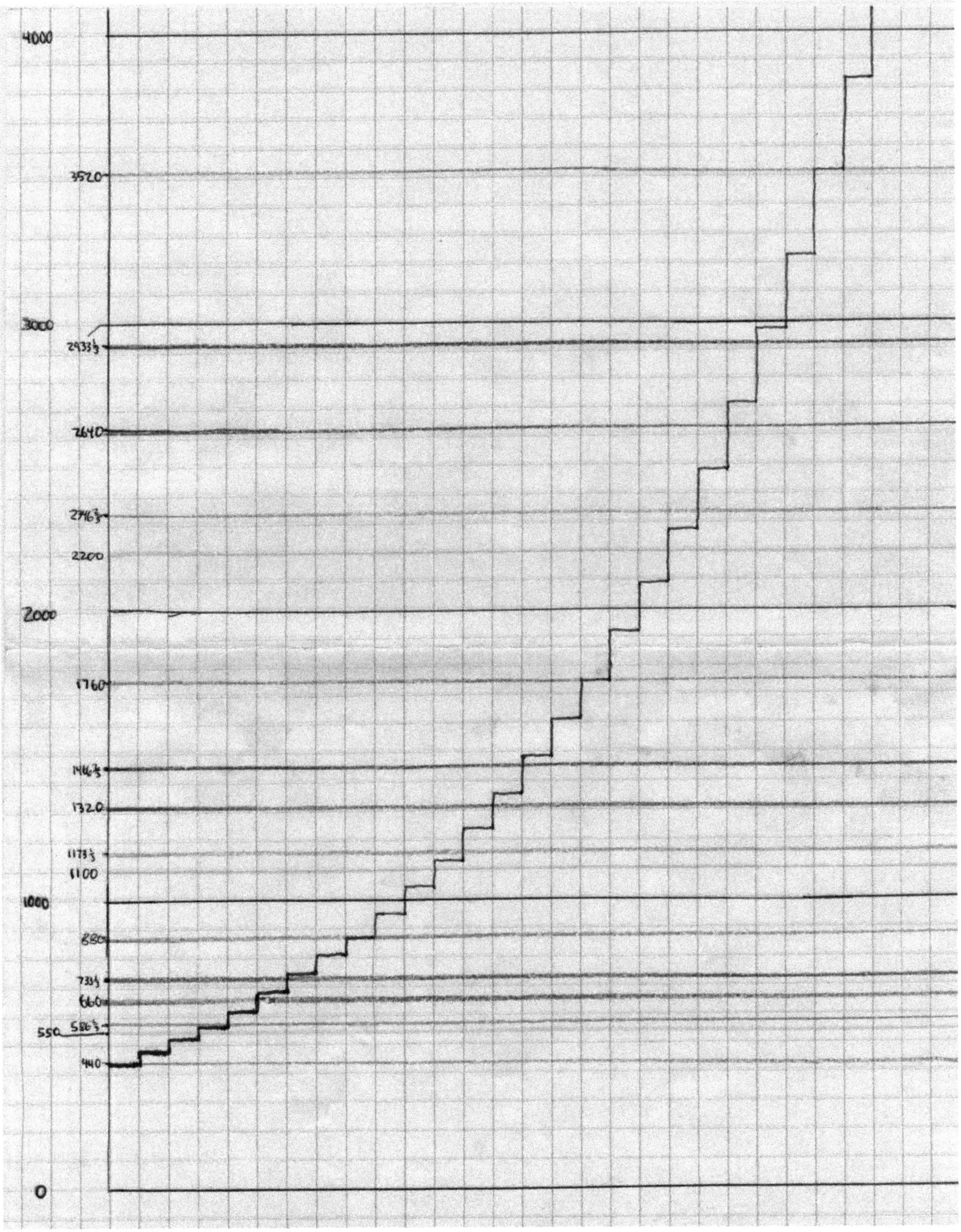

Template for a Musical Scale Graph

Number of Steps per Octave = ____

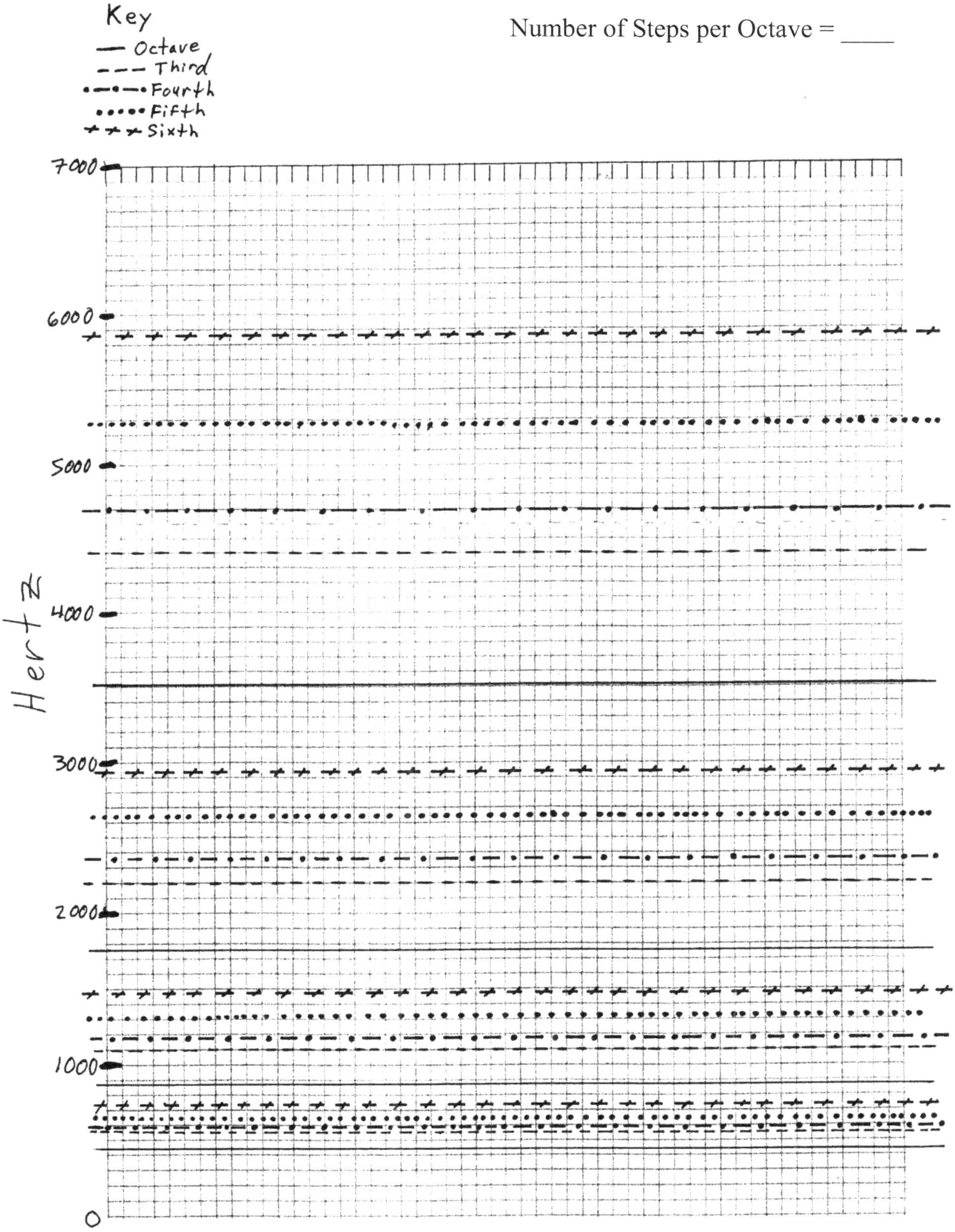

Examples of Keyboards using Different Equitempered Scales

<u>Notes</u>:

- The below drawings are taken from *Harmonie Universelle*, a book published in 1637 by Marin Mersenne, the Parisian theologian, philosopher, mathematician, and "father of acoustics".
- These drawings show prototype piano keyboards using 17, 19, 27 and 31 keys to the octave.

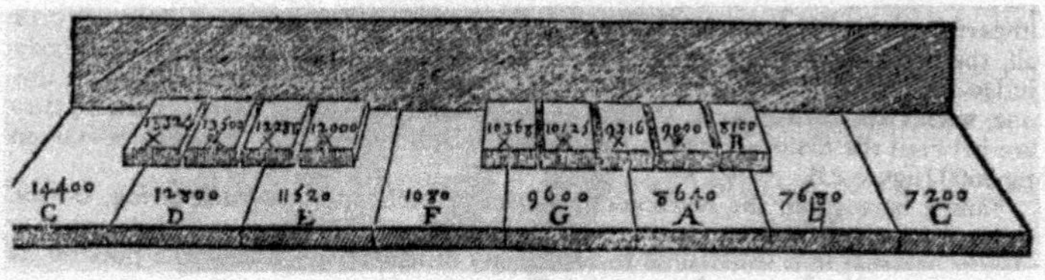

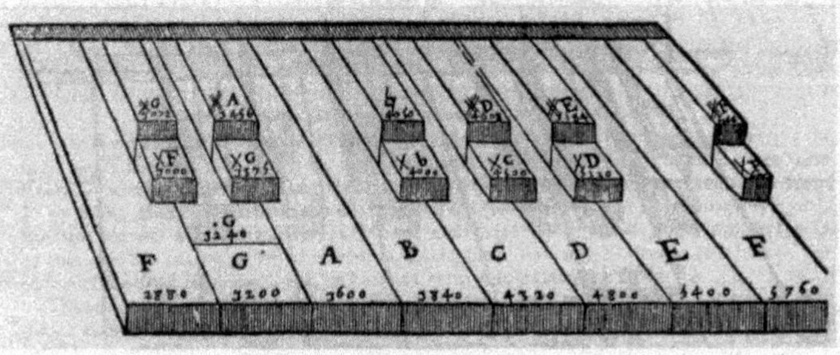

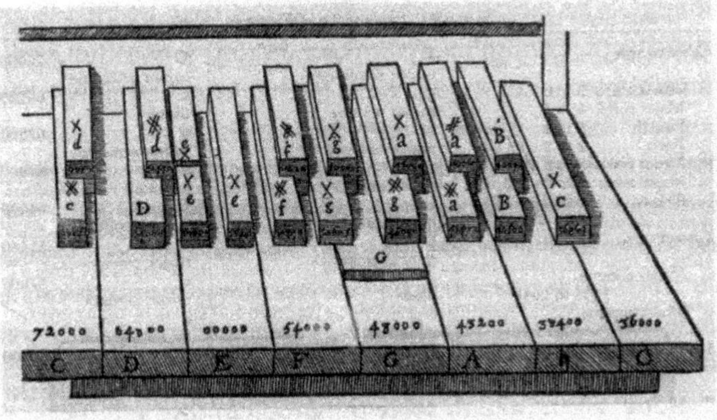

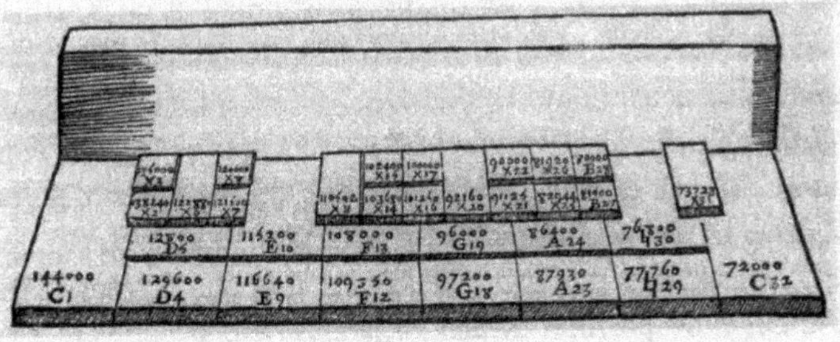

The Circle of Fifths

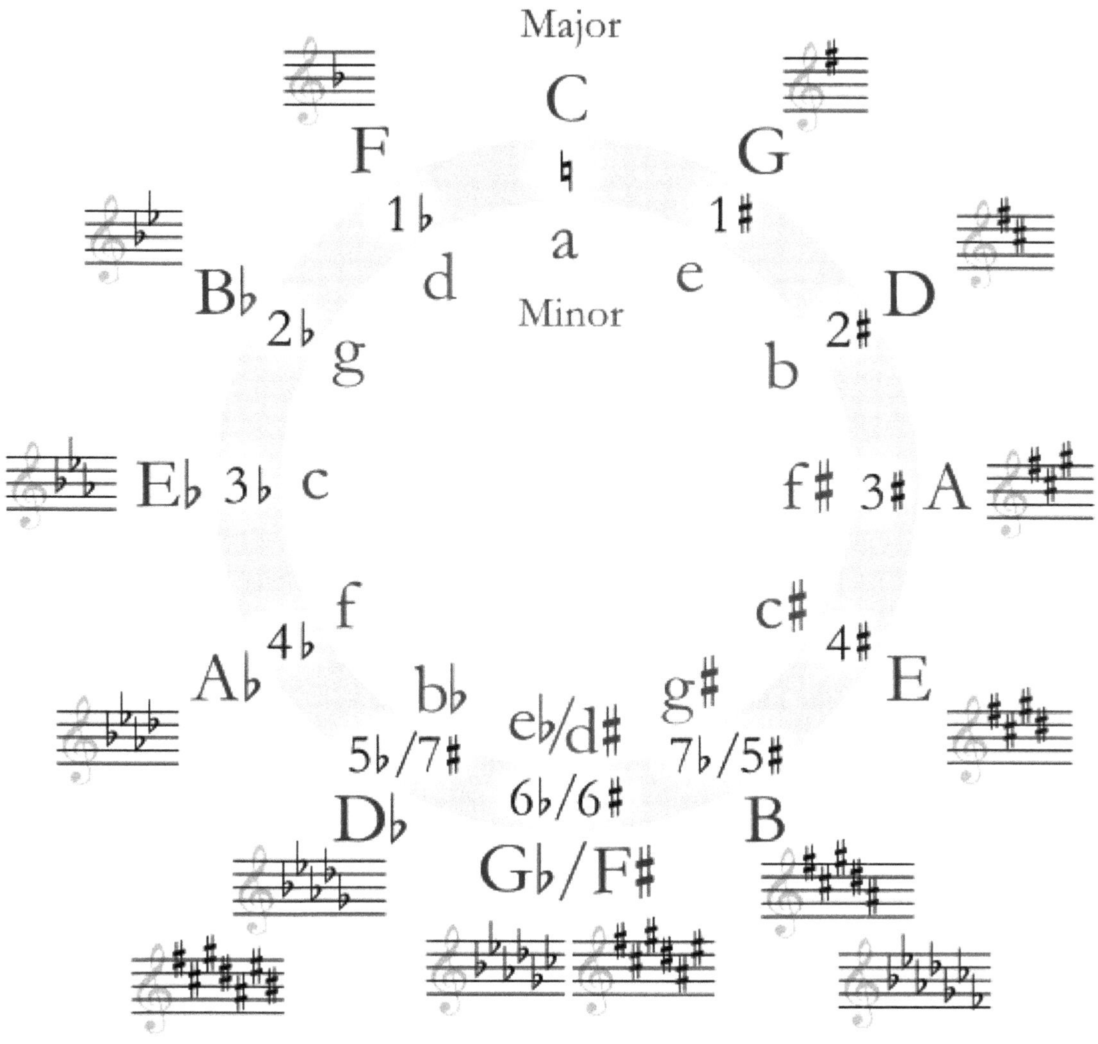

—— *Projective Geometry* (11th Grade Main Lesson) ——

Overview

In many ways, projective geometry – a subject which is unique to the Waldorf math curriculum – is the climax of Waldorf students' multi-year study of geometry. It gives the students a completely different experience of geometry. The thinking involved is both demanding and creative. For many students projective geometry is exciting and refreshing.

We start with a philosophical debate. Under some circumstances, it appears that two parallel lines meet. For example, artists during the Renaissance noticed that two lines, which are known to be parallel, actually meet in the drawing. Historically, it took a couple hundred more years before people dared to question Euclid's fifth postulate, which essentially states that two parallel lines never meet. We then decide to work – perhaps somewhat skeptically at first – with the assumption that two parallel lines meet at infinity. What happens then? This leads us to investigate many different theorems in projective geometry, including theorems from Pappus, Desargues, Pascal, and Brianchon. The topics get more sophisticated during the second half of the course as we study the principle of duality, line-wise conics, and conclude with an in-depth study of polarity.

Lesson plans

Detailed day-by-day lesson plans can be downloaded from our website: **www.JamieYorkPress.com**.

What this unit is

In order to cover all of projective geometry, this unit would have to be infinitely long. (I had to have one bad joke in this book.) In the space given here, I can only cover some of the basic ideas of projective geometry, and include some suggestions about what can be done in the classroom.

Advice for those new to projective geometry

I was completely new to projective geometry when I first started as a Waldorf teacher. I found it strange, challenging, and wonderful. I find that projective geometry takes years of slow, careful study before it completely sinks in. But there is no need to feel intimidated. As opposed to many topics in mathematics, where there is a clear list of topics that ought to be covered, projective geometry is vast and offers many possibilities. Projective geometry courses taught by two teachers could cover completely different topics and theorems and yet still accomplish the same goal: to have the students experience sense-free imaginative thinking and get a brief taste of this amazing subject.

If you are new to the subject, I would suggest the following progression: (1) Read through this unit and study the drawings, which will give you an impression; (2) study Olive Whicher's book, *Projective Geometry*; (3) study my projective geometry lesson plans (found on our website); (4) read Lawrence Edwards' book, *Projective Geometry*; and (5) read H.S.M. Coxeter's book, *Projective Geometry*.

Above all, the best way to really learn projective geometry is to take the time to do many, many drawings yourself. Ideally, all of this study would take place over a period of many months or years.

More than pretty pictures

The purpose of PG is *not* to just make pretty drawings. It is important for the students to understand deeply what the drawings represent. The process in the students' imagination is more important than the finished drawing. I want to encourage the students to experiment; not every drawing has to be in "perfect" finished form. Although I am not fond of having students display their work (people can't get much of an impression of what PG is by looking at a PG drawing), I often have the students complete one complicated drawing, such as the polarity of a curve, as a "final project" which gets displayed in my classroom for a while.

Grades and tests

I question the value of grades for any course, but especially for projective geometry, I have found grading very difficult and counter-productive. I could have one student quickly completing many drawings and making them all look beautiful, and then another student thinking deeply about a couple of drawings, experimenting, and only completing a few drawings that might look less beautiful. How do you grade this? For these reasons, I don't give grades in my projective geometry main lesson. Also, end-of-block tests often have questionable real value. For a number of reasons, I don't give a test during this block. (See also "Grades and Tests" under *Thoughts on Teaching Math* in the Introduction)

Projective geometry topics

What follows below is a description of selected topics from my projective geometry main lesson. Given the vast number of possible topics, I had to decide which topics to include, and, even more difficult, decide which topics to leave out. Another teacher would likely make different decisions.

Although there is no particular theorem that must absolutely be included in a projective geometry course, there are three topics or concepts that, in my opinion, should be given adequate attention:

(1) *Duality*. This is central to projective geometry.
(2) *Linewise conics*. This is not central to projective geometry, but it gives the students a wonderful opportunity to explore and create drawings that seem to penetrate the essence of a conic section.
(3) *Polarity*. For me, this wonderful topic is the highlight and climax of the main lesson block.

Advice for projective geometry drawings

Except for the students' final projects, I don't feel the need to have my students use large paper. No matter how large your paper is, points will sometimes end up inconveniently off the page. I encourage students to experiment first before doing a final drawing of a theorem. A quick rough draft may show that a final point is a bit off the page. What can I do to bring that point onto the page? This is part of the thinking process.

The Complete Triangle in Movement

- The "complete triangle" (or "projective triangle") divides the whole plane into four regions – not seven regions as it first seems. Three of the regions "pass through infinity".
- Have the students start with the triangle at "one o'clock" and color in each region in a different color. Then move to the triangle at two o'clock, keeping the colors of the four regions the same.
- Then we come to the critical moment (at three o'clock) when the lines are parallel. After much thought, and perhaps debate, we realize that the only viable option is that the middle region above the horizontal line is one color, and the region below it is a different color.
- The drawing of all stages of the *Complete Triangle in Movement* is shown on the right.
- We then discover another important question: Where is the apex of the triangle when two sides of the triangle are parallel? This leads us to "Our Postulate" (see below).

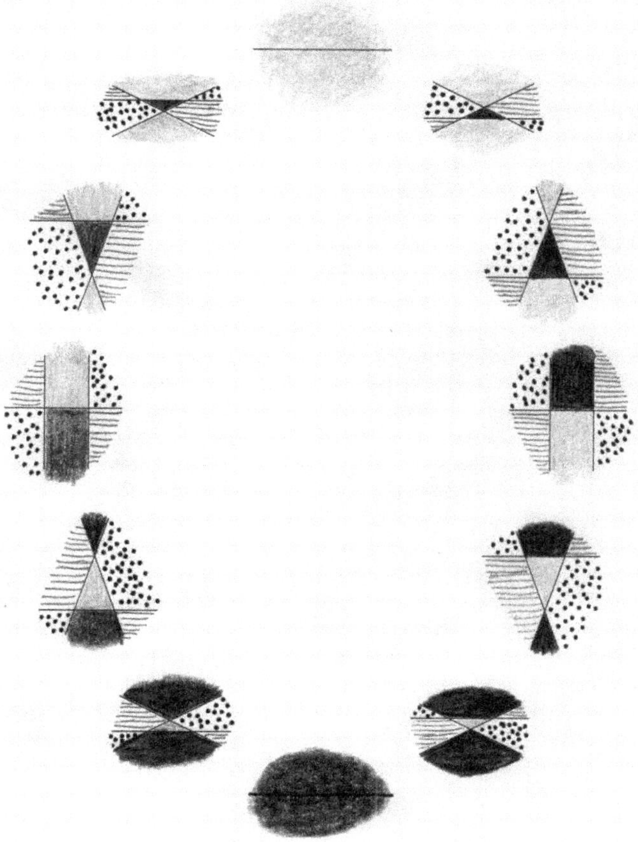

Kepler's Propeller

With the drawing shown here, the two lines intersect at point A. Now imagine that line p rotates clockwise like a propeller, and as it rotates, the point of intersection (A), moves along to the left.

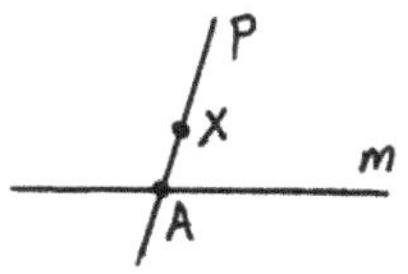

<u>The big question</u>: Where is point A at the instant when the two lines are parallel?

- <u>Option #1</u>: *Euclid's answer:* There is no point – the point disappears for an instant.
- <u>Option #2</u>: *What it seems like:* There are two points – one point infinitely far in each direction.
- <u>Option #3</u>: *The PG answer:* There is one point –infinitely far in both directions at the same time. Projective geometry likes this answer because them we can say there is always one point.

Theorem of Pappus

Given any three points (A, B, C) *on one line and another three points* (A', B', C') *on another line, the three corresponding pairs of lines* (AB' & A'B, AC' & A'C, BC' & B'C) *meet in collinear points.*

- Label points A, B, C on one line (**ℓ**) and A', B', C' on another line (m). (See #1, below.)
- Have each pair of corresponding lines in a different color (i.e., AB' and A'B are both blue, AC' and A'C are both orange, BC' and B'C are both green, etc.). In this way, one of the intersecting points is where two green lines meet, one is where two orange lines meet, and one is where two blue lines meet. (The below drawings have dotted lines instead of colored lines.)
- The theorem says that these three points of intersection must fall on one line – the "Pappus Line".
- *Remember: there are two ways to draw a line*: (1) Given two points; (2) Given a point and a direction
- *Play with Infinity!* Encourage the students to be adventurous and try some of the following:
  - Arrange it so that one of the intersection points is at infinity (see drawing #2, below).
  - Arrange it so that all three intersection points are at infinity (see drawing #3, below).
  - Start by placing A' at infinity, or A and A' at infinity, or A and B' at infinity (see #4 & #5).
  - Put the whole of line **ℓ** at infinity, with points A, B, C in three different directions (see #6).

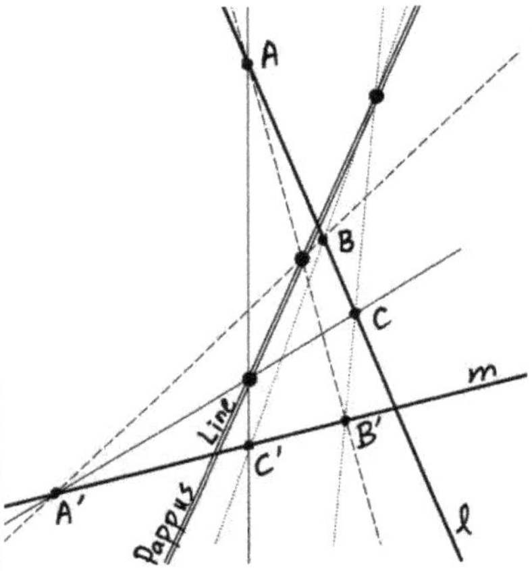

<u>#1</u>: "Normal" drawing of the Theorem of Pappus with all points on the page.

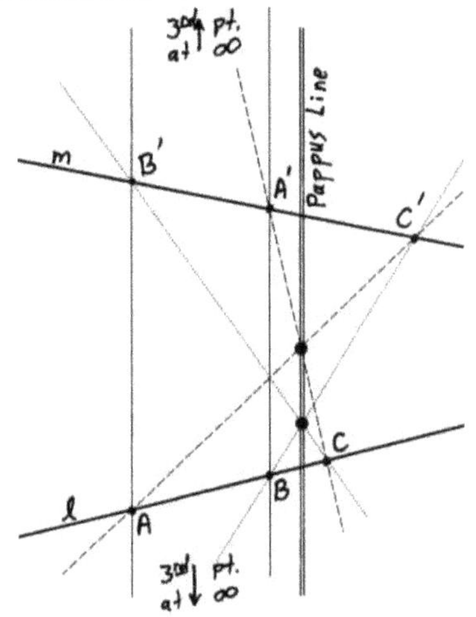

<u>#2</u>: Drawing of the Theorem of Pappus with the third intersecting point at infinity, but the Pappus line is still on the page.

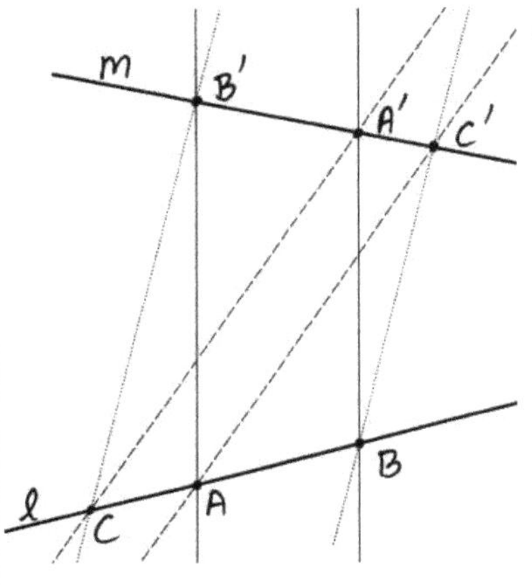

<u>#3</u>: Drawing of the Theorem of Pappus with all three intersecting points at infinity in different directions. <u>The Pappus line is the line at infinity</u>!

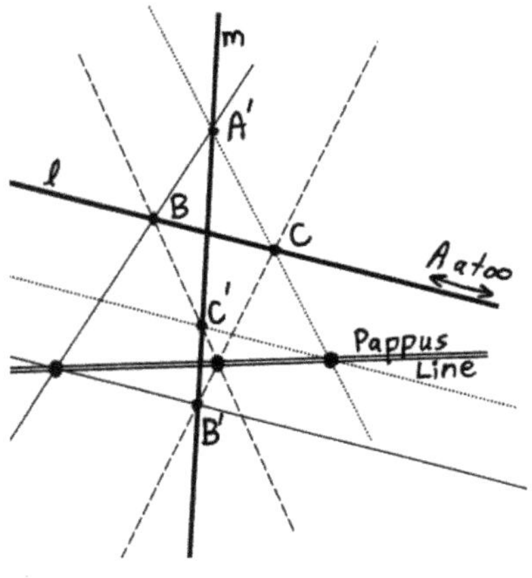

<u>#4</u>: Drawing of the Theorem of Pappus starting with A at infinity. Note that lines AB' and AC' must be parallel to line ~~m~~ ℓ.

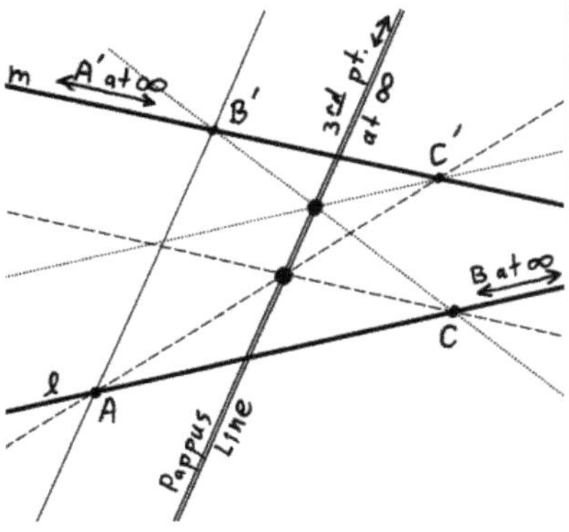

<u>#5</u>: Drawing of the Theorem of Pappus starting with A' and B at infinity. A'B is then the line at infinity.

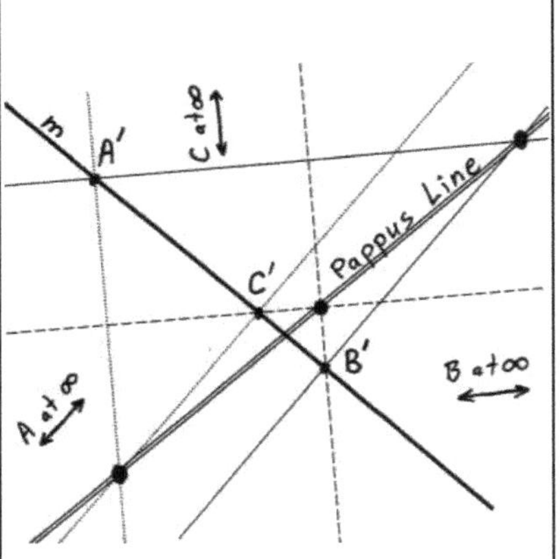

<u>#6</u>: Drawing of the Theorem of Pappus starting with the whole of line **ℓ** at infinity. The points A, B, C are in three different directions.

Our "Postulate": Two parallel lines meet at one point at infinity.

- This idea is supported by the *Complete Triangle in Movement*, by *Kepler's Propeller* (see lesson plans), and the *Theorem of Pappus*. In each case, this postulate eliminates the need for exceptions.
- Of course, it is wonderful to have some healthy debate around this strange concept. But after a while, we agree to accept this (but you don't have to believe it) and see where it takes us.

The Line at Infinity

- This is the same as Kepler's propeller, but raised by one dimension.
- Two parallel planes meet at one infinitely-distant line, which we will call the "line at infinity".
- It is through the Theorem of Pappus that we are led to the idea of the line at infinity. (See drawing #3 on the previous page.)
- It is incorrect (although tempting) to think of *line at infinity* as the line that (like a circle) "bounds" the plane. But, it is not a boundary – you can "go past" it. It is not a circle. The line at infinity is straight even though we have the illusion that it surrounds us!
- The *line at infinity* is the collection of all of the points on a given plane that are infinitely far away.
- A *hyperbola* passes through the line at infinity in two places. An *ellipse* does not intersect the line at infinity. A *parabola* (being the magical instant between an ellipse and a hyperbola) is tangent to the line at infinity (at one point).

Theorem of Pascal

If the vertices of an ordered hexagon lie on a conic, then the three pairs of opposite sides meet in collinear points.

- Start with a circle. Choose six points on the circle labeled in any order. Draw colored lines connecting points: 1→2 green, 2→3 orange, 3→4 purple, 4→5 green, 5→6 orange, 6→1 purple. (In the drawings shown here, we have used dotted and dashed lines instead of color.) Mark the points of intersection of like-colored lines.
- Pascal's Theorem works with any conic!! Students should experiment a lot with circles, ellipses, parabolas, and hyperbolas. And, as always, look for ways to play with infinity (see drawing below, right).
- If we started with a regular hexagon in a circle, with the points labeled in clockwise order, then the Pascal line would be at the line at infinity.

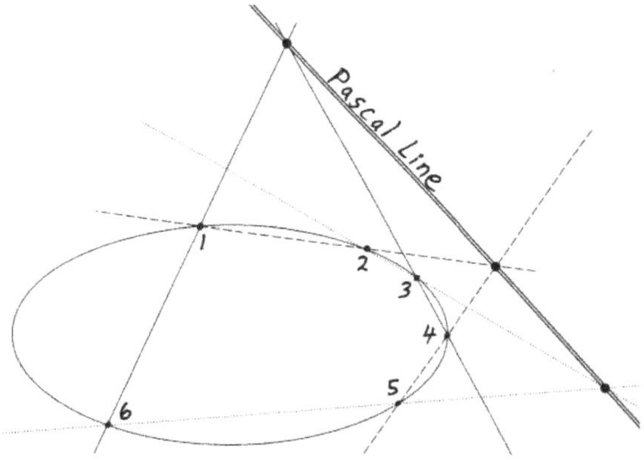

"Normal" drawing of the Theorem of Pascal with the points labeled in clockwise order.

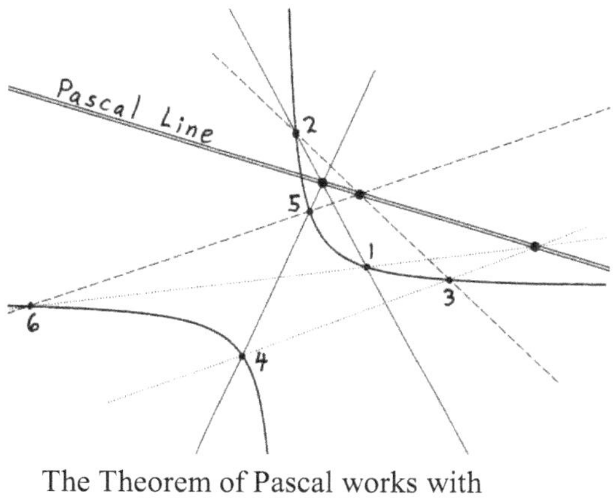

The Theorem of Pascal works with any conic (a hyperbola here) with the points labeled in any order.

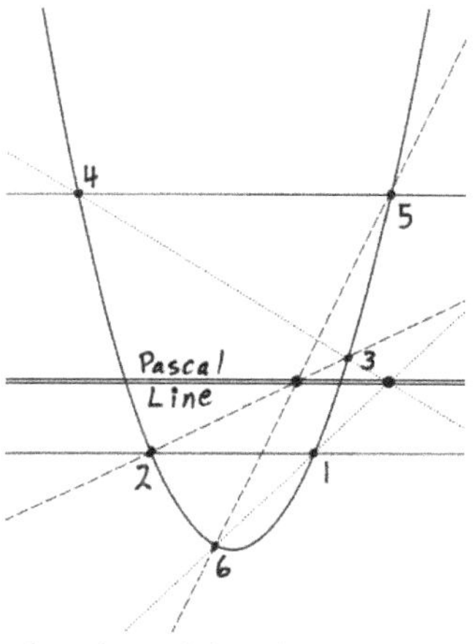

A drawing of the Theorem of Pascal on a parabola where one pair of corresponding lines (1-2 and 4-5) is parallel. The third point of intersection is on the Pascal line at infinity.

Perspectivity

- The general concept of a *perspectivity* is that if two figures are in perspective to a point, then corresponding points can be joined to form concurrent lines (i.e., multiple lines that meet in one point).
- *A two-dimensional perspectivity of a figure from one plane to another.* We can imagine a square on the ground, and a painter drawing the square on a canvas. Looking through one eye, and keeping his head very still, his eye serves as the point of perspectivity. Point A on the ground's square, point A' on the canvas's square (which isn't a proper square) and the painter's eye all lie on a line. Three other lines in space go from the painter's eye through points of the canvas's square, to corresponding points of the ground's square.
- *A two-dimensional perspectivity of two figures on one plane.* The concept and criteria is the same as above; the only difference is that it all takes place on one plane. The below drawings show different examples of a pair of triangles in perspective, with point P as the point of perspectivity. Note that we have drawn "Euclidean" triangles in order to make the triangles easier to see. Proper projective triangles have sides that are infinitely long. The last example (on the right) has one of the triangles with parallel sides (and therefore one of its points at infinity), which works just fine!

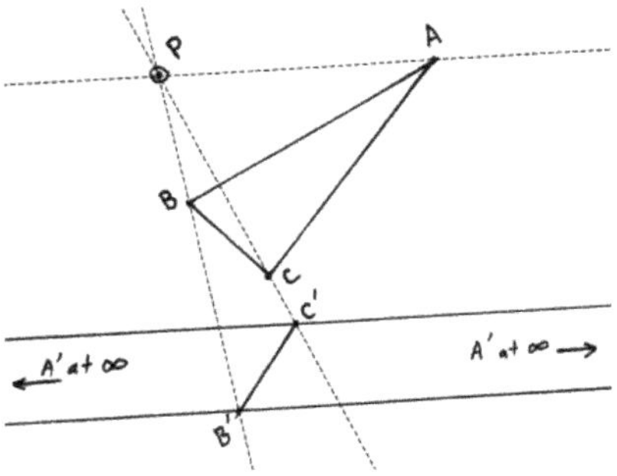

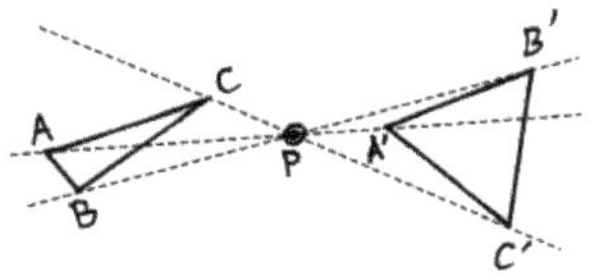

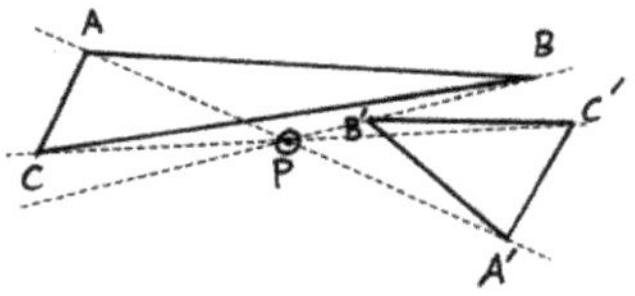

- *A one-dimensional perspectivity of the points on one line to the points on another line.* The below drawings show how the points from line ℓ are perspected through point P onto line m. Note how in the second example point 4 is perspected to infinity.

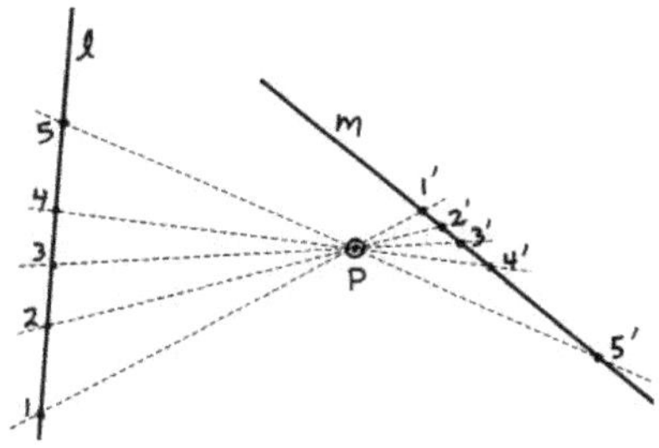

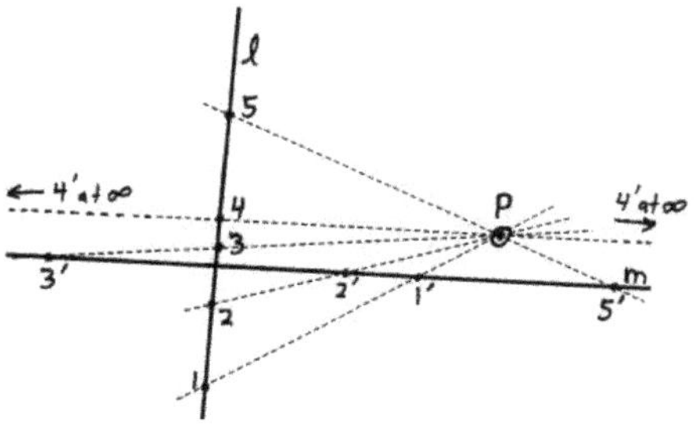

Projectivity

A projectivity is a series of two or more perspectivities.

- Here we will only concern ourselves with *one-dimensional* projectivities.
- We can transform the above two perspectivities into projectivities by simply adding another point of perspectivity (Q) and perspecting the points from line m to line n, as shown in the below drawings. In total, the points (imagine all infinitely many points) on line ℓ have been perspected through point P to line m, and then through point Q to line n. More simply put: *this is a projectivity of the points on line ℓ to the points on line n.*

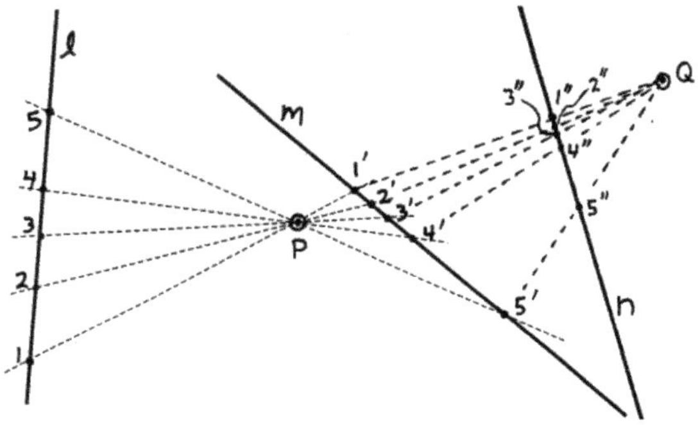

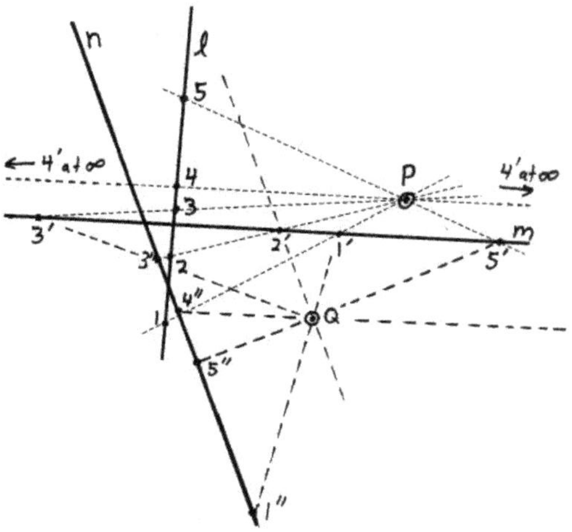

Theorem of Desargues

If two triangles are perspective to a point, then they are also perspective to a line

- To understand the above statement, it is helpful to think about the following two statements:
  - If two figures are in perspective to a point, then *corresponding points form concurrent lines* (see previous page).
  - If two figures are in perspective to a line, then *corresponding lines meet at collinear points*.
  - The above two statements are duals of each other. (See *duality* on the next page.)
- With the three examples below, we show the drawing in two stages: first, starting with two triangles in perspective; then, extending the sides of the triangles to see where corresponding sides intersect (meet). The theorem says that the three points of intersection will always be collinear.
- As with nearly every theorem and drawing in projective geometry, we should look for opportunities to "play with infinity", which is what we have done with the third example.

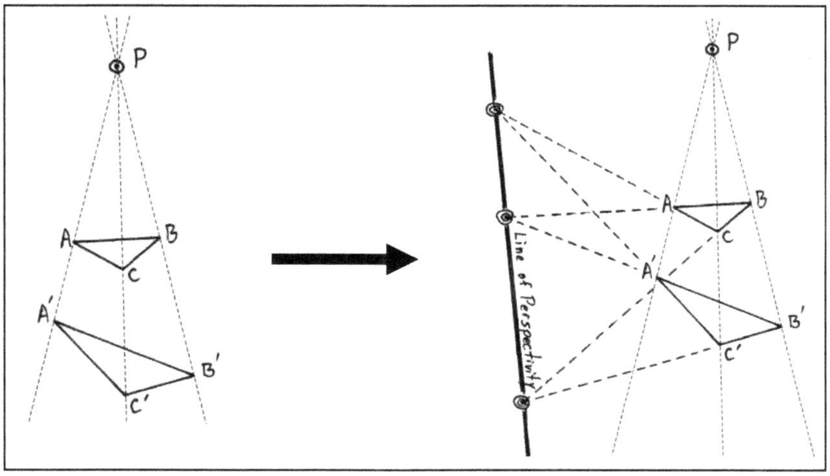

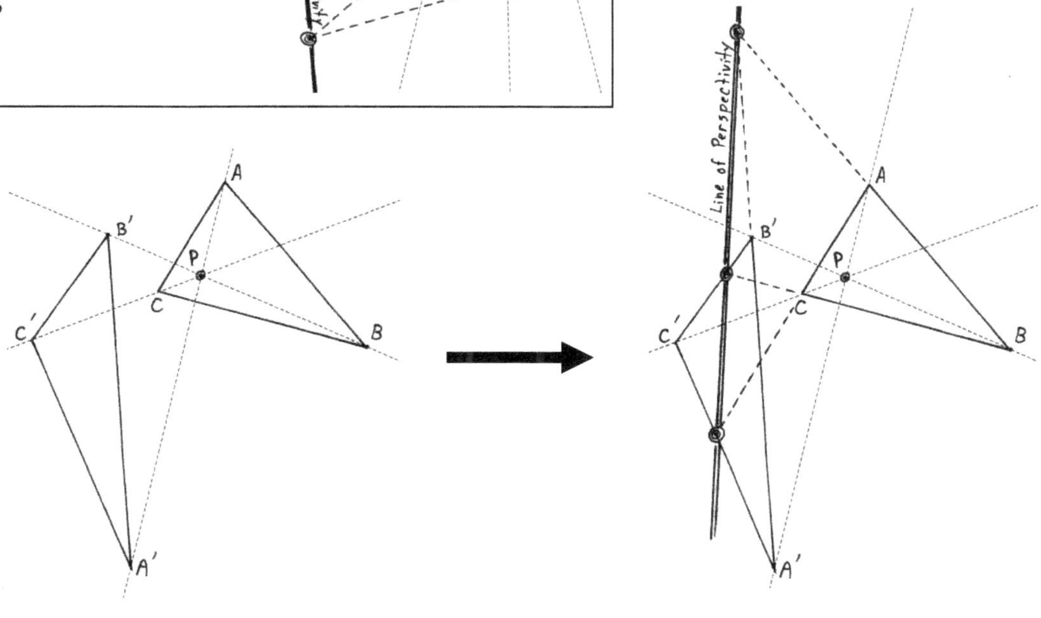

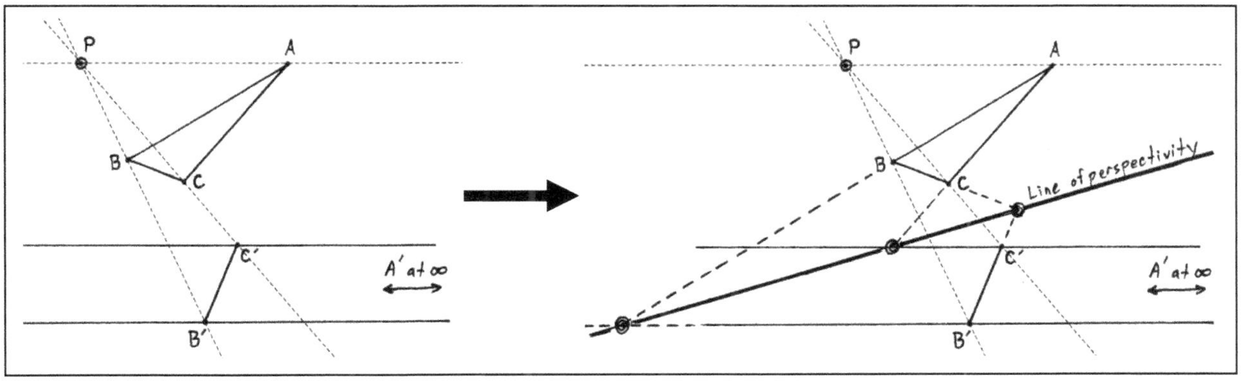

Duality

- The principle of duality is a central (and amazing) property of projective geometry.
- *Two-dimensional duality*. In short, whatever is true for points, is also true for lines. Every theorem or statement in projective geometry has a dual form. If we switch the words (and ideas) "point" and "line", we get another valid theorem or statement. Below are some helpful examples:

Original Statement		**Dual Statement**
Three points are on a line.	→	Three lines pass through a point.
Postulate: Any two points have a common line.	→	Any two (coplanar) lines have a common point.
Quadrangle: Start with 4 points on a plane, no 3 of which are collinear. You can draw 6 lines connecting pairs of points. Using these six lines, we can locate three new points of intersection between lines, which gives us the *diagonal triangle*.	→	*Quadrilateral*: Start with 4 lines on a plane, no 3 of which are concurrent. You can locate 6 points of intersection between pairs of lines. Using these six points, we can draw three new lines connecting points, which gives us the *diagonal triangle*.
The below drawing shows two quadrangles perspective to a point.	→	The below drawing shows two quadrilaterals perspective to a line.

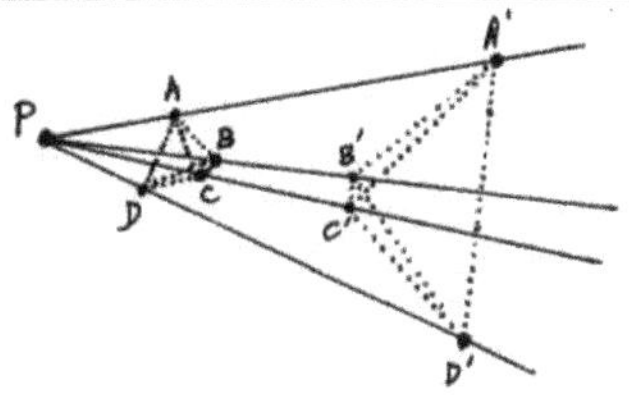

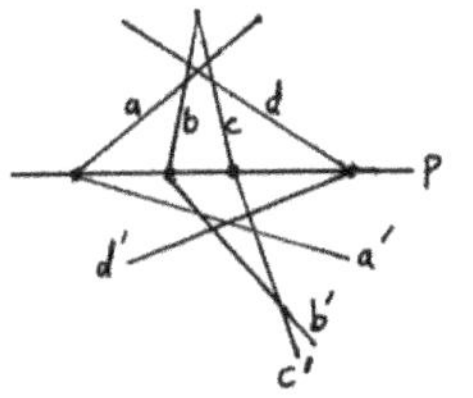

Original Statement		**Dual Statement**
Theorem of Pappus: Given 3 points on one line and 3 points on another line, the 3 corresponding pairs of lines meet in collinear points.	→	*Dual of Pappus*: Given 3 lines through one point and 3 lines through another point, the 3 corresponding pairs of points can be joined in concurrent lines.
Theorem of Pascal: If the vertices of an ordered hexagon lie on a conic, then the three pairs of opposite sides meet in collinear points.	→	*Theorem of Brianchon*: If the sides of an ordered hexagon lie on a conic, then the three pairs of opposite vertices can be joined by concurrent lines.
Theorem of Desargues: If two triangles are perspective to a point, then they are also perspective to a line.	→	*Converse of Desargues*: If two triangles are perspective to a line, then they are also perspective to a point.
The below drawing shows a perspectivity of the points on line ℓ to the points on line m.	→	The below drawing shows a perspectivity of the lines through point L to the lines through point M.

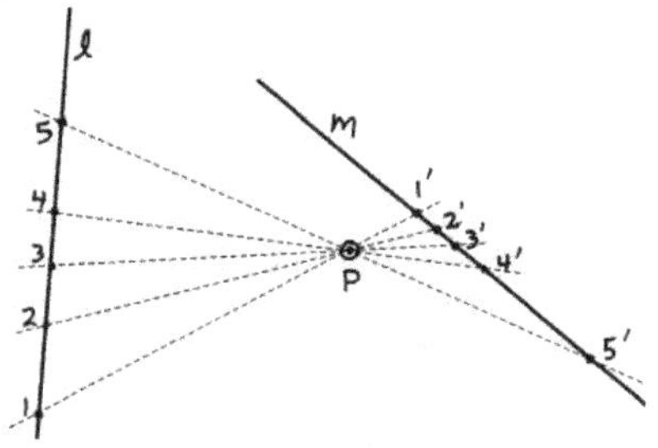

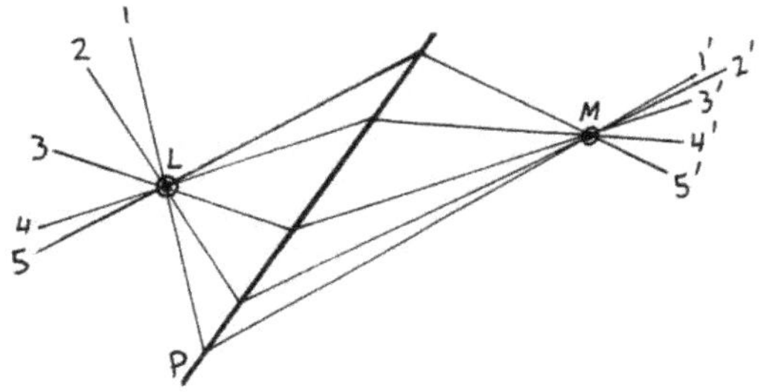

Dual of Pappus

- Once the students are introduced to the idea of duality they need to practice *doing* it. Working through a drawing of the dual of Pappus is an excellent exercise.
- In order to do the dual of the Theorem of Pappus, we do the dual of each step. It helps to first write down the steps that we followed for the drawing of the Theorem of Pappus. (The below instructions correspond with the color-coding I do on the chalkboard.)

Theorem of Pappus

- Draw two (white) lines, ℓ and m.
- Choose three (white) points on each line. Label them A, B, C & A', B', C'.
- Draw lines that join these points:
  - AB' and A'B (green lines)
  - BC' and B'C (orange lines)
  - AC' and A'C (blue lines)
- Mark points of intersection (in yellow) of the same-colored lines.
- The three (yellow) points should be collinear. Draw a (pink) line through them.

Dual of Pappus

- Mark two (white) points, L and M.
- Choose three (white) lines through each point. Label them A, B, C & A', B', C'.
- Find points where these lines intersect:
  - AB' and A'B (green points)
  - BC' and B'C (orange points)
  - AC' and A'C (blue points)
- Draw lines (in yellow) that join same-colored points.
- The three (yellow) lines should be concurrent. Mark a (pink) point where they intersect.

- The below three drawings are examples of the dual of Pappus. As always, look for opportunities to play with infinity! What happens if point M is at infinity? Can you even start with both points, L and M, at infinity? (Yes, you can!) What would that look like?

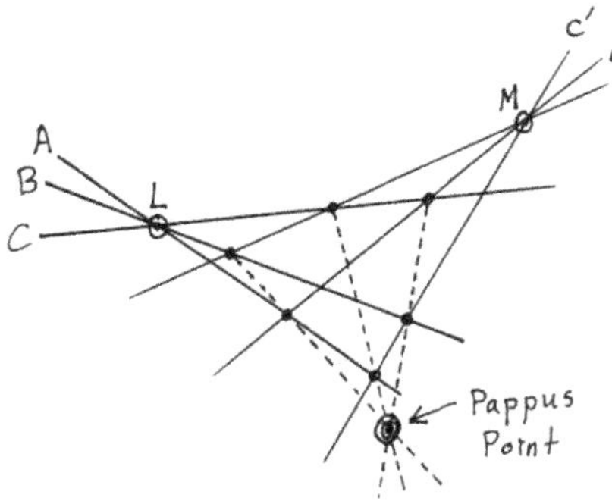

Normal drawing of the Dual of Pappus with everything falling conveniently on the page.

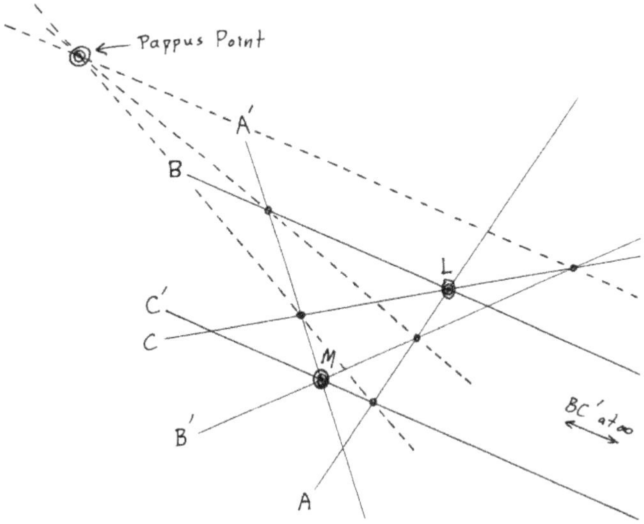

Drawing of the dual of Pappus where I have made B parallel to C'. Notice that the line connecting points B'C and BC' passes through B'C and heads in the direction of BC', which means that it must be parallel to lines B and C'. The Pappus point appears nicely on the page.

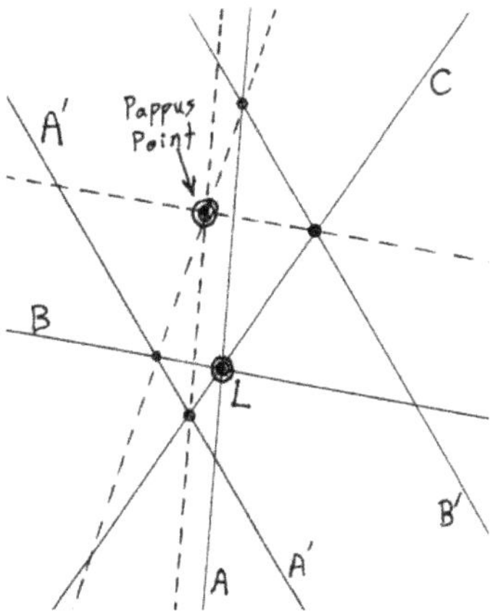

Playing with infinity. In this dual of Pappus drawing, point M is at infinity (which is also the place where lines A' and B' meet), and line <u>C' is the line at infinity</u>. The Pappus point is on the page!

Theorem of Brianchon

If the sides of an ordered hexagon lie on a conic, then the three pairs of opposite vertices can be joined by concurrent lines.

- The Theorem of Brianchon is the dual of the Theorem of Pascal.
- Perhaps the best way to approach this is the same way that we did the dual of Pappus – simply write down detailed steps for how we did the Theorem of Pascal, and then take the dual of each step, substituting the word "point" for "line", "line" for "point", etc. So instead of starting with six ordered points on the conic, we start with six ordered (tangent) lines on the conic. The rest follows quite easily. And – I feel the need to say it again – look for opportunities to play with infinity!
- The three drawings below show examples of the Theorem of Brianchon. Normally I show opposite vertices in the same color – so I need to use three different colors. With the drawings below, I have indicated opposite vertices by highlighting them with squares, triangles, and filled-in circles. Vertices 1-2 and 4-5 are squares, vertices 2-3 and 5-6 are triangles, and vertices 3-4 and 6-1 are circles.
- As with many projective geometry drawings, the greatest challenge can be to figure out where to place the original (tangent) lines and number them in such a way that the final result (in this case, the Brianchon point) appears on the page.
- As always, look for opportunities to play with infinity!

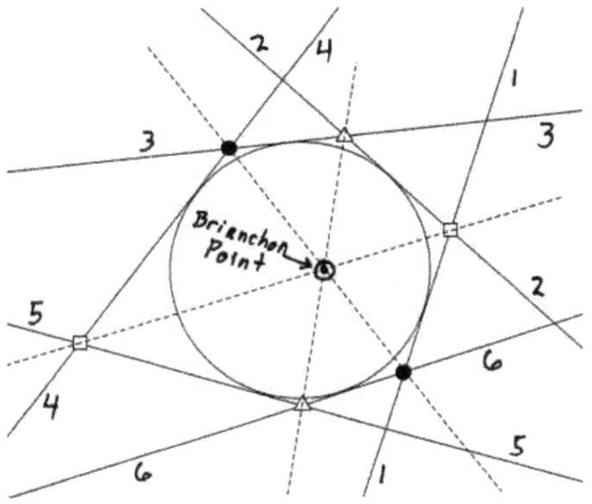

A "normal" looking version of the Theorem of Brianchon where the ordered hexagon is circumscribed around the conic (circle) and the lines are numbered in clockwise order. If it were instead a regular hexagon, then the Brianchon point would be at the center of the circle.

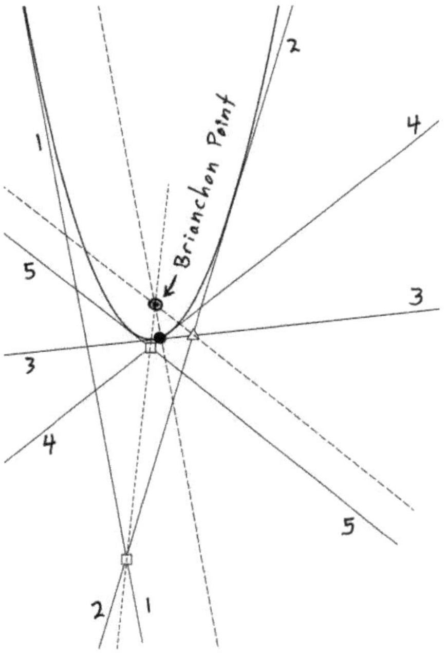

The Theorem of Brianchon with a parabola. Since a parabola is tangent to the line at infinity (see *The Line at Infinity*, above), we have used the line at infinity as tangent line #6. Therefore, the intersection of lines #5 and #6 (shown by a triangle) is the infinitely distant point on line #5. When this point is connected to vertex 2-3 (also shown as a triangle), the line is parallel to line #5. The same can be said for the intersection of lines #1 and #6.

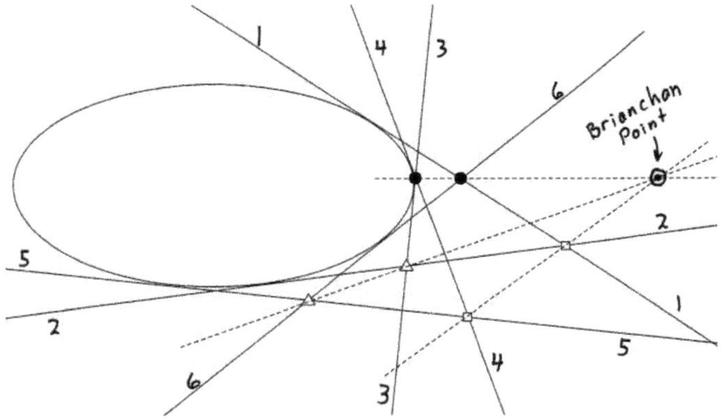

This drawing of the Theorem of Brianchon has lines that are numbered in a random order, and demonstrates that the tangent lines don't have to wrap around the ellipse.

Line-wise Conic

- Be sure to read *Tips for the Line-Wise Conic drawings* from the lesson plans (on our website).
- The step-by-step instructions are as follows:
  1) Choose at random, lines x, y, ℓ, and points P and Q.
  2) Mark 20 points on line x. (The points closest to point P should be the closest together.)
  3) From each one of these 20 points on x, draw a line through point P.
  4) With each one of these 20 lines on P, mark the point that it intersects with line ℓ.
  5) From each one of these 20 points on ℓ, draw a line through point Q.
  6) With each one of these 20 lines on Q, mark the point that it intersects with line y.
  7) Draw the 20 connecting lines (in blue) from each point on x to its corresponding point on y.
  8) The curve is formed by the blue lines.
- I usually have the students attempt one drawing on their own, but it is hard to know if the resulting line-wise conic will appear on the page nicely. This can become unnecessarily frustrating, so I allow their second drawing to be from my *Template for a Line-Wise Conic* (in the following pages), where x, ℓ, P, and Q are all given, as well as the first perspectivity of the 20 points on line x through P onto line ℓ. They simply need to place line y somewhere, and then complete the rest of the drawing.

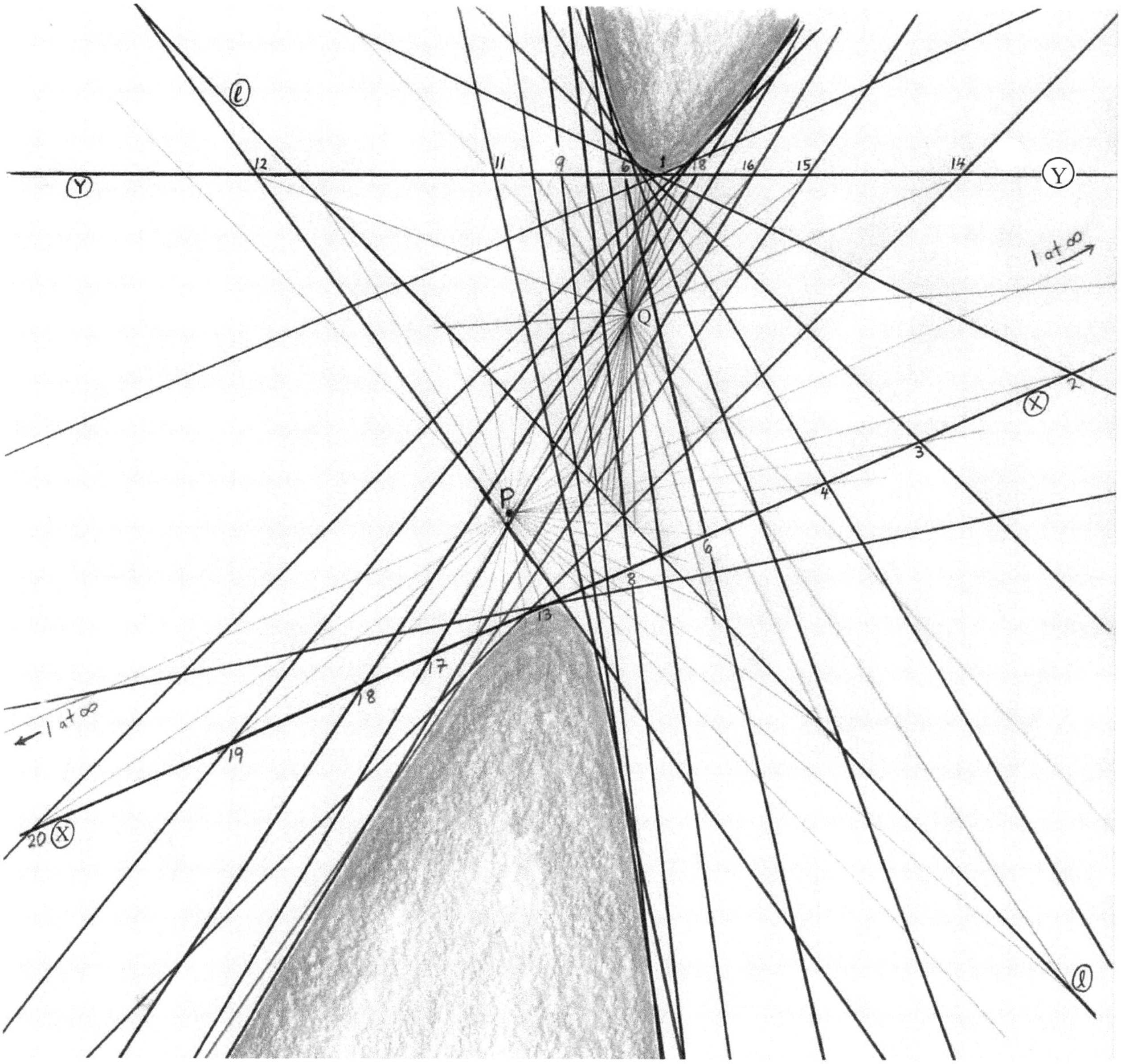

- *Conic Transformation – the Metamorphosis of a an Ellipse into a Hyperbola.*
  - Here is something that I often do with my class. I assign each student a number from 2 to 25, with one special student getting the "number" infinity. Each student begins with the *Template for a Line-Wise Conic*, and then draws line Y horizontally across the page at a distance (in centimeters) up from the bottom of the page equal to their assigned number (assuming that the page has a height of 11 inches or 28 cm). After their drawings are complete, it is wonderful to put all of the drawings together to see the movement.

    The below drawings show four key moments of this transformation. This is a similar transformation that I show in my Descartes block with the "Pappus problem". See the explanation in *The Geometry of Descartes* unit, below.

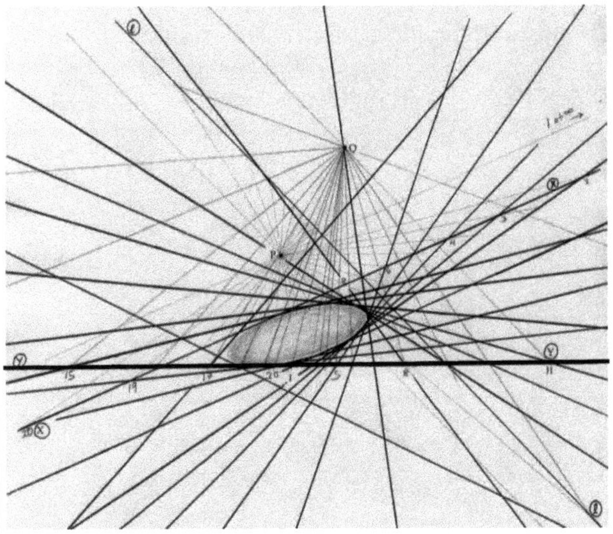

Drawing #1 – Ellipse: Line y is horizontally across the page and attached to the ellipse.

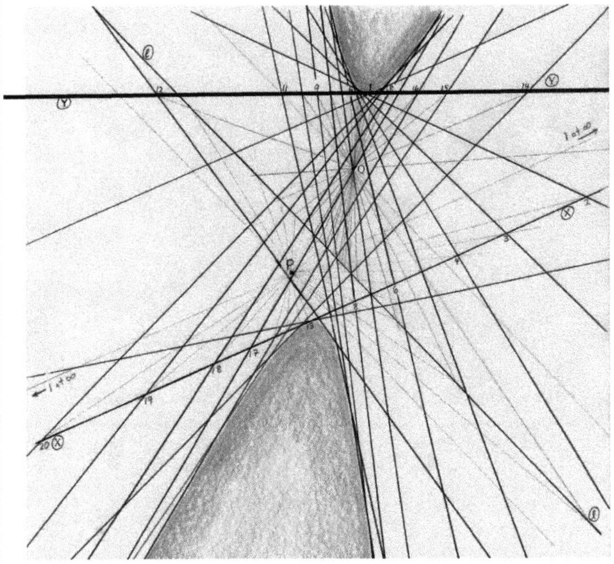

Drawing #4 – Hyperbola: Line y has returned from infinity, and we see how the ellipse has now been turned inside-out.

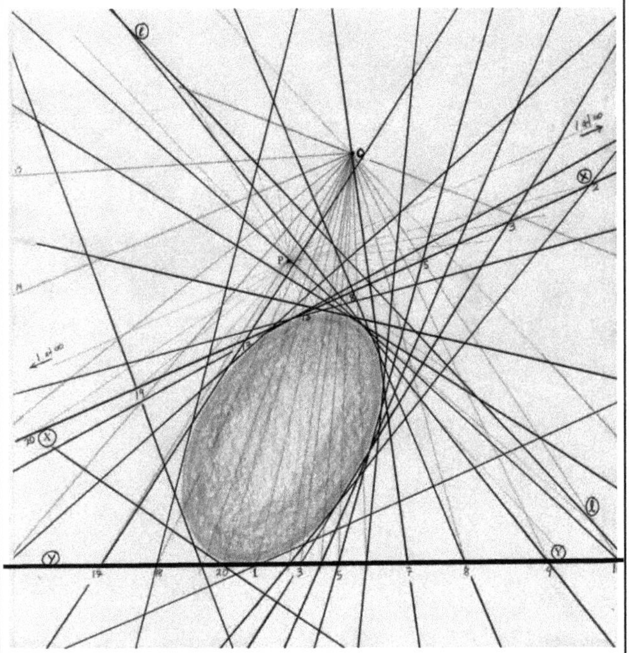

Drawing #2 – Ellipse: Line y moves down the page forcing the ellipse to stretch out.

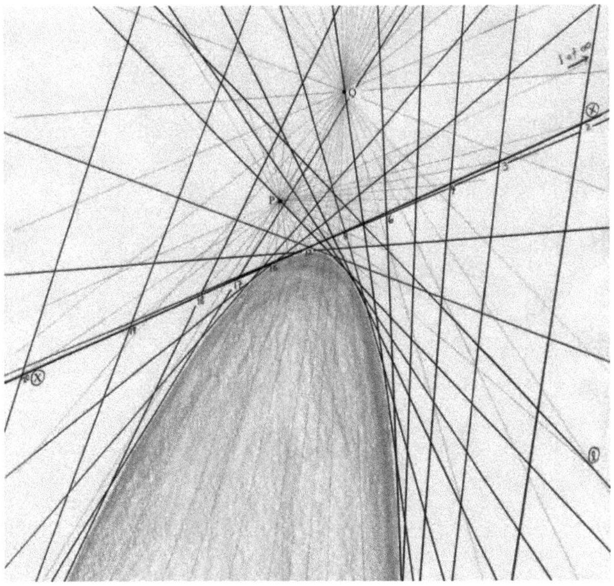

Drawing #3 – Parabola: Line y moves to infinity, stretching the ellipse with it. This shows that a parabola is an ellipse that has been stretched to infinity.

Point-wise Conic

- The point-wise conic drawing is somewhat more difficult than the line-wise conic. Often, due to lack of time, the only students who do this drawing are those who need the extra challenge.
- The step-by-step instructions are simply the dual of the instructions for a line-wise conic:
  1) Choose at random points X, Y, L, and lines p and q.
  2) Draw 20 lines through point X.
     With each one of these 20 lines through X, mark the point that it intersects with line p.
  3) From each one of these 20 points on p, draw a line through point L.
     With each of these 20 lines on L, mark the point that it intersects with line q.
  4) From each one of these 20 points on q, draw a line through point Y.
  5) Mark the 20 points of intersection (in blue) of the corresponding lines passing through x and y.
  6) Draw the curve so that it passes through the blue points as well as points X and Y.
- The step-by-step sequence is shown below. I have started with only 6 lines on X to make it easier to follow. Of course, we should have 20 lines, and make sure that some of them "deal with infinity".

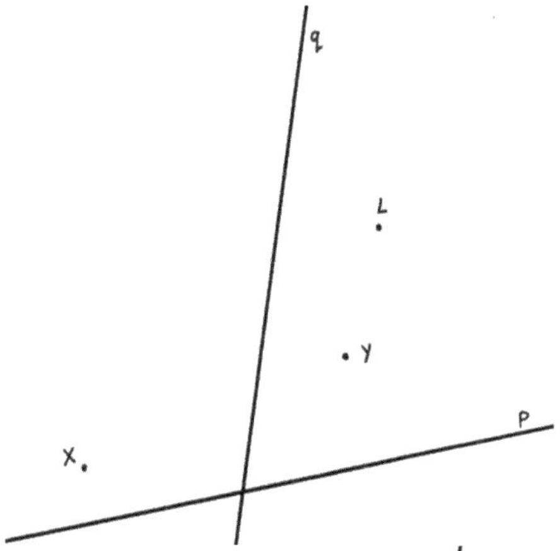

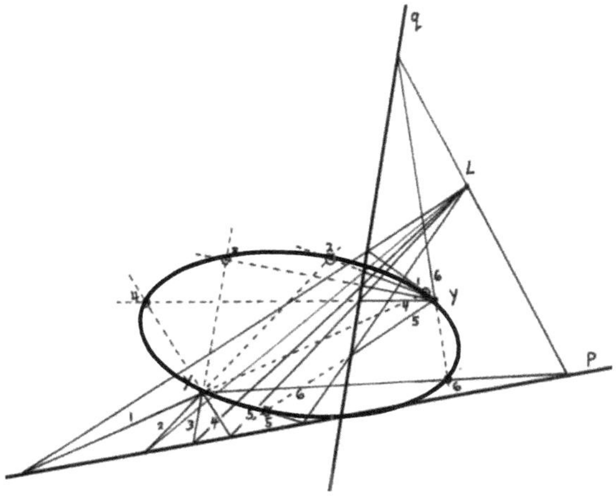

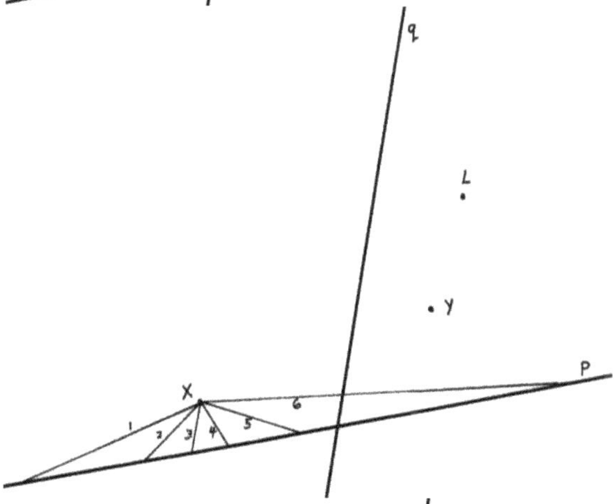

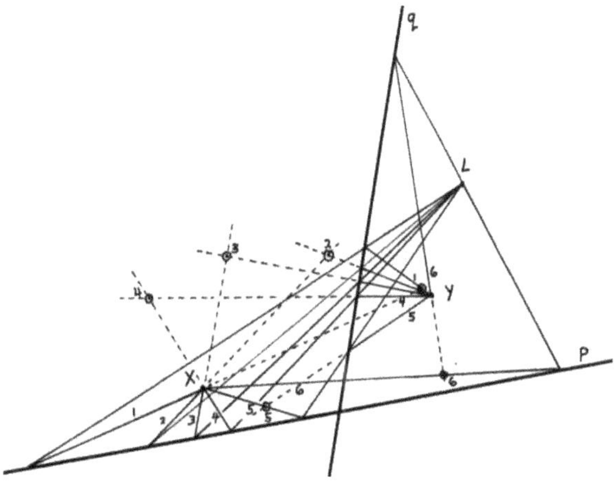

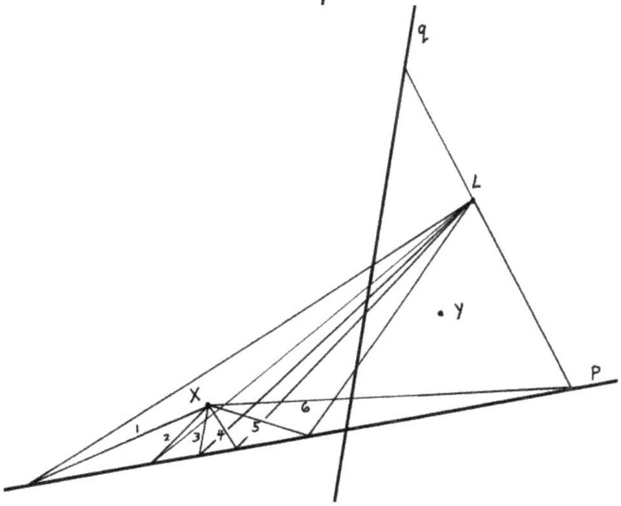

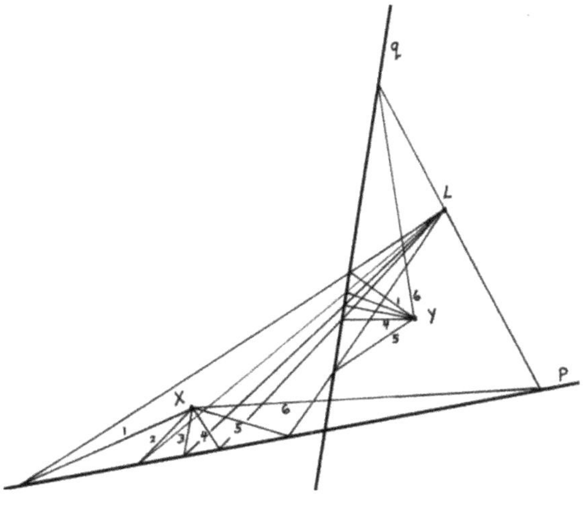

Characterizations of Projective Geometry

The below list is a collection of ideas that can be covered at some point during the main lesson:

- With projective geometry, "normal geometry" gets turned on its head. For example:
  - No such thing as "between". On a line, we can get from A to B by going in either direction.
  - No such thing as a point being "inside" a triangle;
  - We can no longer say that the angles in a triangle add to 180°.
  - There is no measurement, therefore there are no special triangles (isosceles, etc.), no squares, no rectangles, etc. Any circle is just a conic section.

- *Infinity and Dimensions.*
  - On a plane (2D), any two parallel lines (1D) meet at one infinitely distant point (0D); every line (1D) includes one point (0D) at infinity.
  - In space (3D), any two parallel planes (2D) meet at one infinitely distant line (1D); every plane (2D) includes one line (1D) at infinity.
  - In 4D hyperspace, and two parallel 3D spaces meet at one infinitely distant plane (2D); every 3D space includes one plane (2D) at infinity.
- Any given triangle can be transformed through a projectivity to take the shape of any other triangle. Every triangle is identical to every other triangle. In projective geometry, we can say that :
  - *Every triangle is "congruent" to every other triangle.* Similarly, we can say that…
  - *Every conic is "congruent" to every other conic* (an ellipse can be made into a parabola or hyperbola).
  - *Every pair of (coplanar) lines is "congruent" to every other pair of (coplanar) lines.*

The truth about parallel lines

This is important for the teacher to understand…

One hundred years ago, projective geometry textbooks often started with the postulate or assumption that "two parallel lines meet at infinity". Olive Whicher's book starts with this assumption. Many Waldorf teachers believe that in projective geometry it is a fact that "two parallel lines meet at infinity". And, when I teach projective geometry, I start with this "postulate" because I want my students to experience it as it developed historically.

However, *parallel lines don't actually exist in modern projective geometry – nor does infinity.* In true projective geometry, we simply begin with the postulate: "Any two coplanar lines meet at one point."

So what is the truth about parallel lines? Modern physics and mathematics demands a different kind of thinking and understanding to such questions. Our thinking can no longer be as black and white as it used to be – for example, as it was with the ancient Greeks. There isn't a simple answer to this question. Sometimes, the Euclidean idea is helpful (parallel lines never meet), and at other times, it is helpful to think of parallel lines as meeting at infinity.

And, as Euclidean beings, it is helpful, when doing a projective geometry drawing, to think of parallel lines as meeting at one point (in both directions) at infinity.

Harmonic Conjugates

- *Quadrangle*

Any four points (no three of which are collinear) define a quadrangle (PQRS, as shown below, left). There are six lines which can be drawn that connect pairs of the quadrangle's points (as shown below, middle). These six points meet at three new points of intersection: A, C, X, which form the quadrangle's *Diagonal Triangle*. Draw a line (ℓ) through any two of the three points of the diagonal triangle (in the below drawing, we have chosen points A and C). The six lines of the quadrangle meet line ℓ in four points. Points A and C are said to be *harmonic conjugates* of points B and D.

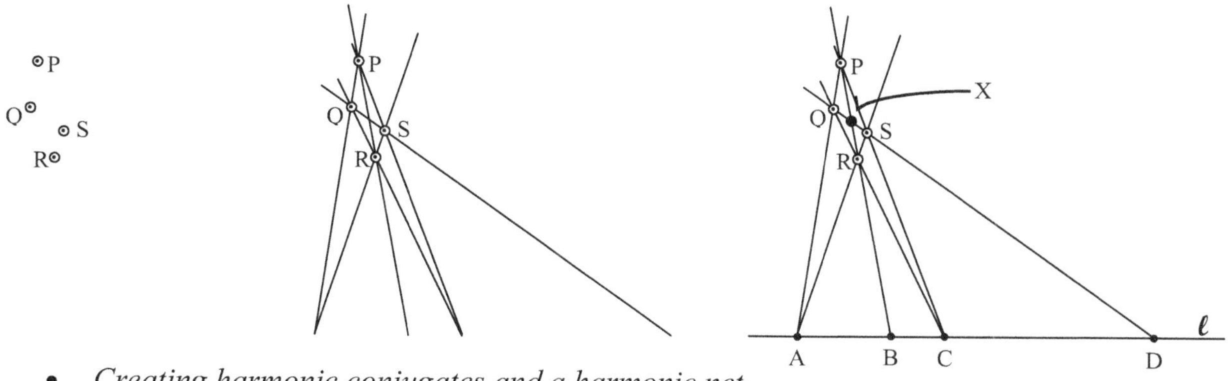

- *Creating harmonic conjugates and a harmonic net*

To create pairs of harmonic conjugates, we essentially work backwards from what was done above. We start with any three points (A, C, D) on a line. Our goal is to locate point B such that points A and C are harmonic conjugates with points B and D. We start by drawing any two lines through point A, and one line through point D. (See below drawings.) This gives us two points of intersection through which we draw two new lines to point C. Two new points of intersection are formed, through which a line is drawn that locates point B.

It is surprising to learn that if we had chosen three different initial lines through points A and D, then we would produce different quadrangles, but the final location of point B would be exactly the same.

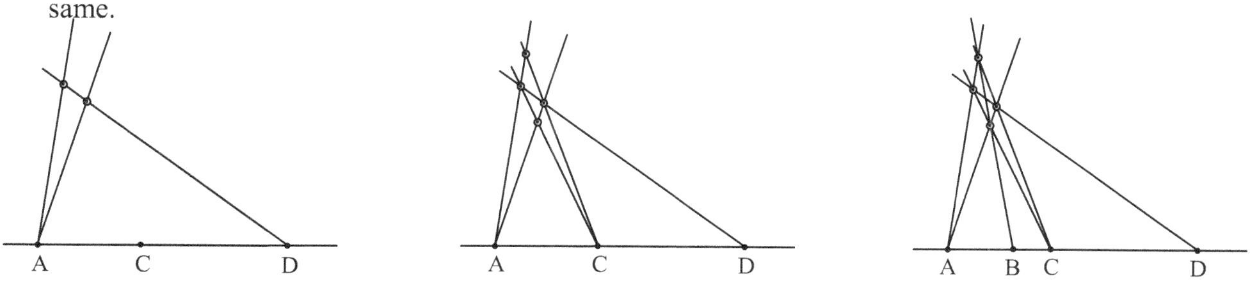

We can also continue to draw lines through new points of intersection in order to create a *harmonic net*, as shown on the right.

Surprisingly, a harmonic net can be used as an alternative coordinate plane to graph algebraic relations and functions – an exercise which is found in our *11th/12th Grade Workbook.*

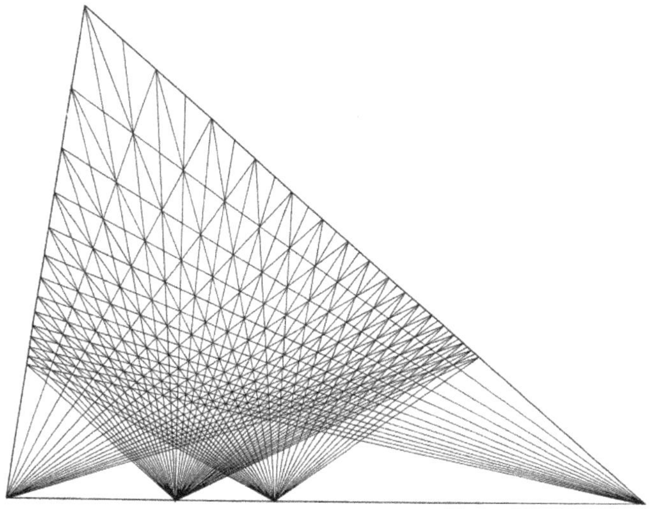

A Harmonic Net

The General Idea of Polarity

- This topic rarely gets the attention it deserves. This topic cultivates spatial imagination, and culminates with elaborate drawings of the polarity of curves. (See the following pages.)
- Generally speaking, we can say that polarity is "specific duality".
  - Our goal is to take the polarity of any curve, which roughly means to "turn it inside-out".
  - Any polarity is done with respect to a "polarity conic". This polarity conic serves as a kind of mirror. To simplify matters, we will always use a circle as the polarity conic, but it could be any conic.
  - We begin with these fundamental ideas:
    - The polar of the "infinitely distant line" (the line at infinity) is the "infinitely inward point" (the center of the circle).
    - The polar of a point (A) on the polarity conic is the line (a) tangent to the polarity conic at that same point, as shown at the right.

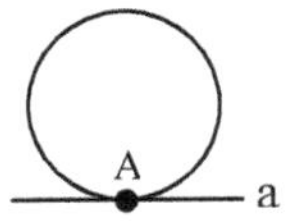

- *Important imagination for polarity.* This 9-frame "video" shows what happens as line a moves.

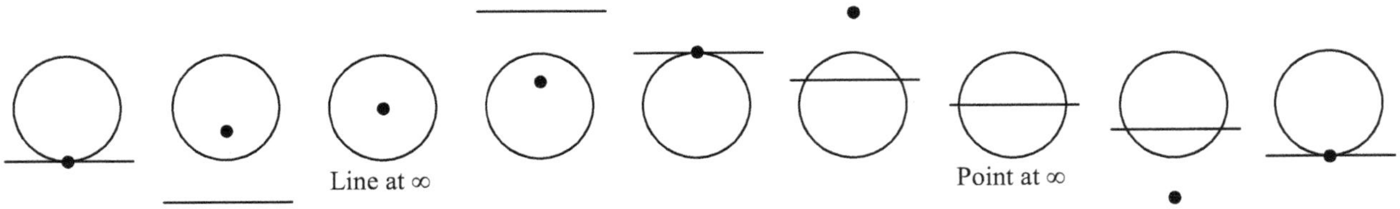

- *Exercises for constructing polarities* – try to have the students discover each one:
  1. *The polar of a point outside the circle.* (See drawing on the right.) From the given point, we first draw two lines that are tangent to the circle. The desired polar line is drawn by connecting the two points of tangency.
  2. *The polar of a line that crosses the circle.* This drawing is the same as for #1, but everything is done in reverse.
  3. *The polar of a line outside the circle.* (See drawing on the right.) We start by choosing any two points on line a. Then we find the polar line of each of these two points. These two lines meet at the desired polar point, A.
  4. *The polar of a point inside the circle.* This drawing is the same as for #3, but everything is done in reverse.

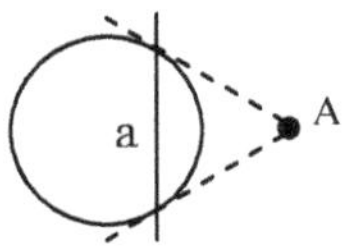

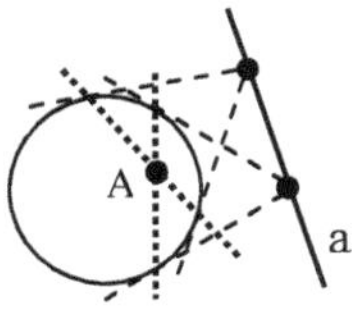

  Notice that #3 and #4 are the most difficult.
  - <u>Important note</u>: You shouldn't just locate the point of tangency (on the circle) "by eye". In order to find the exact point of tangency (where a tangent line exactly touches a circle), use a drawing triangle. Put the triangle's right angle on the circle, have one leg of the triangle pass through the point, and the other leg pass through the circle's center. The right angle will be exactly on the point of tangency. Of course, we should acknowledge that this is "cheating" a bit, because in PG there are no right angles, and, for that matter, no circles. (It is actually possible to construct a tangent to a conic using only a straightedge. See *The Tangent Puzzle* on the following pages.)
- *Polarity of triangles.* Have the students practice several of these drawings. Since any triangle consists of three points and three triangles, we are just repeating the above "exercises".
- *Self-polar triangle.* This is a great puzzle problem that every student should spend some time on. Here are some solutions:
  - There are several "special" cases, including:

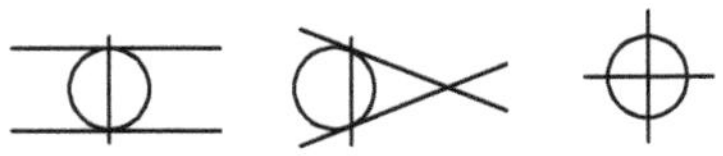

  - Here is a general procedure for a finding a self-polar triangle:
    (1) Choose any point, A, and find its polar line, a.
    (2) Choose any point, B, on line a. Find the polar line, b, to point B. Line b must pass through point A.
    (3) Point C is the intersection of lines a and b; line c connects points A and B.

Chasles' Theorem

A triangle and its polar triangle are always in perspective.

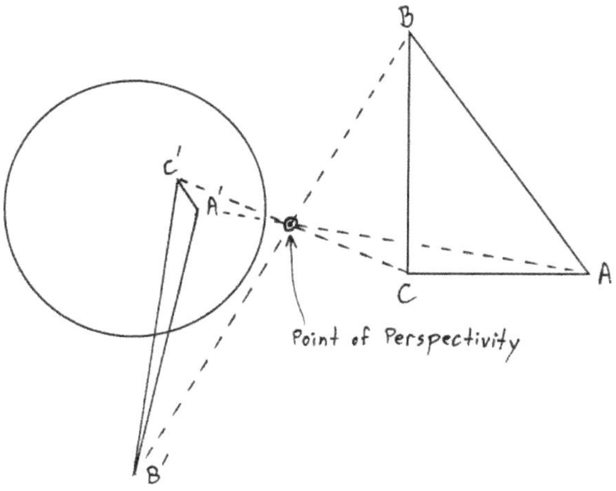

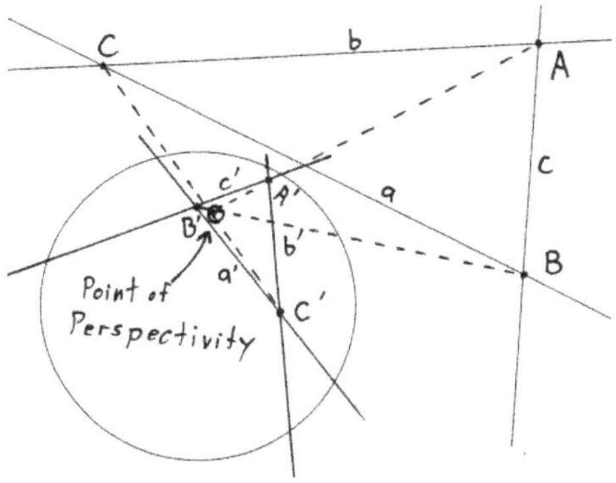

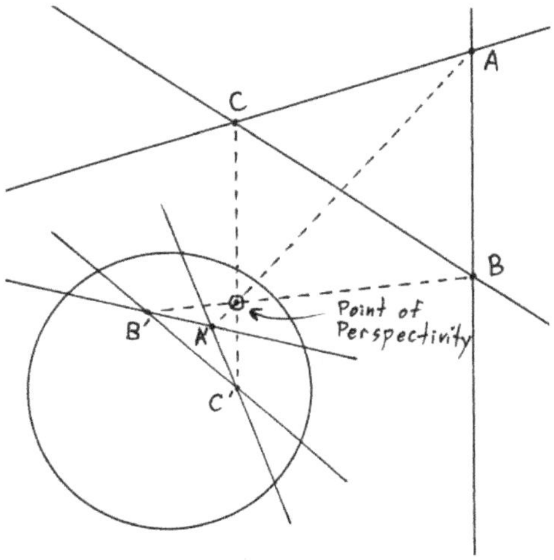

Inscribed Quadrangle Theorem

With any quadrangle inscribed in a conic, its diagonal triangle is self-polar.

Notes:

- A *quadrangle* is any 4 points on a plane, no 3 of which are collinear.
- To find a quadrangle's *diagonal triangle*, we simply draw all 6 lines (dotted in the drawing) connecting pairs of points. Using these six lines, we can locate three new points of intersection between lines, which gives us the *diagonal triangle*.
- As always, the students should be guided toward discovering this extraordinary theorem for themselves.
- This theorem is the key to allowing us to draw tangent lines to conics. (See *The Tangent Puzzle* on the following pages.)

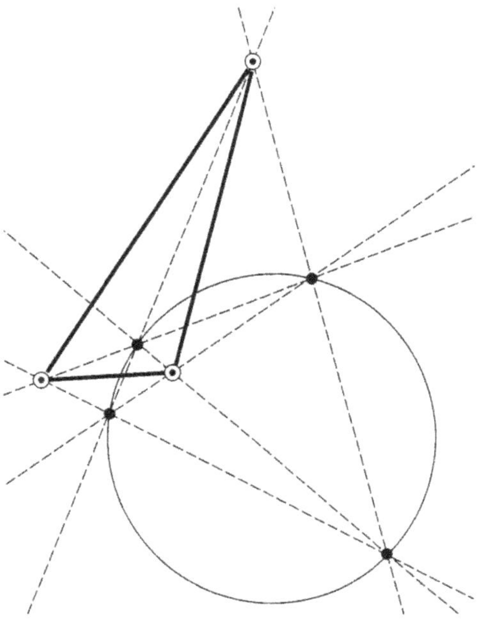

Polarity of Curves

- This is the climax of my projective geometry main lesson block. Polarity drawings of curves require great care from the students, give them a real feeling of accomplishment, and demand a kind of imaginative and rigorous thinking that is hard to find elsewhere in the high school math curriculum.
- Each drawing could take a couple of hours for the students to complete, and may require a significant amount of help from the teacher.

Important tips:

- Instead of thinking of the curve as a collection of points, or, alternatively, as a collection of (tangent) lines, we should think of it as a collection of "locations", where each location on the curve has both a point and a tangent line through that point.
- For most curves, choosing between 25 and 30 points on the original curve should be sufficient. These points should not be equally spread out; the points should be closest together wherever the tangent lines are turning the fastest, and wherever there is a cusp or a point of inflexion. The points should be labeled in numerical order as you travel around the curve. Through each point, tangent lines must be drawn as accurately as possible. Be sure to include tangent lines that pass through the center of the polarity circle, as well as tangent lines that are tangent to both the curve and the polarity circle.
- If we are taking the polar of a tangent line (ℓ) that falls outside the polarity circle, then we need to take the polar of any two points on the line. It is best to have the two points be the point of tangency (A), and the tangent line's infinitely distant point (B). The process is conceptually challenging, but easy to execute. First we take the polar of point A, which is line a (which must cross through the polarity circle). Now we will take the polar of point B (the infinitely distant point on line ℓ). The key is to realize that the polar of a point at infinity is a line that runs through the center of the polarity circle and is *perpendicular to the direction of the point.* Therefore, to get line b, we just draw a perpendicular line to line ℓ, such that it passes through the center of the circle. Now we have found our goal: the polar point to line ℓ; it is point x – the point of intersection of lines a and b. By using a drawing triangle, this can be done very quickly.

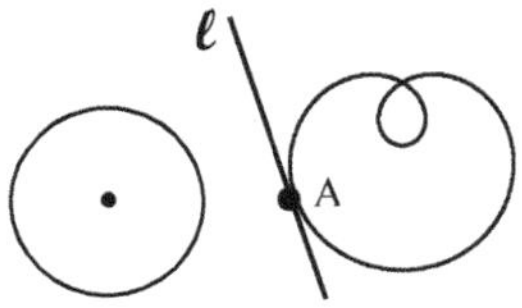

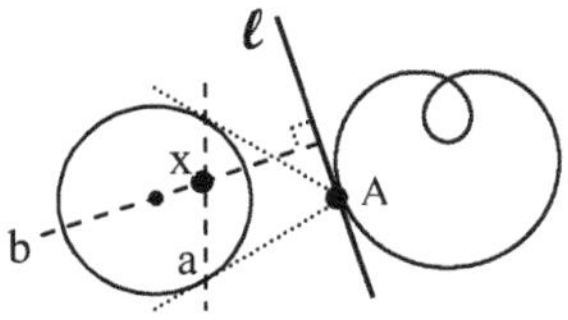

- If we only took the polars of the points of the original curve, then our result would be a collection of tangent lines, and we likely wouldn't be able to tell what the curve really looked like (unless it was a conic). Therefore, it is important to find the polar points of the original curve's tangent lines. If we label the points (of the resulting polar curve) in the same order as the tangent lines of the original curve, then we simply connect the dots in order and see the path of the resulting curve.
- Pay special attention to where the original curve's tangent lines pass through the center of the polarity circle. This tells where (the points of) the polar curve must pass through infinity. *If the original curve's tangent line passes through the center of the polarity circle, then the polar curve must pass through infinity in a direction that is perpendicular to that tangent line.*
- It is very difficult to tell what the resulting curve will look like and (perhaps more importantly) where it will fall on the page by just looking at the original curve and the polarity circle. The placement and size of the polarity circle make a huge difference. For all of these reasons, it is best to use my polarity templates (see the following pages), which make sure the results fall nicely on the page.

Key questions to think about:

- By looking at the original curve and the polarity circle, how can we tell how many times the resulting curve will pass through infinity? Answer: It depends on the number of times the original curve has tangent lines passing through the center of the polarity circle. To show this clearly, draw three limaçons on the board, as shown below.

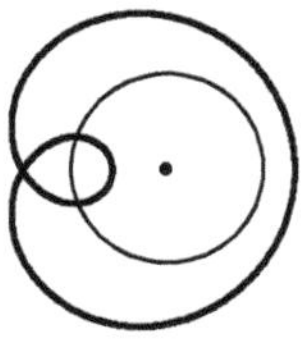

The polar curve passes through infinity twice.

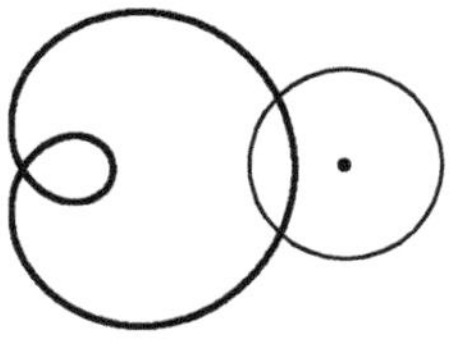

The polar curve passes through infinity four times.

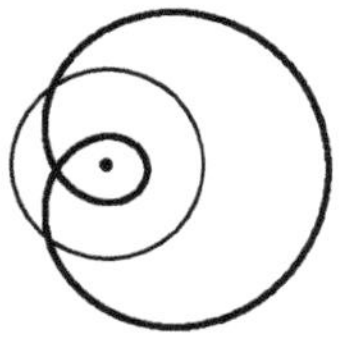

The polar curve doesn't pass through infinity at all.

- If the original curve has a cusp, what is happening here on the polar curve? Answer: You have a point of inflection.
- If the original curve has a point of inflection, what is happening here on the polar curve? Answer: You have a cusp.
- If the original curve has a point where the curve passes through twice, what is happening here on the polar curve? Answer: The polar curve has a tangent line with two points on it.

Polarity of a trefoil

- This is a great first drawing to do for the polarity of a curve. It is relatively easy to construct (because of its symmetry and because all of the tangent lines cross the polarity circle), but it has great thinking behind it.
- Place the polarity circle so that it is tangent to all three pedals, as shown on the right. Make the polarity circle's diameter no larger than about 30% of the width of the page. (You can copy this from my polarity templates in the following pages, or download it from our website.)

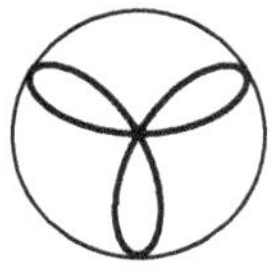

- Most of the "locations" on the curve have tangent lines close to the center of the polarity circle, which result in polar points landing off the page. Therefore, we will only work with locations that are close to the tips of the pedals.
- Working with the natural symmetry of the original curve, we will take the polar of five tangent lines on each pedal, thereby producing a total of 18 points on the resulting polar curve. Points 6, 12, and 18 are all (on top of each other) at the center of the circle.

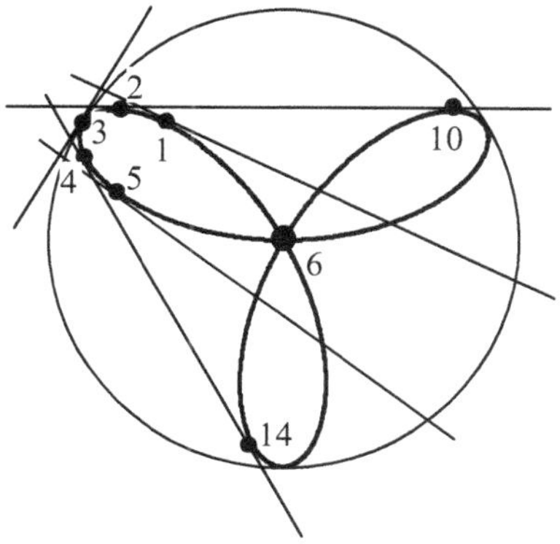

- Note that points 2 and 10 share a common tangent line. So do points 4 and 14, and 8 and 16. This means that the polar of each one of these tangent lines (with two points on it) will be a point with two tangent lines through it – i.e., the polar curve will pass through these points twice.
- The tips of each pedal (points 3, 9, 15) will be self polar (i.e., the original curve and the resulting polar curve will touch one another at these locations).
- The most interesting question is: what happens to the polar curve when the original curve is at the center of the polarity circle (i.e., locations 6, 12, 18)? For starters, we know that because the tangent lines here pass through the center of the polarity circle, then the polar points must be at infinity in a direction that is perpendicular to the tangent lines. But if we observe closely what happens if we travel along the original curve through the center point, we will notice that the tangent line touches the center point, but does not pass through it. This must mean that the polar curve has three places that touch the line at infinity, but doesn't pass through infinity – i.e., it is tangent to the line at infinity!
- The final drawing looks like what is shown here on the right.

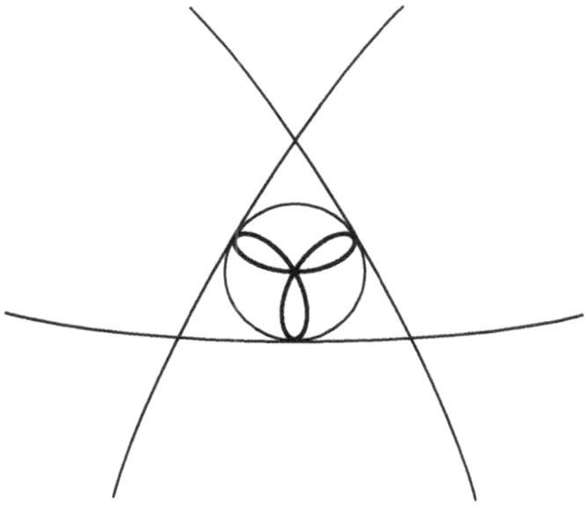

Other curves

- Of course, there are endless possibilities for experimentation with polarities of curves. For any drawing, we can alter things slightly (e.g., change the location of the polarity circle) and see how it changes the resulting polar curve. And we can take the polar of many different curves. It may be best to work with my polarity templates found on the following pages.
- Sample polarity drawings (done by my students) are found on the next page.

Drawings of the Polarity of Curves

(See our website for the full-color images.)

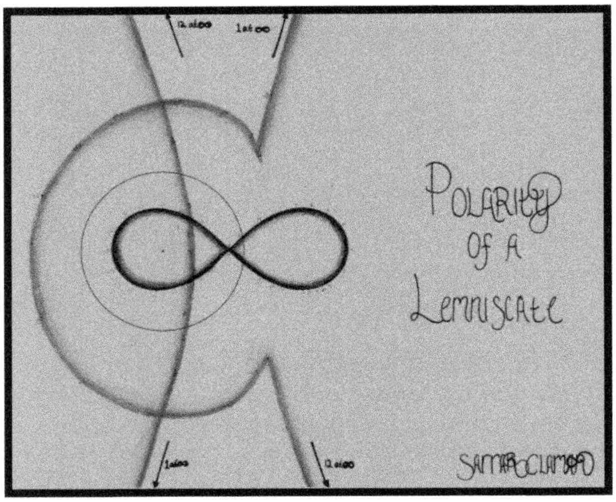

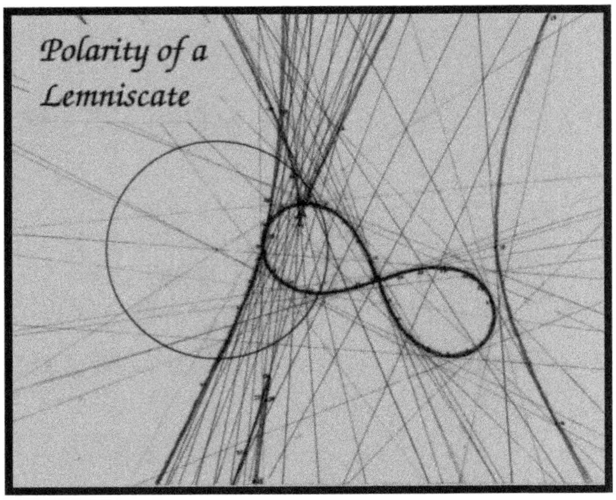

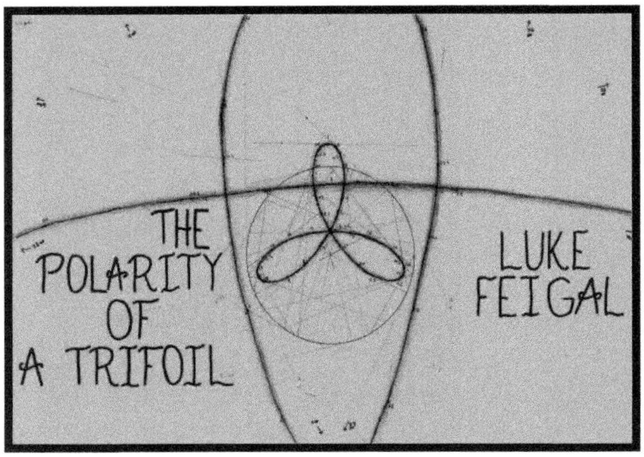

The Tangent Puzzle

Puzzle #1: Find a method to construct a tangent to a conic through a given point outside that conic by using only a straightedge.

Puzzle #2: Find a method to construct a tangent to a conic through a given point on that conic by using only a straightedge.

The key theorem: **The Inscribed Quadrangle Theorem**: *"With any quadrangle inscribed in a conic, its diagonal triangle is self-polar."* (see above, and also Coxeter, p75)

- Construction:
  - Choose a quadrangle (4 points) such that it is inscribed on the conic.
  - Draw the 6 lines connecting these 4 points, and then locate the *diagonal triangle*.
  - This diagonal triangle is always self-polar (i.e., each point of the triangle is polar to the opposite side, etc.).

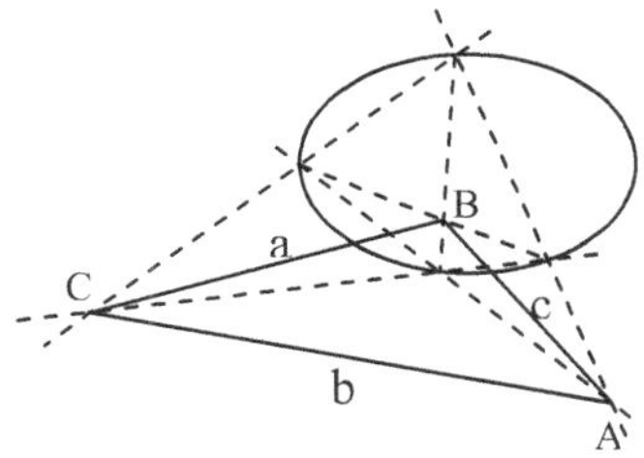

Immediate consequences of the Inscribed Quadrangle Theorem:

*** We can find the polar to a point (not on the conic) without drawing tangents.

Example: Given only a conic and point A, we can find the polar line (a) by doing the following:

1. Draw any two secant lines to the conic that pass through point A. This determines a quadrangle on the conic.
2. Find the *diagonal triangle* to this quadrangle.
3. Point A is one of the points of this diagonal triangle, and the desired polar line to point A is the opposite side (a) of this triangle.

Solution to Puzzle #1: We can now find a method to construct a tangent line to a conic through a given point (A) outside that conic by using only a straightedge.

Solution: To draw a tangent line from point A, simply find the polar line (a) using the above method (see *** above). The two points of tangency through point A are the places where line a (extended) crosses the conic.

Solution to Puzzle #2 – drawing a tangent through a point (P) on the conic:

1. Draw any secant line (ℓ) through point P and choose any two points (F, G) on line ℓ.

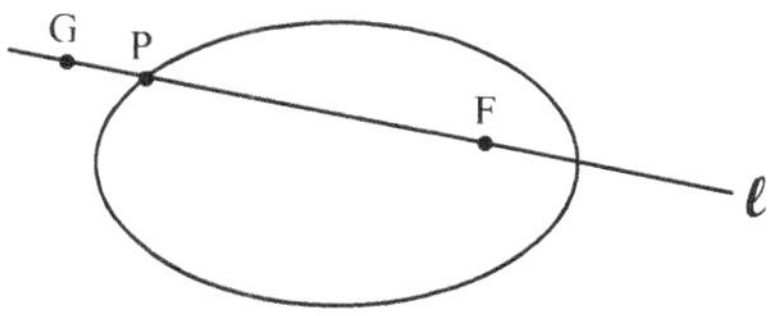

2. Our primary objective is to find the polar to line ℓ without drawing any tangents. We can do this by taking points F and G and finding their polar lines (f and g), by using the above method (see ***). The polar to line ℓ is point Q, which is where lines f and g meet.

3. The desired tangent line is the line connecting P and Q.

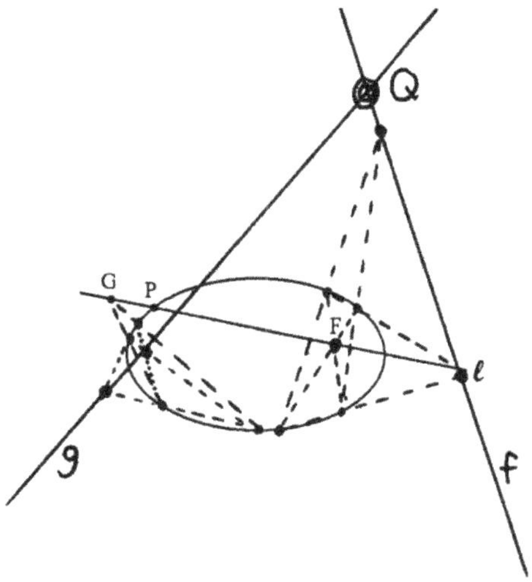

3 Methods for Constructing a Projectivity

(Given 3 pairs of corresponding points)

Background:

The *Fundamental Theorem of Projective Geometry* states that

> "*A projectivity is fully determined by three points on one line, and three corresponding points on another line.*"

In other words, once you know three pairs of corresponding points, a fourth point on either line has a fixed place where its corresponding point on the other line must occur.

The Question:

Given points 1, 2, 3 on line X, and three corresponding points on line Y, how is it possible to construct a projectivity (i.e., determine proper placement of the intermediate line **ℓ**, and the points of perspectivity P and Q) such that the projectivity correctly projects the points from line X to line Y?

Solutions: I know of three possible methods to solve this problem.

Method #1

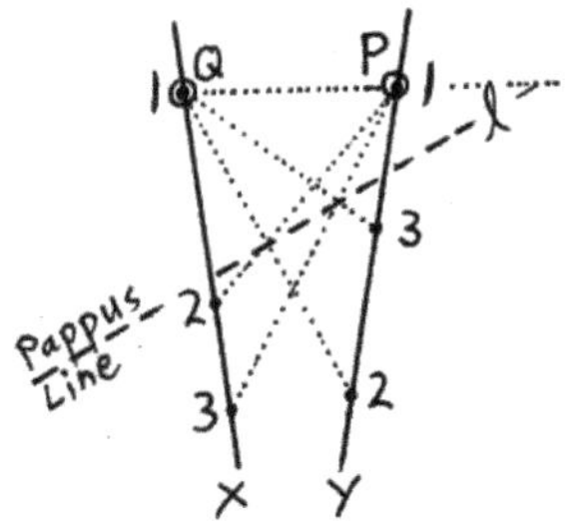

The Pappus line is used as line **ℓ**, and points P and Q coincide with a pair of corresponding points.

Method #2

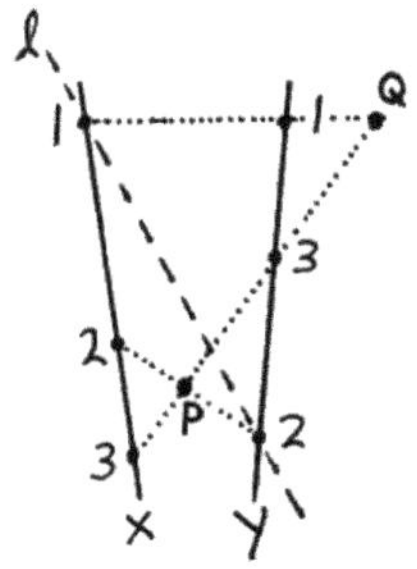

Line **ℓ** is chosen so that it goes through two non-corresponding points. This then determines where P and Q must be placed.

Method #3

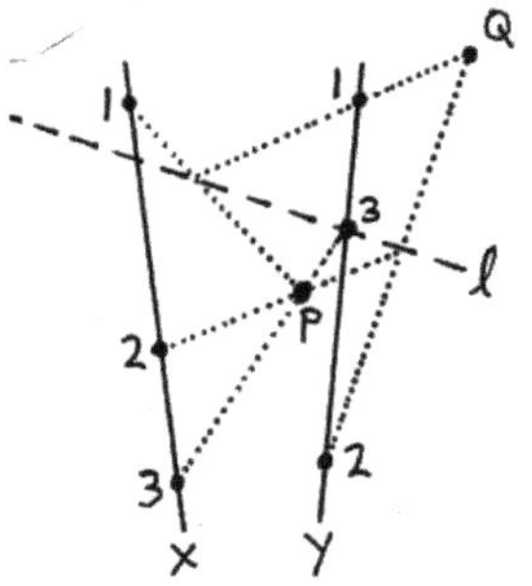

Choose one of the six points. Draw line **ℓ** through this chosen point. Also, place P or Q (you'll have to think about which one) somewhere on the line that connects the chosen point with its corresponding point. This determines where the other point of perspectivity (P or Q) must be. (Note: with the above drawing, it is coincidental that point Q looks to be on the extended line that joins the two points labeled "3".)

Templates for Theorem of Pascal and Theorem of Brianchon

(It may be best to enlarge these.)

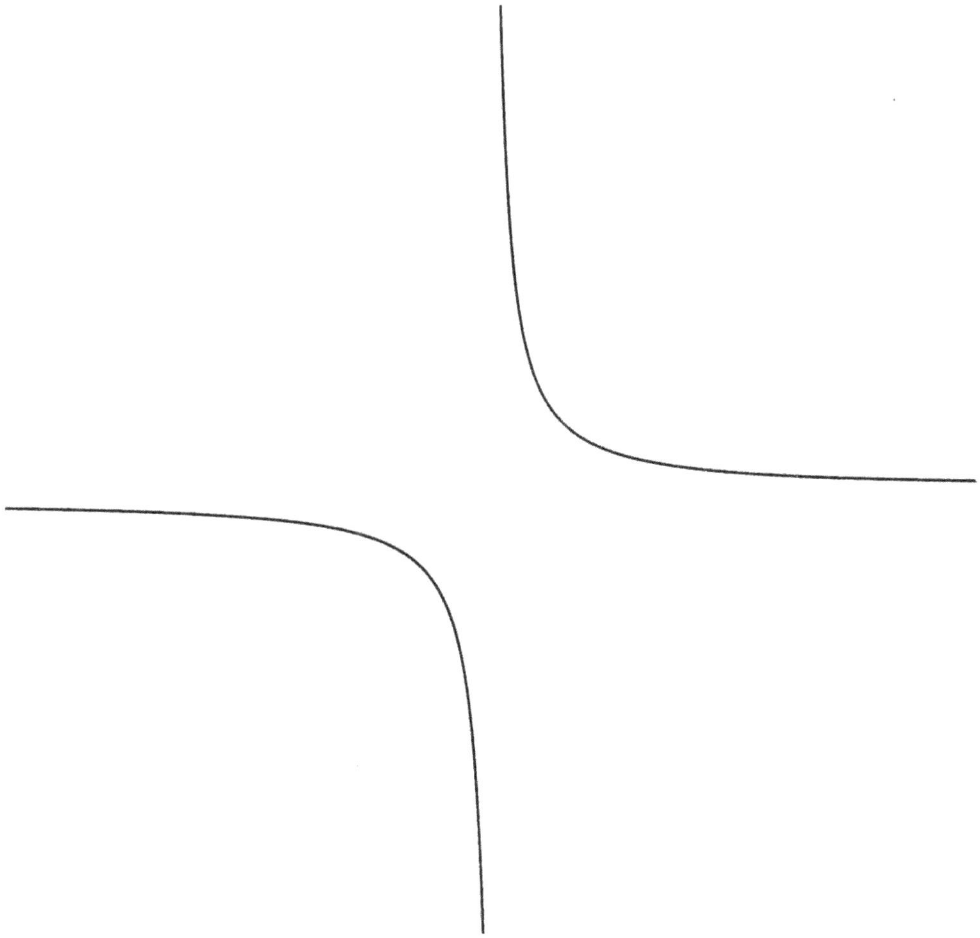

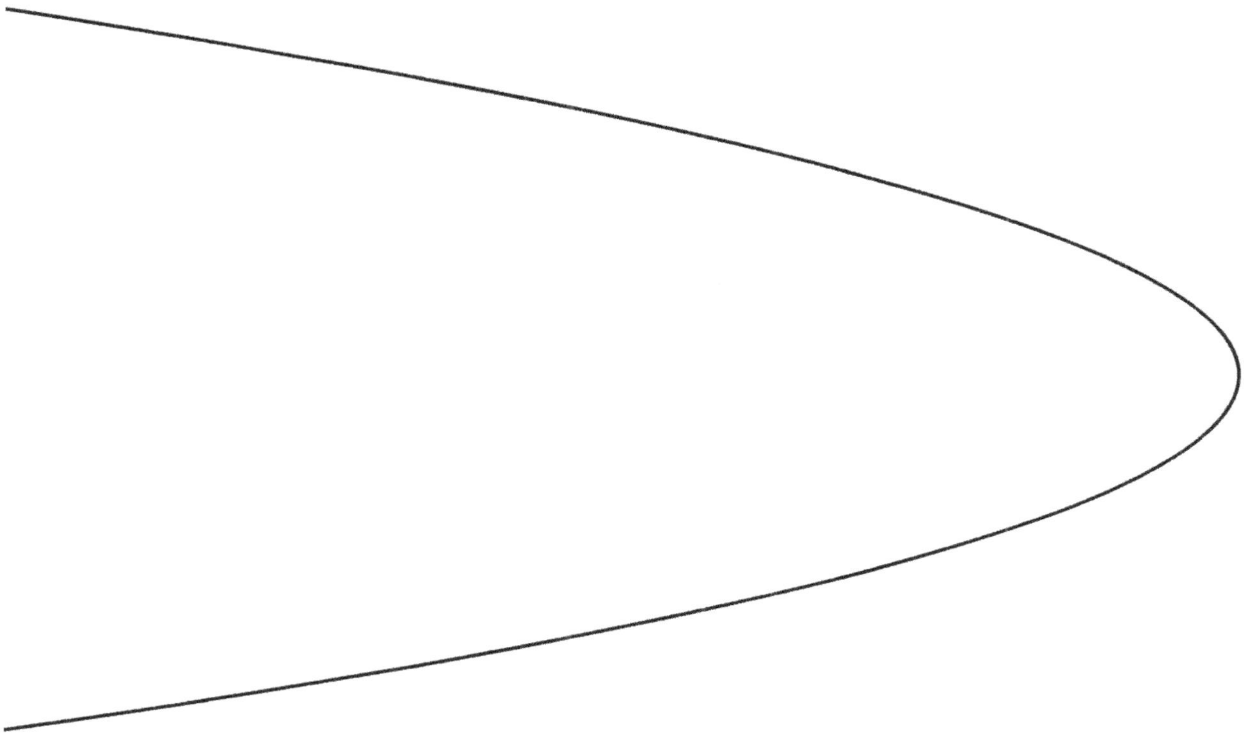

Template for a Line-Wise Conic

(Line y can be drawn anywhere.)

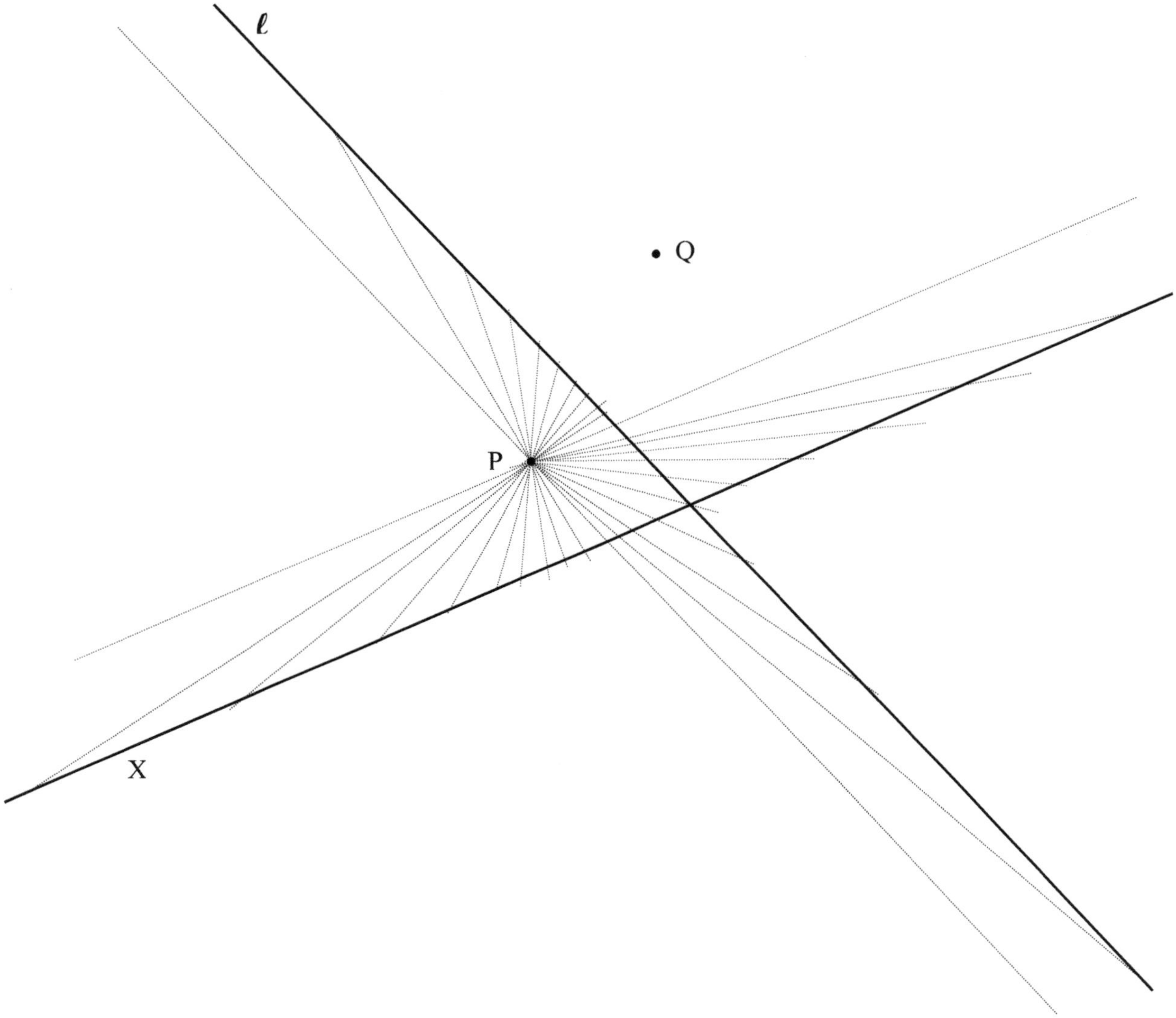

Template for the Polarity of a Conic

Line-wise hyperbola and point-wise parabola

(It may be best to enlarge these.)

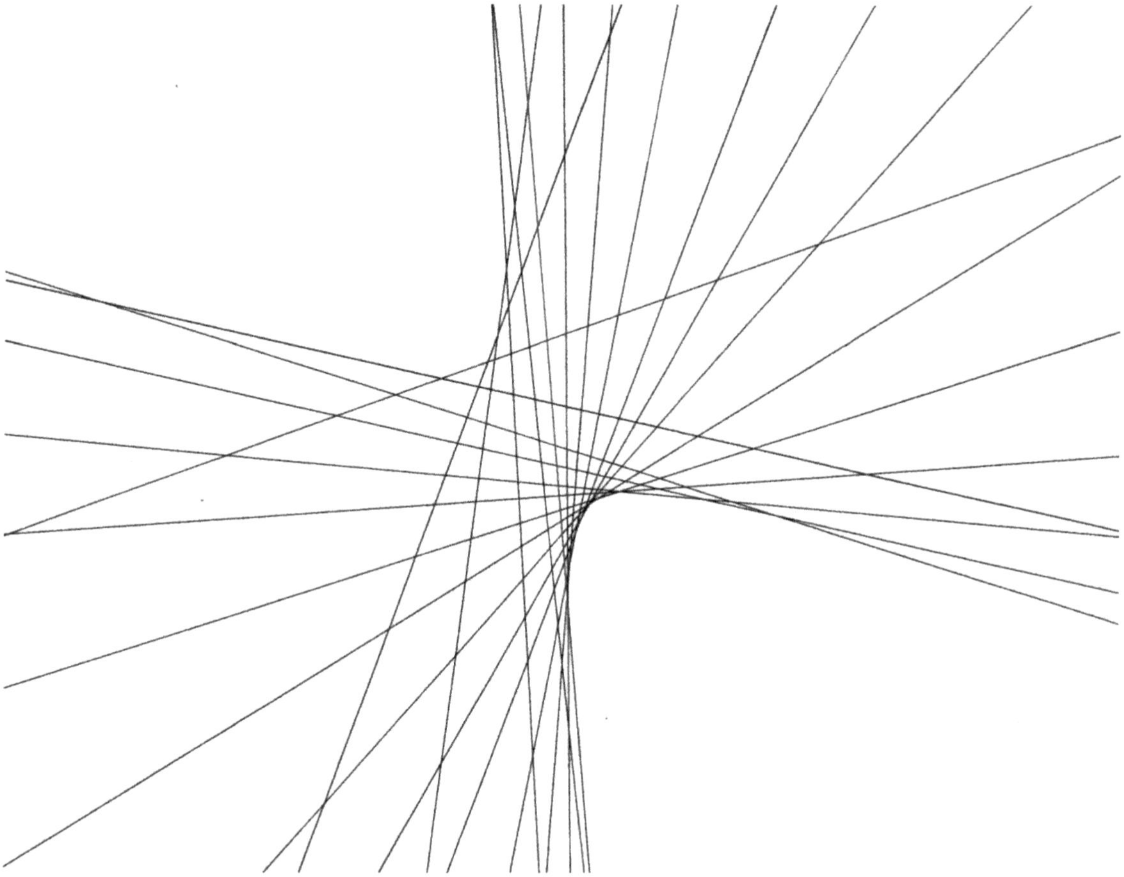

Four Templates for the Polarity of a Limaçon

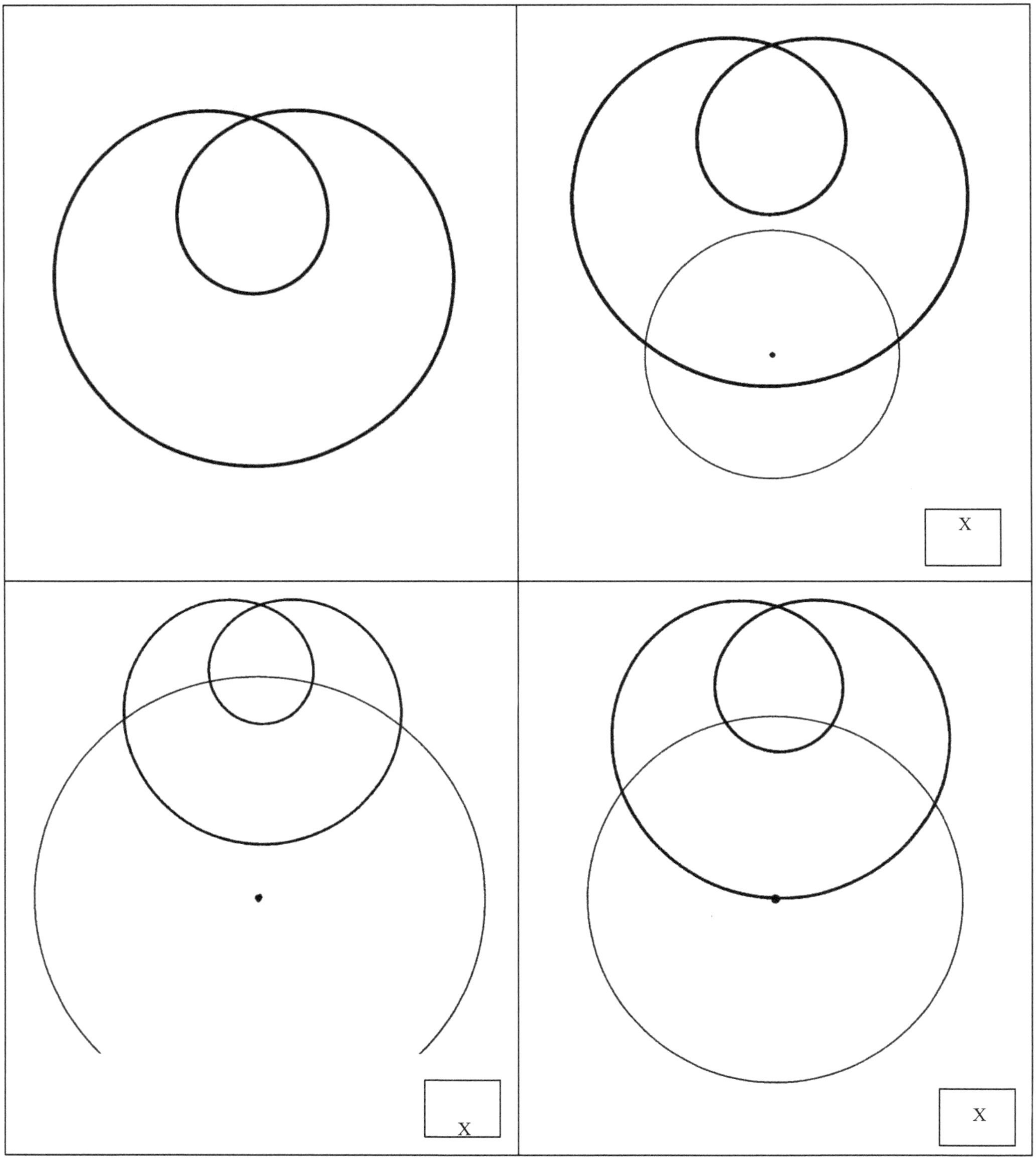

Note: For best results, photocopy this page (without increasing the size), cut out one template, and place it on 8.5 inch by 11 inch paper (A4) in landscape orientation. The "X" shown at the bottom-right of the template indicates the optimal placement of the form, which allows for the polar curve to appear on the page. For larger paper, the size of the form should be increased proportionally. You can also download full-page templates from our website: **www.JamieYorkPress.com**.

Templates for the Polarity of a Cardioid

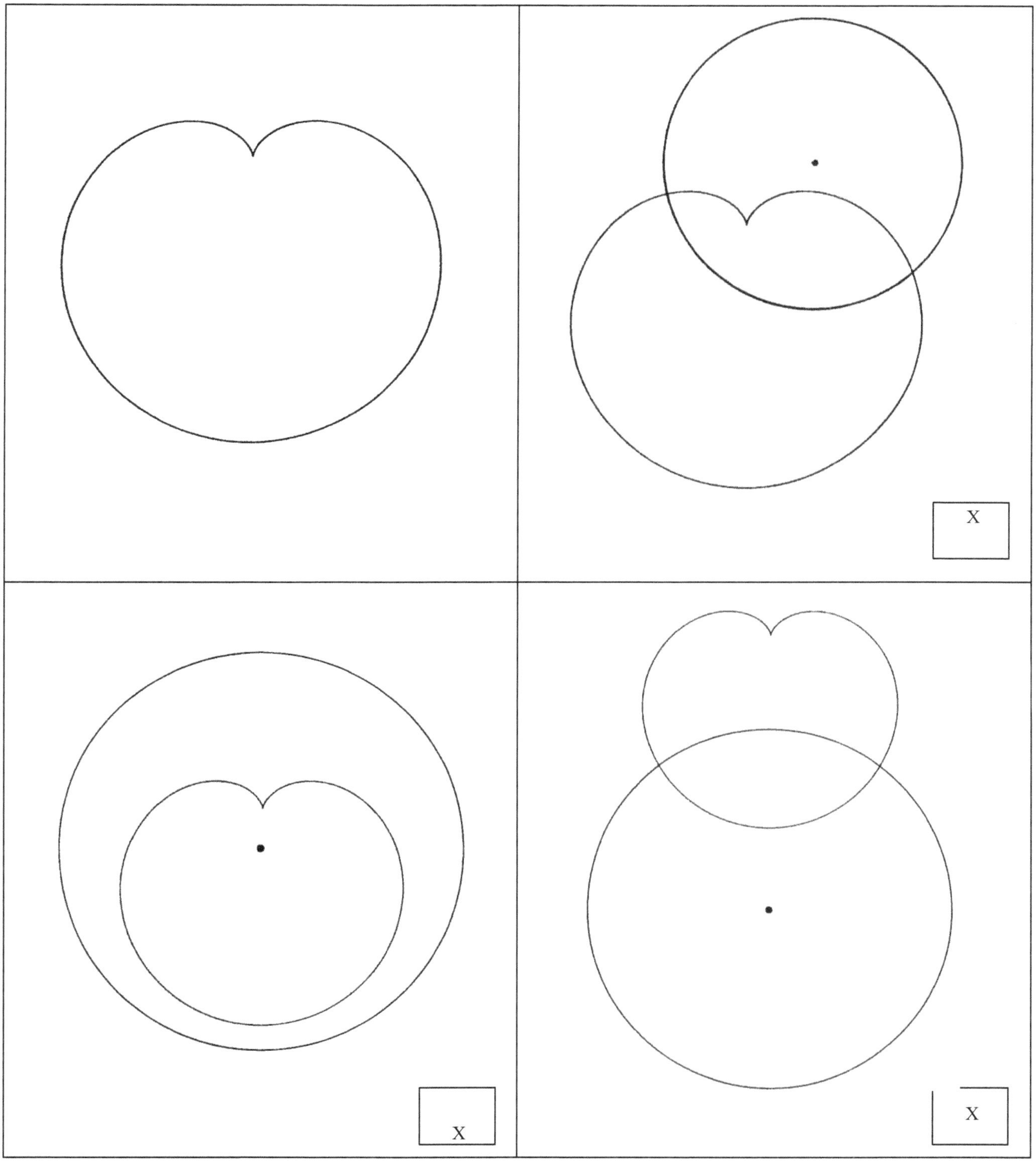

Note: For best results, photocopy this page (without increasing the size), cut out one template, and place it on 8.5 inch by 11 inch paper (A4) in landscape orientation. The "X" shown at the bottom-right of the template indicates the optimal placement of the form, which allows for the polar curve to appear on the page. For larger paper, the size of the form should be increased proportionally. You can also download full-page templates from our website: **www.JamieYorkPress.com**.

Templates for the Polarity of a Lemniscate

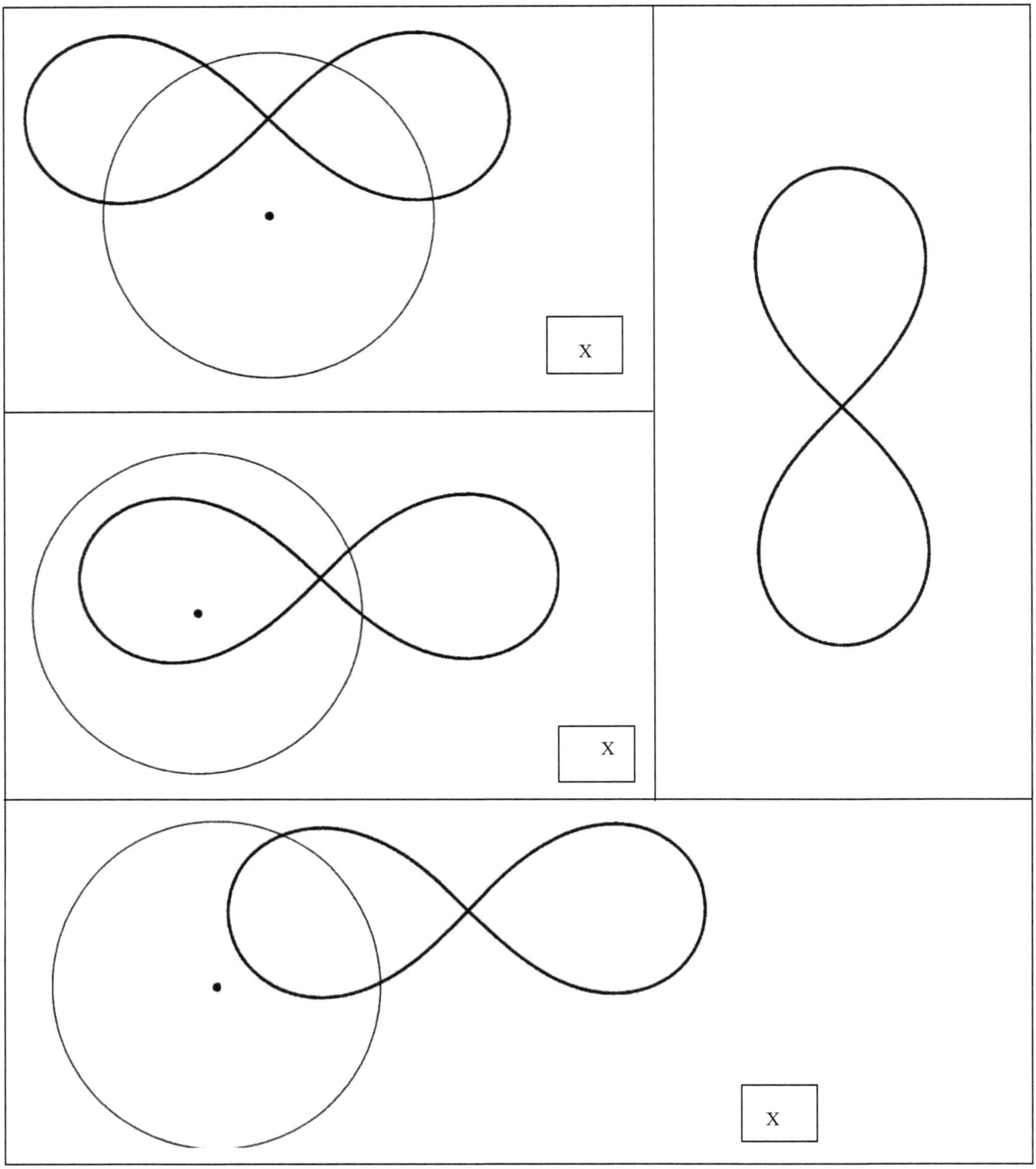

Note: For best results, photocopy this page (without increasing the size), cut out one template, and place it on 8.5 inch by 11 inch paper (A4) in landscape orientation. The "X" shown at the bottom-right of the template indicates the optimal placement of the form, which allows for the polar curve to appear on the page. For larger paper, the size of the form should be increased proportionally. You can also download full-page templates from our website: **www.JamieYorkPress.com**.

More Polarity Templates

Note: For best results, photocopy this page (without increasing the size), cut out one template, and place it on 8.5 inch by 11 inch paper (A4) in landscape orientation. All of these drawings work best when the form is centered on the page. The polarity circle should be about the same size as the form, and either centered on the form, or somewhat overlapping.
You can also download full-page templates from our website: **www.JamieYorkPress.com**.

—— *The Geometry of Descartes* (11th Grade Main Lesson) ——

Full course title: *The Philosophy and Geometry of René Descartes*

Overview

This course is, to a large degree, a history of the evolution of thinking and human consciousness through the lens of philosophy and mathematics.

It is intended to be the students' first introduction to Cartesian (coordinate) geometry. It should be the first main lesson block in eleventh grade, thereby allowing the eleventh grade math track class to thoroughly cover traditional Cartesian geometry through the remainder of the year. It is best if the students have had no exposure to coordinate geometry prior to this block. (Read more about this, above, in the *Introduction*, under "Introducing Cartesian geometry".)

The mathematical objective of this main lesson is to give a historical basis so that the students realize the profound significance of how Descartes' new geometry was able to unite the previous separate fields of algebra and geometry. If this is done well, then the students can really appreciate that coordinate geometry is a powerful mathematical tool, and they learn about how Descartes' new method was the first step on a new course for humanity.

Purpose and intention

What is it that we know for certain? *How* do we know what we know? What is the role of religion in today's society? And the role of science? How did people in Descartes' time and place (Europe) think differently than we do today? These are some of the questions we investigate in this main lesson.

In 1637, the French philosopher, scientist, and mathematician, René Descartes, published a book with the bold title *A Discourse on the Method of Rightly Conducting One's Reason and Searching for the Truth in the Sciences*. The book served as a landmark in modern philosophy. How did it change the way we view our world? It also introduced a powerful and radical method for doing mathematics, which today is known as Cartesian (or coordinate) geometry. How did Descartes come up with this new idea? Perhaps most importantly, Descartes' book introduced a new method for practicing and thinking about science. How did his ideas influence the emerging scientific revolution and shape the way that we think and live today?

This main lesson places an emphasis on classroom discussion and group work. We read through a copy of Descartes' original work to see how he thought differently from how we think today – imagine solving quadratic equations with a compass!

Hopefully this course will allow the students to take another step forward toward a larger goal – a goal that Descartes would have supported – for our students to learn to think for themselves.

Summary of topics

- The "Rectangle and Square Puzzle"
- Descartes' general philosophy:
    - An overview of his book, *Discourse on the Method*
    - Descartes' ideas of duality and the world as a machine
- Descartes' science:
    - His philosophy regarding science
    - His influence in developing a new scientific method
    - An overview of the history of scientific progress
- Descartes' geometry:
    - A detailed study of Descartes' work, *La Géométrie*
    - How Descartes' work was the first step to modern Cartesian geometry
    - How Cartesian geometry united algebra and geometry
    - The Pappus problem
    - How this paved the way for much progress in math and science
- A biography of Descartes' life

Lesson plans and handouts

Detailed day-by-day lesson plans can be downloaded from our website: **www.JamieYorkPress.com**.

I give the students a four-page summary of the main text (which is 60 pages long) of *Discourse on the Method*, which you can also download from our website.

The major reading material is "Book One" of his geometry appendix, *La Géométrie*, which can be found in the book, *The Geometry of René Descartes* (from Dover Publications). You can find copies of this easily on the Internet.

Descartes' philosophy: his four precepts

In section II of the main text of *Discourse on the Method*, he states his four precepts:

1. Don't believe it until you "prove" it to yourself (i.e., think for yourself).
2. Solve complicated problems by the method of "divide and conquer".
3. Proceed from simplest to most complicated.
4. Don't leave anything out (i.e., today, this often amounts to collecting thorough data).

These precepts have formed the basis of how we do science today. The fact that they seem quite obvious is proof that he was quite successful in achieving the goal stated in the title of his book – "*Searching for the Truth in the Sciences*".

Descartes' philosophy: his three maxims

In section III of the main text of *Discourse on the Method*, he states his three maxims:

1. <u>Conservatism</u>. Follow law and custom; adhere to moderate opinions; make no vows or lasting commitments.
2. <u>Decisiveness</u>. Be firm and resolute in your actions.
3. <u>Stoicism</u>. Instead of trying to change the world, try to change your attitude and control your desires.

Descartes' philosophy: "I think, therefore I am"

In section IV of the main text of *Discourse on the Method*, he makes his most famous statement: "I think, therefore I am".

Descartes begins the section by recounting his famous thought experiment. He essentially asks himself, if he was able to doubt all of his beliefs (even the existence of his own body), is there any belief that he could not doubt? He concludes that because he is doubting, he must exist: "I think, therefore I am."

Next Descartes proves that God exists, in short, because "there must of necessity be some other being, more perfect, on whom I depend." God, he says, is a perfect being. Descartes then makes an analogy with geometry: "…consequently it is as certain that God, this Perfect Being, exists, as any geometrical demonstration could be."

A summary of Descartes' geometry

- *Descartes' "Cartesian plane"*. When I first opened Descartes' book, I was eager to read about how he introduced his new method of geometry. I was fully expecting him to start with the standard x-y axis and coordinate plane. Surprisingly, nothing of the sort appears. The closest thing to a coordinate plane appears with his "Pappus problem" (see below) toward the end of the work.
- *Discourse on the Method* has three appendices: *La Dioptrique* (Optics), *Les Météores* (Meteorology), and *La Géométrie*. It is this third appendix for which Descartes is most famous; it is where he lays down the foundation of Cartesian geometry.
- *La Géométrie*, the famous third appendix, is about 100 pages long and is divided into three sections. The first section (*Book I,* which is what this main lesson block concentrates on) contains an explanation of his new geometry, and shows why it is a significant advance over the Greeks. This first section is only 18 pages long (up to page 39, but the pages alternate between French and the English translation), and is, itself, divided into 9 subsections (or parts). It deals with the rectangle & square problem and the Pappus problem. The second section deals with, among other things, a classification of curves, and a method of constructing tangents to curves. The third section deals with solutions to equations of degree two or greater. It is in the third section that he discusses what we now call *Descartes' Rules of Signs*.

- *<u>Book I of La Géométrie</u>*. This is the heart of his introduction to the new geometry. I highly recommend that the students work through these 18 pages, which are dense and foreign. Working through this material successfully with a class requires considerable planning. A summary is helpful. *Book I* is divided into nine parts, A through I, summarized below. The most important parts are A, E, and G.
  - Part A is a general introduction. He states from the start that he has a new method for solving geometric problems whereby the solutions are simply the length of straight lines. It should be read briefly, and needs very little discussion time.
  - Part B gives examples of constructions for multiplying, dividing, and taking square roots. It is three paragraphs long, beginning with "For example, let AB…" at the top of page 5. This is a dense and important passage. In my *Descartes Main Lesson Worksheets* (which can be downloaded from our website), I dedicate the first worksheet to this part B. A full explanation of Part B is in the following pages.
  - Part C introduces the reader to his algebraic terminology. It is three paragraphs long, starting with "Often it is not necessary…" on page 5. When first reading this, it seems incomprehensible, but then you realize what Descartes is doing. The reader in the early 17th century has never seen algebraic notation before. So he needs to explain what a "+" means, what exponents are, etc. Very little class time needs to be spent on this passage.
  - Part D introduces the idea of his new method. It starts on page 6 with, "If, then, we wish …" and runs to page 13. It isn't necessary that all of the details are understood. I have the students read through it quickly, and then simply mention that he is explaining how to formulate an equation, and mentions that his new method allows him to solve all sorts of these equations. He gives examples of such equations and their solutions in Part E.
  - Part E starts on page 13 with "And if it can be solved…". It gives examples of how his method can be used to solve equations by treating them as geometric problems with compass and straightedge solutions. The equations he is solving are three types of quadratic equations – essentially variations of what I call the "rectangle & square problem" (see below for details). This is an important passage. In my *Descartes Main Lesson Worksheets* (which can be downloaded from our website), I dedicate the second worksheet to part E. A full explanation of Part E is in the following pages.
  - Part F starts on page 17 with "This is also evident…" It introduces the Pappus problem, which is a problem that he says the ancient Greeks weren't able to properly solve, but that his new method can solve. Very little class time needs to be spent on this passage.
  - Part G starts on page 25 with "First, I discovered…" This passage talks about how, in general, his method can solve the Pappus problem. Then in Part H, he goes over the specific details of the mathematics. Very little class time needs to be spent on this passage.
  - Part H starts with "Now, since all the angles…" on page 29. This passage is extremely complicated and difficult to follow. I usually have the students read through it quickly to get an impression, then, the next day, I present the whole thing on the board to the class. It is a very challenging presentation for me to do, and for the students to follow – certainly the most difficult hour of the block – but I feel it is important for the students to see it. I tell them that I won't test them on it, and that they don't need to worry about understanding all of the details. A full explanation of Part H is in the following pages. (The end of this passage contains the "seed statement" of Cartesian geometry.)
  - Part I starts with "This method can be used…" on page 34. This ending passage tells briefly about how his method could be used to solve more complicated versions of the Pappus problem. Very little class time needs to be spent on this passage.

The rectangle and square puzzle – a modern version

- This is a puzzle I introduce on day #1 without any reference to its connection to Descartes' work.
- *Question*: What is the height of the rectangle that has a length of 10 cm and has an area equal to the sum of the areas of two squares – one square having the same height as the rectangle, and the other having an area of: (a) 16 cm^2? (b) 15 cm^2 (c) g^2 and the length of the rectangle is f ?

  Solution: The students work in groups to find solutions. Invariably, they draw a diagram, label the height of both the rectangle and the unknown square as x, and then they set up an equation and solve it algebraically. Using this method, they get the following answers:

  (a) $10x = x^2 + 16 \rightarrow x = 2$ or 8 (b) $10x = x^2 + 15 \rightarrow x = 5 \pm \sqrt{10}$

  (c) $fx = x^2 + g^2 \rightarrow x = \frac{f \pm \sqrt{f^2 - 4g^2}}{2}$ Descartes got $z = \frac{1}{2}a \pm \sqrt{\frac{1}{4}a^2 - b^2}$

  which is the same, but he used a, b and z instead of f, g and x.

The rectangle and square puzzle – a Greek Solution[1] (This is for the teacher only)

What is the height of the rectangle (with length f) such that it has an area equal to the sum of the areas of two squares – one square having the same height as the rectangle, and the other having an area of g^2 *?*

The Greeks would have looked at the rectangle & square problem completely differently from how we see it today. For them, every "equation" had geometrical significance; for them, every problem was a geometric puzzle. They would have solved the rectangle & square problem using a compass and a straight edge. The Greek solution is as follows:

1. Given a rectangle of length f and a "fixed" square with side g where $g < \frac{1}{2}f$.
2. Copy f onto a line and label the end points as A and B.
3. Construct the perpendicular bisector of $\overline{AB}$ and label the midpoint C.
4. Copy g onto the perpendicular line $\overline{CD}$.
5. Draw an arc with center at D and with radius $\overline{CB}$, so that it intersects AB at F and E.
6. The desired height of the rectangle is $\overline{EB}$ or $\overline{FB}$.

- The Greeks would have then *pictured* the solution. For example, with the solution $\overline{EB}$, they would have pictured a square on EB, and the rectangle with the same height on AB, so that the rectangle's area is equal to the sum of the areas of the square on EB and the square on CD.

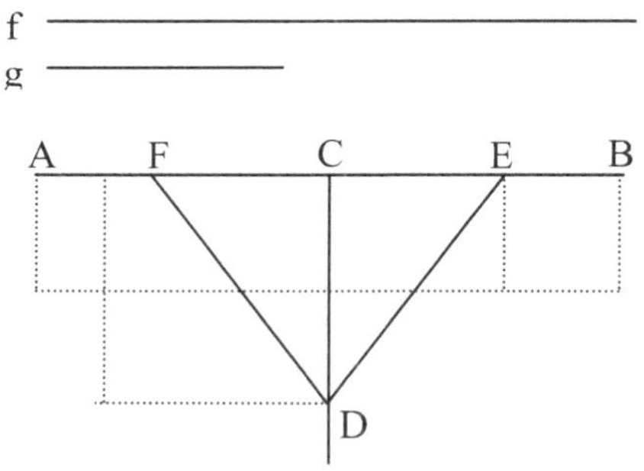

The rectangle and square puzzle – Descartes' solution:

Descartes gives both a geometric solution (unfamiliar to us today) and an algebraic solution (which was unfamiliar to those in his time). His geometric solution is as follows:

- The length of the rectangle is a, and the side of the known square is b. (b must be less than half of the length of a.)
- Draw segment NL equal to ½a. Draw a semicircle having radius NL. Draw LM equal to b and at a right angle to NL. Draw a line parallel to NL passing through M, which intersects the semicircle in two places.
- The possible solutions for the height of the rectangle are given by MQ and MR.

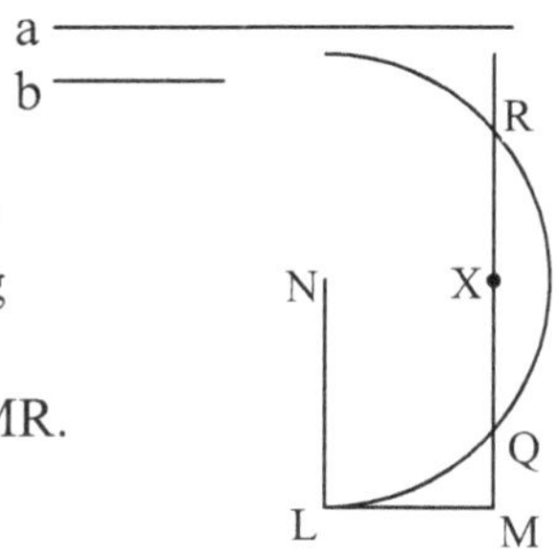

He then states that the algebraic solutions are: $z = \frac{1}{2}a \pm \sqrt{\frac{1}{4}a^2 - b^2}$

Those students who need an extra challenge should try to prove that Descartes' geometric and algebraic solutions are equivalent. We begin by picturing a right triangle connecting the points N, Q, and X (the midpoint of RQ). NQ = NL = ½a, and NX = LM = b. Using the Pythagorean Theorem, we see that:

$$XQ^2 = NQ^2 - NX^2 \rightarrow XQ^2 = (\tfrac{1}{2}a)^2 - b^2 \rightarrow XQ = \sqrt{\tfrac{1}{4}a^2 - b^2}\ (= XR)$$

$$MQ = MX - XQ \rightarrow MQ = \tfrac{1}{2}a - \sqrt{\tfrac{1}{4}a^2 - b^2}$$

$$MR = MX + XR \rightarrow MR = \tfrac{1}{2}a + \sqrt{\tfrac{1}{4}a^2 - b^2} \quad \text{Q.E.D.}$$

---

[1] *The Elements*, translated by Sir Thomas Heath, Vol. I p384 and Vol. II p263; Dover Publications, 1956.

An Explanation for Part B

Here is the whole of Part B taken from his book:

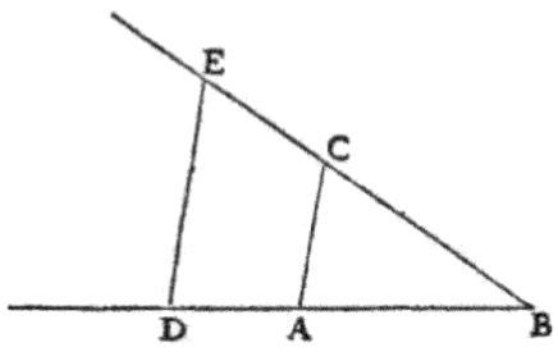

> *For example, let AB be taken as unity, and let it be required to multiply BD by BC. I have only to join the points A and C, and draw DE parallel to CA; then BE is the product of BD and BC.*
>
> *If it be required to divide BE by BD, I join E and D, and draw AC parallel to DE; then BC is the result of the division.*
>
> *If the square root of GH is desired, I add, along the same straight line, FG equal to unity; then, bisecting FH at K, I describe the circle FIH about K as a center, and draw from G a perpendicular and extend it to I, and GI is the required root.*

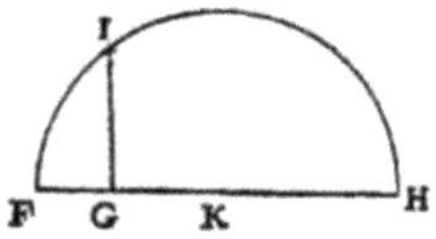

On the first sheet from my *Descartes Main Lesson Worksheets* (which can be downloaded from our website), problem #3 asks the students to follow Descartes' instructions for constructing $a \cdot b$ given the three line segments shown on the right (at 50% of their original size).

Following Descartes' instructions (as stated above for Part B), we copy unity to where AB is in his drawing; copy segment a to BD in his drawing; and then copy segment b to BC in his drawing. This first step of the drawing is shown on the right. (Notes: unity and segment a overlap; the angle between a and b is arbitrary.)

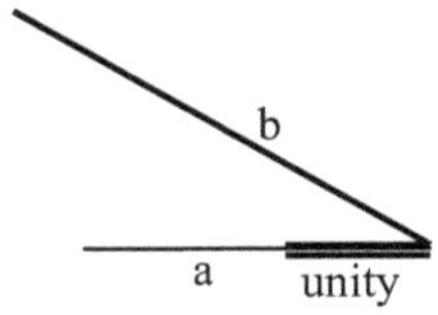

To complete the drawing, and find the desired solution, Descartes tells us to draw a line that connects the end of unity to the end of segment b, and then draw a parallel line (to the one just drawn) that goes from the end of segment a until it meets segment b (extended). The desired solution is the line segment (x) that goes from the start of segment b all the way to the newly found point of intersection.

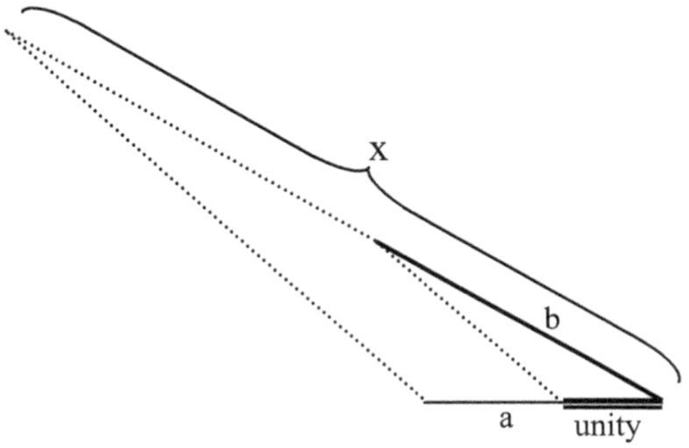

Now we have practiced his construction found in the first paragraph! It is a good extra challenge to ask the students to prove why his construction for multiplication works. They can also check that it works by measuring. For example, if unity is 4cm long, and a and b are 6cm and 8cm (which is 1.5 and 2 times longer than unity), then the solution line, x, should be 12 cm long (which is 3 times longer than unity).

In the second paragraph, Descartes says that in order to perform division, we simply reverse the process. Division appears as practice on my worksheet as problems #4 and #5. In the third and final paragraph, Descartes tells us how to determine the square root of the length of a line segment – again, by using a compass and straightedge.

Descartes makes it look easy! The first step is simply to copy segment a and unity end-to-end (not overlapping this time), and then use this combined length as the diameter of a semi-circle, as shown in the drawing on the right.

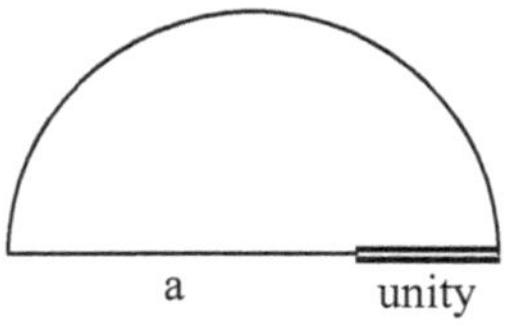

To complete the drawing, all we have to do is draw a perpendicular line up from the meeting point of segment a and unity until it touches the circle. This vertical line segment (x) is the desired solution (see below drawing). We can check by measuring. If unity is 2cm long, and segment a is 18cm long (which is 9 times longer than unity), then x should be 6cm long (which is 3 times longer than unity).

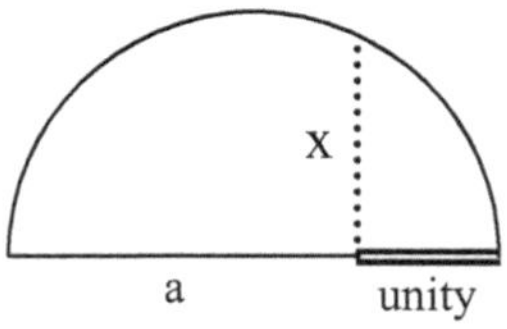

To demonstrate why this method works, try connecting the ends of the line segments in order to form a right triangle inscribed inside the semi-circle. We then have the Altitude of the Hypotenuse Theorem (see *Altitude of the Hypotenuse Theorem* under tenth grade), which says that $x^2 = a \cdot \text{unity}$, which becomes $x = \sqrt{a}$. Voila!

An Explanation for Part E

In Part E, Descartes gives three examples of how his new method can be used to solve quadratic equations. Each example has different signs. For instance, if we had the equation $x^2 = 5x + 6$, he considers the other variations of that equation to be $x^2 = -5x + 6$ and $x^2 = 5x - 6$. We should be wondering why he doesn't also consider $x^2 = -5x - 6$. He doesn't consider it because he would say there are no solutions. Of course, it has two solutions, but they are both negative, and negative numbers were not accepted in Descartes' day.

Descartes' three equations look a bit different than the above equations. He uses x, y, and z as his variables, and a and b as his constants. His three equations are:

$$z^2 = az + b^2 \qquad y^2 = -ay + b^2 \qquad z^2 = az - b^2$$

For each equation, he gives both geometric solutions and algebraic solutions.

Here is the first of the three problems Descartes gives for Part E:

> *For example, if I have $z^2 = az + b^2$, I construct a right triangle NLM with one side LM, equal to b, the square root of the known quantity b^2, and the other side, LN, equal to ½ a, that is, to half the other known quantity which was multiplied by z, which I supposed to be the unknown line. Then prolonging MN, the hypotenuse of this triangle, to O, so that NO is equal to NL, the whole line OM is the required line z. This is expressed in the following way:* $z = \frac{1}{2}a + \sqrt{\frac{1}{4}a^2 + b^2}$

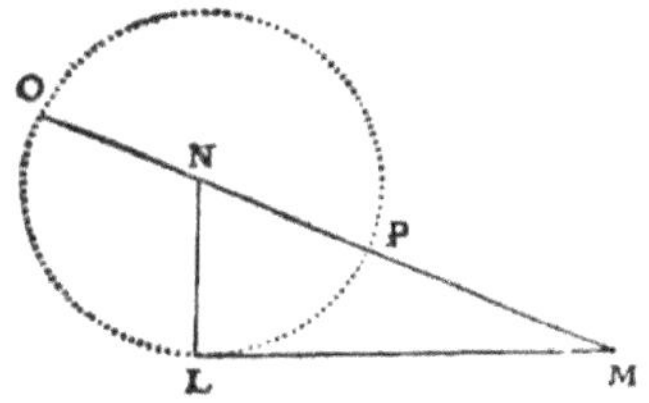

The students have the opportunity to practice this geometric construction on the second sheet from my *Descartes Main Lesson Worksheets* (which can be downloaded from our website). Problem #4 asks the students to follow Descartes' instructions for solving $x^2 = hx + k^2$ given the two line segments shown on the right (at 50% of their original size).

The first step of the geometric construction is to create a right triangle with sides of length ½h and k, and then to construct a circle using ½h as its radius, as shown in the drawing at the right.

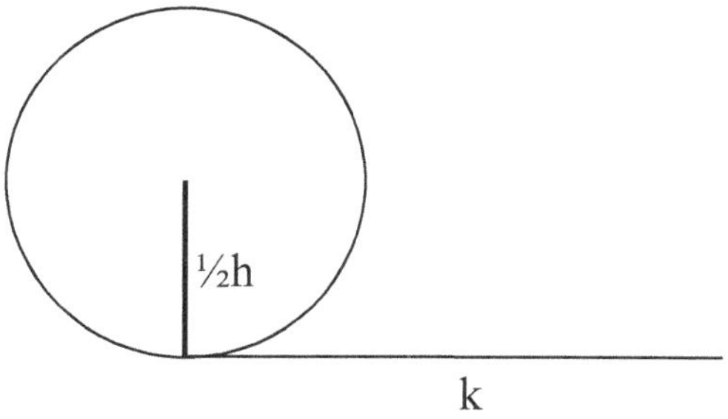

To complete the drawing, and find the desired solution, Descartes tells us to simply draw a line from the end of k through the center and across the whole circle. The desired solution is the length of the whole dotted line (x) as shown in the lower drawing.

If instead, we had been asked to solve $w^2 = -hw + k^2$, then Descartes tells us in the next paragraph (not shown here, and using the similar equation: $y^2 = -ay + b^2$) that the construction is exactly the same, but the desired solution (w in the drawing at the right) is shorter by the length of the circle's diameter.

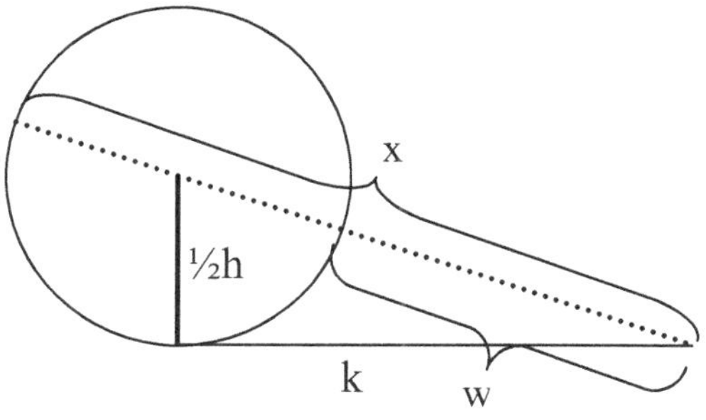

Descartes ends Part E with a third example of solving quadratic equations: $z^2 = az - b^2$. This example leads to two (positive) solutions, and we already have seen this construction with the *rectangle and square puzzle* (see above).

These three examples and their solutions demonstrate to Descartes' readers that he is capable of solving any quadratic equation (assuming it has a positive solution) with a compass and straightedge, and the solution is a line with a determined length. The ability to solve quadratic equations in this way gives Descartes an important tool for his next formidable task: solving the Pappus problem.

The Pappus Problem

Background

This problem is the centerpiece of Descartes' geometric work. Its solution forms the basis for a new kind of geometry – Cartesian geometry – which revolutionized the world of mathematics.

Descartes introduces the Pappus problem in Part F, tells us about how his method can solve it in Part G, and then takes his readers through the mathematics in Part H (for which I have a full explanation after a couple of pages). My intention here is to explain what the Pappus problem is, and what the solution might roughly look like.

The Pappus problem is a fascinating loci puzzle. Descartes' formulation of the problem is more general and complicated than what I will offer here. Without losing the essence of the problem, I simplify it somewhat in order to make it possible for the students to attempt a rough-sketch solution.

The initial drawing

First, we should start with Descartes' drawing, which appears first in Part G and then again in Part H. His drawing (see below, left) shows the four given (solid) lines and one hypothetical solution point (C). My own drawing (see below, right) is a simplified version of Descartes' drawing. Mine shows only the four given lines, labeled w, x, y, z. My lines are in a slightly different orientation than Descartes'.

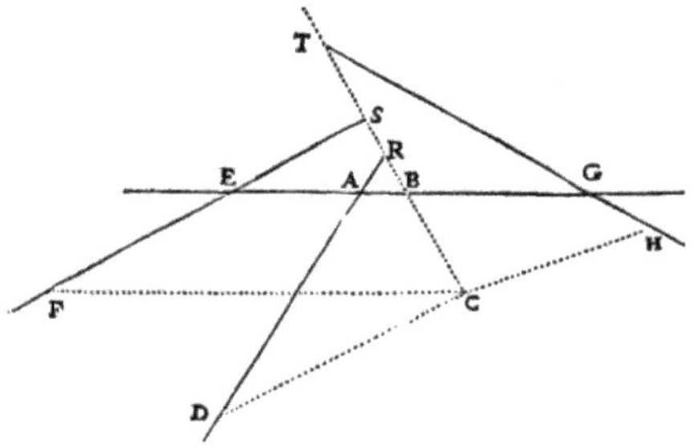

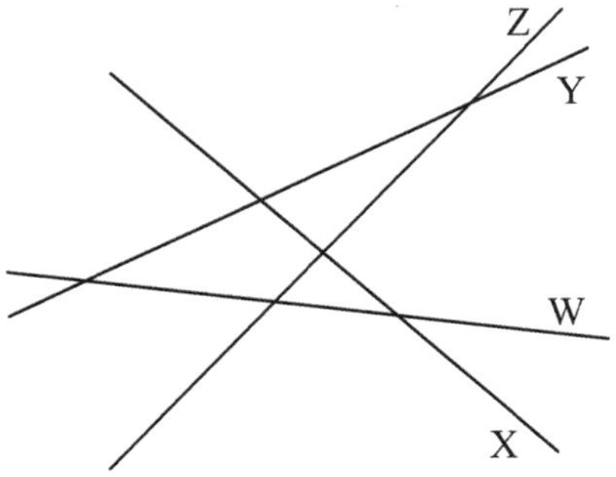

The question

The solution to any loci problem[1] is a locus (collection) of points that satisfy a certain criteria, and when connected, form a curve. In this case, the criteria (which I have slightly simplified) is that, for every point on the curve, the product of the distances to lines w and x must be equal to the product of the distances to lines y and z.

Completing a rough sketch of the solution

Sheet #3 of my *Descartes Main Lesson Worksheets* (which can be downloaded from our website) is the Pappus problem, and the students are asked to make a rough sketch of the solution. They simply guess where one solution point might be, and then they measure with a ruler to see if it is satisfactory. With the below left drawing, point C is 1.4, 1.5, 2.4, and 1.3 centimeters from points w, x, y, and z, respectively. I can see that $y \cdot z$ is considerably greater than $w \cdot x$, so I need to move point C closer (perhaps to the left) to lines y and z. After a significant amount of time, we can see the solution emerge (see below, right); surprisingly, the solution is two curves: a hyperbola, and an ellipse.

A curious person might wonder how the curve changes if the lines move in some manner. The next page shows a transformation of an ellipse into a parabola and then a hyperbola.

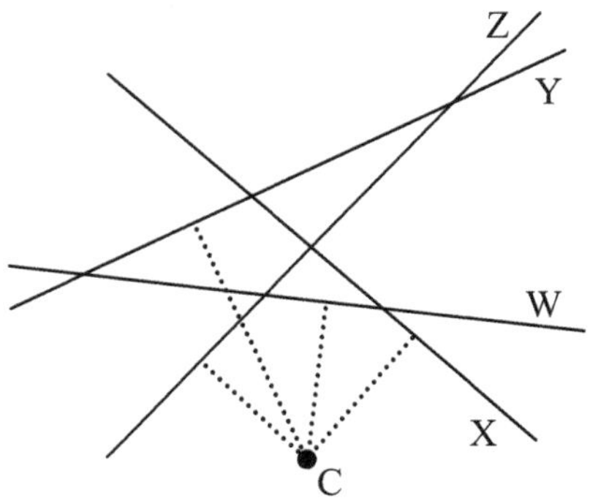

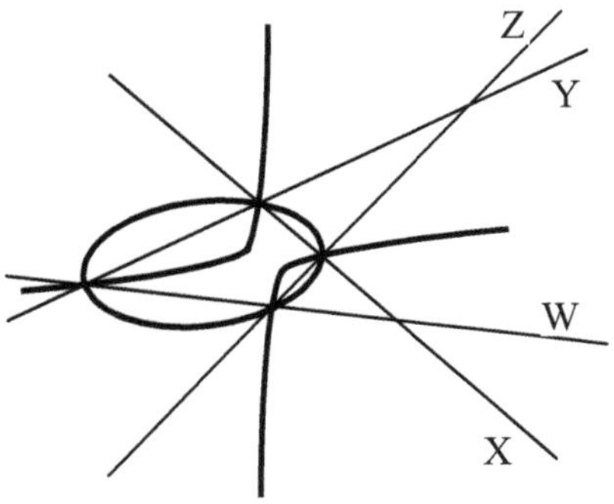

1 for more about the study of "loci", see our *Middle School Source Book* (8th grade geometry).

The Pappus Problem in Movement

The transformation of an ellipse into a parabola and then a hyperbola

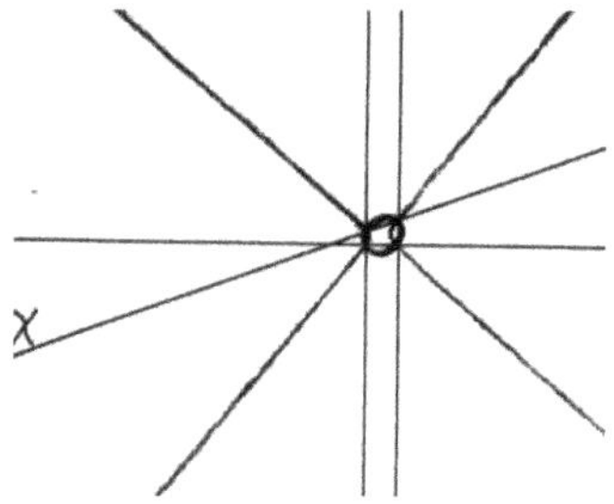

Notes: Lines W (horizontal), Y and Z (vertical) are the same in each drawing. Line X rotates about a fixed point on the horizontal line. The top-left step has one hyperbola (with two branches) and an ellipse. In the second drawing, the hyperbola has degenerated into an "X". The first four drawings show the ellipse growing. The parabola appears in the fifth drawing when line X has a steepness of about $77\frac{1}{3}^\circ$. (It is quite a challenge to determine what this angle must be.) The last two drawings each have two hyperbolas.

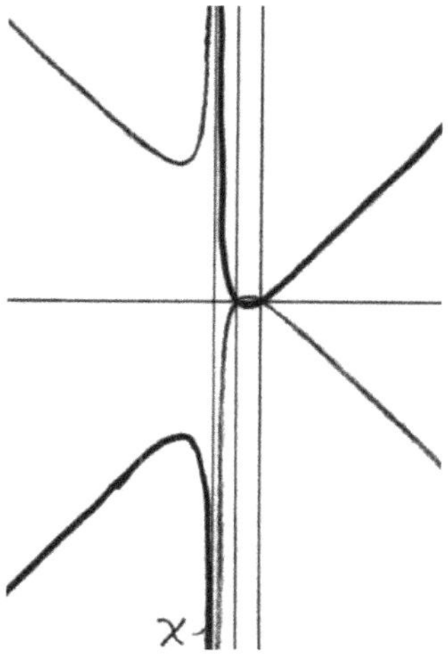

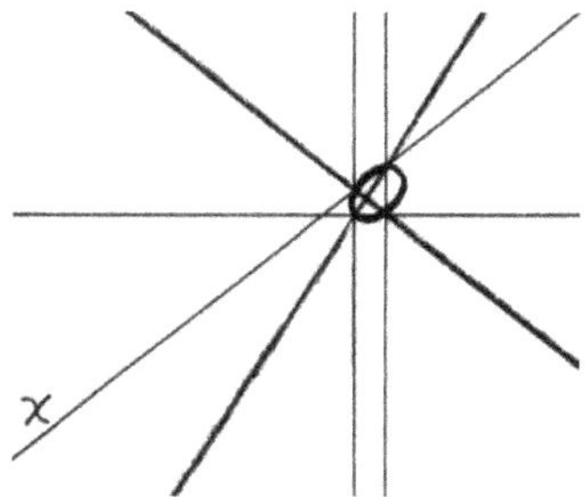

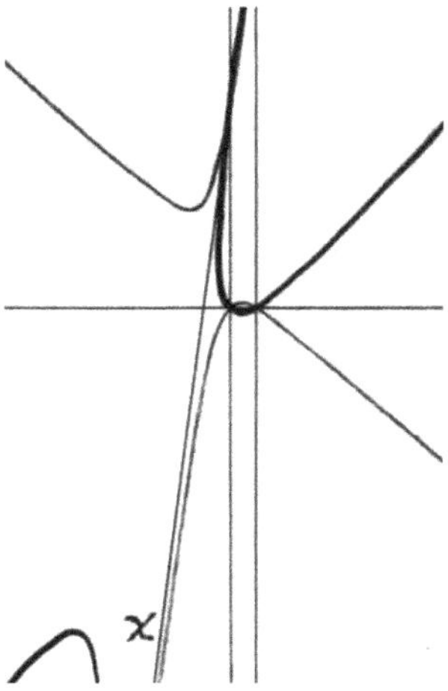

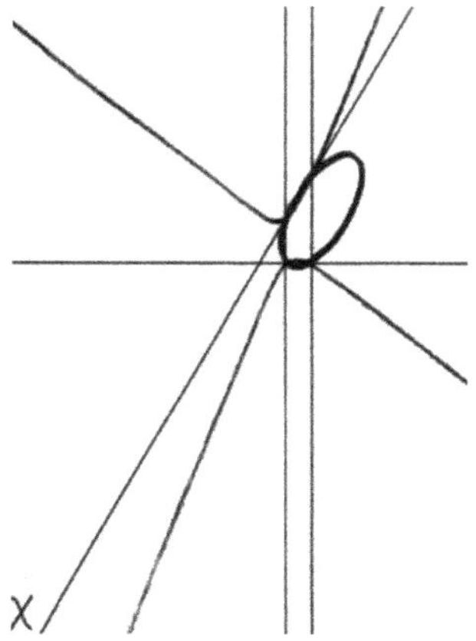

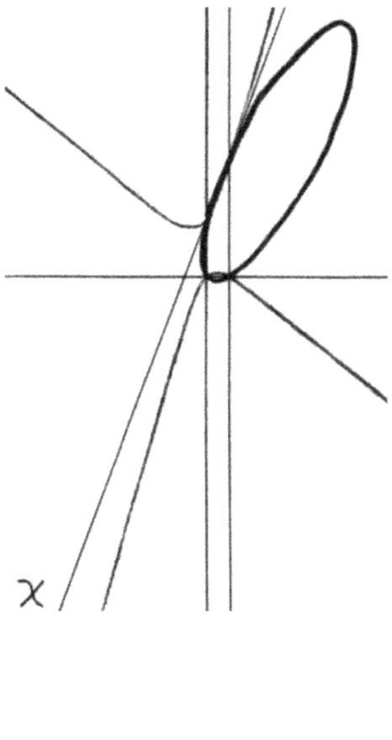

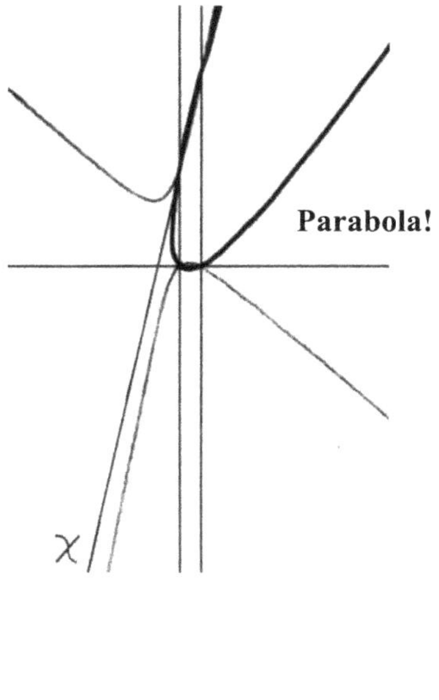

An Explanation of Part H

The Key Ideas

- "Part H" is the culmination of *Book I* of the first appendix, *La Géométrie*, from Descartes' book *Discourse on the Method.*
- This is a summary of what Descartes did in Part H in his treatment of the Pappus problem. The whole passage tells us in detail how you can find one point, C, on the resulting curve.
- We begin with the idea that from point A (the origin) we can travel any given distance, x, along the line EG, and from there (point B) travel a certain distance, y, at the required angle (θ_3), until we arrive at a point (C) on the desired loci curve.
- It is important to note that if we imagine point C moving along the desired loci curve, then all of the triangles (see below) will retain their same shape, angles, and ratios, even though their size will change.
- The goal is to derive a formula that, given any x value, calculates y, or, given any value for y, calculates x.
- The four lines are placed on the page, and we are to find point C on the curve such that the distances to each line – measured at the required angles (θ_1, θ_2, θ_3, θ_4) – satisfy the equation **CB·CF = CH·CD**.

Triangle Ratios (Descartes has chosen to express all of his ratios in terms of z, which could be any number.)

Using ΔARB, let AB:BR = z:b.

$BR = \frac{b \cdot AB}{z}$ since AB = x we get $BR = \frac{b \cdot x}{z}$

Using ΔDRC, let CR:CD = z:c. $CD = \frac{c \cdot CR}{z}$

Using ΔESB, let EB:BS = z:d.

$BS = \frac{d \cdot EB}{z}$ since EB = k+x we get $BS = \frac{dk + dx}{z}$

Using ΔFSC, let CS:CF = z:e. $CF = \frac{e \cdot CS}{z}$

Using ΔBGT, let BG:BT = z:f.

$BT = \frac{f \cdot BG}{z}$ since $BG = \ell - x$ we get $BT = \frac{f\ell - fx}{z}$

Using ΔTCH, let TC:CH = z:g. $CH = \frac{g \cdot CT}{z}$

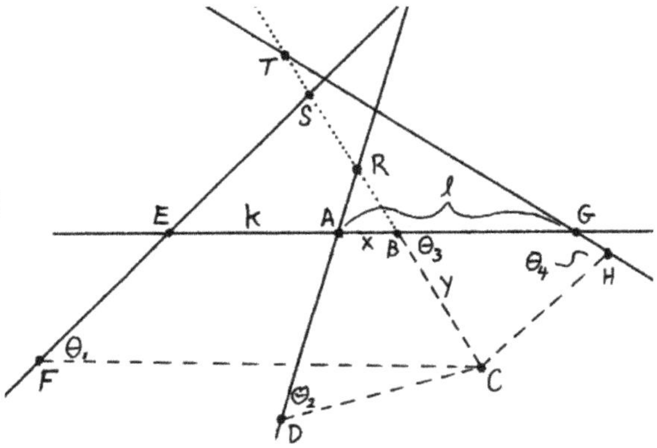

Deriving Formulas for the Four Distances (CB,CF, CH, CD)

- Calculating CB. $\boxed{CB = y}$ (The rest aren't that easy!)
- Calculating CD.

CR = BR+BC. Given BC=y and $BR = \frac{b \cdot x}{z}$ (from above), we get $CR = \frac{b \cdot x}{z} + y$

$CD = \frac{c \cdot CR}{z}$ (from above). Substituting, we get $CD = \frac{c \cdot \left(\frac{b \cdot x}{z} + y\right)}{z}$ → $CD = \frac{cy}{z} + \frac{bcx}{z^2}$ (the second c is missing in the translation) which becomes $\boxed{CD = \frac{czy + bcx}{z^2}}$

- Calculating CF.

CS = BS + CB. Given CB = y and $BS = \frac{dk + dx}{z}$ (from above), we get

$CS = \frac{dk + dx}{z} + y$ → $CS = \frac{dk + dx + zy}{z}$ and $CF = \frac{e \cdot CS}{z}$ (from above). Substituting, we get

$CF = \frac{e \cdot \left(\frac{dk + dx + zy}{z}\right)}{z}$ which becomes $\boxed{CF = \frac{ezy + dek + dex}{z^2}}$

Part H of *La Géométrie* (continued)

- Calculating CH.
  CT = BT + CB. Given CB = y and BT = $\frac{f\ell - fx}{z}$ (from above), we get

  $CT = \frac{f\ell - fx}{z} + y \rightarrow CT = \frac{zy + f\ell - fx}{z}$ and $CH = \frac{g \cdot CT}{z}$ (from above). Substituting, we get

  $CH = \frac{g \cdot \left(\frac{zy + f\ell - fx}{z}\right)}{z}$ which becomes $\boxed{CH = \frac{gzy + fg\ell - fgx}{z^2}}$

- The first sentence at the top of page 34 restates the condition of the Pappus problem:
  CB·CF = CH·CD. This can therefore be expressed as:

  $$y \cdot \left(\frac{ezy + dek + dex}{z^2}\right) = \left(\frac{gzy + fg\ell - fgx}{z^2}\right) \cdot \left(\frac{czy + bcx}{z^2}\right)$$

- In the first sentence on page 33, he says that, with each of the above formulas, x and y are the only variables, and all of the rest (c, b, z, e, d, e, g, f) are given, or easily calculable. Then he says (p34):

  > *Since this condition can be expressed by a single equation into unknown quantities, we may give any value we please to x or y and find the value of the other from this equation...Assigning a value to y we have* $x^2 = \pm ax \pm b^2$*, and therefore x can be found with ruler and compasses by a method already explained. If then we should take successively an infinite number of different values for the line y, we should obtain an infinite number of values for the line x, and therefore an infinite of different points, such as c, by means of which the required curve could be drawn.*

  This essentially forms the seed idea for what has been named after Descartes – Cartesian geometry. Descartes took the first brilliant, but rather cumbersome step, and the world of mathematics quickly developed it into the form that we all know today.

—— *Cartesian Geometry* (11th and 12th Grade) ——

Overview

At a time where nearly everything is taught to children as young as possible, delaying the introduction of Cartesian geometry until eleventh grade certainly seems radical. (Read about our reasons for doing this, above, in the *Introduction* under "Introducing Cartesian geometry".) Cartesian geometry is the largest theme in our *11th/12th Grade Workbook* – there are four units dedicated to this important subject. We find that our students get "caught up" very quickly, and, in the end, they gain a deep understanding and develop solid skills in this subject.

The introduction to Cartesian geometry

Our *11th/12th Grade Workbook* begins with the first unit on Cartesian geometry. The intention is to introduce the subject in the Descartes main lesson (see the above section for details) through René Descartes' work. The students are then able to fully grasp the significance of the step Descartes took, and are prepared and eager to dive into the Cartesian geometry units in the workbook.

Topics covered

The topics covered in our *11th/12th Grade Workbook's* four units on Cartesian geometry are:

Cartesian Geometry, Part I

- Graphing two-variable equations by plotting points from a table
- Overview of graphing lines, circles, parabolas, cubics, etc.
- Focus on graphing lines
- Determining equations of lines given certain conditions
- Using three methods to find common solutions to linear equations

Cartesian Geometry, Part II

- Review of *Cartesian Geometry Part I*
- Graphing parabolas, circles, and ellipses
- Alternate coordinate systems (see below)
- Roots of equations
- Finding common solutions

Cartesian Geometry, Part III

- Review of *Cartesian Geometry Part II*
- Domain and range of functions
- Trig unit circle
- Manipulating graphs of functions
- The Root-Factor Theorem
- Graphing polynomial functions
- Applications of Cartesian geometry

Cartesian Geometry, Part IV

- Review of *Cartesian Geometry Part III*
- Even and odd functions
- Rational functions
- Inverse functions and function properties
- Exponential and logarithmic functions
- Graphing polar equations

For a thorough understanding of the above topics, the teacher is advised to carefully work through the Cartesian geometry units in the workbook, and to also read the *Unit-by-Unit Commentary* in the introduction of the *Teacher's Edition of our 11th/12th Grade Workbook.*

Conics on a Harmonic Net[1]

Alternate coordinate systems – a different representation of $y = x^2$

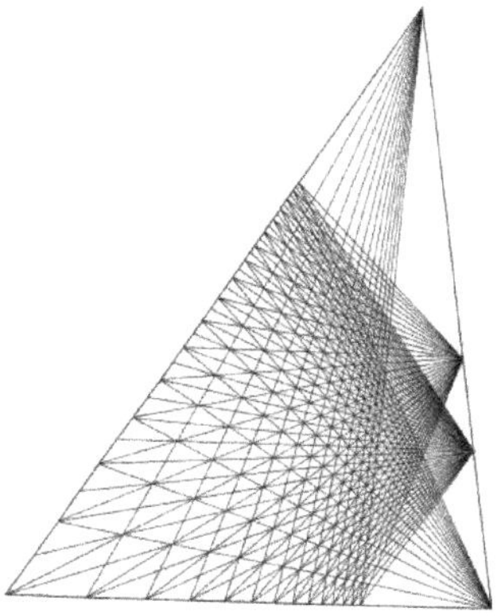

The point of this exercise is to emphasize to the students that, for a given function or relation, the shape of the resulting graph depends upon the coordinate axis we choose. For example, $y = x^2$ produces a parabola if we choose to use the Cartesian coordinate axis. However, if we choose a polar coordinate axis, the graph would be a spiral.

Here, we use a harmonic net as the coordinate axis. Often, a harmonic net is drawn in an eleventh grade projective geometry course. It has four "vanishing points" along the line at infinity (i.e., the horizon), thereby including the diagonals of the "squares" in the drawing. (See drawing on the right, and more details under *Projective Geometry*.) In order to make this into a harmonic net coordinate axis, we don't include the diagonals – although two diagonals are needed as guides, which are erased in the end. The end result looks like a two-point parallel perspective drawing of a checkerboard.

Once this unusual coordinate axis has been created, we define the x-axis by choosing any line that passes through A, and define the y-axis by choosing any line that passes through B. The ellipse and hyperbola show two possible results for graphing $y = x^2$. We should note that if we "nail down" a couple of points on the ellipse, and slide point A infinitely far to the right, and point B infinitely far upwards, then we will get a parabola on a standard Cartesian coordinate axis.

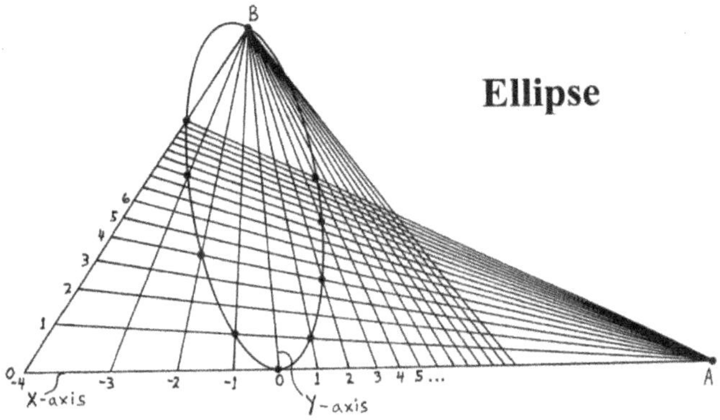

Ellipse

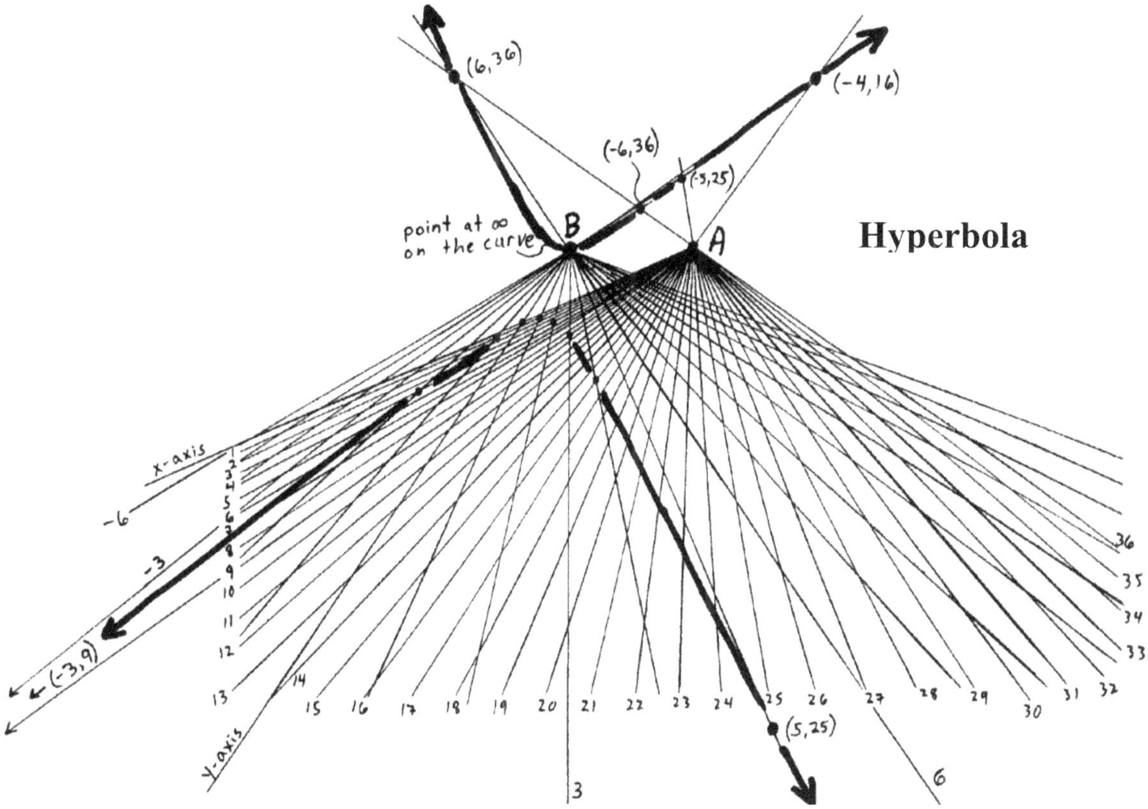

Hyperbola

[1] Thanks to Mikko Bojarsky and Ernst Schuberth for the inspiration for this page.

—— *Trigonometry* (Grades 10-12) ——

Overview

If there is one common weakness in mathematical understanding, amongst even the strongest first-year college students, it is trigonometry. (We should also add logarithms to the list.) Why is this so? My theory is that most high school precalculus textbooks cover all of trigonometry in two or three back-to-back units. It starts by defining sine, cosine, and tangent on the first page (which leaves many students trying for months to remember which one is which), and then it builds, one step at a time, for page after page, until the full edifice of trigonometry has been constructed. No particular step was too difficult or overwhelming, but for even the strongest students, the learning tends to be quite superficial. And superficial learning doesn't stick. Many – if not most – students forget most of what they "learned" shortly after the test is over.

I believe that in order to learn something deeply and (somewhat) permanently, students need to forget it three times – and then review, remember, and deepen it. We have intentionally spaced our four trigonometry units (in our workbooks) over the course of two years. In between each unit, trigonometry is "put to sleep" for months. Then in the next trig unit, the material is "woken up" – the students remember it as we review the material, and then we go deeper. I believe that, with this approach, students leave high school with a deeper and more permanent grasp of trigonometry.

The introduction to trigonometry in tenth grade (*Trigonometry – Part I*)

How can we introduce trigonometry in a meaningful way and still get to the essence of what trigonometry is? The trigonometry unit in our *10th Grade Workbook* attempts to accomplish exactly this, and the end result is a huge mathematical experience. This is in direct contrast to the common textbook "*SohCahToa*" approach, where students quickly memorize sine, cosine and tangent.

Although this unit can be done in track class, it may be best to weave it into a main lesson combined with *surveying,* or some other practical application.

In order to gain a deeper understanding of this unit, the teacher should read the commentary found in the *Teacher's Edition of our 10th Grade Workbook* and also work through the problem sets found in the trigonometry unit.

Trigonometry in depth

The topics covered in our *11th/12th Grade Workbook's* three units on trigonometry are:

Trigonometry, Part II
- Review of Sine and Cosine
- Law of Sines
- Introduction to Tangent
- Special trig triangles (30°-60°-90°; 45°-45°-90°)
- Inverse trig functions
- Estimating trig function values
- Using trig functions to solve triangles
- Solving trig word problems

Trigonometry, Part III
- Review of right triangle trig and the Law of Sines
- Sine, Cosine and Tangent when $90° \leq \theta \leq 180°$
- Law of Cosines
- Law of Tangents
- Solving SSA triangles
- The Six Trig Functions
- Trig identities

Trigonometry, Part IV
- Review of *Trigonometry Part III*
- Graphing trig functions
- Trig identities
- Simplifying trig expressions
- Proving trig identities
- Solving trig equations

For a thorough understanding of the above topics, the teacher is advised to carefully work through the trigonometry units in the workbook, and to also read the *Unit-by-Unit Commentary* in the introduction of the *Teacher's Edition of our 11th/12th Grade Workbook.*

The Trig Unit Circle

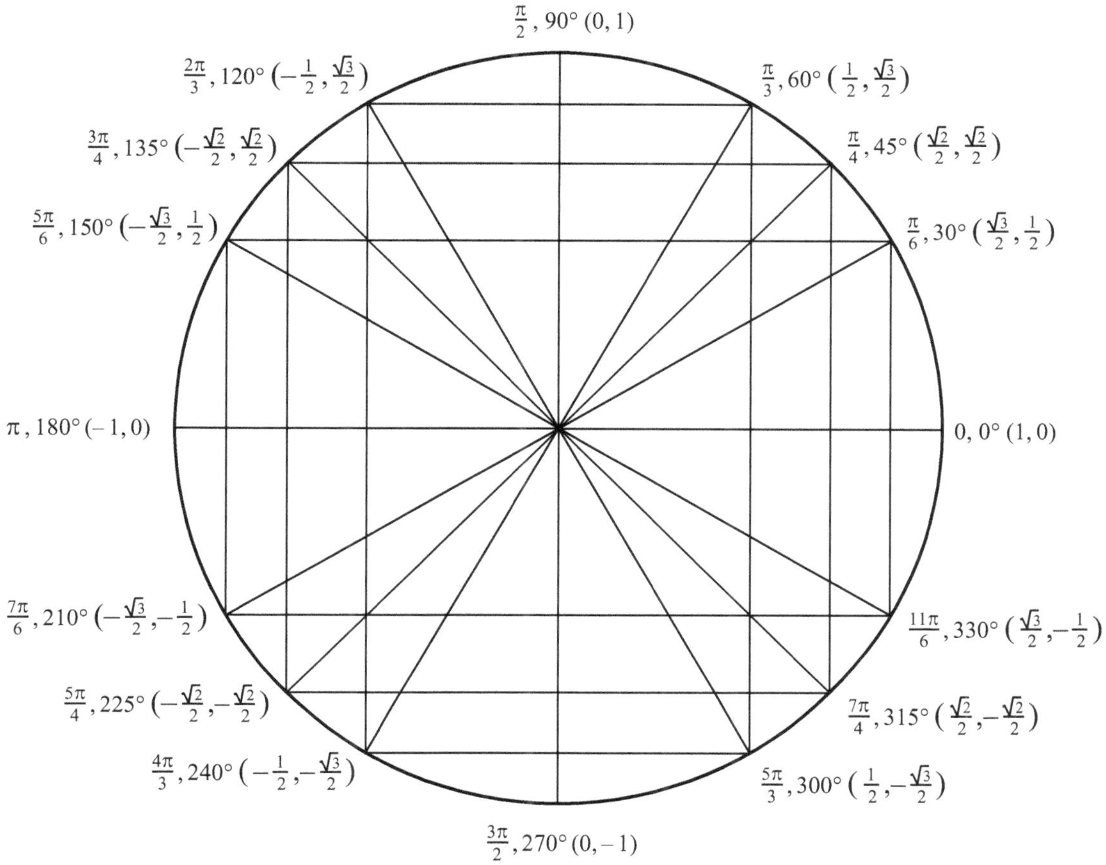

Proofs of the Three Trigonometric Laws

Law of Sines

Note: This exercise appears in the *Intro to Trigonometry* unit (10th grade workbook).

1. An alternative definition of *Sine* involves an angle inscribed in a circle, and the subtended chord. *sin*(α) then answers the question: "*The chord is what proportion of the diameter*?"

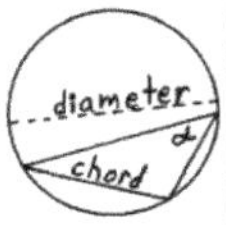

   It is then written as $sin(\alpha) = \frac{\text{chord}}{\text{diameter}}$

2. Given any ΔABC, we can circumscribe a circle around it.

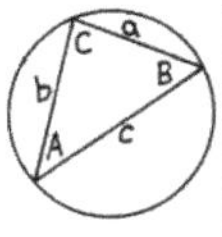

3. Let d be the diameter of the circle. It follows then that:

$$\text{Sin}(A) = \frac{a}{d} \quad \text{and} \quad \text{Sin}(B) = \frac{b}{d}$$

Therefore $d = \frac{a}{\sin(A)} = \frac{b}{\sin(B)}$ and $\boxed{\frac{a}{b} = \frac{sin\,A}{sin\,B}}$

Law of Cosines

Note: This exercise appears in our *11th/12th Grade Workbook*, in the unit *Trigonometry Part III.*

1. Given acute triangle, ΔABC, attach squares to the sides of the triangle, draw the triangle's three altitudes, and label everything as shown below.

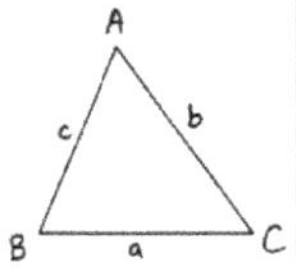

2. Using ΔABX
   AX = c·cos(A).
   Similarly, we have
   CX = a·cos(C)
   BY = c·cos(B)
   CY = b·cos(C)
   AZ = b·cos(A)
   BZ = a·cos(B)

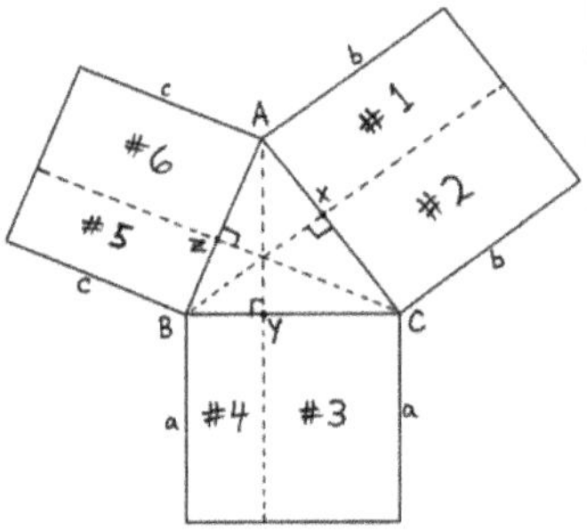

3. The areas of rect#3 = rect#2 = ab·cos(C)
   rect#5 = rect#4 = ac·cos(B)
   rect#6 = rect#1 = bc·cos(A)

4. a^2 = rect#4 + rect#3;
   b^2 = rect#1 + rect#2;
   c^2 = rect#5 + rect#6

5. The final steps are then:

rect#5 + rect#6 + rect#3 = rect#1 + rect#2 + rect#4
c^2 + rect#3 = b^2 + rect#4
c^2 + rect#3 + rect#3 = b^2 + rect#4 + rect#3
c^2 + 2(rect#3) = $b^2 + a^2$

$$\boxed{c^2 = a^2 + b^2 - 2ab\cdot\cos(C)}$$

Law of Tangents

Note: This exercise appears in our *11th/12th Grade Workbook*, in the unit *Trigonometry Part III.*

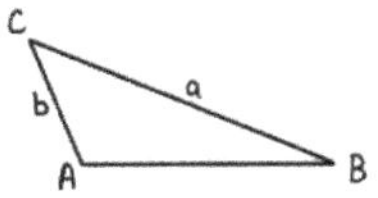

1. Given any triangle, ΔABC, we extend side b upward by the length of side a up to point R. Points P and Q are found by measuring a distance of b away from point C. Lines are then joined as shown in the drawing.

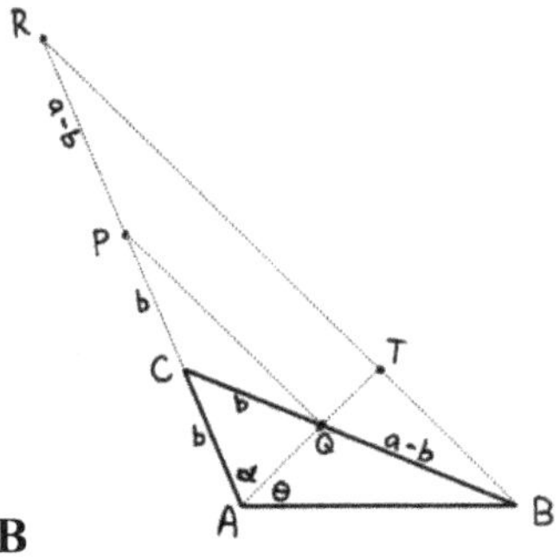

2. ΔCRB ~ ΔCPQ
   ∠CRB ~ ∠CPQ
   PQ is parallel to RB

The angle measures are as follows:

3. $\angle ACQ = 180° - \angle A - \angle B$
   $\alpha = \angle CQA = \angle TQB$
   $\angle PCQ = \angle A + \angle B = \alpha + \angle CQA = 2\alpha$
   $\boldsymbol{\alpha = \frac{1}{2}(\angle A + \angle B)}$

4. $\alpha = \frac{1}{2}(\angle A + \angle B) = \angle CQA = \theta + \angle B$
   $\frac{1}{2}\angle A + \frac{1}{2}\angle B = \theta + \angle B$
   $\boldsymbol{\theta = \frac{1}{2}(\angle A - \angle B)}$

5. $\angle PCQ + \angle CPQ + \angle PQC = 180°$
   $2\alpha + 2\angle PQC = 180° \rightarrow \alpha + \angle PQC = 90°$
   $\boldsymbol{\angle AQP = 90° = \angle ATR}$

6. Let x = AT. Using ΔATB and ΔATR, we get TB = x·tan(θ) and TR = x·tan(α)

7. The last few steps are then:
   ΔTQB ~ ΔPQA ~ ΔRTA
   TB:QB = TR:AR
   x·tan(θ) : (a–b) = x·tan(α) : (a+b)
   x·tan(θ) : x·tan(α) = (a–b) : (a+b)

$$\boxed{\frac{\tan[\frac{1}{2}(A-B)]}{\tan[\frac{1}{2}(A+B)]} = \frac{a-b}{a+b}}$$

where ½(A+B) is the average of ∠A and ∠B and ½(A–B) is the difference between this average and either ∠A or ∠B.

Trigonometric Identities and Laws

Opposite Angle Identities

$\sin(-\theta) = -\sin\theta$
$\cos(-\theta) = \cos(\theta)$
$\tan(-\theta) = -\tan\theta$

Supplementary Angle Identities

$\sin(\pi-\theta) = \sin\theta$
$\cos(\pi-\theta) = -\cos\theta$
$\tan(\pi-\theta) = -\tan\theta$

Pythagorean Identities

$\cos^2\theta + \sin^2\theta = 1$
$1 + \tan^2\theta = \sec^2\theta$
$\cot^2\theta + 1 = \csc^2\theta$

Law of Sines

$\frac{\sin A}{a} = \frac{\sin B}{b}$ or $a:b = \sin A : \sin B$

Law of Cosines

$c^2 = a^2 + b^2 - 2ab\cdot\cos(C)$

Law of Tangents

$$\frac{a+b}{a-b} = \frac{\tan[\frac{1}{2}(A+B)]}{\tan[\frac{1}{2}(A-B)]}$$

Sum/Difference Identities

$\sin(u \pm v) = \sin u \cdot \cos v \pm \cos u \cdot \sin v$

$\cos(u \pm v) = \cos u \cdot \cos v \mp \sin u \cdot \sin v$

$\tan(u \pm v) = \frac{\tan u \pm \tan v}{1 \mp \tan u \cdot \tan v}$

Double-Angle Identities

$\sin 2u = 2 \sin u \cdot \cos u$

$\cos 2u = \cos^2 u - \sin^2 u$
$= 2\cos^2 u - 1 = 1 - 2\sin^2 u$

$\tan 2u = \frac{2 \tan u}{1 - \tan^2 u}$

Half-Angle Identities

$\sin \frac{1}{2}u = \pm\sqrt{\frac{1}{2}(1 - \cos u)}$
(Sign depends on quadrant of angle ½u)

$\cos \frac{1}{2}u = \pm\sqrt{\frac{1}{2}(1 + \cos u)}$
(Sign depends on quadrant of angle ½u)

$\tan \frac{1}{2}u = \frac{1 - \cos u}{\sin u} = \frac{\sin u}{1 + \cos u}$

Co-Function Identities

$\sin(\pi/2 - x) = \cos x$ $\cos(\pi/2 - x) = \sin x$
$\tan(\pi/2 - x) = \cot x$ $\cot(\pi/2 - x) = \tan x$
$\sec(\pi/2 - x) = \csc x$ $\csc(\pi/2 - x) = \sec x$

Power Reducing Identities

$\sin^2 u = \frac{1}{2}(1 - \cos 2u)$
$\cos^2 u = \frac{1}{2}(1 + \cos 2u)$
$\tan^2 u = \frac{1 - \cos 2u}{1 + \cos 2u}$

Sum-to-Product Identities

$\sin u + \sin v = 2\left(\sin \frac{u+v}{2} \cdot \cos \frac{u-v}{2}\right)$

$\sin u - \sin v = 2\left(\cos \frac{u+v}{2} \cdot \sin \frac{u-v}{2}\right)$

$\cos u + \cos v = 2\left(\cos \frac{u+v}{2} \cdot \cos \frac{u-v}{2}\right)$

$\cos u - \cos v = -2\left(\sin \frac{u+v}{2} \cdot \sin \frac{u-v}{2}\right)$

Product-to-Sum Identities

$\sin u \cdot \sin v = \frac{1}{2}[\cos(u-v) - \cos(u+v)]$
$\cos u \cdot \cos v = \frac{1}{2}[\cos(u-v) + \cos(u+v)]$
$\sin u \cdot \cos v = \frac{1}{2}[\sin(u+v) + \sin(u-v)]$

Proofs of the Trigonometric Identities

The Sum/Difference Identities

Everything begins with finding a formula for cos(u-v).

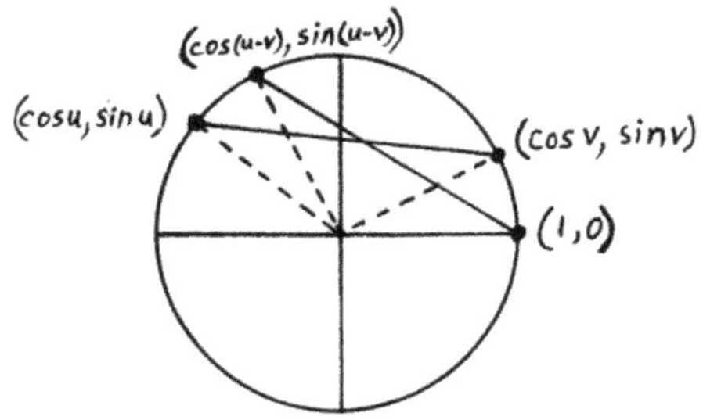

Given the drawing shown at the right, we see two congruent triangles, and therefore the two long sides of the triangles are congruent. From this, and knowing that the distance between any two points (x_1, y_1) and (x_0, y_0) is given by $\sqrt{(x_1-x_0)^2+(y_1-y_0)^2}$, we set the distance between the points (cos(u-v),sin(u-v)) and (1,0) equal to the distance between the points (cos u, sin u) and (cos v, sin v), giving us the equation

$$\sqrt{(\cos(u-v)-1)^2+(\sin(u-v)-0)^2} = \sqrt{(\cos u-\cos v)^2+(\sin u-\sin v)^2}$$

$$(\cos(u-v)-1)^2+(\sin(u-v)-0)^2 = (\cos u-\cos v)^2+(\sin u-\sin v)^2$$

$$\cos^2(u-v)-2\cos(u-v)+1 + \sin^2(u-v) = \cos^2 u-2\cos u\cdot\cos v+\cos^2 v + \sin^2 u-2\sin u\cdot\sin v+\sin^2 v$$

Using the Identity $\sin^2 x+\cos^2 x=1$ in three places, and then dividing both sides of the equation by -2 gives us:

$$\boxed{\cos(u-v) = \cos u\cdot\cos v+\sin u\cdot\sin v}$$

We then let $V=-X$, which gives us: $\boxed{\cos(u+x) = \cos u\cdot\cos x-\sin u\cdot\sin x}$

Letting $U = {}^{\pi}/_2 - Y$ then gives us: $\cos({}^{\pi}/_2 - y + x) = \cos({}^{\pi}/_2 - y)\cdot\cos x - \sin({}^{\pi}/_2 - y)\cdot\sin x$

$$\cos({}^{\pi}/_2 - (y-x)) = \cos({}^{\pi}/_2 - y)\cdot\cos x - \sin({}^{\pi}/_2 - y)\cdot\sin x$$

And using the identity $\cos({}^{\pi}/_2 - \theta) = \sin\theta$ we get $\boxed{\sin(y-x) = \sin y\cdot\cos x - \cos y\cdot\sin x}$

And then letting $X=-W$ gives us $\boxed{\sin(y+w) = \sin y\cdot\cos w + \cos y\cdot\sin w}$

Furthermore, $\tan(u+v) = \frac{\sin(u+v)}{\cos(u+v)} = \frac{\sin u\cdot\cos v+\cos u\cdot\sin v}{\cos u\cdot\cos v-\sin u\cdot\sin v}$ If we divide the numerator and the denominator by cosu·cosv, then we get the identity $\boxed{\tan(u+v) = \frac{\tan u+\tan v}{1-\tan u\cdot\tan v}}$ and then $\boxed{\tan(u-v) = \frac{\tan u-\tan v}{1+\tan u\cdot\tan v}}$

From this, come the **Double-Angle Identities**. We think of sin(2u) as sin(u+u), and use the sum identity for sine given above to get $\boxed{\sin(2u) = 2\sin u\cdot\cos u}$

Similarly, $\boxed{\cos(2u) = \cos^2 u - \sin^2 u = 2\cos^2 u - 1 = 1 - 2\sin^2 u}$

And with tangent we use the identity $\tan(u+v) = \frac{\tan u+\tan v}{1-\tan u\cdot\tan v}$ to get $\boxed{\tan 2u = \frac{2\tan u}{1-\tan^2 u}}$

From there, we can derive the **Power Reducing Identities** from the double-angle identities:

From $\cos 2u = 2\cos^2 u - 1$ we get $\boxed{\cos^2 u = ½(1+\cos 2u)}$

From $\cos 2u = 1-2\sin^2 u$ we get $\boxed{\sin^2 u = ½(1-\cos 2u)}$

And therefore $\boxed{\tan^2 u = \frac{1-\cos 2u}{1+\cos 2u}}$

The **Half-Angle Identities**. We use $\cos^2 u = ½(1+\cos 2u)$ and let $U = ½X$ to get $\boxed{\cos(½x) = \sqrt{½(1+\cos x)}}$

And using $\sin^2 u = ½(1-\cos 2u)$ and letting $U = ½X$, we get $\boxed{\sin(½x) = \sqrt{½(1-\cos x)}}$

It follows then that $\tan(½x) = \frac{\sqrt{½(1-\cos x)}}{\sqrt{½(1+\cos x)}} \rightarrow \sqrt{\frac{½(1-\cos x)}{½(1+\cos x)}}$ and canceling the ½'s and multiplying top and bottom by 1−cosx gives: $\sqrt{\frac{(1-\cos x)^2}{1-\cos^2 x}} \rightarrow \sqrt{\frac{(1-\cos x)^2}{\sin^2 x}} \rightarrow \boxed{\tan(½x) = \frac{1-\cos x}{\sin x}}$

—— *Imaginary and Complex Numbers* (11th Grade) ——

Overview

There are two units on imaginary/complex numbers in our *11th/12th Grade Workbook.* The introduction of these new, strange numbers marks a departure from "ninth grade thinking". Imaginary numbers start out by immediately defying a long-believed rule: "You can't square root a negative number". This gives the students a whole new perspective on mathematics and opens the door to new adventures.

The big hanging question

Too often, mainstream mathematics curricula only allows for a superficial treatment of imaginary/complex numbers. In contrast, we set the stage in *Complex Numbers Part I*, leaving the students to wonder about the big hanging question: "What are the Three Cube Roots of 1?" The students will need to learn much more about Cartesian geometry, trigonometry, and complex numbers in order to solve this question. Leaving a question hanging for so long makes the journey all the more worthwhile.

Complex roots

If the journey is successful, then the students are able to solve the big hanging question in the unit *Complex Numbers Part II.* It is in this second unit that we are able to go into real depth. Through graphing numbers on the complex plane, and using De Moivre's Theorem, not only can we now find the three cube roots of 1 (answers: 1, $-\frac{1}{2}+\frac{\sqrt{3}}{2}i$, $-\frac{1}{2}-\frac{\sqrt{3}}{2}i$), but we can readily find any root of any complex number, such as: the three cube roots of -8i (answers: $2i$, $-\sqrt{3}-i$, $\sqrt{3}-i$); or even the five fifth roots of $16\sqrt{3}-16$ (answers: $2\,\text{cis}(\frac{\pi}{3})$; $2\,\text{cis}(\frac{11\pi}{15})$; $2\,\text{cis}(\frac{17\pi}{15})$; $2\,\text{cis}(\frac{23\pi}{15})$; $2\,\text{cis}(\frac{29\pi}{15})$), which can also be expressed as: $1+\sqrt{3}\,i$, $-1.338+1.486\,i$, $-1.827-0.813\,i$, $0.209-1.989\,i$, $1.956-0.416\,i$) Amazing!

And more amazing!

The unit *Complex Numbers Part II* can be a wonderful culmination to the eleventh grade year. This unit ends with an exploration of Euler's formula, $e^{ix} = \text{cis}(x)$, which leads to several surprising conclusions, including: $e^{i\pi} = -1$, $5^{i} = \text{cis}(\ln 5) \approx -0.0386+0.9993\,i$, and $i^{i} \approx 0.2079$
For details about all of this, read the *Unit-by-Unit Commentary* on *Complex Numbers Part II* in the introduction of the *Teacher's Edition of our 11th/12th Grade Workbook.*

Topics covered

The topics covered in the workbook's two units on imaginary/complex numbers are:

Complex Numbers, Part I

- Review of factoring
- Intro to function notation and evaluating functions
- A brief history of numbers
- Intro to imaginary and complex numbers
- The Fundamental Theorem of Algebra
- "Complex" Factoring
- Simplifying expressions involving *i*
- Equations which have complex number solutions
- The big hanging question: what are the three cube roots of 1?

Complex Numbers, Part II

- Graphing complex numbers in rectangular and polar form
- Absolute value of complex numbers
- Converting between rectangular and polar form
- Laws of complex numbers
- De Moivre's Theorem
- Powers of complex numbers
- Roots of complex numbers (including the three cube roots of 1)
- Euler's formula and Euler's identity
- Raising a real number to the power of *i*
- Raising a complex number to the *i*

For a thorough understanding of the above topics, the teacher is advised to carefully work through the two units in the workbook, and to also read the *Unit-by-Unit Commentary* in the introduction of the *Teacher's Edition of our 11th/12th Grade Workbook.*

A Proof of Euler's Formula

We begin with a formula for e expressed as an infinite series.

$$e = \sum_{j=0}^{\infty} \frac{1}{j!} = \frac{1}{0!} + \frac{1}{1!} + \frac{1}{2!} + \frac{1}{3!} + \frac{1}{4!} + \ldots$$

Furthermore, the below formulas can be derived through higher-level calculus.
(For now you can verify each of them with a calculator. Recall that 0! = 1.)

$$e^{x} = \sum \frac{x^j}{j!} = \frac{1}{0!} + \frac{x}{1!} + \frac{x^2}{2!} + \frac{x^3}{3!} + \frac{x^4}{4!} + \ldots$$

$$\cos(x) = \sum (-1)^j \frac{x^{2j}}{(2j)!} = \frac{1}{0!} - \frac{x^2}{2!} + \frac{x^4}{4!} - \ldots$$

$$\sin(x) = \sum (-1)^j \frac{x^{2j+1}}{(2j+1)!} = \frac{x}{1!} - \frac{x^3}{3!} + \frac{x^5}{5!} - \ldots$$

Notice the similarity between these formulas. The key to relating them is the imaginary number, i. Using the first formula, we replace x with ix, which gives us:

$$e^{ix} = \sum \frac{i^j \cdot x^j}{j!} = \frac{1}{0!} + \frac{i \cdot x}{1!} + \frac{i^2 \cdot x^2}{2!} + \frac{i^3 \cdot x^3}{3!} + \frac{i^4 \cdot x^4}{4!} + \frac{i^5 \cdot x^5}{5!} + \frac{i^6 \cdot x^6}{6!} + \ldots$$

Given that $i^2 = -1$, $i^3 = -i$, $i^4 = 1$, etc., we get:

$$e^{ix} = \sum \frac{i^j \cdot x^j}{j!} = \frac{1}{0!} + \frac{i \cdot x}{1!} - \frac{x^2}{2!} - \frac{i \cdot x^3}{3!} + \frac{x^4}{4!} + \frac{i \cdot x^5}{5!} - \frac{x^6}{6!} - \ldots$$

Now, if we take the terms without i in the numerator, we have the series for cos(x), as given above. And the remaining terms (which have i in the numerator) are equal to $i \cdot \sin(x)$.

Therefore, we have derived Euler's surprising formula:

$$\boxed{e^{ix} = \cos(x) + i\sin(x)}$$ which can also be written as $$\boxed{e^{ix} = \text{cis}(x)}$$

Finally, we plug π into x to get Euler's famous identity: $\boxed{e^{i\pi} = -1}$

—— *Calculus* (12th Grade) ——

Overview

Beginning from a historical perspective, calculus answers four of the unsolved puzzles of the seventeenth century: (1) given a formula for an object's distance, how to find its instantaneous rate of speed; (2) how to find the slope of a line tangent to a given point on a curve; (3) how to find the maximum or minimum value of a function; and (4) how to find areas and volumes of shapes and solids bounded by curves and curved surfaces. In solving these problems and providing the next giant step for the advancement of math and science, calculus is the one of the great achievements of the human mind.

This course focuses on both differential calculus and integral calculus. With differential calculus, we start with the seemingly paradoxical question: if average speed is the change of distance divided by the change of time, then how can we calculate instantaneous speed, since both the change of distance and the change of time are zero? What is zero divided by zero? This leads, over the period of a few days, to the definition of the derivative, thereby providing a method for calculating the instantaneous rate of change.

Integral calculus is introduced through the idea of finding the area under a curve, with the central question being: how can we find a method to add together infinitely many, infinitely thin rectangles? The process to solve the puzzle that the integral presents is at first quite laborious, but eventually we are led to the huge realization – the Fundamental Theorem of Calculus – that the derivative and integral are fundamentally connected. In fact, it is the anti-derivative that provides the key to making integration a relatively simple procedure.

In the end, this introductory calculus course gives the students an experience of the essence of one of the most important fields in mathematics. And for those who will continue their math studies in college, it gives them a firm foundation to ensure success.

Lesson plans

Detailed day-by-day lesson plans can be downloaded from our website: **www.JamieYorkPress.com**.

Discovery sheets

In contrast to nearly every other math main lesson I teach, where skills work is not a central focus, my calculus main lesson is, to some degree, built around worksheets. But these are not normal worksheets; I call them "discovery sheets". The purpose is two-fold: (1) to carefully guide the students along a path of discovery so that they feel that they have discovered the derivative and the integral for themselves; and (2) to systematically build up the students' basic calculus skills so that, at the end of the course, they can take the final exam and walk away feeling that they have firmly learned some basic calculus skills.

These *Discovery Sheets* appear at the end of this section, and can also be downloaded from our website. They may be photocopied by the teacher (in accordance with our permissions agreement stated at the start of this book) and given to students.

Calculus track class

Shortly after the completion of the calculus main lesson, the advanced track class continues its study of calculus by working through the two calculus units found in our *11th/12th Grade Workbook*. The calculus main lesson provides the foundation upon which the workbook's calculus studies build.

The topics covered in the workbook's two calculus units are:

- Review of the calculus main lesson
- Derivatives and anti-derivatives of trig functions
- *Rules for Derivatives*: power rule, product rule, and quotient rule
- Derivatives of $f(x)=e^x$ and $f(x)=\ln x$
- The *Chain Rule*
- Areas and volumes of regions bounded by curves
- Implicit differentiation
- Related rate problems
- Max-min problems

For a thorough understanding of the above topics, the teacher is advised to carefully work through the two units, and to read the *Unit-by-Unit Commentary* in the introduction of the *Teacher's Edition of our 11th/12th Grade Workbook.*

Proofs of the Summation Formulas

The formulas are (for i = 1 to n):

$\Sigma i = \frac{n(n+1)}{2}$; $\Sigma i^2 = \frac{n(n+1)(2n+1)}{6}$; $\Sigma i^3 = \frac{n^2(n+1)^2}{4} = (\Sigma i)^2$; $\Sigma i^4 = \frac{n(n+1)(2n+1)(3n^2+3n-1)}{30}$

Here are two ways that these formulas can be proven:

1. Mathematical Induction

For example, proving Σi^2:

Step 1: We must show that the formula is valid for n = 1. If n=1 then $\Sigma i^2 = 1^2 = 1$.

The formula is $\frac{n(n+1)(2n+1)}{6}$, which for n=1 gives a result of 1. Therefore it is valid for n=1.

Step 2: We must now show that, assuming that the formula is valid for some integer k, that it is also valid for k+1.

Putting k+1 into the formula, we get $\frac{(k+1)(k+2)(2k+3)}{6}$.

To show this is equal to the sum of the squares of all the numbers from 1 to k+1, we get:

$$(1^2 + 2^2 + 3^2 + 4^2 + ... + k^2) + (k+1)^2$$

$$= \frac{k(k+1)(2k+1)}{6} + (k+1)^2$$

factoring out (k+1) as GCF, we get:

$$= \frac{(k+1)[k(2k+1) + 6(k+1)]}{6}$$

$$= \frac{(k+1)[2k^2 + 7k + 6]}{6}$$

$$= \frac{(k+1)(k+2)(2k+3)}{6}$$ therefore it works for k+1

$\therefore$ We have now proven that the formula is correct for all integer values of $k \geq 1$.

2. Proof by summing equations

For example, proving Σi^4:

Using the identity $x^5 - (x-1)^5 = 5n^4 - 10n^3 + 10n^2 - 5n + 1$, we create n equations by first plugging 1 into the above identity, then we create a second equation by plugging in 2 for X, etc., all the way to plugging in n for X. All of this gives us the following n equations:

$$1^5 - 0^5 = 5\cdot1^4 - 10\cdot1^3 + 10\cdot1^2 - 5\cdot1 + 1$$
$$2^5 - 1^5 = 5\cdot2^4 - 10\cdot2^3 + 10\cdot2^2 - 5\cdot2 + 1$$
$$3^5 - 2^5 = 5\cdot3^4 - 10\cdot3^3 + 10\cdot3^2 - 5\cdot3 + 1$$

etc.

$$(n-1)^5 - (n-2)^5 = 5(n-1)^4 - 10(n-1)^3 + 10(n-1)^2 - 5(n-1) + 1$$
$$n^5 - (n-1)^5 = 5n^4 - 10n^3 + 10n^2 - 5n + 1$$

Now add up all n equations (notice that the left side mostly cancels). We get:

$$n^5 = 5(1^4+2^4+3^4 + ... + n^4) - 10(1^3+2^3+3^3 + ... + n^3) + 10(1^2+2^2+3^2 + ... + n^2) - 5(1+2+3 + ... + n) + n$$

which is: $n^5 = 5(\Sigma i^4) - 10(\Sigma i^3) + 10(\Sigma i^2) - 5(\Sigma i) + n$

$$5(\Sigma i^4) = n^5 + 10\frac{n^2(n+1)^2}{4} - 10\frac{n(n+1)(2n+1)}{6} + 5\frac{n(n+1)}{2} - n$$

$$\Sigma i^4 = \frac{6n^5 + 15n^4 + 10n^3 - n}{30}$$

which factors to: $\Sigma i^4 = \frac{n(n+1)(2n+1)(3n^2 + 3n - 1)}{30}$

Some Key Ideas from Calculus

The Derivative

- *What does the derivative mean?*
  - The derivative of a function gives the instantaneous rate of change for any value of x.
  - The development of *Differential Calculus* led to the resolution of three great puzzles: instantaneous speed, slope of a curve, and finding maximums and minimums.
  - For distance, time, and speed…
    - t is the time ; d(t) is the distance; and d'(t) is the instantaneous speed, which is also v(t).
  - For the graph of a function…
    - f(x) is the *height (the y value) of the curve* for a given value of x.
    - f'(x) is the *slope of the curve* for a given value of x. (See "finding the slope of a curve")

The Integral

- *What does the Integral mean?*
  - In concept, the integral allows us to "add together infinitely many, infinitely small things", such as the area of a region bounded by a curve, or the volume of a solid with a curved surface.
- *The Anti-Derivative.* The anti-derivative, F(x), is the inverse of the derivative.
- *Fundamental Theorem of Calculus.* $\int_a^b f(x)\,dx = F(b) - F(a)$
  - Essentially, this theorem gives instructions for *calculating the area under a curve*: We find the anti-derivative, evaluate it at the two x-values, and then subtract.

Example: Find the area under the curve $f(x) = -x^3 + 4x^2$ from $x = 2$ to 4.

Answer: First we find the anti-derivative of f(x), which is $F(x) = -\frac{x^4}{4} + \frac{4x^3}{3}$

$$\int_2^4 f(x)\,dx = F(4) - F(2) \rightarrow 21\tfrac{1}{3} - 6\tfrac{2}{3} \rightarrow \underline{\mathbf{14\tfrac{2}{3}}}$$

Using calculus for graphing

For example, let $f(x) = 2x^3 - x^2 - 4x$

- We can start by plotting points. We then see that the following points are on the graph: (-2,-12); (-1,1); (0,0); (1,-3); (2,4); (3, 33).
- The *roots* of the function are where it crosses the x-axis. It is where f(x) = 0.
  Therefore, we have $0 = 2x^3 - x^2 - 4x$
  Factoring gives us $0 = x(2x^2 - x - 4)$
  so x = 0 is one of the three roots.
  Putting $2x^2 - x - 4$ into the quadratic formula gives us 2 more roots: ≈-1.19, 1.69
- By just plotting points, we can't know exactly where the max and min points (i.e., "peaks" and "valleys") are located.
- *Finding the Slope of a Curve.*
  - To find the slope of the curve at a given x value, we just find f'(x) and then plug in the x value.

Example: Find the slope of f(x) at x = 4.

Answer: $f'(x) = 6x^2 - 2x - 4$
$f'(4) = 6(4)^2 - 2(4) - 4 \rightarrow \underline{\mathbf{84}}$

- *Now we can determine the exact locations of the max and min points.*
  - At every max or min point, the slope of the curve is equal to zero.
  - The slope at any point on the curve is given by the derivative. We need to find the derivative of f(x), which is $f'(x) = 6x^2 - 2x - 4$, and then set it to zero, which gives us:
    $0 = 6x^2 - 2x - 4 \rightarrow 0 = 2(3x^2 - x - 2)$
    $0 = 2(3x + 2)(x - 1) \rightarrow x = -\tfrac{2}{3}, 1$
  - These are the x-coordinates of where the slope is zero. We find the y-coordinates by plugging the x values into f(x).
  - The result is shown here.

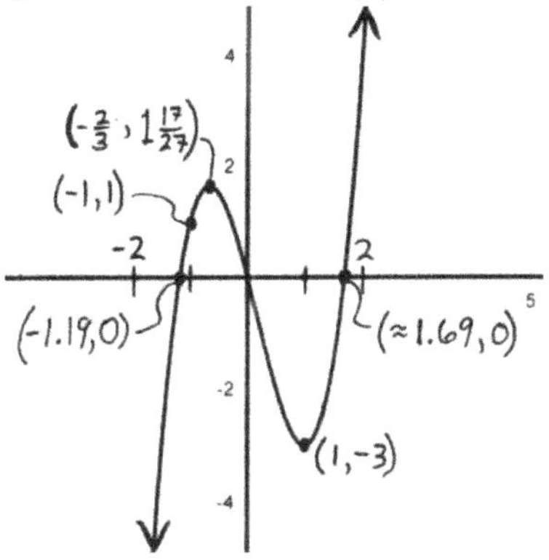

The Evolution of the Integral

Note: This mostly follows the same sequence as is done on sheet #8 from our *Calculus Discovery Sheets*.

Our Goal: To find a formula for the area of the region bounded by the x-axis, the curve $\mathbf{f(x) = x^2}$, and having a right boundary of x = a (where a is any constant).

Step#1: Using 7 rectangles, and a right boundary of x=4.

Some key ideas:

- The width of each rectangle is: $\Delta x = {}^4/_7$.
- The x-coordinate of the right side of the 5th rectangle is: $x_5 = 5\cdot({}^4/_7) \rightarrow \frac{20}{7}$
- The x-coordinate of the right side of the kth rectangle is: $x_k = k\cdot({}^4/_7) \rightarrow \frac{4k}{7}$
- The y-coordinate of any point on the curve is found by using the given function $f(x) = x^2$.

  Example: Find the y-coordinate for x = 1.2.
  Answer: $f(3) = (1.2)^2 \rightarrow$ y-coord is 1.44.
- *The height of the kth rectangle* is the same as the y-coordinate of the right side of the kth rectangle, which is:

  $$f(x_k) = f(\tfrac{4k}{7}) = (\tfrac{4k}{7})^2 \rightarrow \frac{4^2k^2}{7^2}$$
- *The area of the kth rectangle* is the width of the rectangle (Δx) times the height $f(x_k)$,

  which is therefore: $f(x_k)\cdot\Delta x = \frac{4^2k^2}{7^2}\cdot\frac{4}{7} \rightarrow \frac{4^3k^2}{7^3}$
- The sum of the areas of all 7 rectangles is:

  Rect#1 + Rect#2 + Rect#3 +…+ Rect#7

  $$= \frac{4^3 1^2}{7^3} + \frac{4^3 2^2}{7^3} + \frac{4^3 3^2}{7^3} + \ldots + \frac{4^3 7^2}{7^3}$$

  $$= \frac{4^3}{7^3}(1^2 + 2^2 + 3^2 + \ldots + 7^2)$$
- Now we can use the summation formula:

  $$\sum_{k=1}^{n} k^2 = \tfrac{1}{3}n^3 + \tfrac{1}{2}n^2 + {}^1/_6\,n$$

  So the area of 7 rectangles is now:

  $$\frac{4^3}{7^3}\left(\tfrac{1}{3}7^3 + \tfrac{1}{2}7^2 + {}^1/_6\,7\right)$$

  and multiplying in gives us the sum of the areas of the 7 rectangles:

  $$\frac{4^3}{3} + \frac{4^3}{2\cdot 7} + \frac{4^3}{6\cdot 7^2} \approx 26.12$$

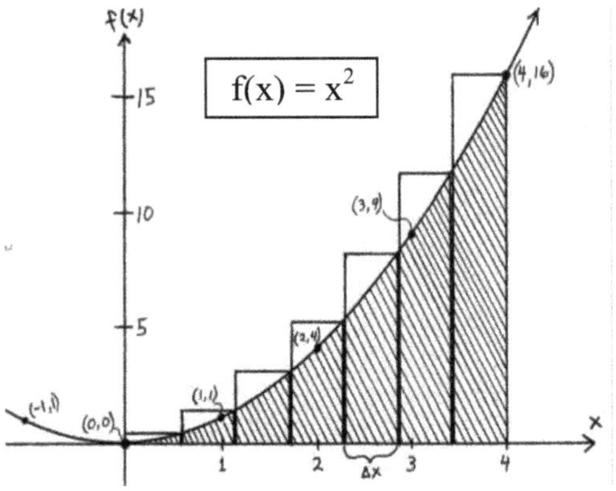

Step#2: Making it more general (but still using the same curve).

- *500 rectangles*. If the shaded area were instead divided into 500 very thin rectangles, the area of these 500 rectangles would be:

  $$\sum_{k=1}^{500} f(x_k)\cdot\Delta x = \frac{4^3}{3} + \frac{4^3}{2\cdot 500} + \frac{4^3}{6\cdot 500^2} \approx 21.40$$
- *n rectangles*. For n rectangles, the shaded area is:

  $$\sum_{k=1}^{n} f(x_k)\cdot\Delta x = \frac{4^3}{3} + \frac{4^3}{2\cdot n} + \frac{4^3}{6\cdot n^2}$$
- *For any right boundary*. If we allow the right boundary to be x = a (instead of x = 4), then the formula becomes:

  $$\boxed{\sum f(x_k)\cdot\Delta x = \frac{a^3}{3} + \frac{a^3}{2n} + \frac{a^3}{6n^2}}$$

Step#3: *The Integral*. The exact area!

- All we need to do now is allow n to approach infinity, which gives us infinitely many, infinitely thin rectangles, and a formula for the exact area:

  $$\boxed{\int_0^a f(x)dx = \lim_{n\to\infty}\sum f(x_k)\cdot\Delta x = \frac{a^3}{3}}$$

Example: Find the area under the curve $f(x) = x^2$ from x = 0 to 4.

Answer: Using the above formula tells us that the exact area of the shaded region is $21\tfrac{1}{3}$.

A Proof of the Product Rule for Differentiation

Given functions u(x) and v(x), our goal is to find a formula for determining the derivative of $u(x)\cdot v(x)$. Using the definition of the derivative, we get:

$\frac{d}{dx}[u(x)\cdot v(x)] = \lim_{h\to 0} \frac{u(x+h)\cdot v(x+h) - u(x)\cdot v(x)}{h}$ now we add and subtract $u(x+h)\cdot v(x)$ in the numerator,

which gives us: $\frac{d}{dx}[u(x)\cdot v(x)] = \lim_{h\to 0} \frac{u(x+h)\cdot v(x+h) - u(x+h)\cdot v(x) + u(x+h)\cdot v(x) - u(x)\cdot v(x)}{h}$

Now we factor: $\frac{d}{dx}[u(x)\cdot v(x)] = \lim_{h\to 0} \left[u(x+h)\frac{v(x+h) - v(x)}{h} + v(x)\frac{u(x+h) - u(x)}{h}\right]$

And after taking the limits of each term separately we get our desired result of:

$$\boxed{\frac{d}{dx}[u(x)\cdot v(x)] = u(x)\frac{dv}{dx} + v(x)\frac{du}{dx}}$$

A similar approach can also be used to prove the quotient rule.

Why Radian Measure is Better than Degrees

The slope of the sine graph (the derivative of sine).

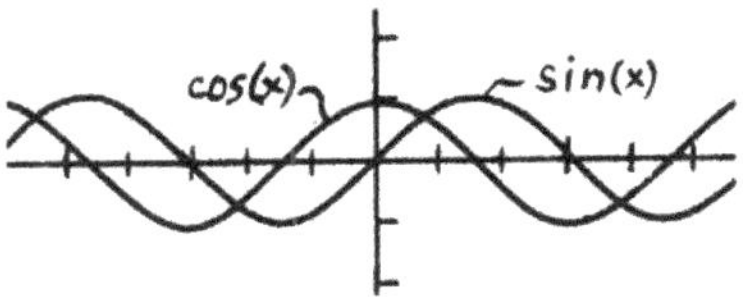

If we graph sin(x) where x is measured in radians and the x-axis is done with the same linear scale as the y-axis (as shown on the right), then we can visually approximate that the slopes of the graph at $x = 0, {}^{\pi}/_{2}, \pi, {}^{3\pi}/_{2}$ are 1, 0, −1, 0, respectively. We know that the values of cos(x) at $x = 0, {}^{\pi}/_{2}, \pi, {}^{3\pi}/_{2}$ are also 1, 0, −1, 0. So it seems reasonable to guess that the derivative (slope) of sin(x) is equal to cos(x).

Comparing radians and degrees

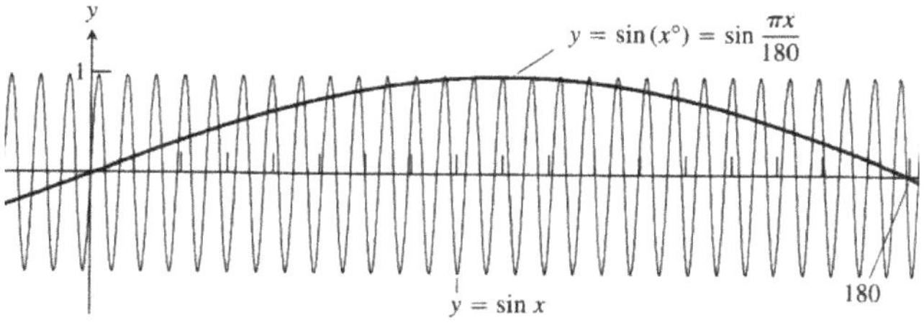

The graph at the right shows both sin(x), where x is measured in radians, and sin(x°), where x° is measured in degrees. Note that each tick mark on the x-axis represents an increment of 10, and that this graph of sin(x) is the same graph shown at the top of the page (next to the graph of cos x), but the scale on the x-axis has been dramatically altered. Now what about the slopes of sin(x) and sin(x°)? As stated above, the slope of sin(x) at a given x value, measured in radians, is equal to the value of cos(x). For example, the slope of sin(x) at x = 0 is equal to 1. (Again, it doesn't appear that way on this graph because of the scale of the axes.) However, we can tell by looking at the graphs that the slope of sin(x) is very different than the slope of sin(x°).

$$\boxed{\frac{d}{dx}\sin(x) = \cos(x) \qquad \frac{d}{dx}\sin(x^\circ) \neq \cos(x^\circ)}$$

Why radians work so well in calculus

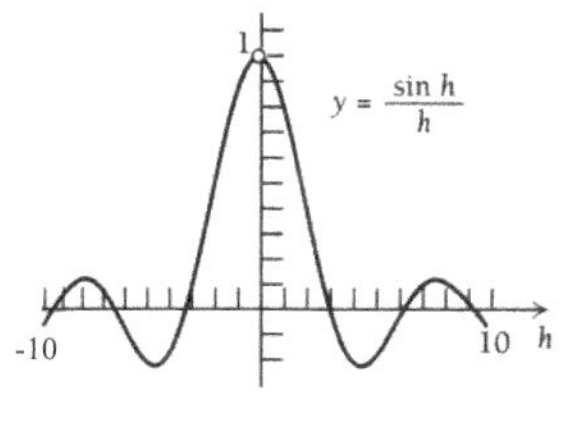

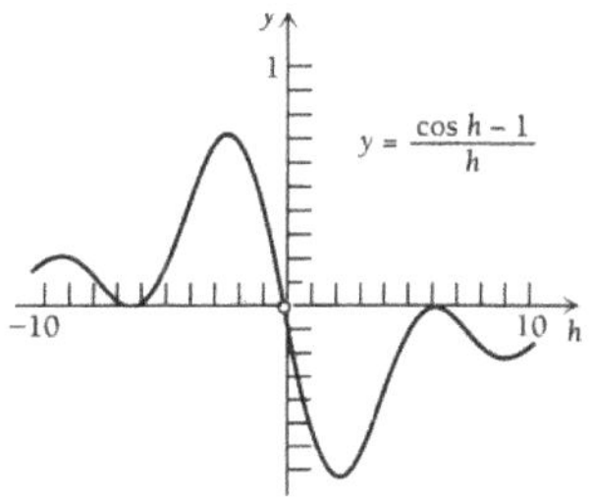

Try this: With a calculator, find the value of $\lim_{x\to 0} \frac{\sin(x)}{x}$. Put in smaller and smaller values for x. What does the result get closer and closer to? Do it first with your calculator in degree mode, and then do it with your calculator in radian mode. Do you get different results? Now do the same with $\lim_{x\to 0} \frac{\cos(x) - 1}{x}$.

This all leads us to answers for two important limits (shown at the right), which are used for deriving the derivatives of sin(x) and cos(x). (See the proofs in our *11th/12th Grade Workbook.*)

$$\boxed{\lim_{x\to 0} \frac{\sin(x)}{x} = 1 \qquad \lim_{x\to 0} \frac{\cos(x) - 1}{x} = 0}$$

Introduction to Calculus
Discovery Sheet #1

Series Formulas

Series Notation

1) Expand and then evaluate each series.

a) $\sum_{i=4}^{9} i$

b) $\sum_{i=0}^{4} 3i$

c) $\sum_{i=0}^{4} 3i+5$

d) $\sum_{i=1}^{3} \frac{1}{2^i}$

e) $\sum_{i=1}^{3} \frac{1}{i^2}$

f) $\sum_{i=1}^{4} 35+5i$

g) $\sum_{i=0}^{3} 40+5i$

h) $\sum_{i=8}^{11} 5i$

2) Rewrite the series in Σ notation, and then evaluate.

a) 5+10+15+20+25+30

b) 7+10+13+16

c) 1+2+3+…+100

Power Series Formula!

3) Multiply.

a) $(x-1)(x+1)$

b) $(x-1)(x^2+x+1)$

c) $(x-1)(x^3+x^2+x+1)$

d) $(x-1)(x^6+x^5+x^4+x^3+x^2+x+1)$

e) $(x-1)\sum_{i=0}^{6} x^i$

f) $(x-1)\sum_{i=0}^{22} x^i$

g) $(x-1)\sum_{i=0}^{n} x^i$

4) *Power Series Formula.* Use the previous problem to state a general formula for…

$\sum_{i=0}^{n} x^i$

5) Evaluate each expression:

a) $(1+3+3^2+3^3+3^4+3^5+3^6)$

b) $(1+2+2^2+\ldots+2^{18})$

c) $\sum_{i=0}^{6} 3^i$

d) $\sum_{i=0}^{18} 2^i$

Infinite Series

What happens if you add up infinitely many numbers? Most people would reply that you get an infinitely large result. But, what if the series had the special characteristic that each step got smaller? Let's see what happens…

6) Consider the following relation: $y = x^n$.
Use a calculator to find y, given that…

a) x=1.1 and n=10

b) x=1.1 and n=50

c) x=1.1 and n=500

d) x=1.1 and n=∞

e) x=0.9 and n=10

f) x=0.9 and n=50

g) x=0.9 and n=500

h) x=0.9 and n=∞

7) What mathematical law is reflected in the above problems?

The Infinite Power Series Formula

The *Power Series Formula* (from above) states:

$$\sum_{i=0}^{n} x^i = \frac{x^{n+1}-1}{x-1}$$

8) If $0<x<1$, what is the value of x^{n+1} as n approaches infinity?

9) *Infinite Power Series Formula.*
What does the *Power Series Formula* become
when $0<x<1$ and n approaches infinity?

10) Evaluate each expression:

a) $1+\left(\frac{1}{2}\right)+\left(\frac{1}{2}\right)^2+\left(\frac{1}{2}\right)^3+\ldots$

b) The Dichotomy $\left(\frac{1}{2}\right)+\left(\frac{1}{2}\right)^2+\left(\frac{1}{2}\right)^3+\ldots$

c) $1+\left(\frac{1}{3}\right)+\left(\frac{1}{3}\right)^2+\left(\frac{1}{3}\right)^3+\ldots$

d) $\left(\frac{1}{3}\right)+\left(\frac{1}{3}\right)^2+\left(\frac{1}{3}\right)^3+\ldots$

e) $\left(\frac{3}{4}\right)+\left(\frac{3}{4}\right)^2+\left(\frac{3}{4}\right)^3+\ldots$

Introduction to Calculus
Discovery Sheet #2

Limits & Average Speed

1) A cyclist is timed over the course of a 3-km ride. He starts his stopwatch as soon as he starts. He reaches the 800m marker at 61.9 seconds, reaches the 2000m marker at 161.4 seconds, and reaches the finish line (3000m) at 240.8 seconds.

a) What is the average speed of the cyclist from the first marker to the second marker?

b) What is the average speed of the cyclist from the second marker to the finish line?

c) What is the average speed of the cyclist from the first marker to the finish line?

d) What is the average speed of the cyclist throughout the whole race?

e) Give a formula for average speed given d_1, d_2, t_1, t_2.

2) What is your average speed…

a) if you go 6 miles in 2 hours?

b) if you go 6 miles in 1 hour?

c) if you go 6 miles in a ½ hour?

d) if you go 6 miles in a $\frac{1}{10}$ hour?

e) if you go 6 miles in a $\frac{1}{100}$ hour?

f) if you go 6 miles in a $\frac{1}{1000}$ hour?

g) if you go 6 miles in 0 hours?

h) if you go 0 miles in 6 hours?

i) if you go 0 miles in 0 hours?

3) Evaluate each limit. Use a calculator in order to find values very close to the given limit.

a) $\lim_{x \to 0} \frac{x^2+5x}{x}$

b) $\lim_{x \to 3} \frac{x^2-9}{x-3}$

c) $\lim_{x \to 3} \frac{x^2+9}{x-3}$

d) $\lim_{x \to 0} \frac{x^3-8x^2}{2x^2}$

e) $\lim_{x \to 5} \frac{x^2+9}{x-3}$

f) $\lim_{x \to 2} \frac{x^2+3x-10}{x-2}$

g) $\lim_{x \to \infty} \frac{6x^2-3x}{2x^2}$

h) Given $0 \le x < 1$ $\lim_{n \to \infty} x^n$

i) $\lim_{x \to \infty} \left(1+\frac{1}{x}\right)^x$

j) $\lim_{x \to \infty} \left(1+\frac{3}{x}\right)^x$

4) **Function Practice.**
Given these functions

$f(x) = 5x - 3$
$g(t) = \sqrt{t+2}$
$p(n) = n^2 + 5$

Evaluate each:

a) f(6)
b) g(23)
c) p(10)
d) g(47)
e) p(4)
f) f(x+2)
g) $p(n^4)$
h) $p(t-4)$

Introduction to Calculus
Discovery Sheet #3

Galileo's Experiment

Galileo wanted to find out the relationship between distance and time when a body (e.g., a ball) is falling. Contrary to popular belief, he didn't drop balls from the Tower of Pisa. His timing instruments wouldn't have been accurate enough for something moving so fast. He needed to slow things down – so he rolled balls down inclined planes.

Although he may have done his experiments somewhat differently, we can imagine him collecting data by rolling a ball down a long inclined plane, and then marking the distance that the ball has traveled after each second has passed. (This makes time the control variable.) If the inclined plane has a 10° angle of inclination, we get the following data:

T (sec) →	0	1	2	3	4	5	6	7	8	9	10
D (meters) →	0	0.851	3.40	7.66	13.6	21.3	30.6	41.7	54.5	68.9	85.1

Questions:

1) What conclusions could Galileo have reached about the relationship of distance and time by looking at the above data? (Look for patterns!)

2) If a car is driving at a constant speed during an entire trip, then we can say that distance is directly proportional to time. What does this mean?

3) Fill in the Blanks, referring to the above inclined plane problem:

   a) The distance is directly proportional to ______________.

   b) The ratio of ________________ to _____________ is a constant.

   c) The *constant of proportionality* is equal to ______________.

   d) A formula that relates distance and time is _____

4) **Average Speed.**
   Find the average speed of the ball…

   a) in the first 10 seconds.

   b) from 2 seconds to 7 seconds.

   c) from 3 seconds to 8 seconds.

   d) from 3 seconds to 5 seconds.

   e) from 3 seconds to 4 seconds.

5) Find the instantaneous speed of the ball at 3 seconds.

6) **Function Practice.**
   Given these functions

$$f(w) = 2w + 8$$
$$d(t) = 10 \cdot t^2$$
$$r(y) = y^2 + 2y - 1$$

   Evaluate each:

a) f(5)	f) r(3y)
b) d(3)	g) f(5w)
c) r(10)	h) f(w+5)
d) d(−2)	i) d(3t)
e) f(0)	j) d(t+3)

Introduction to Calculus
Discovery Sheet #4

Instantaneous Speed, Part I

On the previous worksheet, one of the questions asked us to find the instantaneous speed at the instant that the ball had been rolling for exactly 3 seconds. The (seemingly insurmountable) difficulty with calculating instantaneous speed is that you need to divide the change of distance by the change of speed, and that would result in dividing zero by zero, which seems rather mind-boggling.

We will now work toward finding a general method for determining instantaneous speed.

1) If we adjust the steepness of the inclined plane to about 37.8°, we get a convenient distance formula:

$$d(t) = 3 \cdot t^2$$

Use this distance formula in order to calculate the average speed…

a) from 4 seconds to 6 seconds.
b) from 4 seconds to 5 seconds.
c) from 4 seconds to 4.5 seconds.
d) from 4 seconds to 4.1 seconds.
e) from 4 seconds to 4.01 seconds.
f) from 4 seconds to 4.001 seconds.
g) from 4 seconds to 4.0001 seconds.

2) Find the instantaneous speed at 4 seconds.

3) Now use the same method to find the instantaneous speed at 7 seconds.

4) Explain to one another how each of the following formulas represents average speed:

$$r = \frac{\Delta d}{\Delta t}$$

$$r = \frac{d_2 - d_1}{t_2 - t_1}$$

$$r = \frac{d(t_2) - d(t_1)}{t_2 - t_1}$$

$$r = \frac{d(t+h) - d(t)}{h}$$ "t" is the first time. "h" is change in time.

5) Evaluate each limit. Use a calculator in order to find values very close to the limit.

a) $\lim_{x \to -5} \frac{x^2 - 25}{x + 5}$
b) $\lim_{x \to -5} \frac{x^2}{x + 5}$
c) $\lim_{x \to 0} \frac{5x^2 - 12x}{x}$
d) $\lim_{x \to 2} \frac{5x^2 - 12x}{x}$
e) $\lim_{x \to \infty} \frac{8x^3 - 5}{2x^3}$
f) $\lim_{x \to \infty} x^{1/x}$
g) $\lim_{x \to 0} \frac{\sin x}{x}$
h) $\lim_{x \to 0} \frac{\cos x - 1}{x}$

6) Graph each function

a) $f(x) = x^2 - 7$
b) $f(x) = x^3$
c) $f(x) = \frac{1}{10}x^3$
d) $f(x) = -\frac{1}{10}x^3$

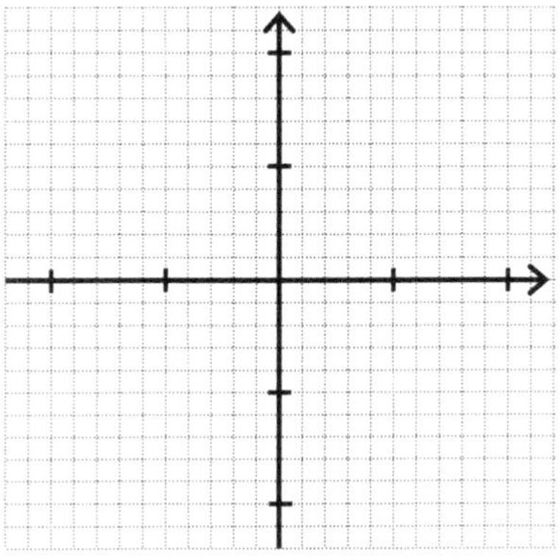

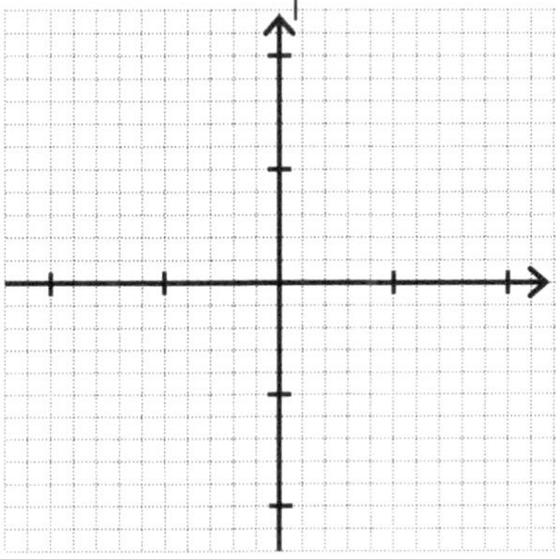

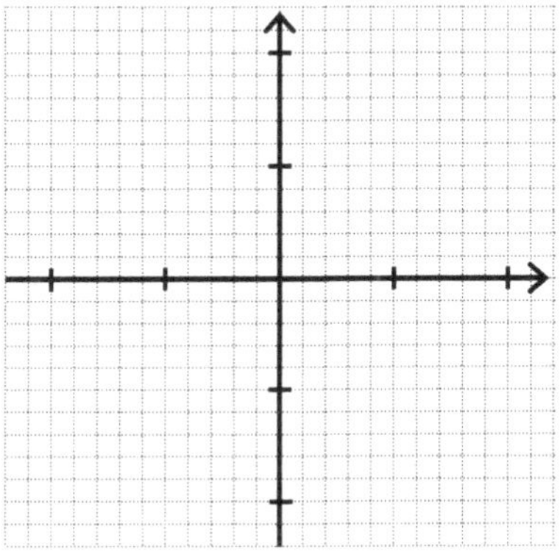

Introduction to Calculus
Discovery Sheet #5

Instantaneous Speed, Part II

1) Using the method from the previous worksheet, find the instantaneous speed…
   a) At 5 seconds, given that the distance formula is $d(t) = 3\cdot t^2$.

   b) At 2 seconds, given that the distance formula is $d(t) = 3\cdot t^2$.

   c) At 10 seconds, given that the distance formula is $d(t) = 3\cdot t^2$

2) The *Calculus Average Speed Formula* is:

$$r = \frac{d(t+h) - d(t)}{h}$$

It is very important that we understand how to use this formula. It will help us to soon arrive at the concept of a derivative.

Use this formula (and show every step!) to do the below problems.

   a) Given $d(t) = 3\cdot t^2$, find the *average speed* from 5 seconds to 8 seconds.

   b) Given $d(t) = 3\cdot t^2$, find the *average speed* from 5 seconds to 12 seconds.

3) **New Formulas!** With each problem below, use the *Calculus Average Speed Formula* in order to derive a new formula. Be sure to show every step.
   a) Given $d(t) = 3\cdot t^2$, give a formula for *average speed*, r, from 5 seconds to 5+h seconds.

   b) Given $d(t) = 3\cdot t^2$, give a formula for *average speed*, r, from t seconds to t+h seconds.

   c) Given $d(t) = 3\cdot t^2$, give a formula for *instantaneous speed*, v(t), at t seconds.

   d) Given $d(t) = k\cdot t^2$, give a formula for *instantaneous speed*, v(t), at t seconds.

4) Graph each function (on separate graph paper).
   a) $f(x) = -x^2 - 3x + 10$
   b) $f(x) = x^3 - 9x$
   c) $f(x) = -x^3 + 9x$
   d) $f(x) = x^3 + x^2 - 6x$

Introduction to Calculus
Discovery Sheet #6

The Derivative, Part I

Formulas for Instantaneous Speed!

On the previous sheet, we took a huge step. We found formulas for calculating average speed, r, and instantaneous speed, v(t). Why is this so important? Because we have managed to get around the paradox of instantaneous speed: dividing zero by zero!

These formulas (from the end of the previous sheet) are:

$$r = 30 + 3h$$

$$r = 6t + 3h$$

$$v(t) = 6t$$

$$v(t) = 2kt$$

1) Explain, once again, what each of the above formulas can be used for, and what each of the variables represents.

2) Use one of the above formulas to solve each.

a) Given $d(t) = 3 \cdot t^2$, find the *average speed* from 5 seconds to 12 seconds.

b) Given $d(t) = 3 \cdot t^2$, find the *average speed* from 3 seconds to 8 seconds.

c) Given $d(t) = 3 \cdot t^2$, find the *instantaneous speed* at 3 seconds.

d) Given $d(t) = 2.2 \cdot t^2$, find the *instantaneous speed* at 4 seconds.

e) Given $d(t) = 0.851 \cdot t^2$, find the *instantaneous speed* at 7 seconds.

f) Given $d(t) = 4.9 \cdot t^2$, find the *instantaneous speed* at 6 seconds.

3) Graph each function (on separate graph paper).

a) $f(x) = x^2 + 5x$

b) $f(x) = \frac{1}{4}x^3 + \frac{1}{2}x$

c) $f(x) = x^4 - 9x^2$

4) **Area Under a Curve**

a) Graph the equation $f(x) = x^2$. Shade in the area bounded by this curve, the x-axis, and the line x = 3.

b) Determine a method for approximating the area of this shaded-in region.

c) How can you make this approximation as accurate as desired?

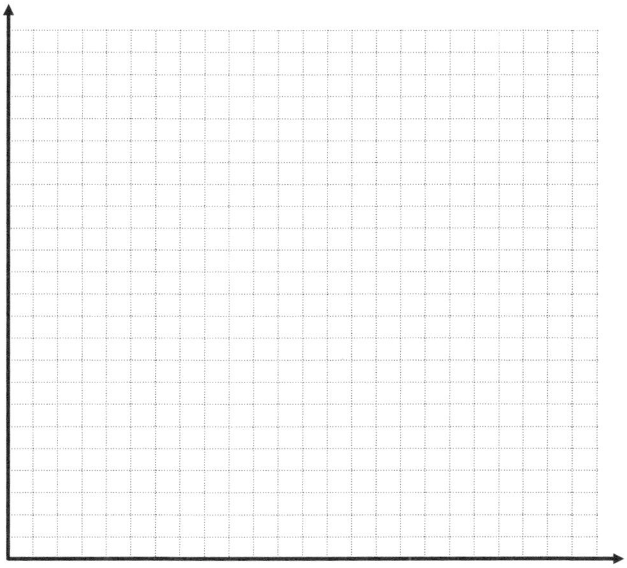

Introduction to Calculus
Discovery Sheet #7

The Derivative, Part II

The Definition of the Derivative.

This is not really a formula. It simply tells us what to do in order to find a formula for the instantaneous rate of change for a given function, $y = f(x)$.

$$f'(x) = \frac{dy}{dx} = \lim_{h\to 0}\frac{f(x+h) - f(x)}{h}$$

1) Use the above definition of the derivative in order to determine the derivative of:

a) $f(x) = x^3$

b) $f(x) = x^2 + 7x$

2) Given what you have learned so far, what do you think the derivative of each function is?

a) $f(x) = x^7$

b) $f(x) = 4x^3$

c) $f(x) = x^5 + 7x^4 - 2x^3 + x^2 - 3x + 8$

3) *Derive the Exponent Law for Derivatives!*
Find $f'(x)$ given $f(x) = k\cdot x^n$

Summation Formulas

$$\sum_{i=1}^{n} i = \tfrac{1}{2}n^2 + \tfrac{1}{2}n$$

$$\sum_{i=1}^{n} i^2 = \tfrac{1}{3}n^3 + \tfrac{1}{2}n^2 + \tfrac{1}{6}n$$

$$\sum i^3 = \tfrac{1}{4}n^4 + \tfrac{1}{2}n^3 + \tfrac{1}{4}n^2 = \left(\sum i\right)^2$$

4) Use one of the above formulas in order to evaluate each series below.

a) $1 + 2 + 3 + \ldots + 30$

b) $1^2 + 2^2 + 3^2 + \ldots + 30^2$

c) $1^3 + 2^3 + 3^3 + \ldots + 100^3$

5) **Slopes of Lines!**
Find the slope of the line that…

a) passes through (5,7) and (3,2).

b) passes through (4,1) and (2,8).

c) passes through (–4,3) and (5,1).

d) passes through (36,23) and (86,43).

e) passes through (x_1,y_1) and (x_2,y_2).

Introduction to Calculus
Discovery Sheet #8

The Integral, Part I

Area Under a Curve (continued)

We will now continue working toward finding the area of the region bounded by the x-axis, the line $x = 4$, and the curve $f(x) = x^2$.

Our strategy is to approximate this area by drawing in a series of thin rectangles (each one with its top, right corner sitting on the curve), and adding up their areas.

We will arbitrarily assign n (the number of rectangles) to be 7, and hope that this gives us insight into the ultimate solution, which is achieved by having the number of rectangles go towards infinity.

1) Give the width of each rectangle (Δx).

2) What is the x-coordinate of the right side of the 5th rectangle (x_5)?

3) What is the x-coordinate of the right side of the kth rectangle (x_k)?

4) What is the height of the kth rectangle?

5) What is the area of the kth rectangle?

Now, we can say that the area of the region is approximately equal to the sum of the 7 rectangles, which would be:

$$\text{Rect}_1 + \text{Rect}_2 + \text{Rect}_3 + \ldots + \text{Rect}_7$$

$$1^2\left(\tfrac{4}{7}\right)^3 + 2^2\left(\tfrac{4}{7}\right)^3 + 3^2\left(\tfrac{4}{7}\right)^3 + \ldots + 7^2\left(\tfrac{4}{7}\right)^3$$

6) Find the sum of the areas of the 7 rectangles by further working the above sequence. (Hint: you'll need to use a summation formula.)

7) In order to derive a general formula, redo the entire above process, but with the number of rectangles equal to n, and the right boundary of the area set at $x = a$ (instead of $x = 4$).

8) Use the above formula to answer the following questions:
   a) What is the area with $x = 4$ as a right boundary, and using 500 rectangles?
   b) What is the area with $x = a$ as a right boundary, and using infinitely many rectangles?

The Integral

The formula found on the last problem is called the *Integral* of f(x). Using calculus notation, the process can be written as:

$$\int_0^a f(x)dx = \lim_{n\to\infty} \sum_{k=1}^{n} f(x_k)\cdot\Delta x$$

(Where the width of the kth rectangle is Δx, and the area of the kth rectangle is $f(x_k)\cdot\Delta x$.)

We have just shown that for $f(x) = x^2$

$$\int_0^a f(x)dx = \frac{a^3}{3}$$

The left side should be read: "The integral of f(x) dx from x equals 0 to a", and it tells us the area under the curve from x = 0 to a.

9) Use the above integral formula to find the exact area under the curve $f(x) = x^2$…
   a) from $x=0$ to $x=4$.
   b) from $x=0$ to $x=5$.
   c) from $x=0$ to $x=9$.

Derivative Practice

10) Given f(x), find the derivative, $\frac{dy}{dx}$.
   a) $f(x) = x^4$
   b) $f(x) = 6x^3$
   c) $f(x) = 5x^6 + 3x$
   d) $f(x) = 7$
   e) $f(x) = 5x^4 - 8x^3 + x^2 + 9x - 7$
   f) $f(x) = -x^8 + 3x^5 - 5x + 3$

Anti-Derivatives!

11) With each given f(x), find its anti-derivative, F(x), such that when you take the derivative of F(x) the result is f(x).
   a) $f(x) = 7x^6$
   b) $f(x) = 9$
   c) $f(x) = 3x$
   d) $f(x) = x^4$
   e) $f(x) = 5x^3 + 8x^2$

Introduction to Calculus
Discovery Sheet #9

The Integral, Part II

The Integral

On the last worksheet, we were given the curve $f(x) = x^2$, and, through a long process of adding together infinitely many infinitely thin rectangles, we found a formula for calculating the area under the curve:

$$\int_0^a f(x)dx = \frac{a^3}{3}$$

This is called the *integral* of f(x), and is used to find the area under f(x) from x = 0 to a. For example, the area under the curve $f(x) = x^2$ from x = 0 to 6 is $\frac{1}{3}(6)^3 = 72$.

1) *A Short-Cut!* Fortunately there is a nice short-cut that enables us to derive the integral of a polynomial. We call this the *Power Rule for Integrals*.

a) What do you think the integral of $f(x) = 5x^2$ is?

b) Fill in the blank in order to state the *Power Rule for Integrals*.

If $f(x) = x^n$

Then $\int_0^a f(x)\,dx =$ ________

c) State in words, the meaning of *Power Rule for Integrals*.

2) With each problem below, first derive a general formula for calculating the area under the curve of f(x), then use it to calculate the requested area.

a) Given $f(x) = x^3$ calculate the area under the curve from x = 0 to x = 2.

b) Given $f(x) = \frac{1}{2}x^2$ calculate the area under the curve from x = 0 to x = 12.

c) Given $f(x) = 5x^4$ calculate the area under the curve from x = 0 to x = 3.

Anti-Derivatives

3) Given $f(x) = x^4$

a) Find $\int_0^a f(x)dx$

b) Find the anti-derivative, F(x).

c) What do the above answers tell you?

4) Given $f(x) = 8x^6$

a) Find f '(x).

b) Find $\int_0^a f(x)dx$

c) Find the anti-derivative, F(x).

d) Find F '(x).

Derivative Practice

5) a) Find f '(x) given $f(x) = \frac{1}{4}x^2 + 8x - 7$

b) Calculate the instantaneous rate of change at x = 6.

6) a) Find f '(x) given $f(x) = x^3 + \frac{1}{2}x^2$

b) Calculate the instantaneous rate of change at x = 2.

Comparing Graphs (*Challenge!*)

For each distance function given below, do the following:

- First, determine its derivative.
- Graph both the function and its derivative on the same graph.
- Lastly, look at the two graphs. Discuss what the graphs say about the movement of the object.

7) $d(t) = 2t$

8) $d(t) = \frac{1}{4}t^2$

9) $d(t) = -\frac{1}{2}t^2 + 3t$

10) $d(t) = t^3 - 6t^2 + 9t + 2$

Introduction to Calculus
Discovery Sheet #10

Tangents & Areas, Part I

** indicates more challenging, but important!

The Connection

We have seen that, for a given function, f(x), we can find a new function, the integral, that helps us find the area under the curve. We also saw how we could take the anti-derivative of f(x), which is F(x).

On the previous sheet, we came to the realization that the integral (which is geometric in nature) and the derivative (which is an algebraic process) are closely related; they are inverses of each other. Thus, the integral and the anti-derivative, F(x), are essentially equal.

What does all of this mean?

Quite simply, we can use F(x), the anti-derivative, to calculate integrals and find areas under curves.

1) Calculate the area under the curve…

a) $f(x) = x^3$ from x = 0 to 2.

b) $f(x) = 7x + 5$ from x = 0 to 4.

c) $f(x) = x^3 - 2x^2 + 3$ from x = 0 to 2.

d) $f(x) = x^3 - 2x^2 + 3$ from x = 0 to 3.

e) $f(x) = x^3 - 2x^2 + 3$ from x = 2 to 3.

f) $f(x) = 5x^4$ from x = 3 to 5.

2) For any given function, f(x), what is F'(x) always equal to?

Working with Curves

3) Given $f(x) = -x^2 + 8x - 12$…

a) Graph f(x)

b) Find f'(x).

c) What does $f(1) = -5$ mean?

d) What does $f'(1) = 6$ mean?

e) Find the slope of the curve at x = 3.

f) Find the slope of the curve at x = 5.

g) Give the points where f(x) = 0.

h) Give the points where f'(x) = 0. (the local min and max coordinates)

i) Calculate the area of the region bounded by the curve and the x-axis.

4) Given $f(x) = x^3 - 9x$…

a) Make a table of values for f(x).

b) Graph f(x) lightly in pencil.

c) Determine f'(x).

d) Find f(–2).

e) Find f'(–2). (Is this a surprise?)

f) Give the points where f(x) = 0.

g) **Give the points where f'(x) = 0. (the local min and max coordinates)

h) Make improvements to your graph of f(x) so that it is very accurate.

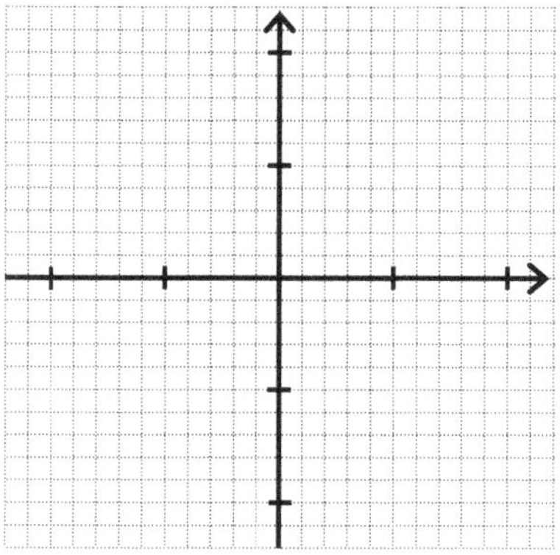
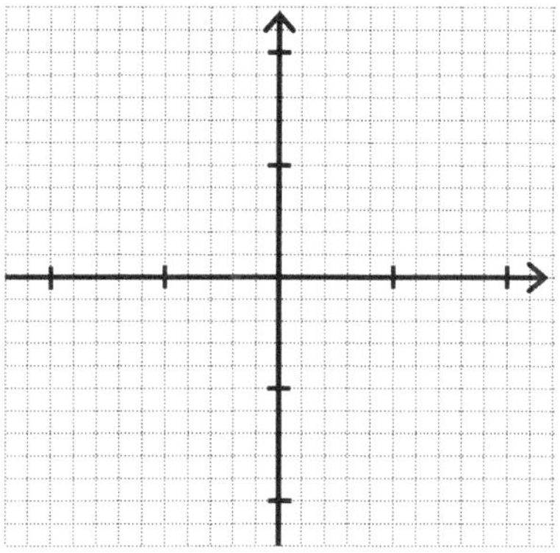
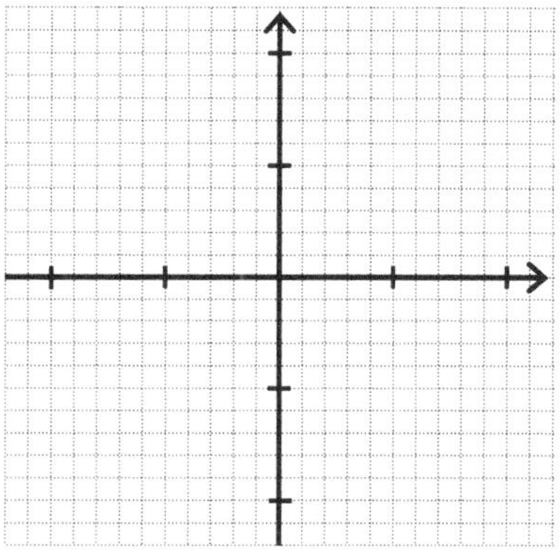

Introduction to Calculus
Discovery Sheet #11

Tangents & Areas, Part II

More Graphing

1) Given $f(x) = -x^3 - 2x^2 + x + 2\ldots$
   a) Graph f(x)
   b) Find f'(x).
   c) Find f(2). What does this mean?
   d) Find f'(2). What does this mean?
   e) Where is x = 5?
   f) Give the points where f(x) = 0.
   g) **Give the points where f'(x) = 0.
   h) Calculate the area of the region bounded by the curve that sits above the x-axis.

2) Given $f(x) = x^3 - 6x^2 + 11x\ldots$
   a) Determine f'(x).
   b) Fill in the below table of values.

x	f(x)	f'(x)
4		
3		
2		
1		
0		
−1		

   c) Give the points where f(x) = 0.
   d) **Give the points where f'(x) = 0. (the local min and max coordinates)
   e) Where on the graph is the slope = 74?
   f) Make a very accurate graph of f(x).

Area Under a Curve

3) Find the area under the curve given…
   a) $f(x) = 2x + 3$, $\int_2^4 f(x)\,dx$
   b) $f(x) = -x^2 + 4x$, $\int_0^4 f(x)\,dx$
   c) $f(x) = x^2 + x - 6$, $\int_{-2}^3 f(x)\,dx$
   d) $f(x) = -x^3 - 2x^2 + x + 2$, $\int_{-1}^1 f(x)\,dx$
   e) $f(x) = x^3 - 6x^2 + 11x$, $\int_1^3 f(x)\,dx$

Speed to Distance Problems (*Challenge!*)

4) The speed (in m/s) of an object is given by the formula $v(t) = 8t + 3$.
   a) What is the formula for its distance?
   b) How far does the ball roll in 10 seconds?

5) A ball, starting from stillness, rolls down an inclined plane. After 5 seconds, its speed is 23m/s.
   a) Find the formulas for distance and instantaneous speed?
   b) What is the steepness of the inclined plane (in degrees)?
   c) How far does the ball roll in 4 seconds?

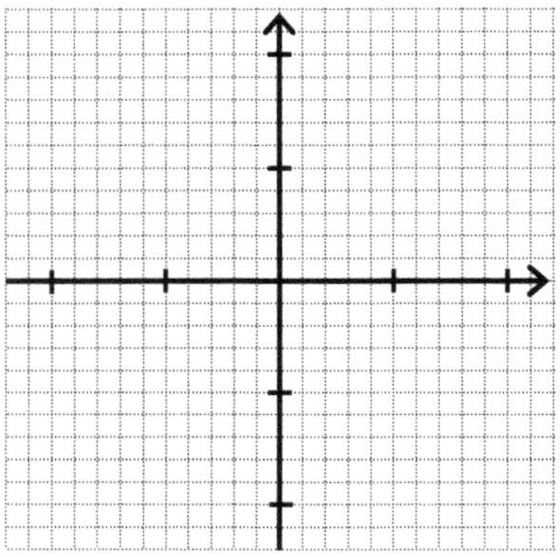
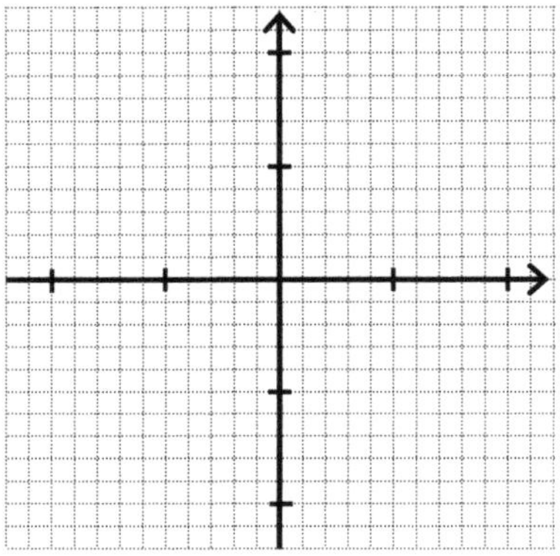
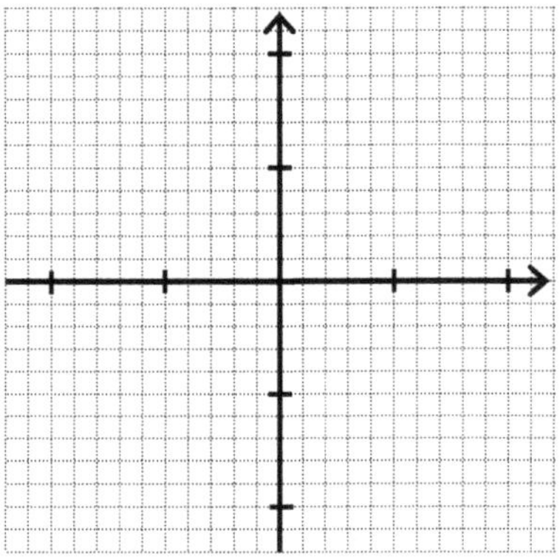

Introduction to Calculus
Review Sheet

1) Given the distance formula $d(t) = 1.5 \cdot t^2 \ldots$
   a) Find the average speed from t = 4 to t = 6.
   b) Find the instantaneous speed at t=6.
   c) Find the average speed from t = 2 to t = 3.
   d) Find the instantaneous speed at t=2.8.

2) Find the derivative, f'(x), of...
   a) $f(x) = x^6$
   b) $f(x) = 10x^3$
   c) $f(x) = 8x$
   d) $f(x) = 5$
   e) $f(x) = 2x^5 - 3x^2 + 7$

3) Find the slope of the line tangent to the curve $f(x) = 2x^2 - 11$ at $x = 2$.

4) Find the anti-derivative, F(x), of...
   a) $f(x) = x^6$
   b) $f(x) = 10x^3$
   c) $f(x) = 8x$
   d) $f(x) = 5$
   e) $f(x) = 2x^5 - 3x^2 + 7$

5) Find the area under the curve given...
   a) $f(x) = 3x^2, \quad \int_2^5 f(x)\,dx$
   b) $f(x) = \frac{x}{3} + 6, \quad \int_{-2}^5 f(x)\,dx$
   c) $f(x) = x^3 - 11x, \quad \int_2^3 f(x)\,dx$

6) Given $f(x) = x^3 - 4x \ldots$
   a) Determine f'(x).
   b) Fill in the below table of values.

x	f(x)	f'(x)
3		
2		
1		
0		
–1		
–2		
–3		

   c) Give the points where f(x) = 0.
   d) Give the points where f'(x) = 0. (the local min and max coordinates)
   e) Find the slope of the line tangent to the curve at x = 3.
   f) Make a very accurate graph of f(x).
   g) What does $f(1) = -3$ mean?
   h) What does $f'(1) = -1$ mean?
   i) What does $F(1) = -1\frac{3}{4}$ mean?

Topics to Study

- Average Speed and Instantaneous Speed
  - How are they different?
  - Why is instantaneous speed problematic?
- Definition of the Derivative
  - Explain what it means.
- The Integral and Area under the Curve
  - How is it that the integral is able to find the exact area under a curve?
- Fundamental Theorem of Calculus
  - What does it mean?
  - Why is it important?

Introduction to Calculus
Challenge Sheet!

On the Earth

The acceleration due to gravity of an object in free fall on earth is 9.8 m/s^2. This means that for every second, the speed increases by 9.8 m/s.

The acceleration (a) of a ball rolling down an inclined plane is $a = 9.8\cdot\sin(\theta)$.

Once we know the acceleration (a), we can then easily derive a distance formula by using $d(t) = ½a\cdot t^2$. In the case of free fall, we then get $d(t) = 4.9\cdot t^2$.

Example: If the inclined plane has a slope of 10°, then $a = 1.702\ m/s^2$, and the distance formula is $d(t) = 0.851\cdot t^2$ (which is what we used on sheet #2).

Example: If the inclined plane has a slope of 37.8°, then $a = 6\ m/s^2$, and the distance formula is $d(t) = 3\cdot t^2$ (which is what we used on sheet #3).

1) A ball is rolled down an inclined plane with a 45° inclination.
   a) Give the formula for the distance that the ball will travel after t seconds. (Assume no friction.)
   b) Give a formula for the instantaneous speed of the ball at t seconds.
   c) Give a formula for the instantaneous speed at the instant that the ball has rolled d meters.

2) A ramp is placed from the ground up to the top of a wall that is 4m above the ground. Find both the time it takes for a ball to roll down the ramp, and find its ending speed, given that the ramp…
   a) has an inclination of 15°.
   b) has an inclination of 30°.
   c) has an inclination of 60°.
   d) has an inclination of 90° (free fall).

On the Moon

The force of gravity is very nearly one-sixth as strong on the moon.

3) Redo problem #2a (above) as if it were on the moon.

4) Given your above answer, what is the ratio (moon:earth) of the times to get to the end of the ramp?

5) What is the ratio (moon:earth) of the speeds at the end of the ramp?

6) How long does it take to freefall 10m on earth, starting from rest?

7) How long does it take to freefall 10m on the moon, starting from rest?

8) What is the ratio of the above two answers?

9) Logan has an 80cm vertical leap (on earth).
   a) How long is she in the air?
   b) With what speed does she take off?
   c) What is her speed after 0.2 sec?
   d) What is her speed when she is 30cm off the ground?
   e) What would be her vertical leap on the moon? (Assume she leaves the ground with the same speed as on earth.) Find the ratio (moon:earth).
   f) How long would she be in the air on the moon?
   Find the ratio (moon:earth).

10) There are two Olympic ski jumps: one on the earth, and one on the moon. If a ball is rolled down each jump, and everything is identical about the two jumps, which ball will go further before landing?

Answers to Sheet #1

1) a) 39 b) 30 c) 55 d) $^7/_8$
e) $1\frac{13}{36}$ f) 190 g) 190 h) 190

2) a) $\sum_{i=1}^{6} 5i = 105$ b) $\sum_{i=1}^{4} 3i+4 = 46$ c) $\sum_{i=1}^{100} i = 5050$

3) a) $x^2 - 1$ b) $x^3 - 1$ c) $x^4 - 1$ d) $x^7 - 1$
e) $x^7 - 1$ f) $x^{23} - 1$ g) $x^{n+1} - 1$

4) $\frac{x^{n+1} - 1}{x - 1}$

5) a) 1093 b) 524,287 c) 1093 d) 524,287

6) a) ≈ 2.59 b) ≈ 117 c) $\approx 4.97 \cdot 10^{20}$ d) ∞
e) ≈ 0.349 f) ≈ 0.00515 g) $\approx 1.32 \cdot 10^{-23}$ h) 0

7) If $0 \le x < 1$ then $\lim_{x \to \infty} x^n = 0$

8) 0

9) If $0 \le x < 1$ then $\sum_{i=0}^{\infty} x^i = \frac{-1}{x-1} = \frac{1}{1-x}$

10) a) 2 b) 1 c) $^3/_2$ d) ½ e) 3

Answers to Sheet #2

1) a) $\approx 12.06\ ^m/_s$ b) $12.59\ ^m/_s$ c) $12.30\ ^m/_s$
d) $12.46\ ^m/_s$ e) $r = \frac{d_2 - d_1}{t_2 - t_1}$

2) a) 3 mph b) 6 mph c) 12 mph d) 60 mph
e) 600 mph f) 6000 mph g) ∞ h) 0 mph i) ?

3) a) 5 b) 6 c) no limit d) – 4 e) 17
f) 7 g) 3 h) 0 i) $e \approx 2.7183$ j) $e^3 \approx 20.08$

4) a) 27 b) 5 c) 105 d) 7 e) 21
f) $5x + 7$ g) $n^8 + 5$ h) $t^2 - 8t + 21$

Answers to Sheet #3

2) If the time goes up, then the distance goes up by the same proportion.

3) a) the square of the time
b) distance to time squared
c) 0.851
d) $d(t) = 0.851\,t^2$

4) a) $8.51\ ^m/_s$ b) 7.66 c) 9.37 d) 6.82 e) 5.94

5) ??

6) a) 18 b) 90 c) 119 d) 40 e) 8
f) $9y^2 + 6y - 1$ g) $10w + 8$ i) $90t^2$
j) $10t^2 + 60t + 90$

Answers to Sheet #4

1) a) $30\ ^m/_s$ b) $27\ ^m/_s$ c) $25.5\ ^m/_s$ d) $24.3\ ^m/_s$
e) $24.03\ ^m/_s$ f) $24.003\ ^m/_s$ g) $24.0003\ ^m/_s$

2) $24\ ^m/_s$ 3) $42\ ^m/_s$

5) a) – 10 b) no limit c) – 12 d) – 2
e) 4 f) 1 g) 1 h) 0

6) a)
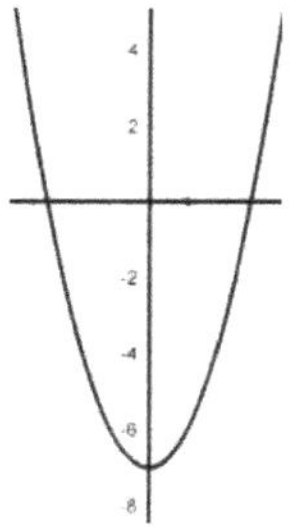

b)
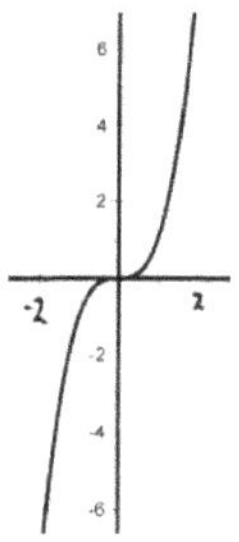

c)
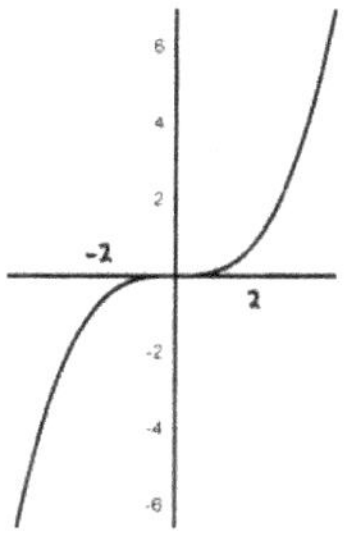

d)
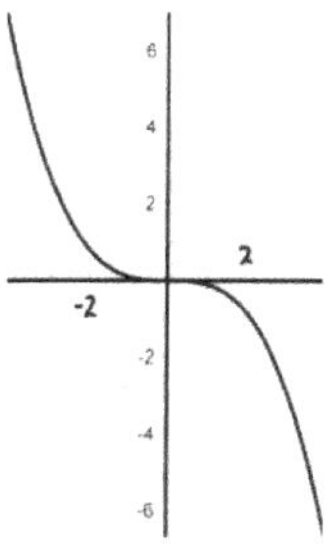

Answers to Sheet #5

1) a) $30\ ^m/_s$ b) $12\ ^m/_s$ c) $60\ ^m/_s$

2) a) $39\ ^m/_s$ b) $51\ ^m/_s$

3) a) $r = 30 + 3h$ b) $r = 6t + 3h$
c) $v(t) = 6t$ d) $v(t) = 2\,k\,t$

4) a)
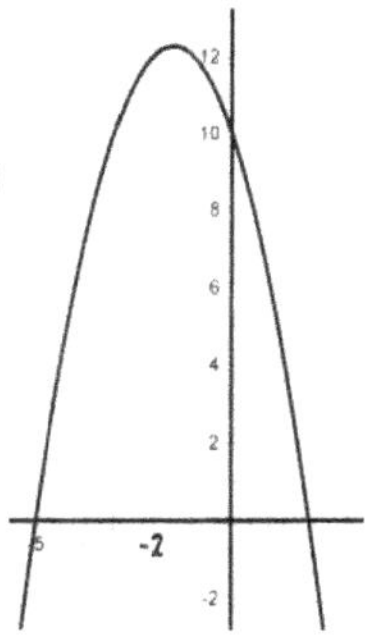

b)
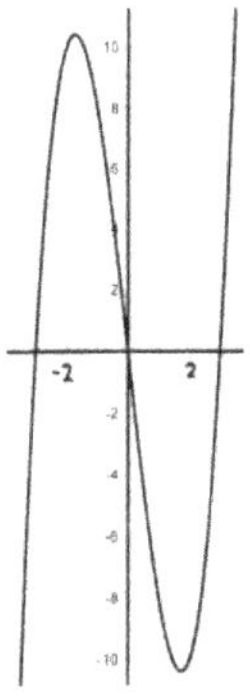

c)
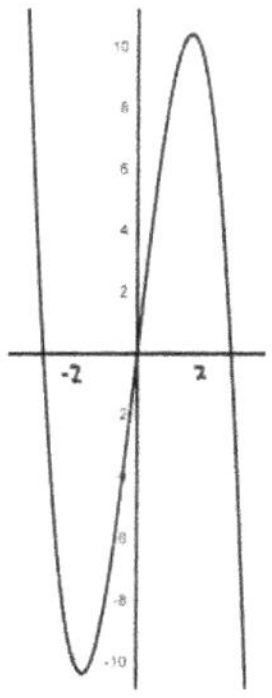

d)
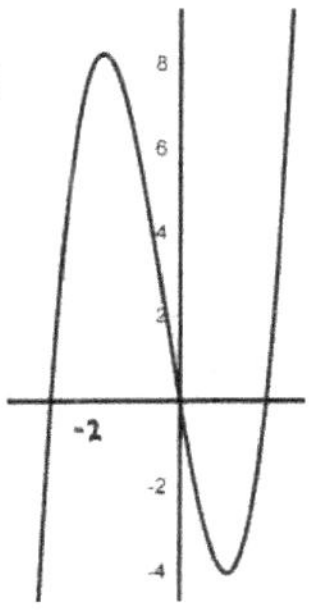

Answers to Sheet #6

2) a) $r = 51\ ^{m}/_{s}$ b) $r = 33\ ^{m}/_{s}$ c) $v = 18\ ^{m}/_{s}$
d) $v = 17.6\ ^{m}/_{s}$ e) $v \approx 11.9\ ^{m}/_{s}$ f) $v = 58.8\ ^{m}/_{s}$

3) a)
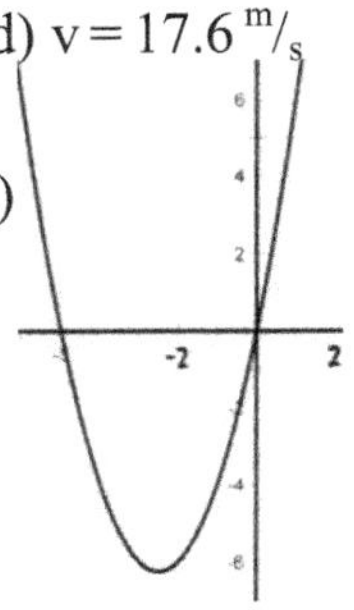

b)
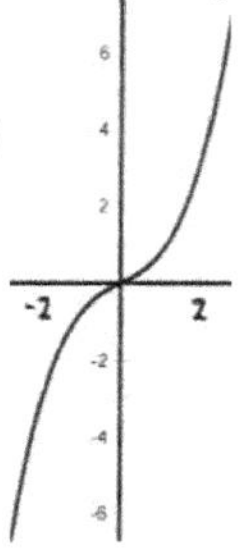

c)
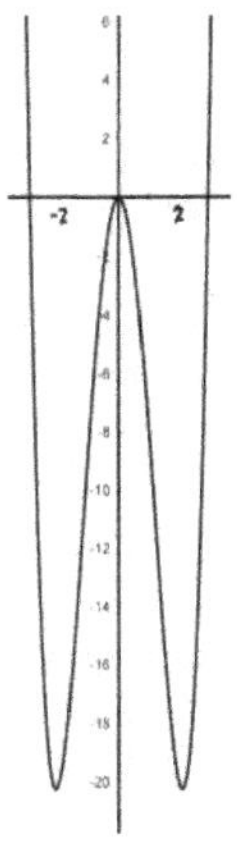

Answers to Sheet #7

1) a) $f(x) = x^3$ We will need f(x+h)

$f(x+h) = (x+h)^3 = x^3 + 3x^2h + 3xh^2 + h^3$

Using the definition to find the derivative:

$$f'(x) = \lim_{h\to0} \frac{f(x+h) - f(x)}{h}$$

$$f'(x) = \lim_{h\to0} \frac{(x^3 + 3x^2h + 3xh^2 + h^3) - (x^3)}{h}$$

$$f'(x) = \lim_{h\to0} \frac{3x^2h + 3xh^2 + h^3}{h}$$

$$f'(x) = \lim_{h\to0} \frac{h(3x^2 + 3xh + h^2)}{h}$$

$$f'(x) = \lim_{h\to0} 3x^2 + 3xh + h^2$$

Now we can plug in 0 for h, which gives us

Our desired answer: $\mathbf{f'(x) = 3x^2}$

1) b) $f(x) = x^2 + 7x$ We will need f(x+h)

$f(x+h) = (x+h)^2 + 7(x+h)$

$= x^2 + 2xh + h^2 + 7x + 7h$

Using the definition to find the derivative:

$$f'(x) = \lim_{h\to0} \frac{f(x+h) - f(x)}{h}$$

$$f'(x) = \lim_{h\to0} \frac{(x^2 + 2xh + h^2 + 7x + 7h) - (x^2 + 7x)}{h}$$

$$f'(x) = \lim_{h\to0} \frac{2xh + h^2 + 7h}{h}$$

$$f'(x) = \lim_{h\to0} \frac{h(2x + h + 7)}{h}$$

$$f'(x) = \lim_{h\to0} 2x + h + 7$$

Now we can plug in 0 for h, which gives us

Our desired answer: $\mathbf{f'(x) = 2x + 7}$

2) a) $7x^6$ b) $12x^2$ c) $5x^4 + 28x^3 - 6x^2 + 2x - 3$

3) $f'(x) = k \cdot n \cdot x^{n-1}$

4) a) 465 b) 9455 c) 25,502,500

5) a) $^5/_2$ b) $-^7/_2$ c) $-^2/_9$ d) $^2/_5$ e) $\frac{y_2 - y_1}{x_2 - x_1}$

Answers to Sheet #8

1) $\frac{4}{7}$ 2) $5 \cdot \frac{4}{7} \rightarrow \frac{20}{7}$ 3) $k \cdot \frac{4}{7} \rightarrow \frac{4k}{7}$

4) $\frac{k^2 4^2}{7^2}$ 5) $\frac{k^2 4^3}{7^3}$

6) $1^2\left(\frac{4}{7}\right)^3 + 2^2\left(\frac{4}{7}\right)^3 + 3^2\left(\frac{4}{7}\right)^3 + \ldots + 7^2\left(\frac{4}{7}\right)^3$

$= \frac{4^3}{7^3}\left(1^2 + 2^2 + 3^2 + \ldots + 7^2\right) = \sum_{i=1}^{7} i^2$

Now we use the summation formula:

$\sum_{i=1}^{n} i^2 = \frac{1}{3}n^3 + \frac{1}{2}n^2 + \frac{1}{6}n$, which gives us:

$\frac{4^3}{7^3}\left(\frac{1}{3}7^3 + \frac{1}{2}7^2 + \frac{1}{6}7\right) \rightarrow \frac{4^3}{3} + \frac{4^3}{2\cdot7} + \frac{4^3}{6\cdot7^2}$

$\mathbf{\approx 26.12}$

7) Following the same process, we get:
$\frac{a^3}{n^3}\left(\frac{1}{3}n^3 + \frac{1}{2}n^2 + \frac{1}{6}n\right) \rightarrow \frac{a^3}{3} + \frac{a^3}{2\cdot n} + \frac{a^3}{6\cdot n^2}$

8) a) ≈ 21.40
b) as n approaches infinity, the second two factional terms approach zero. Therefore the answer is $\frac{a^3}{3}$.

9) a) $21\frac{1}{3}$ b) $41\frac{2}{3}$ c) 243

10) a) $4x^3$ b) $18x^2$ c) $30x^5 + 3$ d) 0
e) $20x^3 - 24x^2 + 2x + 9$ f) $-8x^7 + 15x^4 - 5$

11) a) $F(x) = x^7 + C$
b) $F(x) = 9x + C$
c) $F(x) = \frac{3x^2}{2} + C$
d) $F(x) = \frac{x^5}{5} + C$
e) $F(x) = \frac{5x^4}{4} + \frac{8x^3}{3} + C$

Answers to Sheet #9

1) a) $\frac{5a^3}{3}$ b) $\int_0^a f(x)\,dx = \frac{a^{n+1}}{n+1}$

2) a) $= \frac{a^4}{4}$; $a = 4 \rightarrow$ area = 4

b) $= \frac{a^3}{6}$; $a = 12 \rightarrow$ area = 288

c) $= a^5$; $a = 3 \rightarrow$ area = 243

3) a) $\frac{a^5}{5}$ b) $\frac{x^5}{5} + C$

4) a) $48x^5$ b) $\frac{8a^7}{7}$ c) $\frac{8x^7}{7}+C$ d) $8x^6$

5) a) $f'(x) = ½x + 8$ b) $f'(6) = 11$

6) a) $f'(x) = 3x^2 + x$ b) $f'(2) = 14$

7) $d'(t) = v(t) = 2$
The object is moving at a constant speed

8) $d'(t) = v(t) = ½t$
One possibility is to imagine a car moving toward a wall. "d" is the distance away from the wall. The car steadily decelerates, touches the wall, and then goes backwards with steady acceleration.

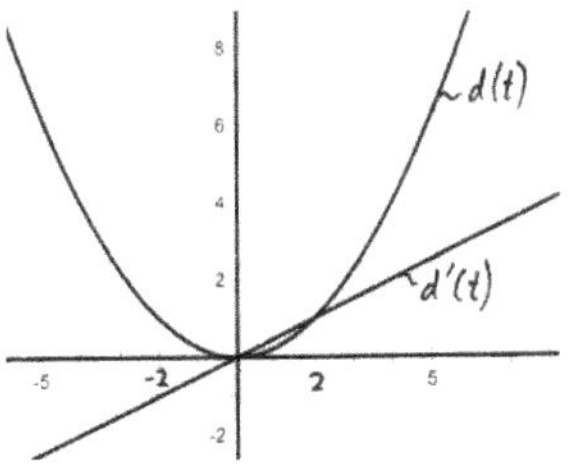

9) $d'(t) = v(t) = -t + 3$
One possibility is that the object is thrown up an inclined plane, and "d" is the object's distance uphill from a mark on the plane. Note that the maximum height (above the mark) is when t = 3, which is also when the height is zero.

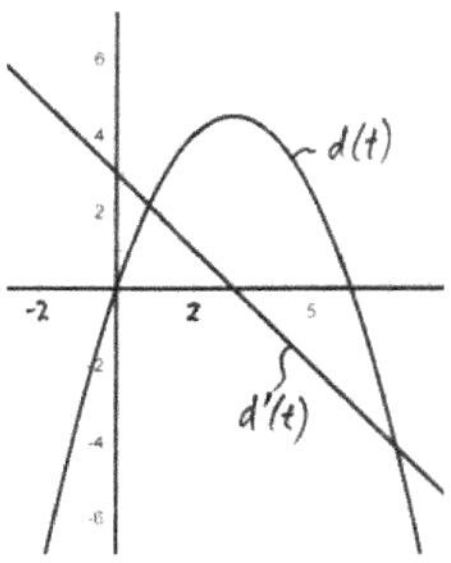

10) $d'(t) = v(t) = 3t^2 - 12t + 9 = 3(t-1)(t-3)$
As opposed to the above problem, this case does not have constant acceleration. We can imagine that "d" is the height above the ground of a rocket. There are two moments when the rocket stops moving up (or down), and that's when its speed is zero.

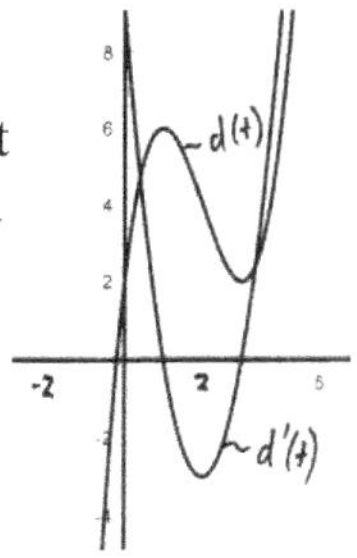

Answers to Sheet #10

1) a) $F(x) = \frac{x^4}{4}$; $F(2) = 4$

b) $F(x) = \frac{7x^2}{2} + 5x$; $F(4) = 76$

c) $F(x) = \frac{x^4}{4} - \frac{2x^3}{3} + 3x$; $F(2) = 4⅔$

d) Same as above; $F(3) = 11¼$

e) $F(3) - F(2) = 11¼ - 4⅔ = 6\frac{7}{12}$

f) $F(x) = \frac{x^5}{5}$; $F(5) - F(3) = 3125 - 243 = 2882$

2) $F'(x) = f(x)$

3) a) See graph at right

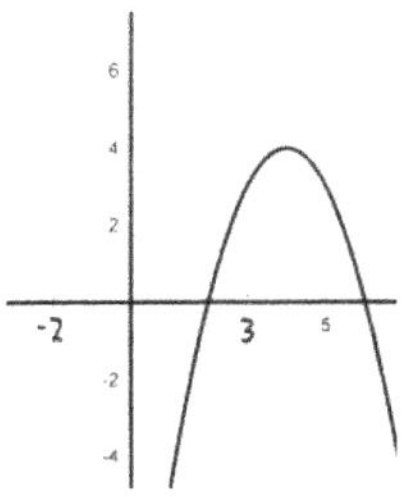

b) $f'(x) = -2x + 8$
c) When x = 1, the y-value is –5
d) When x = 1, the slope of the curve is 6
e) $f'(3) = 2$
f) $f'(5) = -2$
g) $0 = -x^2 + 8x - 12 \rightarrow (2,0)\,;(6,0)$
h) $0 = -2x + 8 \rightarrow x = 4;\ f(4) = 4$
The local max (slope = 0) is (4,4)
i) $F(x) = -\frac{x^3}{3} + 4x^2 - 12x$; roots are 2 and 6
$F(6) - F(2) = 0 - (-10⅔)$; Area = 10⅔

4) c) $f'(x) = 3x^2 - 9$ d) 10 e) 3

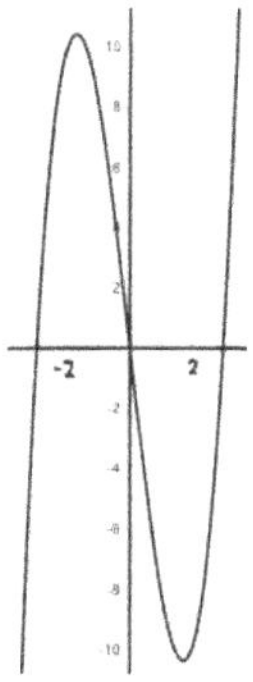

f) $f(x) = 0$ gives the roots:
(-3,0); (0,0); (3,0)
g) $0 = 3x^2 - 9 \rightarrow x^2 = 3$
$x = \pm\sqrt{3} \approx \pm 1.73$ To find the y-values, we plug into f(x).
$f(\sqrt{3}) \approx -10.4;\ f(-\sqrt{3}) \approx 10.4$
Max & min at (1.73, -10.4); (-1.73, 10.4)

Answers to Sheet #11

1) Given $f(x) = -x^3 - 2x^2 + x + 2$...
a) See graph on next page with #2.
b) $f'(x) = -3x^2 - 4x + 1$
c) $f(2) = -12$. (2,–12) is a point on the curve.
d) $f'(2) = -19$. At x = 2, the slope is –19.
e) y = –168 when x = 5. It is the point (5,–168)
f) y = 0 at (–2,0); (–1,0); (1,0).
g) We set the derivative equal to zero, and then use the quadratic formula.
Ans: (0.215, 2.11); (–1.55, –0.631)
h) $\int_{-1}^{1} f(x)\,dx = F(1) - F(-1)$

$F(x) = -\frac{x^4}{4} - 2\frac{x^3}{3} + \frac{x^2}{2} + 2x$

$F(1) = -¼ - ⅔ + ½ + 2 = 1\frac{7}{12}$

$F(-1) = -¼ + ⅔ + ½ - 2 = -1\frac{1}{12}$

Area = $F(1) - F(-1) = 1\frac{7}{12} - (-1\frac{1}{12}) = \mathbf{2\frac{2}{3}}$

2) a) $f'(x) = 3x^2 - 12x + 11$

b)

x	f(x)	f'(x)
4	12	11
3	6	2
2	6	-1
1	6	2
0	0	11
-1	-18	26

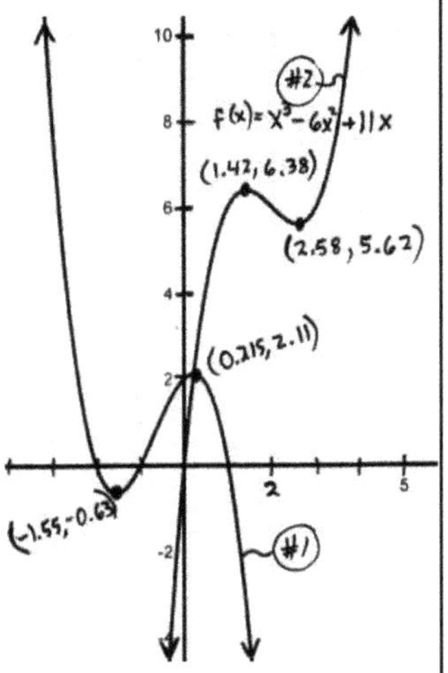

c) The only place it crosses the x-axis is (0,0).

d) Max and Min are (2.58, 5.62); (1.42, 6.38)

e) We solve $74 = 3x^2 - 12x + 11$ to get $x = -3, 7$.
Ans: (–3, –114) and (7,126)

3) a) $F(x) = x^2 + 3x$; Area = F(4) – F(2) = **18**

b) F(4) = **10⅔** c) $-4\frac{1}{2} - 11\frac{1}{3} = \mathbf{-15\frac{5}{6}}$

d) $1\frac{7}{12} - (-1\frac{1}{12}) =$ **2⅔** e) 15¾ – 3¾ = **12**

4) a) $d(t) = 4t^2 + 3t$
b) 430m

5) a) $v(t) = 4.6t$ and $d(t) = 2.3t^2$
b) $\sin^{-1}(2.3 \div 4.9) \approx 28.0°$
c) 36.8m

Answers to Review Sheet

1) a) Using one of the average speed formulas:

$$r = \frac{d(6) - d(4)}{6 - 4} \to \frac{54 - 24}{6 - 4} \to \frac{30}{2} \to \mathbf{15m/s}$$

b) Here are three ways to do this:

- Plug in two time values *very* close to 6.
- Plug in t = 6 and t = 6+h into the calculus average speed formula, then, after the H cancels, put zero in for h.
- Recall that the instantaneous speed formula for an inclined plane is v(t) = 2kt. In this case k = 1.5. Therefore v(t) = 3t

Each method yields the answer: **18m/s**

1) c) 7.5 m/s d) 8.4 m/s

2) a) $f'(x) = 6x^5$ b) $f'(x) = 30x^2$ c) $f'(x) = 8$
d) $f'(x) = 0$ e) $f'(x) = 10x^4 - 6x$

3) $f'(x) = 4x$; $f'(2) = 4 \cdot 2 =$ **8**

4) a) $F(x) = \frac{x^7}{7} + C$ b) $F(x) = \frac{5x^4}{2} + C$ c) $F(x) = 4x^2 + C$
d) $F(x) = 5x + C$ e) $F(x) = \frac{x^6}{3} - x^3 + 7x + C$

5) a) $F(x) = x^3 \to F(5) - F(2) \to 125 - 8 \to$ **117**

b) $F(x) = \frac{x^2}{6} + 6x \to 34\frac{1}{6} - (-11\frac{1}{3}) \to$ **45½**

c) $F(x) = \frac{x^4}{4} - \frac{11x^2}{2} \to -29\frac{1}{4} - (-18) \to$ **–11¼**

6) a) $f'(x) = 3x^2 - 4$

b)

x	f(x)	f'(x)
3	15	23
2	0	8
1	–3	–1
0	0	–4
–1	3	–1
–2	0	8
–3	–15	23

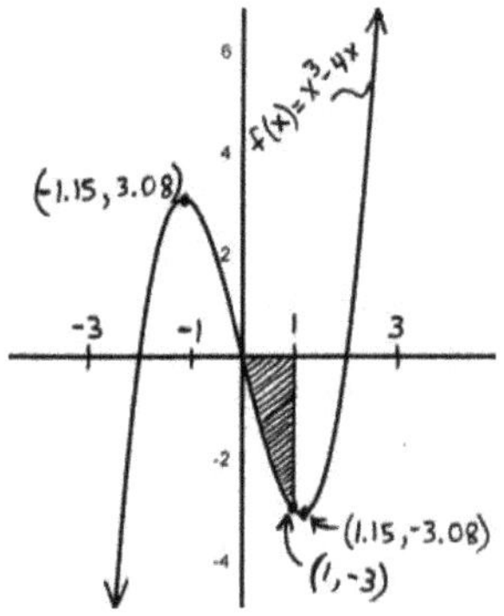

c) It crosses the x-axis at **(0,0); (2,0); (–2,0)**.

d) $f'(x) = 0 = 3x^2 - 4 \to x = \pm 1.15$
the y-coordinates are $f(\pm 1.15) = \mp 3.08$
Therefore the Max/Min points are:
(1.15, –3.08); (–1.15, 3.08)

e) The slope at x = 3 is f'(3) → **23**

f) See graph above.

g) At x = 1 the y-coordinate is –3.

h) At x = 1 the slope is –1.

i) The area (shaded) from x = 0 to 1 is –1¾.

Answers to Challenge Sheet

1)a) $d(t) = 3.46t^2$ b) $v(t) = 6.93t$ c) $v(d) = 3.72\sqrt{d}$

2) a) $v(t) = 2.536t$; $d(t) = 1.268t^2$
d = 15.45m ; t = 3.49 sec ; v = 8.86 m/s
b) t = 1.81 sec ; v = 8.86 m/s
c) t = 1.04 sec ; v = 8.86 m/s
d) t = 0.904 sec ; v = 8.86 m/s

3) t = 8.53 sec ; v = 3.618 m/s

4) moon : earth = $\sqrt{6}$: 1

5) moon : earth = 1 : $\sqrt{6}$ or $\sqrt{6}$: 6

6) 1.43 sec 7) 3.50 sec

8) moon : earth = $\sqrt{6}$: 1

9) a) 0.808 sec b) 3.96 m/s c) 2.0 m/s

d) $v(t) = 3.96 - 9.8t \to d(t) = 3.96t - 4.9t^2$
$0.3 = 3.96t - 4.9t^2 \to t = 0.0846$
v(0.0846) = 3.13 m/s

e) 6:1 ratio → 4.8 m f) 4.848 sec

—— ***Philosophy of Math*** (12th Grade) ——

Background

As I stated in the introduction (see "Twelfth grade math – The Grand Finale"), the students' final math course in high school should leave them feeling inspired and saying: "Wow, mathematics is truly remarkable!" The final topic needs to be something that inspires the teacher. Additionally, the twelfth grade year is the year of synthesis. So we look for topics that give the students a sense that what they are learning right now is in some way a culmination of everything they have learned through the years.

For all of the above reasons, Philosophy of Math is the final course that I teach to my twelfth graders. I acknowledge that a large part of the reason for this topic is that it is a passion of mine – but there is nothing wrong with that; another teacher could choose a different topic to end the year with.

Lesson plans and worksheets

Day-by-day lesson plans and worksheets can be downloaded from **www.JamieYorkPress.com**.

Format

For my situation, this course is a one-quarter track class – around thirty 45-minute lessons, or a total of about 23 classroom hours. It could also work as a main lesson. I teach this course to all of the twelfth grade class – advanced and regular sections combined.

Overview

In the middle of the nineteenth century, two subjects that have always been considered centerpieces of human thought – science and mathematics – were shaken to their core. In the world of science, it was the emergence of the theories of quantum and relativity that shook the world of physics. While many educated people are at least familiar with the terms "quantum" and "relativity", and the brilliant minds that brought it all about (Einstein, Bohr, Heisenberg, Planck, etc.), the story of the "foundational crisis of mathematics", and its implications for the world of mathematics, is known by very few people. This course tells this *great story* (see below), and in the process, investigates some of classic questions.

Essays and articles

The following is a list of possible readings for this course – much of which is found on the Internet:

- Excerpts from *A Mathematician's Apology* by G. H. Hardy
- *Mathematics as an Art* by John Williams Navin Sullivan
- *Mathematics and the Metaphysicians* by Bertrand Russell
- *Mathematical Creation* by Henri Poincaré
- *The Crisis in Intuition* by Hans Hahn
- *Paradox Lost and Paradox Regained* by Kasner and Newman
- Excerpts from *The Western Heritage from the Earliest Times to the Present* by Stewart Easton
- *Mathematical Platonism and its Opposites* by Barry Mazur
- Excerpts from *What is Mathematics, Really?* by Reuben Hersh
- *Intuitionistic Reflections on Formalism* by Luitzen Brouwer
- *On the Infinite* by David Hilbert
- Excerpts from Rebecca Goldstein's book: *Incompleteness: The Proof and Paradox of Kurt Gödel*

A video documentary

One of the highlights of this course is a video documentary that I show the students in the second week. This extraordinary, award-winning documentary is Simon Singh's "Fermat's Last Theorem", which tells the story of Andrew Wiles' journey to prove Fermat's Last Theorem. The documentary came out in 1996 on the BBC program Horizon and UKTV. It can be found on the Internet.

Course textbook (a graphic novel!?)

I was thrilled when I was first given a copy of *Logicomix* (subtitled: "An Epic Search for Truth"). Here was the *Great Story* I had been telling in this course for many years, in the form of a graphic novel – and a New York Times bestseller! This book now serves as a reader for my course. Bertrand Russell serves as the main protagonist, and the story spans the entire foundational crisis. The book highlights Russell's struggles with his work, *Principia Mathematica*, paints a picture of conflicting philosophical beliefs between great minds (Russell, Poincaré, Hilbert, Wittgenstein, Gödel), and, to some degree, concludes with Gödel's incompleteness theorems – the proof that ends the great struggle.

Questions to wrestle with

Here is a list of some of the question that can be wrestled with during this course:

- What is mathematics? What do most people think that mathematics is?
- How is math different from science?
- Is math discovered or created?
- If math is discovered, and it "has always been there", how did it get there? Who created it? God?
- Is mathematics an art? How is a mathematician different than a normal artist?
- What does it mean to be a mathematician?
- What is the dominant philosophy today?
- How do we gain knowledge?
- Is philosophy important? Can a dominant philosophy influence our daily lives and politics?
- What are the implications of Gödel's proof?

Puzzles

I carefully select some puzzles, interspersed throughout the course, that help to elucidate a central point: mathematics is above all an experience of struggle and discovery. The puzzles I typically do are:

- *Cut Plane* (from our book, *Fun with Puzzles, Games and More!*).
  Question: Ten planes divide space into how many regions?
  Answer: 176 (See our puzzle book, or the lesson plans for a full explanation.)
- *Perfect Number Puzzle.*
  Question: A perfect number is a number where the sum of all of its factors (except for itself) is equal to itself. The first three perfect numbers are 6, 28, and 496. Find the next two perfect numbers.
  Answer: 8128 and 33,550,336. Euclid's perfect number formula is $P = (2^{(N-1)})\cdot(2^N - 1)$
- *Hilbert's Infinite Hotel.*
  Question: If a hotel with infinitely many rooms is full, how many new guests can be accommodated?
  Answer: We can even accommodate infinitely many buses arriving at the hotel – each bus with infinitely many passengers. (See lesson plans for a full explanation.)
- *Goldbach's Conjecture.* (worksheet #2)
  Question: Which even numbers can be expressed as the sum of two prime numbers, and what property can be stated regarding this?
  Answer: The conjecture (which hasn't been proven) states: "Every even number can be expressed as the sum of two prime numbers."
- *Difference of Two Squares.* (worksheet #2)
  Question: What numbers can be expressed as the difference of two square numbers, and what property can be stated regarding this?
  Answer: The theorem states: "Every prime number, except for 2, can be expressed as the difference of two square numbers in one and only one way."
- *The Sum of Two Squares.* (worksheet #3)
  Question: In how many ways can a number be expressed as the sum of two square numbers, and what property can be stated regarding this?
  Answer: There are three statements to be made:
  - If a number is prime and has a remainder of 1 after dividing it by 4, then it can be expressed as the sum of two square numbers in one and only one way.
  - If a number is prime and has a remainder of 3 after dividing it by 4, then it is not possible to express it as a sum of two square numbers.
  - If a number is not prime, then there are a variety of possibilities – the number may be expressed as the sum of two square numbers in one way, in multiple ways, or not at all.
- *Russell's Paradox.* (worksheet #2)
  Question: If R is the set of all sets that don't include themselves as a member, then is R a member of itself?
  Answer: Worksheet #2 builds up to an understanding of this paradox.
- *Fermat's Little Theorem.* (worksheet #3)
  Question: If p and n are any natural numbers, and $Q = n^p - n$, then under what conditions is Q evenly divisible by p?
  Answer: The theorem states: "If p is a prime number, n is any other natural number, and $Q = n^p - n$ then the Q is divisible by p."

A (very abbreviated) summary of *The Great Story – An Epic Search for Truth*

I tell my students that the story of the "foundational crisis" is one of the greatest stories ever told. It has complex characters, conflict, struggle, disappointment, and hope. The plot is dramatic, and the conclusion is so unexpected and shocking that, even today, much of the mathematical community seems to operate under the premise that it never really happened.

ACT I – Perfect truth (300 BC – 1820 AD)

We already set the stage for the story in tenth grade – going back some 2300 years – when we studied Euclid's *Elements*. Euclid's work is an axiomatic system comprised of 465 theorems, and encompasses much of the known mathematics at that time. The truth of these theorems rests upon five postulates, or self-evident truths. Because of the truth of these five postulates, and the flawless logic that is followed with each proof, *The Elements* is considered to be the perfect model of truth. It is *THE* math textbook for over 2000 years. To a large degree, it is the foundation upon which the rest of the mathematical world is built. This is where we leave things with the tenth grade, and that was where the world of mathematics found itself at the start of the 19th century – very comfortably believing that Euclid was unshakeable, and therefore mathematical truth was irrefutable.

ACT II – The fall of Euclid (1820 – 1870)

But what about the fifth postulate? It certainly isn't as obvious as the first four postulates. The famous fifth postulate (known as the *Parallel Postulate*) reads:

> *If a line falling on two lines makes the interior angles on the same side less than two right angles, the two lines, if produced indefinitely, meet on that side on which the angles are less than two right angles.*

Certainly, if you take the time to make a drawing and think it through, then it is clearly true. But wouldn't *The Elements* be even better – wouldn't the foundation be even stronger – if we could prove the fifth postulate based upon the first four postulates? For centuries, mathematicians try to prove the fifth postulate. But nobody succeeds. And then, the unthinkable happens. Not suddenly, but slowly. Slowly over the first few decades of the 19th century, the mathematical world comes to the cruel realization that the fifth postulate *is not necessarily true*. We can assume it to be true, and then we end up with Euclid. But we can also assume something completely different and contradictory to the fifth postulate, and then we end up with a completely different *and equally valid* geometry. This opens the door for the development of new geometries (e.g., projective geometry and non-Euclidean geometry).

ACT III – New hopes are shattered (1870 – 1902)

As we enter the second half of the 19th century, Euclid is no longer the only possible truth; the unshakable foundation is gone. In place of the ancient Greeks' reliance on geometry, much of mathematics now relies on algebra, or more properly: formal analysis (calculus, differential equations, and functional analysis). But what is the foundation for analysis? Enter stage left: the rise of formal logic. There is hope that the foundation can be rebuilt. Georg Cantor's *set theory* provides some of the tools needed for the new field of formal logic. Cantor's ideas are quite controversial – are there really different "sizes" of infinity?

But it's Gottlob Frege who takes the torch and runs with it. Frege wants to show that mathematics grows out of logic. His world of logic is destined to become the new foundation for mathematics. In the process, Frege invents axiomatic predicate logic. His monumental works (*Begriffsscrift* and *Grundgesetze der Arithmetik*) take more than 25 years to complete. Certainly, his time would be well spent if it indeed became the new, unshakeable foundation. But just as Frege is laying the last few bricks (his final book was about to go to press), Bertrand Russell writes his famous letter to Frege (in 1902), informing him of a paradox within his work. Frege is understandably crushed as is shown by the comment he adds to the appendix of the book: "Hardly anything more unfortunate can befall a scientific writer than to have one of the foundations of his edifice shaken after the work is finished."

ACT IV – Stormy times and more uncertainty (1902 – 1922)

It seems that a powder keg has been ignited. David Hilbert, one of the foremost mathematicians of the time, sums it up nicely, stating: "The present state of affairs where we run up against the paradoxes is intolerable. If mathematical thinking is defective, where are we to find truth and certitude?" Mathematicians even begin to doubt if there is any truth behind mathematics. Bertrand Russell expresses a dramatic sentiment shared by several others: "Mathematics may be defined as the subject in which we never know what we are talking about, nor whether what we are saying is true." (He is referring to axioms that are no longer self-evident truths, and to "primitive undefined terms".)

Has mathematics really become just a meaningless game?

The mathematical world becomes bitterly divided into philosophical camps. The *Logicists* are led by Bertrand Russell, who is determined to pick up the pieces of Frege's work and see it to a successful completion. David Hilbert, the powerful leader of the *Formalists*, believes that the real solution is through a formal proof to show the consistency of arithmetic. And then there are the *Intuitionists*– the hecklers and thorns-in-the-sides of the formalists and logicists. Many of the intuitionists are great and well-respected mathematicians, such as Leopold Kronecker, Henri Poincaré, and L.E.J. Brouwer. But the intuitionists stand philosophically in direct contrast to the likes of Russell and Hilbert. Kronecker believes that whole numbers were given to us by God. Poincaré says: "Arithmetic cannot be justified by an axiomatic foundation. Our intuition precedes such a structure." And Brouwer insists: "Our intuition, not logic or experience, determines the soundness and acceptability of ideas."

Hilbert and Russell feel a sense of deep responsibility to save mathematics from the heresy of the intuitionists. Hilbert's "program" aims to prove that arithmetic (the theory of natural numbers) is *consistent*. Russell and Whitehead, on the other hand, work tirelessly for ten years on their version of what Frege had started. Their three-volume work, *Principia Mathematica* (published in 1910-13), is written in the language of formal logic. Nobody can wade through the 2000-page tome, let alone judge whether it has successfully achieved its goal. Is *Principia Mathematica* both *consistent* and *complete*?[1] Has it provided a new, unshakable foundation for mathematics? For nearly 20 years, nobody really knows the answer to that question.

ACT V – An Unexpected Ending (1922 – 1931)

As we enter the 1920's, the uncertainty and precarious position of mathematics has not improved. The tension between Hilbert and Brouwer grows more tense. In 1922, a group of mathematicians and philosophers begins to meet weekly in a Vienna café. The "Vienna Circle" soon gains influence over many intellectuals of the time. Their new brand of philosophy (later called *Logical Positivism*) pronounces as "meaningless" any statement that cannot be supported with empirical evidence. Mathematics, in their eyes, is not about truth at all; it fact it is completely devoid of meaning whatsoever. The only real purpose of math is as a language to be used in science. The Vienna Circle has an unlikely guru: the young, radical philosopher, Ludwig Wittgenstein. He publishes a work, *Tractatus Logico Philosophicus*, which is intended to "resolve for good all problems of philosophy".

In the late 1920's, an introverted graduate student and logician, Kurt Gödel, attends the Vienna Circle's weekly meetings. He sits quietly on the side, takes it all in, and slowly becomes more and more convinced that the Vienna Circle's philosophy is desperately wrong. Gödel is a Platonist; he believes that math is meaningful. And he wants to prove it! He stops attending the Vienna Circle meetings in 1928, and works on his proof for three years. His (now famous) *Incompleteness Theorems* state:

- Any formal, axiomatic system that encompasses arithmetic (such as *Principia Mathematica*) is essentially incomplete.
- If *Principia Mathematica* is consistent, then the consistency cannot be proven within that system.

Principia Mathematica suffers a fatal blow. Gödel's theorems dramatically and unexpectedly put an end to both the foundational crisis and the 2,400-year-long "epic search for truth". Hilbert and Russell wanted to give a firm foundation for all mathematics by eliminating intuition from mathematics. Gödel's proof seems to show that math cannot proceed without intuition. He believes that mathematical reality must exceed all formal attempts to contain it.

There is no unshakable foundation for mathematics to replace Euclid's *Elements*. What are the implications?

Epilogue (1931 – present)

Many people misunderstood the implications of Gödel's proof. Gödel "defeated" Russell and Hilbert, but sadly, the logical positivists (Vienna Circle) saw it as further evidence of the meaninglessness of math, and this attitude continues to have an impact on mathematics education today.

After Sputnik (the Soviets' first satellite in 1957), America became focused on beating the Soviets. Through this narrow lens, the purpose of mathematics education became to produce more scientists in an effort to win this mad race. Over the past few decades, the world has changed in many ways – socially, economically, and politically. Perhaps now more than ever, there is a realization that mathematics education needs to be overhauled. Opinions differ about where to place the blame, and how to fix it. New mathematics curricula have come and gone. Math textbooks are thicker, "prettier" (more graphics and fancier "packaging"), and more expensive – but less effective than ever. The trends are clear: an increase in teaching to standardized tests; more reliance on technology-driven learning; and teaching more advanced material at a younger and younger age.

And the results? A superficial understanding of material; a loss of a "sense of number"; an inability to do simple calculations in your head; no time left for depth, discovery, or true problem solving. In short, mathematics has become meaningless for most students.

But we must not give up. We all need to become math missionaries. We need to embark on a crusade to make math meaningful.

---

[1] an axiomatic system is said to be "consistent" if it is free of any contradictions. It is "complete" as long as every theorem (or statement or formula) that is true can be proven to be true within that system.

Cantor's Set Theory

Proof that <u>the rational numbers are countable</u> (which means they can be put into a one-to-one correspondence with the counting numbers):

- Make a 2-D array which encompasses all of the rational numbers in the following way: the first row is $^1/_1$, $^2/_1$, $^3/_1$, etc., the second row is $^1/_2$, $^2/_2$, $^3/_2$, etc., the third row is $^1/_3$, $^2/_3$, $^3/_3$, etc.
- Now we can number all of them along diagonals so that #1 is $^1/_1$, and #2 is $^2/_1$, #3 is $^1/_2$, #4 is $^3/_1$, #5 is $^2/_2$, #6 is $^1/_3$, #7 is $^4/_1$ #8 is $^3/_2$, etc.
- Thus, the rational numbers can be put into a one-to-one correspondence with the counting numbers.

Proof that <u>the algebraic numbers are countable</u>:

- Every algebraic number is a (complex number) solution to an algebraic equation in this form:
  $a_n x^n + a_{n-1}x^{n-1} + a_{n-2}x^{n-2} + \ldots + a_1 x^1 + a_0 x^0 = 0$, where a_i is an integer, and n is a positive integer.
- Our goal is to find a systematic method for putting all of the algebraic numbers into a specific order, thereby matching them in a one-to-one correspondence with the counting numbers.
- Let A(i) be the ith algebraic number.
- Let $K = n + |a_n| + |a_{n-1}| + |a_{n-2}| + \ldots + |a_1| + |a_0|$, where K represents the "index" of the equation.
- Usually, there are several algebraic equations for a given index, K. Some of these equations have multiple solutions. Some of these solutions will be ignored because they are algebraic numbers that were found with an equation from a smaller index. Of all of the new (complex number) solutions to the equations produced by a given index, we will order them (from least to greatest) according to their complex components, and then their real components.
- There are no equations where K = 0 or K = 1 that yield any algebraic numbers as solutions.
- Of the equations where K = 2, only one algebraic number (x = 0) is produced. Therefore A(1) = 0
- Of the equations where K = 3, only two new algebraic numbers (x = –1, 1) are produced. Therefore A(2) = –1, and A(3) = 1
- Of the equations where K = 4, six new algebraic numbers ($x = \pm 2, \pm\frac{1}{2}, \pm i$) are produced. Therefore $A(4) = -i$, $A(5) = -2$, $A(6) = -\frac{1}{2}$, $A(7) = \frac{1}{2}$, $A(8) = 2$, $A(9) = i$.
- Of the equations where K = 5, twenty new algebraic numbers (including $x = \pm\sqrt{2}, \pm\sqrt{2}\,i, \pm\phi$) are produced, thereby giving us the values of A(10) through A(29).
- This can be continued indefinitely for all values of K.
- Therefore all of the algebraic numbers can be put into a one-to-one correspondence with the counting numbers.

Proof that <u>the real numbers are not countable</u>:

- Every real number has a specific and unique decimal representation.
- <u>Assumption</u>: The real numbers between 0 and 1 are countable.
- It is therefore possible to write down <u>all</u> of the real numbers between 0 and 1 in a systematic order (but not according to size) from $a_1, a_2, a_3, \ldots$ etc., thereby matching them in a one-to-one correspondence with the counting numbers.
- Let d be a 2-D array such that for any number, a_n, the ith digit of a_n is given by $d_{n,i}$.
  This means that the 4th number in our list, a_4, has a decimal expansion of:
  $a_4 = 0\,.\,d_{4,1}\,d_{4,2}\,d_{4,3}\,d_{4,4}\,d_{4,5}\ldots$ (So if $a_4 = 0.463872048\ldots$, then $d_{4,6} = 2$)
- Now we will create a new number, j, between 0 and 1. We assign its first digit to be anything but $d_{1,1}$ and the 2nd digit to be anything but $d_{2,2}$, and the 3rd digit to be anything but $d_{3,3}$, etc.
- j is not equal to a_1 because they have different first digits; j is not equal to a_2 because they have different second digits; j is not equal to a_3 because they have different third digits, etc.
  j is not equal to any number on our list. We have therefore found a real number between 0 and 1 that is not on the list, so the list does not include all of the real numbers.
- Therefore, our assumption is false; the real numbers are *not* countable.
- <u>Corollary</u>: There exists at least one irrational number that is not algebraic. (These numbers are called *transcendental numbers*.)
- <u>Corollary</u>: The transcendental numbers are *not* countable. (Loosely speaking, this means that there are "far more" *transcendental numbers*, than there are rational or algebraic numbers.)
- <u>Corollary</u>: The transcendental numbers and the irrational numbers have the same order, or *cardinal number* (i.e., they can be mapped into a one-to-one correspondence with each other).

A Timeline for the Foundational Crisis and the Vienna Circle

1874: Cantor introduces *Set Theory*. Rational and algebraic numbers are "countable", but the irrational numbers are not.

1879: Frege publishes *Begriffsscrift,* which works toward the development of formal logic.

1893: Frege publishes *Grundgesetze der Arithmetik, Vol I,* which aims to be the new foundation of mathematics.

1899: Hilbert states his 22 axioms for Euclidean geometry. Axioms are no longer considered to be self-evident truths.

1900: Hilbert gives his famous lecture at the International Congress of Mathematicians in Paris. He presents 23 problems that the world of mathematics should be focusing on in the new century, including (1) a proof of *Cantor's Continuum Hypothesis*, and (2) a proof that arithmetic is consistent.

1902/1903: Frege publishes *Grundgesetze der Arithmetik, Vol II.* However, just before it is completed, Russell finds a paradox that shakes the work's foundation.

1910: Russell and Whitehead publish the first volume of *Principia Mathematica.*

1920: Hilbert begins work on "Hilbert's Program" which is a further development of *formalism*, and is intended to develop a new foundation for mathematics.

1922: Wittgenstein publishes *Tractatus Logico Philosophicus.*

1922: Schlick organizes the *Vienna Circle* along with Carnap and Hahn.

1931: Gödel publishes his Incompleteness Theorems.

1936: Schlick is assassinated. The Vienna Circle ends.

Ages of Key People

Person	Age in 1910	Age in 1922	Age in 1931
Immanuel Kant (1724-1804)			
Leopold Kronecker (1823-1891)			
Ernst Mach (1838-1916)	72		
Georg Cantor (1845-1918)	65		
Gottlob Frege (1848-1925)	62	74	
Henri Poincaré (1854-1912)	56		
David Hilbert (1862-1943)	48	60	69
Bertrand Russell (1872-1970)	38	50	59
Hans Hahn (1879-1934)	31	43	52
L.E.J. Brouwer (1881-1966)	29	41	50
Moritz Schlick (1882-1936)	28	40	49
Ludwig Wittgenstein (1889-1951)	21	33	42
Rudolf Carnap (1891-1970)	19	31	40
Kurt Gödel (1906-1978)	4	16	25

Gödel's Proof – Gödel Numbers

Table of Symbols within PM and *Gödel numbering*

Symbol	Gödel #	Meaning	Symbol	Gödel #	Meaning
~	1	not	(	8	left parenthesis
∨	2	or	)	9	right parenthesis
⊃	3	if…then…	,	10	comma
∃	4	there exists…	+	11	plus
=	5	equals	·	12	multiplication
0	6	zero	x	13	variable
s	7	successor of	y	17	variable
			z	19	variable

Note: ss0 stands for 2.

Vocabulary

PM: the given formal axiomatic system within which all the axioms, definitions, and rules are given. PM is assumed to be the system given in *Principia Mathematica* (by Russell and Whitehead), but could be any formal axiomatic system that includes the basic properties of arithmetic (e.g., addition, multiplication).

formula: a well-formed formula (wff) or statement within the system PM that is made according to the rules. A formula may be either true or false. A formula becomes a *theorem* once it is proven. "x =" is not a proper formula. Examples of proper formulas include:

x = ssss0, which means "x equals 4"
sssss0 = ss0 + ss0, which means "5 equals 2 + 2"
(∃x)(x = ss0 + sss0), which means "there exists an x such that x equals 2+3"
(∃x)(x = ss0) ⊃ (∃y)(~(y = 0)), which means "If there exists x such that x equals 2, then there exists y such that y is not equal to 0."

proof: A sequence of formulas, each one of which is justified according to the rules and axioms, and the last formula in the proof is the theorem that is to be proven.

Gödel numbering:

- The key idea is that any possible formula or proof can be coded as a unique Gödel number, and any Gödel number can be decoded to get the formula or proof that it represents.
- To determine what a Gödel number represents, we break it down into its prime factorization.
- The bases of the prime factorization of any Gödel number are always consecutive prime numbers.
- The Gödel number of a single formula is such that each exponent in the prime factorization tells us a symbol in the formula.
- The Gödel number of a proof – or perhaps an entire system of proofs – is such that each exponent in the prime factorization is itself the Gödel number of a single formula.

Question: What is the formula represented by the Gödel number 31104000000?
Solution: We break down the number into its prime factorization, which is $2^{13}\cdot 3^{5}\cdot 5^{6}$. The exponents tell us that the three symbols are "x", "=", and "0". The formula is "x = 0".

Question: What is the Gödel number for the formula "z = ss0 + y" ?
Solution: The Gödel number is given by multiplying out $2^{19}\cdot 3^{5}\cdot 5^{7}\cdot 7^{7}\cdot 11^{6}\cdot 13^{11}\cdot 17^{17}$.

Question: What is the Gödel number for the formula (∃x)(x = ss0) ⊃ (∃y)(~(y = 0)) ?
(The solution is left for you to figure out!)

Question: What is the Gödel number for this proof?:
x = sss0
y = x
y = sss0

Solution: The first formula has the Gödel number $2^{13}\cdot 3^{5}\cdot 5^{7}\cdot 7^{7}\cdot 11^{7}\cdot 13^{6}$, which we will call a.
The second formula has the Gödel number $2^{17}\cdot 3^{5}\cdot 5^{13}$, which we will call b.
The third formula has the Gödel number $2^{17}\cdot 3^{5}\cdot 5^{7}\cdot 7^{7}\cdot 11^{7}\cdot 13^{6}$, which we will call c.
Therefore, the whole proof has the Gödel number $2^{a}\cdot 3^{b}\cdot 5^{c}$

Question: What is the Gödel number for the whole of *Principia Mathematica*?
(This is left for you to imagine!)

Gödel's Proof – Functions & Formulas

I. Key Ideas

1. *Truth and Certainty*. Whether a statement is true or not is a different matter than whether or not the statement can be proven as true or false. For example, the statement "Lions are mammals" may be true, but it cannot be proven within PM.
2. *Meta-Mathematics*. During the "foundational crisis", meta-mathematics emerged as an important field of study. Meta-mathematics is when we "stand above" a mathematical system and make statements about it. Examples of meta-mathematical statements include: "Euclid proved 465 theorems in *The Elements*"; "PM is consistent." Quite amazingly, Gödel found a way to create formulas within PM that were, at the same time, meta-mathematical statements about PM.
3. *If a formula and its negation (opposite) can both be proven as true, the system is inconsistent.*
4. *If a system is inconsistent, then any formula (even one that is obviously false) can be proven as true*. For example, *if* it could be proven within a system that 2+2 = 4 and that 2+2 = 5, *then* there is a contradiction, and therefore the system is inconsistent. It would then follow that any formula within the system could be proven as true (e.g., 4 = 5; 7 = 8; 21 = 24, etc.).
5. *If, within a given mathematical system, there exists a (presumably false) formula that cannot be proven as true, then the system is consistent.* This is the contrapositive of the above statement. (Using another example, the contrapositive of "If it's snowing, then it's not hot", is "If it's hot, then it's not snowing.")
6. *In order to prove that a system is consistent, we only need to be able to find one (presumably false) formula within the system that cannot possibly be proven as true.* For example, if we can prove, by using the axioms of the system, that there is no possible way to prove that 3+9 = 7, then we have proven that the system is consistent. (Note: proving that 3+9 = 7 is false is very different from proving that it could never be proven as true.)
7. *With any mathematical system, if there exists one true formula that is not provable within the system, then that system is incomplete.*

II. Functions.
Gödel found a way to express both of the following functions within PM.

Dem(z,w) "Dem" is short for "demonstrate", which is another word for "prove". It answers the question: "Is z a proof of w?" This function is true only if the sequence of formulas given by the Gödel number z is a proof of the formula given by the Gödel number w (formula w would be the last formula in proof z).

Sub(a,b,c) "Sub" is short for "substitute". This is a bizarre but important function. a is the Gödel number of a formula. b is the Gödel number of a variable. c represents a number or symbol. Sub(a,b,c) tells us to take the formula with Gödel number a, find all occurrences of the variable indicated by Gödel number b, and then replace them with the symbol c. The Gödel number of the resulting formula is what Sub(a,b,c) is equal to.

Example: If the formula x = y + z is given by the Gödel number k, then sub(k,17,7) returns the Gödel number of the formula x = 7 + z.

Example: If the formula (∃x)(x = y + z) is given by the Gödel number m, then sub(m,17,m) returns the Gödel number of the formula (∃x)(x = m + z).

III. Formulas.
The key to Gödel's brilliance is that he finds a way to express certain important meta-mathematical statements about PM within the system of PM. He does this by using two amazing statements – each one is a meta-mathematical statement that is expressed within PM. (Note that for now, we are not saying whether either formula is true, or not.)

Formula B: (∃w) ~(∃z) Dem(z,w)

This reads as: "There exists a formula w such that there does *not* exist a proof (z) of w", or: "w is not provable". **Formula B is the equivalent of saying: "PM is consistent".**

Formula G: ~(∃x) Dem(x,[sub(n,17,n)])

This statement is very important, but difficult to comprehend. You must first know that n is the Gödel number of the formula ~(∃x) Dem(x,[sub(y,17,y)]). Formula G then reads, "There does *not* exist an x such that x is a proof of the formula given by the Gödel number that results from sub(n,17,n)." In other words, the statement that results from sub(n,17,n), *which is Formula G itself*, is not provable. Gödel has now created a meta-mathematical self-referential statement.

Formula G says: "Formula G is not provable."

The two above formulas are used as centerpieces in Gödel's proof.

Gödel's proof – The Central Argument

Note: This proof uses formulas B and G (see previous sheet, *Gödel's Proof – Functions & Formulas*).
What follows is only an outline of the central argument of the proof.[1]

The following steps are justified by using formulas, axioms, and rules from within PM.

1. Assumption: PM is consistent, which means Formula B is true.
2. G says, "G is not provable." Its negation, ~G, says, "G is provable".
   - *If*, somehow, G could be proven as true, then ~G is provable.
   - *If*, somehow, ~G could be proven as true, then G is provable.

   (Gödel proved the two above statements within the system of PM.)
3. We know that "*if a formula and its negation can both be proven as true, then the system is inconsistent*" (see previous page). We have just discovered that if PM *is* consistent (step #1), and *if* G or its negation could somehow be proven as true, then we would arrive at a contradiction. Therefore we can say: If PM is consistent (step #1), then *G is not provable*.

Now, using meta-mathematical reasoning…

4. We have just shown that G is not provable (assuming that PM is consistent). But, G says "G is not provable." Now, meta-mathematically stepping out of PM, we can see that G is true. Therefore, we can say: *G is true, but not provable within PM.*
5. We have now found a statement, expressible within PM, that is true but not provable. We also know that: "*With any mathematical system, if there exists one true formula that is not provable within the system, then that system is incomplete.*" (See previous page)

Conclusion #1: *If PM is consistent, then it is incomplete.*[2, 3]

6. The statement "PM is incomplete" is the equivalent of saying: "There exists one true formula of PM that is not provable." We have now discovered that G is such a formula. Therefore, we can now say that G has the following new meaning: "PM is incomplete".
7. Assumption: Formula B (which says: "PM is consistent") is provable.
8. We now can say the following:
   - From Conclusion #1: "If PM is consistent, then PM is incomplete"
   - Which also means: "If B [is true], then G [is true]."
   - Which leads us to: "If B is provable, then G is provable."
9. In summary, if we assume that PM is consistent (B is true, step #1) and assume that the consistency is provable (B is provable, step #7), then it must follow (from step #8) that *G is provable*.
10. However, we said in step #3, in contradiction, that if PM is consistent, then G is *not* provable. Therefore, our assumption (step #7) is incorrect; B, which says "PM is consistent", is not provable.

Conclusion #2: *If PM is consistent, then the consistency cannot be proven.*[4]

---

[1] The teacher should read *Gödel's Proof* (by Ernest Nagel and James Newman, NYU Press, 2001, 2nd edition) for an excellent account of Gödel's Proof.

[2] Gödel also proves that PM is *essentially* incomplete, which means that even if the system is "repaired" by adding more axioms so that it can handle any problematic formulas (like G), then another true, but unprovable formula can always be constructed. And Gödel proves that this is true of *any* formal, axiomatic system that encompasses the elementary properties of whole numbers, including addition and multiplication.

[3] The meta-mathematical statement, "If PM is consistent then PM is incomplete" (step #5), can be expressed within PM by the formula (which can be abbreviated a $\supset$ G):

$$[(\exists w) \sim(\exists z)\ \mathrm{Dem}(z,w)] \supset [\sim(\exists x)\ \mathrm{Dem}(x,[\mathrm{sub}(n,17,n)])]$$

[4] To be more precise, I quote Ernst and Nagel (p107): "If PM is consistent, its consistency cannot be proven by any meta-mathematical reasoning that can be mirrored within PM itself. It does *not* exclude [the possibility of] a meta-mathematical proof of the consistency of PM. What it excludes is a proof of consistency that can be mirrored inside of PM…Proofs that cannot be mirrored inside the systems that they concern are not finitistic; they [therefore] do not achieve the proclaimed objectives of Hilbert's original program."

Appendix

Unit Conversion Table

* Denotes that it should be memorized as given in parentheses.

Weight

* 1 lb = 16 oz
* 1 kg ≈ 2.2046 (2.2) lb
* 1 oz ≈ 28.35 g
1 g ≈ 0.0353 oz
1 lb ≈ 0.4536 kg
* 1 U.S. ton = 2000 lb
* 1 metric ton = 1000 kg

Volume

* 1 tablespoon = 3 teaspoons
* 1 fl oz = 2 tablespoons
* 1 cup = 8 fl oz
* 1 pt = 2 cups = 16 fl oz
* 1 qt = 2 pt = 32 fl oz
* 1 gal = 4 qt = 128 fl oz ≈ 3.785 ℓ
* 1 mℓ = 1cm^3 (exactly!)
* 1 ℓ ≈ 1.0567 (1.06) qt ≈ 33.8 fl oz
1 fl oz ≈ 29.58 mℓ ≈ 1.804 in^3
1 qt ≈ 57.75 in^3 ≈ 0.9464 ℓ
1 gal ≈ 231.0 in^3 ≈ 0.134 ft^3
1 ft^3 = 1728 in^3 ≈ 7.481 gal
1 in^3 ≈ 0.554 fl oz ≈ 16.39 cm^3
1 m^3 = 1000 ℓ ≈ 35.31 ft^3
1 cord (of wood) = 128 ft^3

Area

* 1 acre ≈ area of square with side of 70 yards
* 1 hectare = 10,000 m^2 (100m·100m) ≈ 2.471 acres
1 acre = 4840 yd^2 ≈ 0.405 hectare
1 mile^2 = 640 acres ≈ 2.590 km^2
1 ft^2 = 144 in^2
1 m^2 = 10,000 cm^2 ≈ 10.764 ft^2
1 in^2 ≈ 6.452 cm^2

Length

* 1 yd = 36 in
* 1 in ≈ 2.5400 (2.54) cm
* 1 m ≈ 3.2808 (3.28) ft
* 1 mile = 5280 feet ≈ 1.6093 (1.61) km
* 1 km ≈ 0.6214 (0.62) mi
1 cm ≈ 0.39370 in
1 m ≈ 39.370 in ≈ 1.09yd
1 ft ≈ 0.3048m

Speed

1 m/s = 3.6 km/h ≈ 2.237 mph ≈ 3.281 ft/sec

Density[1]

Density conversion factors:

$$1\frac{\text{g}}{\text{cm}^3} = 1000\frac{\text{kg}}{\text{m}^3} \approx 62.43\frac{\text{lb}}{\text{ft}^3} \approx 0.578\frac{\text{oz}}{\text{in}^3}$$

$$1\frac{\text{oz}}{\text{in}^3} \approx 1.73\frac{\text{g}}{\text{cm}^3}$$

Water[1] (at a maximum density of 4°C)

$$= 1\frac{\text{g}}{\text{cm}^3} \text{ or } 1\frac{\text{kg}}{\ell} \text{ or } 1000\frac{\text{kg}}{\text{m}^3}$$

$$\approx 0.578\frac{\text{oz}}{\text{in}^3} \text{ or } 1.043\frac{\text{oz}}{\text{fl oz}}$$

$$\approx 62.43\frac{\text{lb}}{\text{ft}^3} \text{ or } 8.345\frac{\text{lb}}{\text{gal}}$$

Air $1.29\frac{\text{oz}}{\text{ft}^3}$ or $1.29\frac{\text{kg}}{\text{m}^3}$ (coincidentally!)

Aluminum	$169\frac{\text{lb}}{\text{ft}^3}$	or	$2.70\frac{\text{g}}{\text{cm}^3}$
Iron	$443\frac{\text{lb}}{\text{ft}^3}$	or	$7.10\frac{\text{g}}{\text{cm}^3}$
Mercury	$843\frac{\text{lb}}{\text{ft}^3}$	or	$13.5\frac{\text{g}}{\text{cm}^3}$
Gold	$1204\frac{\text{lb}}{\text{ft}^3}$	or	$19.3\frac{\text{g}}{\text{cm}^3}$

Useful Distances

Average Radius of the Earth:	3960 mi (6371 km)
Polar Circumference of Earth:	24859 mi (40,005 km)
Equatorial Circum. of Earth:	24902 mi (40,076 km)
Surface Area of the Earth:	197,000,000 mi^2 (510,000,000 km^2)
Total land area of the Earth:	57,500,000 mi^2 (149,000,000 km^2)
Radius of the Sun:	432,000 mi (696,000 km)
Radius of the Moon:	1080 mi (1738 km)
Distance to the Moon:	239,000 mi (384,400 km)
Distance to the Sun:	93,000,000 mi (150,000,000 km)
One light year:	5.8784x10^{12} mi (9.46x10^{12} km)
Distance to the nearest star:	2.53x10^{13} mi (4.07x10^{13} km)

Temperature Conversions

C = $^5/_9$ (F − 32)
F = $^9/_5$ C + 32

[1] Density always reads as weight per volume. For example, the density of gold is 1204 lb/ft^3, which tells us that a cubic foot of gold weighs 1204 pounds. The density of gold can also be given as 19.3 g/cm^3, which says that a cubic centimeter weighs 19.3 grams.

- Note that water has a density of exactly 1 oz/fl.oz. at 212°F when it is *least* dense.
- It is perhaps more useful to give densities in terms of g/cm^3 because we can easily compare it to water, which has a density of exactly 1 g/cm^3 (1 cm^3 of water weighs 1 gram). For example, with gold's density of 19.3 g/cm^3, we can say that gold is 19.3 times heavier than water.

Power and Base Tables

2nd Power

N	N^2
1	1
2	4
3	9
4	16
5	25
6	36
7	49
8	64
9	81
10	100

3rd Power

N	N^3
1	1
2	8
3	27
4	64
5	125
6	216
7	343
8	512
9	729
10	1000

4th Power

N	N^4
1	1
2	16
3	81
4	256
5	625
6	1296
7	2401
8	4096
9	6561
10	10000

5th Power

N	N^5
1	1
2	32
3	243
4	1024
5	3125
6	7776
7	16807
8	32768
9	59049
10	100000

6th Power

N	N^6
1	1
2	64
3	729
4	4096
5	15625
6	46656
7	117649
8	262144
9	531441
10	1000000

Base 2

N	2^N
1	2
2	4
3	8
4	16
5	32
6	64
7	128
8	256
9	512
10	1024

Base 3

N	3^N
1	3
2	9
3	27
4	81
5	243
6	729
7	2187
8	6561
9	19683
10	59049

Base 4

N	4^N
1	4
2	16
3	64
4	256
5	1024
6	4096
7	16384
8	65536
9	262144

Base 5

N	5^N
1	5
2	25
3	125
4	625
5	3125
6	15625

Base 6

N	6^N
1	6
2	36
3	216
4	1296
5	7776
6	46656

Base 7

N	7^N
1	7
2	49
3	343
4	2401
5	16807
6	117649

Base 8

N	8^N
1	8
2	64
3	512
4	4096
5	32768
6	262144

Base 9

N	9^N
1	9
2	81
3	729
4	6561
5	59049
6	531441

Table of Common Logarithms

Note: Looking up row 73 and column 8 we read 8681, which means both $\log_{10} 7.38 \approx 0.8681$ and $10^{0.8681} \approx 7.38$

	0	1	2	3	4	5	6	7	8	9
10	0000	0043	0086	0128	0170	0212	0253	0294	0334	0374
11	0414	0453	0492	0531	0569	0607	0645	0682	0719	0755
12	0792	0828	0864	0899	0934	0969	1004	1038	1072	1106
13	1139	1173	1206	1239	1271	1303	1335	1367	1399	1430
14	1461	1492	1523	1553	1584	1614	1644	1673	1703	1732
15	1761	1790	1818	1847	1875	1903	1931	1959	1987	2014
16	2041	2068	2095	2122	2148	2175	2201	2227	2253	2279
17	2304	2330	2355	2380	2405	2430	2455	2480	2504	2529
18	2553	2577	2601	2625	2648	2672	2695	2718	2742	2765
19	2788	2810	2833	2856	2878	2900	2923	2945	2967	2989
20	3010	3032	3054	3075	3096	3118	3139	3160	3181	3201
21	3222	3243	3263	3284	3304	3324	3345	3365	3385	3404
22	3424	3444	3464	3483	3502	3522	3541	3560	3579	3598
23	3617	3636	3655	3674	3692	3711	3729	3747	3766	3784
24	3802	3820	3838	3856	3874	3892	3909	3927	3945	3962
25	3979	3997	4014	4031	4048	4065	4082	4099	4116	4133
26	4150	4166	4183	4200	4216	4232	4249	4265	4281	4298
27	4314	4330	4346	4362	4378	4393	4409	4425	4440	4456
28	4472	4487	4502	4518	4533	4548	4564	4579	4594	4609
29	4624	4639	4654	4669	4683	4698	4713	4728	4742	4757
30	4771	4786	4800	4814	4829	4843	4857	4871	4886	4900
31	4914	4928	4942	4955	4969	4983	4997	5011	5024	5038
32	5051	5065	5079	5092	5105	5119	5132	5145	5159	5172
33	5185	5198	5211	5224	5237	5250	5263	5276	5289	5302
34	5315	5328	5340	5353	5366	5378	5391	5403	5416	5428
35	5441	5453	5465	5478	5490	5502	5514	5527	5539	5551
36	5563	5575	5587	5599	5611	5623	5635	5647	5658	5670
37	5682	5694	5705	5717	5729	5740	5752	5763	5775	5786
38	5798	5809	5821	5832	5843	5855	5866	5877	5888	5899
39	5911	5922	5933	5944	5955	5966	5977	5988	5999	6010
40	6021	6031	6042	6053	6064	6075	6085	6096	6107	6117
41	6128	6138	6149	6160	6170	6180	6191	6201	6212	6222
42	6232	6243	6253	6263	6274	6284	6294	6304	6314	6325
43	6335	6345	6355	6365	6375	6385	6395	6405	6415	6425
44	6435	6444	6454	6464	6474	6484	6493	6503	6513	6522
45	6532	6542	6551	6561	6571	6580	6590	6599	6609	6618
46	6628	6637	6646	6656	6665	6675	6684	6693	6702	6712
47	6721	6730	6739	6749	6758	6767	6776	6785	6794	6803
48	6812	6821	6830	6839	6848	6857	6866	6875	6884	6893
49	6902	6911	6920	6928	6937	6946	6955	6964	6972	6981
50	6990	6998	7007	7016	7024	7033	7042	7050	7059	7067
51	7076	7084	7093	7101	7110	7118	7127	7135	7143	7152
52	7160	7168	7177	7185	7193	7202	7210	7218	7226	7235
53	7243	7251	7259	7267	7275	7284	7292	7300	7308	7316
54	7324	7332	7340	7348	7356	7364	7372	7380	7388	7396

	0	1	2	3	4	5	6	7	8	9
55	7404	7412	7419	7427	7435	7443	7451	7459	7466	7474
56	7482	7490	7497	7505	7513	7521	7528	7536	7544	7551
57	7559	7566	7574	7582	7589	7597	7604	7612	7619	7627
58	7634	7642	7649	7657	7664	7672	7679	7686	7694	7701
59	7709	7716	7723	7731	7738	7745	7752	7760	7767	7774
60	7782	7789	7796	7803	7810	7818	7825	7832	7839	7846
61	7853	7860	7868	7875	7882	7889	7896	7903	7910	7917
62	7924	7931	7938	7945	7952	7959	7966	7973	7980	7987
63	7993	8000	8007	8014	8021	8028	8035	8041	8048	8055
64	8062	8069	8075	8082	8089	8096	8102	8109	8116	8122
65	8129	8136	8143	8149	8156	8162	8169	8176	8182	8189
66	8195	8202	8209	8215	8222	8228	8235	8241	8248	8254
67	8261	8267	8274	8280	8287	8293	8300	8306	8312	8319
68	8325	8332	8338	8344	8351	8357	8363	8370	8376	8382
69	8389	8395	8401	8407	8414	8420	8426	8432	8439	8445
70	8451	8457	8463	8470	8476	8482	8488	8494	8500	8507
71	8513	8519	8525	8531	8537	8543	8549	8555	8561	8567
72	8573	8579	8585	8591	8597	8603	8609	8615	8621	8627
73	8633	8639	8645	8651	8657	8663	8669	8675	8681	8686
74	8692	8698	8704	8710	8716	8722	8727	8733	8739	8745
75	8751	8756	8762	8768	8774	8780	8785	8791	8797	8802
76	8808	8814	8820	8825	8831	8837	8842	8848	8854	8859
77	8865	8871	8876	8882	8887	8893	8899	8904	8910	8915
78	8921	8927	8932	8938	8943	8949	8954	8960	8965	8971
79	8976	8982	8987	8993	8998	9004	9009	9015	9020	9026
80	9031	9036	9042	9047	9053	9058	9063	9069	9074	9080
81	9085	9090	9096	9101	9106	9112	9117	9122	9128	9133
82	9138	9143	9149	9154	9159	9165	9170	9175	9180	9186
83	9191	9196	9201	9207	9212	9217	9222	9227	9232	9238
84	9243	9248	9253	9258	9263	9269	9274	9279	9284	9289
85	9294	9299	9304	9310	9315	9320	9325	9330	9335	9340
86	9345	9350	9355	9360	9365	9370	9375	9380	9385	9390
87	9395	9400	9405	9410	9415	9420	9425	9430	9435	9440
88	9445	9450	9455	9460	9465	9469	9474	9479	9484	9489
89	9494	9499	9504	9509	9513	9518	9523	9528	9533	9538
90	9542	9547	9552	9557	9562	9567	9571	9576	9581	9586
91	9590	9595	9600	9605	9610	9614	9619	9624	9628	9633
92	9638	9643	9647	9652	9657	9661	9666	9671	9676	9680
93	9685	9690	9694	9699	9704	9708	9713	9717	9722	9727
94	9731	9736	9741	9745	9750	9754	9759	9764	9768	9773
95	9777	9782	9786	9791	9796	9800	9805	9809	9814	9818
96	9823	9827	9832	9836	9841	9845	9850	9854	9859	9863
97	9868	9872	9877	9881	9886	9890	9895	9899	9903	9908
98	9912	9917	9921	9926	9930	9934	9939	9943	9948	9952
99	9956	9961	9965	9970	9974	9978	9983	9987	9991	9996

Table of Sines and Cosines

α	sin(α)	cos(α)	α	sin(α)	cos(α)	α	sin(α)	cos(α)	α	sin(α)	cos(α)
0.0°	0.00000	1.00000	22.5°	0.38268	0.92388	45.0°	0.70711	0.70711	67.5°	0.92388	0.38268
0.5°	0.00873	0.99996	23.0°	0.39073	0.92050	45.5°	0.71325	0.70091	68.0°	0.92718	0.37461
1.0°	0.01745	0.99985	23.5°	0.39875	0.91706	46.0°	0.71934	0.69466	68.5°	0.93042	0.36650
1.5°	0.02618	0.99966	24.0°	0.40674	0.91355	46.5°	0.72537	0.68835	69.0°	0.93358	0.35837
2.0°	0.03490	0.99939	24.5°	0.41469	0.90996	47.0°	0.73135	0.68200	69.5°	0.93667	0.35021
2.5°	0.04362	0.99905	25.0°	0.42262	0.90631	47.5°	0.73728	0.67559	70.0°	0.93969	0.34202
3.0°	0.05234	0.99863	25.5°	0.43051	0.90259	48.0°	0.74314	0.66913	70.5°	0.94264	0.33381
3.5°	0.06105	0.99813	26.0°	0.43837	0.89879	48.5°	0.74896	0.66262	71.0°	0.94552	0.32557
4.0°	0.06976	0.99756	26.5°	0.44620	0.89493	49.0°	0.75471	0.65606	71.5°	0.94832	0.31730
4.5°	0.07846	0.99692	27.0°	0.45399	0.89101	49.5°	0.76041	0.64945	72.0°	0.95106	0.30902
5.0°	0.08716	0.99619	27.5°	0.46175	0.88701	50.0°	0.76604	0.64279	72.5°	0.95372	0.30071
5.5°	0.09585	0.99540	28.0°	0.46947	0.88295	50.5°	0.77162	0.63608	73.0°	0.95630	0.29237
6.0°	0.10453	0.99452	28.5°	0.47716	0.87882	51.0°	0.77715	0.62932	73.5°	0.95882	0.28402
6.5°	0.11320	0.99357	29.0°	0.48481	0.87462	51.5°	0.78261	0.62251	74.0°	0.96126	0.27564
7.0°	0.12187	0.99255	29.5°	0.49242	0.87036	52.0°	0.78801	0.61566	74.5°	0.96363	0.26724
7.5°	0.13053	0.99144	30.0°	0.50000	0.86603	52.5°	0.79335	0.60876	75.0°	0.96593	0.25882
8.0°	0.13917	0.99027	30.5°	0.50754	0.86163	53.0°	0.79864	0.60182	75.5°	0.96815	0.25038
8.5°	0.14781	0.98902	31.0°	0.51504	0.85717	53.5°	0.80386	0.59482	76.0°	0.97030	0.24192
9.0°	0.15643	0.98769	31.5°	0.52250	0.85264	54.0°	0.80902	0.58779	76.5°	0.97237	0.23345
9.5°	0.16505	0.98629	32.0°	0.52992	0.84805	54.5°	0.81412	0.58070	77.0°	0.97437	0.22495
10.0°	0.17365	0.98481	32.5°	0.53730	0.84339	55.0°	0.81915	0.57358	77.5°	0.97630	0.21644
10.5°	0.18224	0.98325	33.0°	0.54464	0.83867	55.5°	0.82413	0.56641	78.0°	0.97815	0.20791
11.0°	0.19081	0.98163	33.5°	0.55194	0.83389	56.0°	0.82904	0.55919	78.5°	0.97992	0.19937
11.5°	0.19937	0.97992	34.0°	0.55919	0.82904	56.5°	0.83389	0.55194	79.0°	0.98163	0.19081
12.0°	0.20791	0.97815	34.5°	0.56641	0.82413	57.0°	0.83867	0.54464	79.5°	0.98325	0.18224
12.5°	0.21644	0.97630	35.0°	0.57358	0.81915	57.5°	0.84339	0.53730	80.0°	0.98481	0.17365
13.0°	0.22495	0.97437	35.5°	0.58070	0.81412	58.0°	0.84805	0.52992	80.5°	0.98629	0.16505
13.5°	0.23345	0.97237	36.0°	0.58779	0.80902	58.5°	0.85264	0.52250	81.0°	0.98769	0.15643
14.0°	0.24192	0.97030	36.5°	0.59482	0.80386	59.0°	0.85717	0.51504	81.5°	0.98902	0.14781
14.5°	0.25038	0.96815	37.0°	0.60182	0.79864	59.5°	0.86163	0.50754	82.0°	0.99027	0.13917
15.0°	0.25882	0.96593	37.5°	0.60876	0.79335	60.0°	0.86603	0.50000	82.5°	0.99144	0.13053
15.5°	0.26724	0.96363	38.0°	0.61566	0.78801	60.5°	0.87036	0.49242	83.0°	0.99255	0.12187
16.0°	0.27564	0.96126	38.5°	0.62251	0.78261	61.0°	0.87462	0.48481	83.5°	0.99357	0.11320
16.5°	0.28402	0.95882	39.0°	0.62932	0.77715	61.5°	0.87882	0.47716	84.0°	0.99452	0.10453
17.0°	0.29237	0.95630	39.5°	0.63608	0.77162	62.0°	0.88295	0.46947	84.5°	0.99540	0.09585
17.5°	0.30071	0.95372	40.0°	0.64279	0.76604	62.5°	0.88701	0.46175	85.0°	0.99619	0.08716
18.0°	0.30902	0.95106	40.5°	0.64945	0.76041	63.0°	0.89101	0.45399	85.5°	0.99692	0.07846
18.5°	0.31730	0.94832	41.0°	0.65606	0.75471	63.5°	0.89493	0.44620	86.0°	0.99756	0.06976
19.0°	0.32557	0.94552	41.5°	0.66262	0.74896	64.0°	0.89879	0.43837	86.5°	0.99813	0.06105
19.5°	0.33381	0.94264	42.0°	0.66913	0.74314	64.5°	0.90259	0.43051	87.0°	0.99863	0.05234
20.0°	0.34202	0.93969	42.5°	0.67559	0.73728	65.0°	0.90631	0.42262	87.5°	0.99905	0.04362
20.5°	0.35021	0.93667	43.0°	0.68200	0.73135	65.5°	0.90996	0.41469	88.0°	0.99939	0.03490
21.0°	0.35837	0.93358	43.5°	0.68835	0.72537	66.0°	0.91355	0.40674	88.5°	0.99966	0.02618
21.5°	0.36650	0.93042	44.0°	0.69466	0.71934	66.5°	0.91706	0.39875	89.0°	0.99985	0.01745
22.0°	0.37461	0.92718	44.5°	0.70091	0.71325	67.0°	0.92050	0.39073	89.5°	0.99996	0.00873
									90.0°	1.00000	0.00000

Z-Score Table for Standard Normal Distribution

The table entries represent the area under the standard normal curve from μ to the specified value of z.

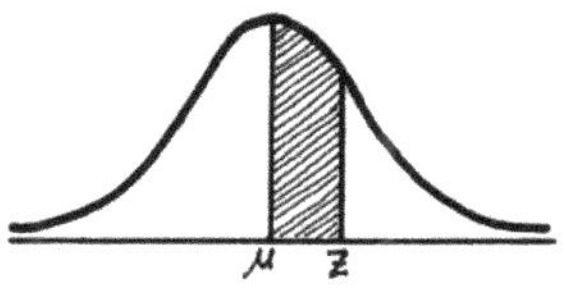

Example: What percentage of the data lies between the mean (μ) and 1.47 standard deviations (z) above the mean?
Answer: The table tells us 42.92%.

	.00	.01	.02	.03	.04	.05	.06	.07	.08	.09
0.0	0.0000	0.0040	0.0080	0.0120	0.0160	0.0199	0.0239	0.0279	0.0319	0.0359
0.1	0.0398	0.0438	0.0478	0.0517	0.0557	0.0596	0.0636	0.0675	0.0714	0.0753
0.2	0.0793	0.0832	0.0871	0.0910	0.0948	0.0987	0.1026	0.1064	0.1103	0.1141
0.3	0.1179	0.1217	0.1255	0.1293	0.1331	0.1368	0.1406	0.1443	0.1480	0.1517
0.4	0.1554	0.1591	0.1628	0.1664	0.1700	0.1736	0.1772	0.1808	0.1844	0.1879
0.5	0.1915	0.1950	0.1985	0.2019	0.2054	0.2088	0.2123	0.2157	0.2190	0.2224
0.6	0.2257	0.2291	0.2324	0.2357	0.2389	0.2422	0.2454	0.2486	0.2517	0.2549
0.7	0.2580	0.2611	0.2642	0.2673	0.2704	0.2734	0.2764	0.2794	0.2823	0.2852
0.8	0.2881	0.2910	0.2939	0.2967	0.2995	0.3023	0.3051	0.3078	0.3106	0.3133
0.9	0.3159	0.3186	0.3212	0.3238	0.3264	0.3289	0.3315	0.3340	0.3365	0.3389
1.0	0.3413	0.3438	0.3461	0.3485	0.3508	0.3531	0.3554	0.3577	0.3599	0.3621
1.1	0.3643	0.3665	0.3686	0.3708	0.3729	0.3749	0.3770	0.3790	0.3810	0.3830
1.2	0.3849	0.3869	0.3888	0.3907	0.3925	0.3944	0.3962	0.3980	0.3997	0.4015
1.3	0.4032	0.4049	0.4066	0.4082	0.4099	0.4115	0.4131	0.4147	0.4162	0.4177
1.4	0.4192	0.4207	0.4222	0.4236	0.4251	0.4265	0.4279	0.4292	0.4306	0.4319
1.5	0.4332	0.4345	0.4357	0.4370	0.4382	0.4394	0.4406	0.4418	0.4429	0.4441
1.6	0.4452	0.4463	0.4474	0.4484	0.4495	0.4505	0.4515	0.4525	0.4535	0.4545
1.7	0.4554	0.4564	0.4573	0.4582	0.4591	0.4599	0.4608	0.4616	0.4625	0.4633
1.8	0.4641	0.4649	0.4656	0.4664	0.4671	0.4678	0.4686	0.4693	0.4699	0.4706
1.9	0.4713	0.4719	0.4726	0.4732	0.4738	0.4744	0.4750	0.4756	0.4761	0.4767
2.0	0.4772	0.4778	0.4783	0.4788	0.4793	0.4798	0.4803	0.4808	0.4812	0.4817
2.1	0.4821	0.4826	0.4830	0.4834	0.4838	0.4842	0.4846	0.4850	0.4854	0.4857
2.2	0.4861	0.4864	0.4868	0.4871	0.4875	0.4878	0.4881	0.4884	0.4887	0.4890
2.3	0.4893	0.4896	0.4898	0.4901	0.4904	0.4906	0.4909	0.4911	0.4913	0.4916
2.4	0.4918	0.4920	0.4922	0.4925	0.4927	0.4929	0.4931	0.4932	0.4934	0.4936
2.5	0.4938	0.4940	0.4941	0.4943	0.4945	0.4946	0.4948	0.4949	0.4951	0.4952
2.6	0.4953	0.4955	0.4956	0.4957	0.4959	0.4960	0.4961	0.4962	0.4963	0.4964
2.7	0.4965	0.4966	0.4967	0.4968	0.4969	0.4970	0.4971	0.4972	0.4973	0.4974
2.8	0.4974	0.4975	0.4976	0.4977	0.4977	0.4978	0.4979	0.4979	0.4980	0.4981
2.9	0.4981	0.4982	0.4982	0.4983	0.4984	0.4984	0.4985	0.4985	0.4986	0.4986
3.0	0.4987	0.4987	0.4987	0.4988	0.4988	0.4989	0.4989	0.4989	0.4990	0.4990
3.1	0.4990	0.4991	0.4991	0.4991	0.4992	0.4992	0.4992	0.4992	0.4993	0.4993
3.2	0.4993	0.4993	0.4994	0.4994	0.4994	0.4994	0.4994	0.4995	0.4995	0.4995
3.3	0.4995	0.4995	0.4995	0.4996	0.4996	0.4996	0.4996	0.4996	0.4996	0.4997
3.4	0.4997	0.4997	0.4997	0.4997	0.4997	0.4997	0.4997	0.4997	0.4997	0.4998
3.5	0.4998	0.4998	0.4998	0.4998	0.4998	0.4998	0.4998	0.4998	0.4998	0.4998
3.6	0.4998	0.4998	0.4998	0.4999	0.4999	0.4999	0.4999	0.4999	0.4999	0.4999

The Cubic Formula

The general cubic equation: $x^3 + ax^2 + bx + c = 0$

We then substitute for x using: $x = (y - \frac{a}{3})$

Which simplifies to: $y^3 + (b - \frac{a^2}{3})y + (\frac{2a^3}{27} - \frac{ab}{3} + c) = 0$

If we let: $p = b - \frac{a^2}{3}$ and $q = \frac{2a^3}{27} - \frac{ab}{3} + c$

Then we have an equation in the form of: $y^3 + py + q = 0$, (by Cardano, 1545.)

To solve this new equation, we let: $D = (\frac{1}{3}p)^3 + (\frac{1}{2}q)^2$

There are three possibilities:

If $D > 0$ then there is <u>one real solution</u>: $y = \sqrt[3]{-\frac{q}{2} + \sqrt{D}} + \sqrt[3]{-\frac{q}{2} - \sqrt{D}}$

If $D = 0$ then there are <u>two real solutions</u>: $y_1 = \mp 2\sqrt{-\frac{p}{3}}$; $y_2 = \pm\sqrt{-\frac{p}{3}}$

(y_2 is a double root) Use top sign if q is positive, bottom sign if q negative.

If $D < 0$ then there are <u>three real solutions</u>: Using $\alpha = \cos^{-1}\left|\frac{q}{2\sqrt{-(p/3)^3}}\right|$

$$y_1 = \mp 2\sqrt{-p/3}\cos(\alpha/3)$$
$$y_2 = \mp 2\sqrt{-p/3}\cos(\alpha/3 + 120°)$$
$$y_3 = \mp 2\sqrt{-p/3}\cos(\alpha/3 + 240°)$$

Use top sign if q is positive, bottom sign if q negative.

Example #1: Solve $x^3 - 2x^2 - 2x - 3 = 0$.

Solution: We first substitute $x = y + \frac{2}{3}$ (because $a = -2$), and we get

$p = -\frac{10}{3}$ and $q = -\frac{133}{27}$ which gives us the new equation $y^3 - \frac{10}{3}y - \frac{133}{27} = 0$.

We now get $D = \frac{169}{36}$ (or $4.69\overline{4}$), which is greater than zero, so using

$y = \sqrt[3]{-\frac{q}{2} + \sqrt{D}} + \sqrt[3]{-\frac{q}{2} - \sqrt{D}}$ we get $y = \frac{7}{3}$. Since $x = y + \frac{2}{3}$, our answer is <u>$x = 3$</u>.

Example #2: Solve $x^3 - 4x^2 + x + 6 = 0$.

Solution: We first substitute $x = y + \frac{4}{3}$ in for x and get

$p = -\frac{13}{3}$ and $q = \frac{70}{27}$ which gives us the new equation $y^3 - \frac{13}{3}y + \frac{70}{27} = 0$.

We now get $D = -1.\overline{3}$, which is less than zero, so we find $\alpha = 41.69366°$, and our three solutions for y are $y_1 = -\frac{7}{3}$, $y_2 = \frac{5}{3}$, $y_3 = \frac{2}{3}$.

And, finally, using $x = y + \frac{4}{3}$, we get our final answers of $x_1 = -1$, $x_2 = 3$, $x_3 = 2$.

Example #3: Solve $x^3 + 9x^2 + 24x + 16 = 0$.

Solution: We substitute $x = y - 3$ and get $p = -3$, $q = -2$. Our new equation is $y^3 - 3y - 2 = 0$.
We now get $D = 0$, which means there are two solutions for y:

$y_1 = 2$, $y_2 = -1$, leading to our final solutions of $x_1 = -1$, $x_2 = -4$.

Quotes

On Mathematics

1. “Geometry existed before creation.” -- Plato
2. “God forever geometrizes.” -- Plato
3. “Let no one ignorant of geometry enter here.” -- inscription above Plato’s Academy
4. “Wherever there is number, there is beauty.” -- Proclus
5. “There is no royal road to geometry.” -- Euclid
6. “[Paradoxes of the infinite arise] only when we attempt, with our finite minds, to discuss the infinite, assigning to it those properties which we give to the finite and limited.” -- Galileo
7. “The book of nature is written in the language of mathematics.” -- Galileo
8. “The merit of painting lies in the exactness of reproduction. Painting is a science and all sciences are based on mathematics. No human inquiry can be a science unless it pursues its path through mathematical exposition and demonstration.” -- Leonardo Da Vinci
9. “With me, everything turns into mathematics.” -- Descartes
10. “I have discovered a truly marvelous proof of this [theorem], which however, the margin is not large enough to contain.” -- Pierre de Fermat (referring to his “last theorem”)
11. “Besides language and music, mathematics is one of the primary manifestations of the free creative power of the human mind.” -- Hermann Weyl
12. “Mathematics is the Queen of the Sciences.” -- Carl Friedrich Gauss
13. “Projective geometry is all geometry.” -- Arthur Cayley
14. “The whole of mathematics consists in the organization of a series of aids to the imagination in the process of reasoning.” -- Alfred North Whitehead
15. “The advancement and perfection of mathematics are intimately connected with the prosperity of the State.” -- Napoleon
16. “A mathematician who is not also something of a poet will never be a complete mathematician.” -- Karl Weierstrass
17. “The mathematician does not study pure mathematics because it is useful; he studies it because he delights in it and he delights in it because it is beautiful.” -- Henri Poincaré
18. “The essence of mathematics is in its freedom.” -- Georg Cantor
19. “Pure mathematics is, in its way, the poetry of logical ideas.” -- Albert Einstein
20. “Do not worry too much about your difficulties in mathematics, I can assure you that mine are still greater.” -- Albert Einstein
21. “How can it be that mathematics, a product of human thought independent of experience, is so admirably adapted to the objects of reality?” -- Albert Einstein
22. “Science without religion is lame; religion without science is blind.” -- Albert Einstein
23. “When you are courting a nice girl, an hour seems like a second. When you sit on a red-hot cinder, a second seems like an hour. That’s relativity.” -- Albert Einstein
24. “The moving power of mathematical invention is not reasoning, but imagination.” -- Augustus de Morgan
25. “All mathematicians share...a sense of amazement over the infinite depth and the mysterious beauty and usefulness of mathematics.” -- Martin Gardner
26. “Fear it no less than the sensual passions because it, too, may take up all your time and deprive you of your health, peace of mind, and happiness. For God’s sake, please give it up.” -- Wolfgang Farkas Bolyai’s advice in a letter (ca. 1830) to his son, Janos Bolyai, who was in the process of discovering non-Euclidean geometry.
27. “Out of Nothing, I have created a strange new universe.” -- Janos Bolyai, speaking of his discovery of a non-Euclidean geometry.

28. “There are 10 types of people in the world: those who understand binary, and those who don't.”
29. “The lottery is a tax on people who are bad at math.”
30. “Mathematics is a body of knowledge, but it contains no truths.” -- Morris Kline
31. “Mathematics takes us still further from what is human, into the region of absolute necessity, to which not only the actual world, but every possible world, must conform.” -- Bertrand Russell
32. “Mathematics, rightly viewed, possesses not only truth, but supreme beauty.” -- B. Russell
33. “Math is the subject in which we never know what we are talking about, nor whether what we are saying is true.” -- Bertrand Russell
34. “Beauty is the first test; there is no permanent place in the world for ugly mathematics.” -- Godfrey Harold Hardy, A Mathematician's Apology (1940)
35. “The study of mathematics is apt to commence in disappointment.” -- Alfred North Whitehead
36. “Numbers are the free creation of the human mind.” -- Richard Dedekind
37. “Good, he did not have enough imagination to become a mathematician.” -- David Hilbert's response upon hearing that one of his students quit mathematics in order to study poetry.
38. “Before beginning [to try to prove Fermat's Last Theorem] I would have to put in three years of intensive study, and I haven't that much time to squander on a probable failure.” -- D. Hilbert
39. “Admittedly, the present state of affairs where we run up against the paradoxes is intolerable. Just think, the definitions and deductive methods which everyone learns, teaches, and uses in mathematics, the paragon of truth and certitude, lead to absurdities! If mathematical thinking is defective, where are we to find truth and certitude?” -- David Hilbert
40. “The Good Lord made all the integers; the rest is man's doing.” -- Leopold Kronecker
41. “We know that God exists because mathematics is consistent and we know that the devil exists because we cannot prove the consistency.” -- Andre Weil
42. “A man is like a fraction whose numerator is what he is and whose denominator is what he thinks of himself. The larger the denominator, the smaller the fraction.” -- Tolstoy
43. “In the fall of 1972, President Nixon announced that the rate of increase of inflation was decreasing. This was the first time a president used the third derivative to advance his case for reelection.” -- Hugo Rossi
44. “If men had known how to permeate the soul with mathematics in the right way in the arithmetic lessons during these past years, we should not now have Bolshevism in Eastern Europe.” --Rudolf Steiner (Oxford, August 1922)
45. “The student of mathematics must get rid of all arbitrary thinking and follow purely the demands of thought. In thinking in this way, the laws of the spiritual world flow into him. This regulated thinking leads to the most spiritual truths.” -- Rudolf Steiner (Oxford, August 1922)
46. “Mathematics is a practical field in that it serves to free the students from the bonds of authority.” -- from *Finding the Path* by Bengt Ulin
47. “Mathematics is the music of reason.” -- from *A Mathematician's Lament* by Paul Lockhart
48. “To do mathematics is to engage in an act of discovery and conjecture, intuition and inspiration; to be in a state of confusion – not because it makes no sense to you, but because you gave it sense and you still don't understand what your creation is up to.” -- Paul Lockhart
49. “If you deny students the opportunity to pose their own problems, make their own conjectures and discoveries, to be wrong, to be creatively frustrated, to have an inspiration, and to cobble together their own explanations and proofs – you deny them mathematics itself.” -- P. Lockhart
50. “Mathematics is not a language; it's an adventure.” -- Paul Lockhart
51. “Mathematics arose from the awakening of the human soul. The mathematician does not look for truth with a practical purpose. To cultivate mathematics only for its practical purpose is to despoil the soul of mathematics.” -- from *The Man Who Counted* by Malba Tahan
52. “Mathematics is one of the surest ways for a man to feel the power of thought and the magic of the spirit. Mathematics is one of the eternal truths and, as such, raises the spirit to the same level on which we feel the presence of God. Without dreams or imagination, mathematics is impoverished; it is lifeless.” -- from *The Man Who Counted* by Malba Tahan

On Education and Life

53. "He who asks a question is a fool for five minutes; he who does not ask a question remains a fool forever." -- Confucius
54. "When I get a little money, I buy books. If any is left, I buy food and clothes." -- Erasmus
55. "The length of your education is less important than its breadth, and the length of your life is less important than its depth." -- Marilyn vos Savant
56. "Your work is to discover your work and then with all your heart to give yourself to it." -- Buddha
57. "The world is not given to you by your parents. It is loaned to you by your children." -- Kenyan proverb
58. "A mind is a fire to be kindled, not a vessel to be filled." -- Plutarch
59. "It is not enough to have a good mind. The main thing is to use it well." -- René Descartes
60. "The more you know, the less sure you are." -- Voltaire
61. "The greater our knowledge increases, the greater our ignorance unfolds." -- John F. Kennedy
62. "Nothing was ever achieved without enthusiasm." - Emerson
63. "Learning without thought is labor lost; thought without learning is perilous." -- Confucius
64. "True pleasure lies not in the discovery of truth, but in the search for it." -- Tolstoy
65. "God grant me the serenity to accept the things I cannot change, the courage to change the things I can, and the wisdom to know the difference." -- Reinhold Niebuhr
66. "Imagination is more important than knowledge. Knowledge is limited; imagination encircles the world." -- Albert Einstein
67. "Everything that is really great and inspiring is created by the individual who can labor in freedom." -- Albert Einstein
68. "The most beautiful thing we can experience is the mysterious. It is the source of all true art and science." -- Albert Einstein
69. "It is the supreme art of the teacher to awaken joy in creative expression and knowledge." -- Albert Einstein
70. "I have no particular talent. I am only inquisitive." -- Albert Einstein
71. "The value of an education is not the learning of many facts, but the training of the mind to think something that cannot be learned from textbooks." -- Albert Einstein
72. "God does not play dice." -- Albert Einstein
73. "God not only plays dice. He also sometimes throws the dice where they cannot be seen." -- Stephen Hawking
74. "Black holes are where God divided by zero." -- Steven Wright
75. "I have come to the frightening conclusion that I am the decisive element. It is my personal approach that creates the climate. It is my daily mood that makes the weather. I possess tremendous power to make life miserable or joyous. I can be a tool of torture or an instrument of inspiration; I can humiliate or humor; hurt or heal. In all situations, it is my response that decides whether a crisis is escalated or de-escalated, and a person humanized or de-humanized. If we treat people as they are, we make them worse. If we treat people as they ought to be, we help them become what they are capable of becoming." -- Johann Wolfgang von Goethe
76. "General opinion is starting to make out that we live in a world of hatred and greed, but I don't see that…It seems to me that love is everywhere. Often it's not particularly dignified or newsworthy, but it's always there...If you look for it, I've got a sneaky feeling you'll find that love actually is all around." -- opening line from the movie *Love Actually.*

Suggested Reading

for high school math teachers

George Adams, Physical and Ethereal Spaces. Rudolf Steiner Press, London, 1978.

George Adams and Olive Whicher, The Plant between Sun and Earth. Shambala Publications, 1982.

Hermann Baravalle, The Waldorf Approach to Arithmetic. Parker Courtney Press, 1996

Glen van Brummelen, Heavenly Mathematics: the Forgotten Art of Spherical Trigonometry. Princeton University Press, 2012.

E. T. Bell, Men of Mathematics. Touchstone, 1965.

H. S. M. Coxeter, Projective Geometry. Springer-Verlag, 1987.

René Descartes, La Géométrie. Dover Publications, 1954.

Lawrence Edwards, Projective Geometry. Second Edition, Floris Books, 2003.

Lawrence Edwards, Vortex of Life. Floris Books, 1993.

Euclid, The Thirteen Books of the Elements. Dover Publications, 1956.

Amos Franceschelli, Mathematics in the Classroom: Mine Shaft and Skylight. Mercury Press, 1998.

Matila Ghyka, The Geometry of Art and Life. Dover Publications, 1977.

Rebecca Goldstein, Incompleteness: The Proof and Paradox of Kurt Gödel. Atlas books, 2005.

David Hilbert and S. Cohn-Vossen, Geometry and the Imagination. Chelsea Publishing, 1990.

H. E. Huntley, The Divine Proportion. Dover Publications, 1970.

Morris Kline, Mathematical Thought from Ancient to Modern Times. Oxford University Press, 1972.

Imre Lakatos, Proofs and Refutations. Cambridge University Press, 1976.

Louis Locher-Ernst, Space and Counterspace. AWSNA Publications, 2003.

Miranda Lundy, Sacred Geometry. Wooden Books, 1998.

Ernest Nagel and James Newman, Gödel's Proof, 2nd edition. NYU Press, 2001.

Nigel Pennick, Sacred Geometry. Capall Bann Publishing, 1994.

Martyn Rawson, Tobias Richter, eds., The Educational Tasks and Content of the Steiner Waldorf Curriculum. Steiner Schools Fellowship Publications, 2003.

Frederic Rosen (editor and translator), The Algebra of Mohammed Ben Musa [al-Khwarizmi]. Kessinger Publishing, ISBN#1-4179-4914-7

Herb Swanson, Geometry for the Waldorf High School. AWSNA Publications Committee, 1987.

Renwick Sheen, Geometry and the Imagination. AWSNA Publications Committee, 1994.

Karl Stockmeyer, R. Steiner's Curriculum for Waldorf Schools. Steiner Schools Fellowship Pub., 1991.

Daud Sutton, Platonic & Archimedean Solids. Wooden Books, 2002.

Malba Tahan, The Man Who Counted. W.W. Norton & Company, 1993.

Bengt Ulin, Finding the Path AWSNA Publications, 1991.

Peter Taylor, A Senior High School Mathematics Textbook. This is now found online at http://www.mast.queensu.ca/~peter/inprocess/contents.htm.

Hermann Weyl, Symmetry. Princeton University Press, 1983.

Olive Whicher, Projective Geometry London: Rudolf Steiner Press,1971.

Jamie York, Making Math Meaningful. A series of books for lower school, middle school, and high school math. www.JamieYorkPress.com.

Index

E

F

G

N

O

P

Q

R

S